Chemistry

experiment and theory

Solutions Manual

Bernice G. Segal
Barnard College

JOHN WILEY & SONS
New York Chichester Brisbane Toronto Singapore

ISBN 0 471 80974 8

Printed in the United States of America

10 9 8 7 6 5 4 3 2 1

Solutions to Problems: Introduction

I.1. The best way to see how many significant figures a number possesses is to express the number in scientific (exponential) notation.

	number	exponential notation	no. of sig. figs.
(a)	0.01000	1.000×10^{-2}	4
(b)	2400	2.4×10^{3}	2
(c)	0.0000706	7.06×10^{-5}	3
(d)	0.1023	1.023×10^{-1}	4
(e)	60,200	6.02×10^{4}	3
(f)	0.004	4×10^{-3}	1
(g)	208,842,000	2.08842×10^{8}	6
(h)	0.003240	3.240×10^{-3}	4

I.2.

	4 sig. figs.	3 sig. figs.	2 sig. figs.
(a)	16.00	16.0	16
(b)	1.007	1.01	1.0
(c)	2.876×10^{4}	2.88×10^{4}	2.9×10^{4}
(d)	2.604×10^{6}	2.60×10^{6}	2.6×10^{6}
(e)	2.045×10^{-3}	2.05×10^{-3}	2.0×10^{-3}

I.3. Rearrange the definition of density, Eq. (I-6), to solve for the volume.

$$\text{volume} = \frac{\text{mass}}{\text{density}} = \frac{59.69\ \text{g}}{1.4832\ \text{g}\cdot\text{mL}^{-1}} = 40.24\ \text{mL}$$

I.4.

	number	exponential notation	no. of sig. figs.
(a)	0.0002008	2.008×10^{-4}	4
(b)	20,772,000	2.0772×10^{7}	5
(c)	0.010570	1.0570×10^{-2}	5
(d)	7030	7.03×10^{3}	3

I.5.

(a) 12. The factor 2.1 has only 2 significant figures, so the answer is only valid to 2 significant figures.

(b) 3.41×10^{-1}. The factor 0.00323 has only 3 significant figures.

(c) 1.98×10^{-4}. The factors 0.928 and 0.00520 have only 3 significant figures.

(d) 1.51×10^{-2}. Do the subtraction required to calculate the numerator first. The numerator is 0.241, which has only 3 significant figures, so the answer can only be expressed to 3 significant figures.

(e) 1.36×10^{-2}. The numerator is 0.861, which has only 3 significant figures.

I.6. To convert to the Kelvin scale, add 273.15.

(a) 24 + 273.15 = 297 K. Since the Celsius temperature, 24°C, is only known to the units place, the Kelvin temperature is also only known to the units place.

(b) 25.0 + 273.15 = 298.2 K

(c) 26.8 + 273.15 = 299.95 = 300.0 K

(d) 24.35 + 273.15 = 297.50 K

(e) 77 + 273.15 = 350 K

I.7.

(a) (1) 7.58×10^{2} (2) 1.02×10^{-2} (3) 6.40×10^{-3} (4) 31.0

(b) (1) 4.4×10^{2} (2) 2.0×10 (3) 7.9×10^{-3} (4) 6.9×10^{4}

I.8. A density has the same numerical value in $g \cdot L^{-1}$ and in $kg \cdot m^{-3}$.

$$\left(\frac{10^3\ g}{1\ kg}\right)\left(\frac{1000\ cm^3}{1\ L}\right)\left(\frac{1\ m}{10^2\ cm}\right)^3 = \left(\frac{10^3\ g}{1\ kg}\right)\left(\frac{10^3\ cm^3}{1\ L}\right)\left(\frac{1\ m^3}{10^6\ cm^3}\right)$$

$$= \frac{1\ g \cdot L^{-1}}{1\ kg \cdot m^{-3}}$$

I.9.

(a) The number 52,000 has experimental uncertainty. The reporter did not count every single person, but made an estimate.

(b) There are exactly 3 feet in a yard. The number 3 in this case is known to an infinite number of significant figures.

(c) Weighing involves using a scale or balance and therefore any weight has experimental uncertainty.

(d) The number 1307 is exact. The hospital keeps an exact count of babies born.

(e) The number 2000 is exact. This is a defined quantity.

(f) The number of oranges is exactly 18.

(g) The apples have to be weighed on a scale. The number 4 has experimental uncertainty.

I.10.

$$\text{volume} = \frac{\text{mass}}{\text{density}} = \frac{234.9\ \text{g}}{0.99707\ \text{g}\cdot\text{mL}^{-1}} = 235.6\ \text{mL} = 0.2356\ \text{L}$$

I.11. $$\left(\frac{3.87\ \text{g}}{1\ \text{min}}\right)\left(\frac{60\ \text{min}}{1\ \text{h}}\right)\left(\frac{24\ \text{h}}{1\ \text{day}}\right)\left(\frac{7\ \text{day}}{1\ \text{wk}}\right)\left(\frac{1\ \text{lb}}{453.6\ \text{g}}\right) = \frac{86.0\ \text{lb}}{1\ \text{wk}}$$

I.12. As $5.00\text{x}10^2$ g of water is only known to the units place, the answer can only be given to the units place.

$$\begin{array}{r} 500. \\ +\ \ 1.464 \\ +\ \ 3.74 \\ \hline 505.2 \end{array} \longrightarrow 505\ \text{g or } 5.05\text{x}10^2\ \text{g}$$

I.13.

(a) 20.7 Only valid to the first decimal place, as 15.9 is only known to the first decimal place.

(b) 127.91 (c) 211 (d) 56.08 (e) 233.39

(f) $6.3\text{x}10^4$. The value 1.28 is insignificant compared to $6.3\text{x}10^4$. The first term would have to be known to 5 significant figures before 1.28 could be added to it significantly. $6.3000\text{x}10^4 + 1.28 = 6.3001\text{x}10^4$.

I.14. $$\left(\frac{2.0\ \text{mile}}{18.0\ \text{min}}\right)\left(\frac{1\ \text{min}}{60\ \text{s}}\right)\left(\frac{1\ \text{km}}{0.6214\ \text{mile}}\right)\left(\frac{10^3\ \text{m}}{1\ \text{km}}\right) = 3.0\ \text{m}\cdot\text{s}^{-1}$$

I.15. mass of 1 doz. eggs = 12(56.49 g) = 677.9 g

The 12 is an exact number, so the answer should be given to 4 significant figures.

I.16. mass of H_2O in flask = (45.0078 − 20.0324) g = 24.9754 g

$$\text{Volume} = \frac{\text{mass}}{\text{density}} = \frac{24.9754\ \text{g}}{0.99681\ \text{g}\cdot\text{mL}^{-1}} = 25.055\ \text{mL}$$

I.17. volume of block = (5.0 in.)(3.0 in.)(2.0 in.)
= 30.0 in.^{3}

As the density is given in g·cm^{-3}, we need the volume in cubic centimeters and not in cubic inches. We must therefore derive the conversion factor from cm^3 to in.^{3}.

$$\left(\frac{2.540\ \text{cm}}{1\ \text{in.}}\right)^3 = \frac{16.39\ \text{cm}^3}{1\ \text{in.}^3}$$

(a) $$\text{mass of block} = \left(8.92\ \frac{\text{g}}{\text{cm}^3}\right)\left(\frac{16.39\ \text{cm}^3}{1\ \text{in.}^3}\right)(30\ \text{in.}^3)$$

$$= 4.39\text{x}10^3\ \text{g} = 4.4\text{x}10^3\ \text{g}$$

As each dimension of the block is only known to 2 significant figures, the volume of the block and the mass of the block are also only known to 2 significant figures.

(b) The conversion factor from grams to pounds is found in Appendix A.

$$(4.39\text{x}10^3\ \text{g})\left(\frac{1\ \text{lb}}{453.6\ \text{g}}\right) = 9.7\ \text{lb}$$

Note that we use the value of the mass in grams before rounding and then round the mass in pounds to 2 figures.

I.18.

(a) $$\frac{(0.8600)(0.0742)}{(0.08206)(297.4)} = 2.61\text{x}10^{-3} \quad \text{valid to 3 figures.}$$

(b) $$\frac{32.97643 - 32.1402}{112.41 + 32.064} = \frac{0.8362}{144.47} = 5.788\text{x}10^{-3}$$

I.19. $$\left(3.4\ \frac{\text{m}}{\text{s}}\right)\left(\frac{60\ \text{s}}{1\ \text{min}}\right)\left(\frac{60\ \text{min}}{1\ \text{h}}\right)\left(\frac{1\ \text{km}}{10^3\ \text{m}}\right)\left(\frac{0.6214\ \text{mile}}{1\ \text{km}}\right) = 7.6\ \frac{\text{mile}}{\text{h}}$$

I.20.

(a)	(b)	(c)
78.5	115	125.66
+273.15	+273.15	+273.15
351.6 K	388 K	398.81 K

I.21. Rearrange the definition of density to solve for the mass: mass = (density)·(volume). Since the density is given in g·cm^{-3} we need the volume of the tube in cm^3.

$$\text{volume of cylinder} = (\text{area})(\text{height}) = \pi r^2 h$$

We must give the radius, r, and height, h, in centimeters in order to obtain the volume in cubic centimeters.

diameter = d = 9.0 mm = 0.90 cm Hence, r = d/2 = 0.45 cm
height = h = 68.3 cm

$$\text{volume} = V = \pi(0.45\text{ cm})^2(68.3\text{ cm}) = 43.45\text{ cm}^3$$

$$\text{mass} = \left(13.594\ \frac{\text{g}}{\text{cm}^3}\right)(43.45\text{ cm}^3) = 590.7\text{ g}$$

Since the diameter of the tube is only known to 2 figures, the volume is only good to 2 figures, and therefore the mass can only be given to 2 figures. The correct answer is mass = $5.9\text{x}10^2$ g.

I.22. Since by definition, density = mass/volume, we must find the mass of the liquid.

$$\begin{array}{r} 62.8365\text{ g} \\ -\ 18.4631\text{ g} \\ \hline 44.3734\text{ g} \end{array} = \text{mass of liquid}$$

Hence, $\text{density} = \dfrac{44.3734\text{ g}}{50.02\text{ mL}} = 0.8871\text{ g}\cdot\text{mL}^{-1}$

I.23.

$$2{,}602{,}000 + 142{,}320 - 204{,}190 + 33{,}286 = 2{,}573{,}416$$

Since the population is known only to the nearest 1000, the answer should be given as $2.573\text{x}10^6$.

I.24. mass = (density)(volume) Thus the mass of 45.00 mL of this solution is

$$\left(1.082\ \frac{\text{g}}{\text{mL}}\right)(45.00\text{ mL}) = 48.69\text{ g}$$

Of this amount, 20.0% is fructose and 80.0% is water. Hence

$$\text{mass fructose} = (0.200)(48.69\text{ g}) = 9.74\text{ g}$$

As the 20.0% is only known to 3 figures, the answer should be given to 3 figures.

I.25. pressure dry H_2 = 758.3 − 21.068 = 737.2 mmHg

I.26. On the Kelvin scale: −164 + 273 = 109 K

$$^{\circ}F = \frac{9}{5}(^{\circ}C) + 32 = \frac{9}{5}(-164) + 32 = -263\ ^{\circ}F$$

I.27.

$$\text{mass ethanol} = \left(0.7893\ \frac{g}{mL}\right)(40.0\ mL) = 19.57\ g$$

$$\text{mass water} = \left(0.99823\ \frac{g}{mL}\right)(62.5\ mL) = 62.39\ g$$

$$\text{total mass} = 81.96\ g$$

$$\%\ \text{ethanol by weight} = \left(\frac{19.57\ g}{81.96\ g}\right) \times 100 = 23.9\%$$

There are only 3 significant figures in the masses of ethanol and water, and therefore in the % ethanol, because the volumes are only known to 3 significant figures.

I.28.

$$^{\circ}F = \frac{9}{5}(^{\circ}C) + 32 = \frac{9}{5}(-189.69) + 32 = -341.44 + 32$$

$$= -309.44\ ^{\circ}F$$

Both 9/5 and 32 are exact numbers in this formula.

On the Kelvin scale: −189.69 + 273.15 = +83.46 K

I.29.

$$\left(\frac{10^3\ g}{1\ kg}\right)\left(\frac{1\ cm^3}{1\ mL}\right)\left(\frac{1\ m}{10^2\ cm}\right)^3 = \frac{10^3\ g\cdot m^3}{10^6\ kg\cdot mL} = \frac{1\ g\cdot mL^{-1}}{10^3\ kg\cdot m^{-3}}$$

To convert from grams per milliliter to kilograms per cubic meter, multiply by

$$\frac{10^3\ kg\cdot m^{-3}}{1\ g\cdot mL^{-1}}$$

Hence if a density is, for example, 1.62 $g\cdot mL^{-1}$, it is $1.62 \times 10^3\ kg\cdot m^{-3}$.

Solutions to Exercises, Chapter 1.

1. The symbol K represents the element potassium (kalium in Latin), atomic number 19. All isotopes of K have 19 protons and 19 electrons. The number of neutrons is A - 19, where A is the mass number. It is useful to tabulate the answers to the question.

	No. protons	No. electrons	No. neutrons
^{39}K	19	19	20
^{40}K	19	19	21
^{41}K	19	19	22

2. The atomic number of mercury, Hg, is 80. All isotopes of Hg have 80 protons and 80 electrons.

	^{196}Hg	^{198}Hg	^{199}Hg	^{200}Hg	^{201}Hg	^{202}Hg	^{204}Hg
No. protons	80	80	80	80	80	80	80
No. electrons	80	80	80	80	80	80	80
No. neutrons	116	118	119	120	121	122	124

3.

	No. protons	No. electrons	No. neutrons
^{19}F	9	9	10
^{19}Ne	10	10	9
^{19}O	8	8	11

4.

	Be	Mg	Ca	Sr	Ba
atomic number, Z	4	12	20	38	56
electrons in core	2	10	18	36	54

5. The atomic weight is the weighted average of the naturally occurring isotopes:

$$\text{atomic weight} = (0.604)(68.9257) + (0.396)(70.9249)$$

$$= 41.63 + 28.09 = 69.72 = 69.7$$

Since the natural abundances are only known to 3 figures, each term in the sum is only good to 3 figures, and the answer should be reported as 69.7.

6. The atomic weight of Cl is 35.453. This means that one mole, or N_A atoms, has a mass of 35.453 g. The average mass of one atom is

$$\frac{35.453 \text{ g}\cdot\text{mol}^{-1}}{6.022045\text{x}10^{23} \text{ atoms}\cdot\text{mol}^{-1}} = 5.8872\text{x}10^{-23} \text{ g}\cdot\text{atom}^{-1}$$

In nature there are two chlorine isotopes, ^{35}Cl and ^{37}Cl. The 35.453 g for N_A chlorine atoms is the mass of a mixture of ^{35}Cl atoms and ^{37}Cl atoms. There is no chlorine atom with a mass of $5.8872\text{x}10^{-23}$ g; that value is the average mass, weighted according to the natural abundances, of a ^{35}Cl atom and a ^{37}Cl atom.

7. One mole of copper weighs 63.546 g, which is $6.3546\text{x}10^{-2}$ kg.

8. The ratio of the average masses of atoms of two different elements is the same as the ratio of their atomic weights.

$$\frac{\text{average mass of an atom of Au}}{\text{average mass of an atom of Ag}} = \frac{196.9665}{107.868} = 1.82600$$

9(a).

$$\text{mol. wt. } C_{12}H_{22}O_{11} = 12(12.011) + 22(1.0079) + 11(15.9994)$$

$$= 144.13_2 + 22.173_8 + 175.993_4$$

$$= 342.30 \text{ g}\cdot\text{mol}^{-1}$$

9(b).

$$\% \text{ by weight C} = \left(\frac{\text{mass of C in one mole of sucrose}}{\text{mass of one mole of sucrose}}\right) \text{x } 100$$

$$= \left(\frac{12(12.011)}{342.30}\right)\text{x}100 = \left(\frac{144.13}{342.30}\right)\text{x}100 = 42.107\%$$

10. $\text{mol. wt. } C_6H_8O_7 = 6(12.011) + 8(1.0079) + 7(15.9994)$

$$= 72.066 + 8.0632 + 111.996 = 192.125$$

$$\text{No. mol } C_6H_8O_7 = \frac{\text{wt. in grams}}{\text{mol. wt. in g·mol}^{-1}} = \frac{4.892 \text{ g}}{192.125 \text{ g·mol}^{-1}}$$

$$= 2.546 \times 10^{-2} \text{ mol}$$

In each mole of citric acid ($C_6H_8O_7$) there are six moles of C. Thus the number of moles of carbon in 4.892 g of citric acid is $6(2.546 \times 10^{-2}) = 0.1528$ mol of carbon.

11.

$$\text{mol. wt. cholesterol} = 27(12.011) + 46(1.0079) + 15.9994$$

$$= 324.29_7 + 46.363_4 + 15.9994 = 386.66$$

$$\text{No. moles cholesterol} = \frac{13.97 \text{ g}}{386.66 \text{ g·mol}^{-1}} = 3.613 \times 10^{-2} \text{ mol}$$

There are 46 moles of H per mole of $C_{27}H_{46}O$. The number of moles of H in this 13.97 g sample is therefore $46(3.613 \times 10^{-2}) = 1.662$ mol.

12.

$$\text{mol. wt. } NaHCO_3 = 22.9898 + 1.0079 + 12.011 + 3(15.9994)$$

$$= 84.007 \text{ g·mol}^{-1}$$

$$\%\text{ of O in } NaHCO_3 \text{ by weight} = \frac{3(15.9994)}{84.007} \times 100 = 57.14\%$$

<u>Any sample</u> of $NaHCO_3$ is 57.14% oxygen. Thus the weight of oxygen in 0.8561 g of $NaHCO_3$ is (0.5714)(0.8561) = 0.4891 g of O.

An alternative method of solving this problem is the following:

$$\text{No. mol } NaHCO_3 = \frac{0.8561}{84.007} = 0.01019 \text{ mol}$$

$$\text{No. mol O} = 3(\text{No. mol } NaHCO_3) = 3(0.01019)$$

$$= 0.03057 \text{ mol O atoms}$$

mass of O = (No. mol O)(at. wt. O)

$$= (0.03057 \text{ mol})(15.9994 \text{ g}\cdot\text{mol}^{-1}) = 0.4891 \text{ g of O.}$$

13. mol. wt. $KMnO_4$ = 39.0983 + 54.9380 + 4(15.9994)

$$= 158.0339 \text{ g}\cdot\text{mol}^{-1}$$

$$\text{No. mol } KMnO_4 \text{ in sample} = \frac{7.238 \text{ g}}{158.0339 \text{ g}\cdot\text{mol}^{-1}} = 0.04580 \text{ mol}$$

No. mol O atoms = 4(No. mol $KMnO_4$) = 4(0.04580) = 0.1832 mol

One mole contains 6.022045×10^{23} atoms. Therefore,

$$\text{No. O atoms} = (6.022 \times 10^{23} \text{ atoms}\cdot\text{mol}^{-1})(0.1832 \text{ mol})$$

$$= 1.103 \times 10^{23} \text{ atoms of oxygen.}$$

14. When an atom loses one valence electron, it becomes a singly positively charged ion. The cations of these elements are therefore Li^+, Na^+, K^+, Rb^+, and Cs^+.

15. The compound must be electrically neutral. Hence there must be two Na^+ ions for each SO_4^{2-} ion, and the formula is Na_2SO_4.

16. No. mol SO_4^{2-} = 3{No. mol $La_2(SO_4)_3\cdot 9H_2O$} = 3(0.394)

$$= 1.182 \text{ mol } SO_4^{2-} \text{ ions}$$

No. mol H_2O = 9{No. mol $La_2(SO_4)_3\cdot 9H_2O$} = 9(0.394)

$$= 3.546 \text{ mol } H_2O$$

17. You must look up the atomic number of each of the atoms. When the same calculations are done repetitively, it is a good idea to tabulate the results.

atom	protons	electrons	ion	protons	electrons
Mg	12	12	Mg^{2+}	12	10
Al	13	13	Al^{3+}	13	10
F	9	9	F^-	9	10
Rb	37	37	Rb^+	37	36
Br	35	35	Br^-	35	36
Se	34	34	Se^{2-}	34	36

18. The formula weight of $(CH)_n$ is (12.011 + 1.0079)n = 13.019n. Thus 13.019n = 78.1, and n = 6, an exact integer. The molecular weight given has been rounded to 3 figures. The molecular formula of benzene is C_6H_6.

19. The empirical formula is $(C_3H_2Cl)_n$, which has a molecular weight of 73.502n. Thus 73.502n = 147.0, and n = 2 exactly. The value of n must be an integer; it is the molecular weight that has been rounded. The molecular formula of para-dichlorobenzene is therefore $C_6H_4Cl_2$.

20. Consider a 100.0 g sample of propane. It contains 81.71 g of C and 18.29 g of H. In this sample,

$$\text{No. mol C} = \frac{81.71\ \text{g}}{12.011\ \text{g/mol}} = 6.803\ \text{mol C}$$

$$\text{No. mol H} = \frac{18.29\ \text{g}}{1.0079\ \text{g/mol}} = 18.14_7\ \text{mol H}$$

$$\text{molar ratio} = \frac{\text{No. mol H}}{\text{No. mol C}} = \frac{18.147}{6.803} = \frac{2.667}{1}$$

The number 2.667 is clearly <u>not</u> an integer to three figures. Multiply the ratio 2.667/1 by successive integers, until you obtain a ratio of two integers, to three significant figures.

$\frac{2.667}{1} = \frac{5.33}{2} = \frac{8.00}{3}$ Thus 8/3 is the correct molar ratio.

The empirical formula of propane is therefore $(C_3H_8)_n$. Note that it is customary to write the C before the H in a compound containing only C and H (a hydrocarbon). The molecular weight of $(C_3H_8)_n$ is $n\{3(12.011) + 8(1.0079)\}$ = 44.1n. As the molecular weight is 44 $g \cdot mol^{-1}$, n must be 1 exactly. The molecular formula of propane is C_3H_8; its exact molecular weight is 44.096 g/mol.

21. (a)

$$\frac{\text{No. mol NO(g) formed}}{\text{No. mol Cu(s) used}} = \frac{2}{3}$$

(b)

$$\frac{\text{No. mol Cu(s) used}}{\text{No. mol } H^+(aq) \text{ used}} = \frac{3}{8}$$

22.

$$\text{No. mol of } O_2 \text{ to be produced} = \frac{1.758 \text{ g}}{2(15.9994) \text{ g/mol}} = \frac{1.758 \text{ g}}{31.9988 \text{ g/mol}}$$

$$= 0.05494 \text{ mol } O_2$$

$$\frac{\text{No. mol } KClO_3 \text{ used}}{\text{No. mol } O_2 \text{ formed}} = \frac{2}{3}$$

$$\text{No. mol } KClO_3 \text{ used} = (2/3)(\text{No. mol } O_2 \text{ formed})$$

$$= (2/3)(0.05494) = 3.663 \times 10^{-2} \text{ mol } KClO_3$$

$$\text{mass of } KClO_3 \text{ needed} = (\text{No. mol } KClO_3)(\text{mass 1 mol } KClO_3)$$

$$\text{formula wt. } KClO_3 = 39.0983 + 35.453 + 3(15.9994)$$

$$= 122.550 \text{ g} \cdot \text{mol}^{-1}$$

$$\text{mass of } KClO_3 \text{ needed} = (3.663 \times 10^{-2} \text{ mol})(122.550 \text{ g} \cdot \text{mol}^{-1})$$

$$= 4.489 \text{ g of } KClO_3$$

23.

$$\text{No. mol Zn} = \frac{6.283 \text{ g}}{65.38 \text{ g/mol}} = 9.610 \times 10^{-2} \text{ mol of Zn}$$

$$\frac{\text{No. mol } Ag^+ \text{ used}}{\text{No. mol Zn(s) used}} = \frac{2}{1}$$

$$\text{No. mol } Ag^+ \text{ used} = 2(\text{No. mol Zn used})$$

$$= 2(9.610 \times 10^{-2} \text{ mol}) = 1.922 \times 10^{-1} \text{ mol}$$

No. mol $AgNO_3$ used = No. mol Ag^+ used = 1.922×10^{-1} mol

$$\frac{\text{No. mol Ag(s) formed}}{\text{No. mol Ag}^+ \text{ used}} = \frac{2}{2} = \frac{1}{1}$$

Therefore, No. mol Ag(s) formed = 1.922×10^{-1} mol

mass Ag(s) formed = (No. mol Ag)(at. wt. Ag in g/mol)

= $(1.922 \times 10^{-1}$ mol)(107.868 g/mol) = 20.73 g of solid Ag

24.
$$\frac{\text{No. mol } I_2 \text{ formed}}{\text{No. mol } MnO_4^- \text{ used}} = \frac{5}{2}$$

Thus, No. mol MnO_4^- used = (2/5)(No. mol I_2 formed)

= (2/5)(0.8155 mol) = 0.3262 mol

No. mol $KMnO_4$ used = No. mol MnO_4^- used = 0.3262 mol

formula wt. $KMnO_4$ = 39.0983 + 54.9380 + 4(15.9994)

= 158.0339 $g \cdot mol^{-1}$

mass $KMnO_4$ needed = (0.3262 mol)(158.0339 g/mol) = 51.55 g

25. Molecular weight of C_3H_8 = 3(12.011) + 8(1.0079)

= 44.096 $g \cdot mol^{-1}$

No. mol C_3H_8 = $\frac{37.570 \text{ g}}{44.096 \text{ g/mol}}$ = 0.85200 mol

No. mol C = 3(No. mol C_3H_8) = 2.5560 mol C

No. mol CO_2 = No. mol C = 2.5560 mol CO_2

Alternatively, we could write a balanced equation for the combustion:

$$C_3H_8(g) + 5\ O_2(g) \longrightarrow 3CO_2(g) + 4H_2O(liq)$$

From the coefficients of the equation we obtain

$$\text{No. mol } CO_2 = 3(\text{No. mol } C_3H_8) = 2.5560 \text{ mol } CO_2$$

$$\text{Mol. wt. } CO_2 = 12.011 + 2(15.9994) = 44.010 \text{ g·mol}^{-1}$$

$$\text{mass } CO_2 \text{ produced} = (44.010 \text{ g·mol}^{-1})(2.5560 \text{ mol}) = 112.49 \text{ g}$$

26. Molecular weight of Br_2 = 2(79.904) = 159.81 g/mol

$$\text{No.mol } Br_2 = \frac{30.2022 \text{ g}}{159.808 \text{ g/mol}} = 0.18899 \text{ mol}$$

The balanced equation for the reaction is

$$3Br_2(liq) + 2Al(s) \longrightarrow 2AlBr_3(s)$$

Hence, $\text{No. mol } AlBr_3 = \frac{2}{3}(\text{No. mol } Br_2) = \frac{2}{3}(0.18899 \text{ mol})$

$$= 0.12599 \text{ mol } AlBr_3$$

$$\text{Formula wt. } AlBr_3 = 26.9815 + 3(79.904) = 266.69 \text{ g·mol}^{-1}$$

$$\text{Mass } AlBr_3 \text{ produced} = (266.69 \text{ g/mol})(0.12599 \text{ mol}) = 33.601 \text{ g}$$

27. Formula wt. CaO = 40.08 + 16.00 = 56.08 g·mol^{-1}

$$\text{Mol. wt. } CO_2 = 12.011 + 2(15.9994) = 44.010 \text{ g·mol}^{-1}$$

$$\text{No. mol CaO} = \frac{0.892 \text{ g}}{56.08 \text{ g/mol}} = 1.59\text{x}10^{-2} \text{ mol}$$

$$\text{No. mol } CO_2 = \frac{0.738 \text{ g}}{44.01 \text{ g/mol}} = 1.68\text{x}10^{-2} \text{ mol}$$

Since CaO and CO_2 combine in a 1:1 molar ratio, there is excess CO_2, and CaO is the limiting reagent. The maximum yield of $CaCO_3$ is $1.59\text{x}10^{-2}$ mol, as

$$\frac{\text{No. mol } CaCO_3 \text{ formed}}{\text{No. mol CaO used}} = \frac{1}{1}$$

Formula weight of $CaCO_3$ = 100.09 $g{\cdot}mol^{-1}$. Hence, the maximum yield of $CaCO_3$ is (1.59×10^{-2} mol)(100.09 $g{\cdot}mol^{-1}$) = 1.59g.

28. The molecular weight of C_3H_8 is 44.096, and of O_2 is 31.9998 g/mol.

$$\text{No. mol } C_3H_8 = \frac{2.760 \text{ g}}{44.096 \text{ g/mol}} = 6.259 \times 10^{-2} \text{ mol}$$

$$\text{No. mol } O_2 = \frac{14.886 \text{ g}}{31.9998 \text{ g/mol}} = 0.4652 \text{ mol}$$

Each mole of C_3H_8 combines with 5 moles of O_2. To use up all the C_3H_8 in the reaction, 5(0.06259 mol) = 0.3130 mol of O_2 are needed. As there is excess O_2, C_3H_8 is the limiting reagent.

$$\text{No. mol } CO_2 \text{ formed} = 3(\text{No. mol } C_3H_8 \text{ used}) = 3(0.06259)$$

$$= 0.18777 \text{ mol } CO_2$$

$$\text{maximum yield } CO_2 = (44.010 \text{ g}{\cdot}\text{mol}^{-1})(0.18777 \text{ mol}) = 8.264\text{g}$$

29. Mol. wts.: CH_3OH 32.042, CH_3COOH 60.052, and

CH_3COOCH_3 74.079 $g{\cdot}mol^{-1}$

$$\text{No. mol } CH_3OH \text{ added} = \frac{9.04 \text{ g}}{32.04 \text{ g/mol}} = 0.282 \text{ mol}$$

$$\text{No. mol } CH_3COOH \text{ added} = \frac{15.78 \text{ g}}{60.052 \text{ g/mol}} = 0.2628 \text{ mol}$$

As there is excess CH_3OH, the limiting reagent is CH_3COOH. The maximum yield of CH_3COOCH_3 is 0.2628 mol, or (0.2628 mol)(74.079 g/mol) = 19.47 g.

$$\%\text{ yield} = \left(\frac{\text{actual yield}}{\text{maximum yield}}\right) \times 100 = \left(\frac{18.36 \text{ g}}{19.466 \text{ g}}\right) \times 100 = 94.32\%$$

Solutions to Multiple Choice Questions, Chapter 1.

1. **(d)** The sample with the largest number of atoms will be the sample with the largest number of moles of atoms, because a mole contains 6.022×10^{23} atoms. Since all samples weigh 1 gram, and

$$\text{No. mol} = \frac{\text{mass in grams}}{\text{formula wt. in g/mol}}$$

the substance with the smallest formula weight will be the one for which the number of moles is largest. Both O_2 and N_2 are diatomic, and the number of moles of atoms is twice the number of moles of the molecules. Of the three solids (Ni, Ca, and B), boron has the smallest atomic weight. The molecular weight of N_2 is 28.0134, so the number of moles of N atoms is

$$2\times\left(\frac{1.00\ \text{g}}{28.0134\ \text{g/mol}}\right) = \frac{1.00}{14.0067}\ \text{mol of N atoms}$$

The number of moles of B atoms is larger, it is (1.00/10.81) mol.

Note that you can answer this question without using Avogadro's number or actually calculating the number of moles or the number of atoms of any of these substances. You are asked for a comparison, and need only find out which of these 5 elements has the smallest atomic weight.

2. **(a)** There are two factors to be considered: the number of atoms per molecule, and the molecular weight of the substance. There are 3 atoms per molecule for CO_2, 8 for C_2H_6, 26 for C_8H_{18}, 2 for LiF, and 14 for B_4H_{10}. The molecular weights are 44 for CO_2, 30 for C_2H_6, 114 for C_8H_{18}, 25.9 for LiF, and 53.3 for B_4H_{10}. The number of atoms is directly proportional to the number of moles of atoms, which is 3(1/44) = 0.068 for CO_2, and 2(1/25.9) = 0.077 for LiF. The others have many more atoms per molecule, and therefore a larger number of moles of atoms.

3. **(c)** In $(NH_4)_2SO_4$, $\frac{\text{No. mol of O atoms}}{\text{No. mol of H atoms}} = \frac{4}{8} = \frac{1}{2}$

4. **(c)** In $(NH_4)_3PO_4$, $\frac{\text{No. mol of O atoms}}{\text{No. mol of H atoms}} = \frac{4}{12} = \frac{1}{3}$

Thus, No. mol O atoms = (1/3)(No. mol H atoms)

$= (1/3)(3.18) = 1.06$ mol O atoms

5. **(e)** The atomic weight of Cu is 63.546 $g{\cdot}mol^{-1}$. Thus the number of moles of Cu is

$$\frac{3.782\ g}{63.546\ g/mol} = 5.951_6 x 10^{-2}\ \text{mol Cu}$$

In $CuSO_4{\cdot}5H_2O$, $\frac{\text{No. mol O}}{\text{No. mol Cu}} = \frac{9}{1}$ Note that there are 4 O atoms per SO_4^{2-} ion, and one O atom per H_2O.

Thus, No. mol O in sample = 9(No. mol Cu) = $9(5.951_6 x 10^{-2})$

$= 5.356_4 x 10^{-1}$ mol O atoms.

mass of O = $(5.356_4\ \text{mol})(15.9994\ g{\cdot}mol^{-1}) = 8.570g$ O

6. **(d)** A 1.1596 g sample of this compound contains 1.000 g of X. It must therefore contain 0.1596 g of O.

$$\text{No. mol O} = \frac{0.1596\ g}{15.9994\ g/mol} = 9.975_4 x 10^{-3}\ \text{mol O}$$

In X_2O_3, $\frac{\text{No. mol X}}{\text{No. mol O}} = \frac{2}{3}$

Therefore, No. mol X = $(2/3)(9.975_4 x 10^{-3}) = 6.650 x 10^{-3}$ mol X

$$\frac{\text{wt. in grams of X}}{\text{atomic wt. of X}} = \text{No. mol X}$$

$$\text{at. wt. of X} = \frac{\text{wt. in g of X}}{\text{No. mol of X}} = \frac{1.000}{6.650 x 10^{-3}} = 150.4\ g{\cdot}mol^{-1}$$

Element X is samarium, Sm, Z = 62. The compound is Sm_2O_3.

7. (b) The number of moles of Ag in a 1.00 g sample is

$$\frac{1.00\ g}{107.868\ g/mol} = 9.27\times10^{-3}\ mol\ Ag$$

$$\text{In } Ag_2S, \quad \frac{\text{No. mol Ag}}{\text{No. mol } Ag_2S} = \frac{2}{1}$$

Thus, No. mol Ag_2S = (1/2)(No. mol Ag) = $4.63_5\times10^{-3}$ mol Ag_2S

Formula weight of Ag_2S = 2(107.87) + 32.06 = 247.80 g/mol

The weight of Ag_2S needed to yield 1.00 g of Ag is therefore

$$(4.63_5\times10^{-3}\ mol)(247.80\ g\cdot mol^{-1}) = 1.14_9\ g = 1.15\ g$$

Let x = the weight of ore needed. Then the weight of Ag_2S is 1.34% of x, or 0.0134x = 1.14_9 g, and x = 85.7 g of ore.

Alternative method: Let x = wt. of ore that must be processed. Then,

wt. of Ag_2S in ore = 0.0134x

How many moles of Ag_2S are in x grams of ore? As the formula weight of Ag_2S is 247.80 g/mol,

$$\text{No. mol } Ag_2S \text{ in ore} = \frac{0.0134x\ g}{247.80\ g/mol}$$

$$\text{No. mol Ag} = 2(\text{No. mol } Ag_2S) = \frac{2(0.0134x)}{247.80}$$

No. grams Ag = (No. mol Ag)(at. wt. in g/mol)

$$= \frac{2(0.0134x)(107.87)}{247.80}$$

$$= 1.167\times10^{-2}x = 1.00\ g\ of\ Ag$$

Hence $x = \dfrac{1.00}{1.167\times10^{-2}}$ = 85.7 g of ore are needed.

8. (d) On the right-hand side there are 5x2 + 6 = 16 mol of O atoms. Therefore there must be 16 mol of O atoms, or 8 mol of O_2 molecules on the left.

9. (b) There must be 2 moles of C atoms on the right, therefore the coefficient of CO_2 is 2. There must be 6 moles of H atoms on the right, therefore the coefficient of H_2O is 3. The ratio of the coefficients of CO_2 to H_2O is therefore 2/3.

10. (c)

Mol. wt. C_2H_5OH = 2(12.011) + 6(1.0079) + 15.9994 = 46.07

Mass 1.2 mol of C_2H_5OH = (1.2 mol)(46.07 g/mol) = 55.3 g

$$\text{Density} = \frac{\text{mass in g}}{\text{volume in mL}} = 0.7893 \text{ g/mL}$$ Hence,

$$\text{volume in mL} = \frac{\text{mass in g}}{0.7893 \text{ g/mL}} = \frac{55.3 \text{ g}}{0.7893 \text{ g/mL}} = 70 \text{ mL}$$

11. (e)

Mol. wt. camphor = 10(12.011) + 16(1.0079) + 15.9994

$= 152.24 \text{ g·mol}^{-1}$

$25.0 \text{ mg} = 25.0\times10^{-3} \text{ g, or } 2.50\times10^{-2} \text{ g}$

$$\text{No. mol camphor} = \frac{2.5\times10^{-2} \text{ g}}{152.24 \text{ g/mol}} = 1.64\times10^{-4} \text{ mol}$$

Each molecule of camphor contains 27 atoms (10C, 16H, 1 O).

$$\text{No. atoms} = (1.64\times10^{-4} \text{ mol})\left(6.022\times10^{23} \frac{\text{molecules}}{\text{mol}}\right)\left(27 \frac{\text{atoms}}{\text{molecule}}\right)$$

$= 2.67\times10^{21}$ atoms in 25.0 mg of camphor.

12. **(d)** Mol. wt. = {3(12) + 4(1) + 16}n = 56n. There is no need for more figures because the molecular weight given has a large uncertainty. Thus 56n ~ 170, and n is exactly 3. The value of n must be an exact integer; it is the molecular weight that is uncertain. The compound is therefore $C_9H_{12}O_3$, and its exact molecular weight is 9(12.011) + 12(1.0079) + 3(15.9994) = 168.19 g/mol. 170±5 means between 165 and 175. The value 168.19 is within these limits.

13. **(a)** Consider a 100.00 g sample of this compound. It contains 65.03 g Ag, 15.68 g Cr, and 19.29 g O.

$$\text{No. moles Ag} = \frac{65.03\ \text{g}}{107.868\ \text{g/mol}} = 0.6029\ \text{mol Ag}$$

$$\text{No. moles Cr} = \frac{15.68\ \text{g}}{51.996\ \text{g/mol}} = 0.3016\ \text{mol Cr}$$

$$\text{No. moles O} = \frac{19.29\ \text{g}}{15.9994\ \text{g/mol}} = 1.206\ \text{mol O}$$

Molar ratios:

$$\frac{\text{No. mol Ag}}{\text{No. mol Cr}} = \frac{0.6029}{0.3016} = 1.999 = 2.00$$

$$\frac{\text{No. mol O}}{\text{No. mol Cr}} = \frac{1.206}{0.3016} = 3.999 = 4.00$$

The simplest formula of this compound is Ag_2CrO_4.

14. **(e)** In one mole of cortisone, the weight of C is 21(12.011) g, or 252.23 g C per mole of cortisone. By the definition of a weight percentage,

$$\frac{\text{wt. of C in 1 mol}}{\text{mol. wt. of cortisone}} = 0.6998$$

Thus, $\text{mol. wt. of cortisone} = \dfrac{252.23}{0.6998} = 360.4\ \text{g/mol}$

15. (b)

Mol. wt. benzoic acid = 7(12.011) + 6(1.0079) + 2(15.9994)

= 122.12 g/mol

$$\text{No. mol } C_6H_5COOH = \frac{24.4\ g}{122.12\ g/mol} = 0.200 \text{ mol}$$

The mass of 70 mL of CH_3OH is (70 mL)(0.791 $g \cdot mL^{-1}$) = 55.4 g

Mol. wt. CH_3OH = 12.011 + 4(1.0079) + 15.9994

= 32.04 $g \cdot mol^{-1}$

$$\text{No. mol } CH_3OH = \frac{55.4\ g}{32.04\ g/mol} = 1.73 \text{ mol } CH_3OH$$

Benzoic acid and methanol react in a 1:1 molar ratio. In this mixture there is excess CH_3OH. Thus benzoic acid is the limiting reagent. The maximum amount of methyl benzoate that can be produced is 0.200 mol.

Mol. wt. $C_6H_5COOCH_3$ = 8(12.011) + 8(1.0079) + 2(15.9994)

= 136.15 $g \cdot mol^{-1}$.

maximum yield methyl benzoate = (0.200 mol)(136.15 g/mol)

= 27.2_3 g

The actual yield of methyl benzoate was 21.6g. Thus,

$$\%\ \text{yield} = \left(\frac{21.6\ g}{27.23\ g}\right) x100 = 79.3\%$$

16. (d) The atomic number of Rb is 37. Hence ^{85}Rb has (85-37) = 48 neutrons. The atomic number of Sr is 38. Since 38 + 48 = 86, ^{86}Sr also has 48 neutrons.

17. (b) Since $N_A = 6.0 \times 10^{23}$, 2.0×10^{23} atoms is 1/3 mol of atoms.

No. mol Be atoms = $(3.0\ g)/(9.0\ g \cdot mol^{-1})$ = 1/3 mol atoms

No. mol O atoms = $2(8.0\ g)/(32.0\ g \cdot mol^{-1})$ = 1/2 mol of O

as there are 2 atoms of O per molecule of O_2.

18. (e) Tellurium, Te, is atomic number 52. To form an anion with a charge of -2 requires the addition of 2 electrons. Since the neutral atom has 52 electrons, there are 54 in the Te^{2-} ion.

19. (b) Nitrogen dioxide, NO_2, is one of the few gases that are intensely colored. Its red-brown color is distinctive.

20. (a) Laughing gas, used as an anesthetic, is dinitrogen oxide, N_2O, (also called nitrous oxide). Inhaling small amounts of N_2O causes a giddy sensation. It must be mixed with oxygen when it is administered, or death by suffocation results.

21. (d) Note that the question asks only for an approximate value of the natural abundance. We can therefore use the mass number as the mass of each isotope. One can say immediately that the percentage of ^{63}Cu must be greater than 50%, because the atomic weight of Cu is significantly less than 64, and a 50/50 mixture of masses 63 and 65 would result in an atomic weight of 64. Thus we need only consider the two choices (d) and (e). If you try (d) first you find 0.70(63) + 0.30(65) = 63.6, very close to the actual atomic weight. It is clear that the natural abundance of the ^{63}Cu isotope is approximately 70%. If you try (e) first, you find 0.90(63) + 0.10(65) = 63.2, much further from the actual atomic weight. To be certain, though, you would have to do the calculation for both 70% and 90% if you had tried 90% first.

Solutions to Problems, Chapter 1.

1.1. (a)

Mol. wt. $Mg_2P_2O_7 = 2(24.305) + 2(30.97376) + 7(15.9994)$

$= 222.553\ g{\cdot}mol^{-1}$

No. mol $Mg_2P_2O_7 = \dfrac{1.0864\ g}{222.553\ g/mol} = 0.0048815_3$

$= 4.8815x10^{-3}$ mol

(b) In $Mg_2P_2O_7$, $\dfrac{\text{No. mol P}}{\text{No. mol } Mg_2P_2O_7} = \dfrac{2}{1}$ Hence,

No. mol P = 2(No. mol $Mg_2P_2O_7$) = $2(4.88153x10^{-3})$

$= 9.7631x10^{-3}$

(c) By the law of conservation of mass, the number of moles of P in the original compound must be the same as the number of moles of P in the product, or $9.7631x10^{-3}$ mol.

mass of P = (No. moles of P)(at. wt. of P in $g{\cdot}mol^{-1}$)

$= (9.7631x10^{-3}\ mol)(30.97376\ g/mol) = 0.30240\ g$

Note that the only piece of data used so far has been the mass of $Mg_2P_2O_7$, which is known to 5 significant figures. Therefore you should use the molecular weight of $Mg_2P_2O_7$ to 6 figures, and give all answers to 5 figures.

(d) % P by weight in sample = $\left(\dfrac{0.30240\ g}{0.7970\ g}\right)x100 = 37.94\%$

As the mass of the original compound is given to 4 figures, the weight percentage should only be reported to 4 figures.

1.2. The atomic weight of magnesium is given by

$(0.7870)(23.98504)+(0.1013)(24.98584)+(0.1117)(25.98259)$

$= 18.87_6 + 2.531 + 2.902 = 24.31\ g{\cdot}mol^{-1}$ of Mg

1.3. First calculate the % of oxygen in histidine.

$$\% \text{ O} = 100.00 - 46.45 - 5.85 - 27.08 = 20.62\% \text{ O}$$

Consider a 100.00 g sample of histidine. It contains 46.45 g of C, 5.85 g of H, 27.08 g of N, and 20.62 g of O. The number of moles of each atom in this 100.00 g sample is

$$\text{No. mol C} = \frac{46.45 \text{ g}}{12.011 \text{ g/mol}} = 3.867 \text{ mol C}$$

$$\text{No. mol H} = \frac{5.85 \text{ g}}{1.0079 \text{ g/mol}} = 5.80_4 \text{ mol H}$$

$$\text{No. mol N} = \frac{27.08 \text{ g}}{14.007 \text{ g/mol}} = 1.933 \text{ mol N}$$

$$\text{No. mol O} = \frac{20.62 \text{ g}}{15.999 \text{ g/mol}} = 1.289 \text{ mol O}$$

The smallest of these is the number of moles of O; therefore calculate the molar ratio of each of the other atoms to oxygen.

$$\frac{\text{moles C}}{\text{moles O}} = \frac{3.867}{1.289} = \frac{3}{1}, \qquad \frac{\text{moles H}}{\text{moles O}} = \frac{5.804}{1.289} = \frac{4.50}{1},$$

$$\frac{\text{moles N}}{\text{moles O}} = \frac{1.933}{1.289} = \frac{1.50}{1}, \qquad \frac{\text{moles O}}{\text{moles O}} = \frac{1.289}{1.289} = \frac{1}{1}$$

Thus the molar ratio C:H:N:O = 3:4.5:1.5:1. To make these all integers, multiply each by 2. The molar ratio C:H:N:O = 6:9:3:2. The empirical formula of histidine is therefore $(C_6H_9O_2N_3)_n$.

1.4. The only two elements in the compound are Gd and O, so the composition is 86.76% Gd and 13.24% O, by weight. In a 100.00 g sample,

$$\text{No. mol Gd} = \frac{86.76 \text{ g}}{157.25 \text{ g/mol}} = 0.5517 \text{ mol Gd}$$

$$\text{No. mol O} = \frac{13.24\ \text{g}}{15.9994\ \text{g/mol}} = 0.8275\ \text{mol O}$$

$$\text{Molar ratio:} \quad \frac{\text{No. mol O}}{\text{No. mol Gd}} = \frac{0.8275}{0.5517} = \frac{1.50}{1} = \frac{3}{2}$$

The empirical formula is therefore $(Gd_2O_3)_n$. Note that when writing formulas of compounds, metals are written before nonmetals.

1.5. The molecular weight of C_6H_5COOH is 122.123 $g{\cdot}mol^{-1}$ Thus,

$$\text{No. mol benzoic acid} = \frac{2.9310\ \text{g}}{122.123\ \text{g/mol}} = 2.4000\times10^{-2}\ \text{mol}$$

$$\frac{\text{No. mol } CO_2 \text{ formed}}{\text{No. mol } C_6H_5COOH \text{ used}} = \frac{7}{1}$$

$$\text{No. mol } CO_2 \text{ formed} = 7(\text{No. mol } C_6H_5COOH \text{ used})$$

$$= 7(2.4000\times10^{-2}\ \text{mol}) = 0.16800\ \text{mol } CO_2$$

1.6. (a) Mol. wt. $C_9H_{13}N$ = 135.21 $g{\cdot}mol^{-1}$. In a 62.87 g sample,

$$\text{No. mol amphetamine} = \frac{62.87\text{g}}{135.21\ \text{g/mol}} = 0.4650\ \text{mol}$$

(b) There are 23 atoms per molecule of amphetamine (9C, 13H, 1N).

In an 18.04 g sample, $\text{No. mol } C_9H_{13}N = \frac{18.04\ \text{g}}{135.21\ \text{g/mol}}$

$$\text{No. of atoms} = \left(\frac{18.04}{135.21}\ \text{mol}\right)\left(6.022\times10^{23}\ \frac{\text{molecules}}{\text{mol}}\right)\left(23\ \frac{\text{atoms}}{\text{molecule}}\right)$$

$$= 1.848\times10^{24} \text{ atoms in 18.04 g of amphetamine}$$

Note that it is not necessary to calculate the number of moles of amphetamine, as it is not asked for.

(c) Mass of 4.50 mol $C_9H_{13}N$ = (4.50 mol)(135.21 g/mol)

$$= 608._4 \text{ g}$$

$$\text{Density} = \frac{\text{mass in g}}{\text{volume in mL}} = 0.949 \text{ g/mL} \qquad \text{Hence,}$$

$$\text{volume} = \frac{608.4 \text{ g}}{0.949 \text{ g/mL}} = 641 \text{ mL}$$

(d) Mol. wt. $H_2O = 2(1.0079) + 15.9994 = 18.0152 \text{ g·mol}^{-1}$

$$\text{No. mol } H_2O = \frac{117.1 \text{ g}}{18.0152 \text{ g/mol}} = 6.500 \text{ mol of } H_2O$$

In H_2O, $\frac{\text{No. mol H}}{\text{No. mol } H_2O} = \frac{2}{1}$; No. mol H = 2(6.500) = 13.00 mol H

How many moles of amphetamine contain 13.00 mol of H atoms? Since the formula is $C_9H_{13}N$, exactly 1 mol of amphetamine, or 135.21 g of amphetamine, contains 13.00 mol of H atoms.

1.7. (a) $\frac{\text{No. mol } Mn^{2+} \text{ formed}}{\text{No. mol } Fe^{2+} \text{ used}} = \frac{1}{5}$ Hence,

No. mol Mn^{2+} formed = (1/5)(No. mol Fe^{2+} used)

$$= (1/5)(1.360\text{x}10^{-3}) = 2.720\text{x}10^{-4} \text{ mol}$$

(b) No. mol Fe^{3+} formed = No. mol Fe^{2+} used = $1.360\text{x}10^{-3}$ mol

(c) $$\frac{\text{No. mol } MnO_4^- \text{ used}}{\text{No. mol } Fe^{2+} \text{ used}} = \frac{1}{5}$$

No. mol MnO_4^- used = $2.720\text{x}10^{-4}$ mol

(d) $$\frac{\text{No. mol } Fe^{2+}}{\text{No. mol } FeSO_4\cdot 7H_2O} = \frac{1}{1}$$

$$\text{No. mol } FeSO_4{\cdot}7H_2O = 1.360\text{x}10^{-3} \text{ mol}$$

$$\text{Mol. wt. } FeSO_4 = 55.847 + 32.06 + 4(15.9994) = 151.90 \text{ g/mol}$$

$$\text{Mol. wt. } FeSO_4{\cdot}7H_2O = 151.90 + 7(18.0153) = 278.01 \text{ g/mol}$$

$$\text{mass } FeSO_4{\cdot}7H_2O = (1.360\text{x}10^{-3} \text{ mol})(278.01 \text{ g/mol}) = 0.3781 \text{ g}$$

1.8. By the law of conservation of mass, all the Br originally in the $YbBr_3$ will be in the AgBr precipitate. Thus we should find the number of moles of Br in the AgBr.

$$\text{Formula wt. AgBr} = 107.868 + 79.904 = 187.772 \text{ g}{\cdot}\text{mol}^{-1}$$

$$\text{No. mol AgBr} = \frac{1.8027 \text{ g}}{187.772 \text{ g/mol}} = 9.6005\text{x}10^{-3} \text{ mol AgBr}$$

As there is 1 mol Br per mole AgBr, there are $9.6005\text{x}10^{-3}$ mol of Br in the AgBr, and there were $9.6005\text{x}10^{-3}$ mol of Br in the $YbBr_3$ originally.

$$\text{In } YbBr_3, \quad \frac{\text{No. mol Yb}}{\text{No. mol Br}} = \frac{1}{3}$$

$$\text{Thus,} \quad \text{No. mol Yb} = (1/3)(\text{No. mol Br}) = (1/3)(9.6005\text{x}10^{-3})$$

$$= 3.2002\text{x}10^{-3} \text{ mol}$$

$$\text{No. mol } YbBr_3 = \text{No. mol Yb} = 3.2002\text{x}10^{-3} \text{ mol}$$

$$\text{No. mol } YbBr_3 = \frac{1.3209 \text{ g } YbBr_3}{\text{mol. wt. } YbBr_3} = 3.2002\text{x}10^{-3} \text{ mol}$$

$$\text{Hence,} \quad \text{mol. wt. } YbBr_3 = \frac{1.3209 \text{ g}}{3.2002\text{x}10^{-3} \text{ mol}} = 412.76 \text{ g/mol}$$

At. wt. Yb + 3(79.904) = 412.76. Therefore,

$$\text{At. wt. Yb} = 412.76 - 3(79.904) = 173.05 \text{ g}{\cdot}\text{mol}^{-1}$$

Note: the uncertainty in the mol. wt. of $YbBr_3$, and therefore in the at. wt. of Yb, is in the second decimal place.

1.9. (a)

Formula wt. Al_2O_3 = 2(26.9815) + 3(15.9994) = 101.961 g/mol

$$\text{No. mol } Al_2O_3 = \frac{0.3272\ g}{101.961\ g/mol} = 3.209 \times 10^{-3}\ mol$$

(b) The number of moles of Al is conserved, that is, it does not change when a chemical reaction occurs.

$$\text{In } Al_2O_3, \quad \frac{\text{No. mol Al}}{\text{No. mol } Al_2O_3} = \frac{2}{1} \qquad \text{Hence}$$

No. mol Al = $2(3.209 \times 10^{-3}$ mol) = 6.418×10^{-3} mol Al. There are 6.418×10^{-3} mole of Al in both the Al_2O_3 precipitate and in the original sample, by the law of conservation of mass.

(c) mass Al = (No. mol Al)(at. wt. Al in g/mol)

$$= (6.418 \times 10^{-3}\ mol)(26.9815\ g/mol) = 1.732 \times 10^{-1}\ g$$

$$\%\text{ by weight of Al} = \left(\frac{\text{mass Al}}{\text{mass sample}}\right) \times 100 = \left(\frac{0.17317\ g}{2.7022\ g}\right) \times 100$$

$$= 6.408\%$$

(d) In $Al_2(SO_4)_3$, $\dfrac{\text{moles } Al_2(SO_4)_3}{\text{moles Al}} = \dfrac{1}{2}$, therefore

No. mol $Al_2(SO_4)_3$ = $(1/2)(6.418 \times 10^{-3}$ mol) = 3.209×10^{-3} mol

Formula wt. $Al_2(SO_4)_3$ = 2(26.9815) + 3(32.06) + 12(15.9994)

= 342.14 g/mol

mass $Al_2(SO_4)_3$ = $(3.209 \times 10^{-3}$ mol)(342.14 g/mol) = 1.098 g

$$\%\ Al_2(SO_4)_3 \text{ in original sample} = \left(\frac{1.098\ g}{2.7022\ g}\right) \times 100 = 40.63\%$$

1.10. The atomic weight of oxygen is calculated as

$$(0.99759)(15.99491) + (0.00037)(17) + (0.00204)(18)$$

$$= 15.956_4 + 0.0063 + 0.036_7 = 15.999$$

All three terms in the sum are known to three decimal places, so the sum is also known to three decimal places, and the atomic weight of oxygen is therefore known to 5 figures.

1.11. (a) If 10.6×10^{10} α-particles are emitted per second, and each becomes a helium atom, we can calculate the number of helium atoms formed in one year from the sample of radium.

$$\left(10.6 \times 10^{10} \ \frac{\text{He atoms}}{\text{s}}\right)\left(60 \ \frac{\text{s}}{\text{min}}\right)\left(60 \ \frac{\text{min}}{\text{hr}}\right)\left(24 \ \frac{\text{hr}}{\text{da}}\right)\left(365 \ \frac{\text{da}}{\text{yr}}\right)$$

$$= 3.34 \times 10^{18} \ \frac{\text{He atoms}}{\text{yr}}$$

The mass of 3.34×10^{18} He atoms = 22.0×10^{-3} mg = 22.0×10^{-6} g. Thus the mass of one He atom is

$$\frac{22.0 \times 10^{-6} \text{ g}}{3.34 \times 10^{18} \text{ He atoms}} = 6.58 \times 10^{-24} \text{ g per He atom}$$

(b) One mole of He has a mass of 4.0026 g. We want to find the number of atoms in one mole. We calculated the mass of one He atom in part (a). Use the units to determine how to obtain N_A:

$$\frac{4.0026 \text{ g/mol}}{6.58 \times 10^{-24} \text{ g/atom}} = 6.08 \times 10^{23} \text{ atom/mol} = N_A$$

1.12. (a) coulombs = (amps)(seconds)

$$= (5.00 \times 10^{-2} \text{ A})(1.75 \text{ hr})\left(60 \ \frac{\text{min}}{\text{hr}}\right)\left(60 \ \frac{\text{s}}{\text{min}}\right) = 315 \text{ C}$$

(b) $$\text{No. mol Ag deposited} = \frac{\text{mass Ag deposited}}{\text{at. wt. Ag}} = \frac{0.352\ g}{107.868\ g/mol}$$

$$= 3.26\times10^{-3}\ \text{mol}$$

(c) $$\frac{315\ \text{coulombs}}{3.26\times10^{-3}\ \text{mol Ag}} = \frac{x\ \text{coulombs}}{1\ \text{mol Ag}}$$

$$x = 9.66\times10^{4}\ \text{C per mole of Ag deposited}$$

(d) $$\left(9.66\times10^{4}\ \frac{C}{mol}\right)\left(\frac{1\ \text{electron}}{1.602\times10^{-19}\ C}\right) = 6.03\times10^{23}\ \frac{\text{electrons}}{\text{mol}}$$

Note how dimensional analysis enables you to figure out the correct arithmetical process for obtaining the answer.

1.13. The atomic weight of vanadium is 50.94 daltons. (A dalton and an amu are identical.) Let n = no. of V atoms per hemovanadin molecule. Then the mass of V atoms in the molecule is 50.94n daltons.

$$\%\ V\ \text{by weight} = \left(\frac{50.94n}{2.4\times10^{5}}\right)\times100 = 0.51 \qquad \text{Solving for n,}$$

$$n = \frac{(0.51)(2.4\times10^{5})}{50.94\times100} = 24.0 = 24\ \text{V atoms per hemovanadin}$$

1.14. The equation for the reaction is not given. Let us begin by writing the unbalanced equation showing reactants and products, and then balancing the equation.

<u>Unbalanced</u>: $Na(s) + O_2(g) \rightarrow Na_2O(s)$

As there are 2 O atoms on the left-hand side in O_2, and only 1 on the right, in Na_2O, we multiply the Na_2O by 2. That will result in 4 Na atoms on the right, so we must multiply the Na(s) by 4. We obtain:

$$4Na(s) + O_2(g) \rightarrow 2Na_2O(s)$$

It is also correct to write $2Na(s) + 1/2\ O_2(g) \rightarrow Na_2O(s)$.

$$\text{Mol. wt. } Na_2O = 2(22.9898) + 15.9994 = 61.9790 \text{ g·mol}^{-1}$$

$$\text{No. mol Na(s)} = \frac{4.5980 \text{ g}}{22.9898 \text{ g/mol}} = 0.20000 \text{ mol Na}$$

The equation tells us

$$\text{No. mol } Na_2O \text{ formed} = (1/2)(\text{No. mol Na used})$$

The maximum yield of Na_2O is therefore (1/2)(0.20000) = 0.10000 mol of Na_2O, or 6.19790 grams. As only 5.8750 g were obtained,

$$\% \text{ yield} = \left(\frac{5.8750 \text{ g}}{6.1979 \text{ g}}\right) \text{x}100 = 94.79\%$$

1.15. (a)

$$\text{Mol. wt. } (C_6H_5)_3P = 18(12.011) + 15(1.0079) + 30.97376$$

$$= 262.29 \text{ g/mol triphenyl phosphine}$$

$$\text{No. mol } (C_6H_5)_3P = \frac{2.63 \text{ g}}{262.29 \text{ g/mol}} = 1.00\text{x}10^{-2} \text{ mol}$$

$$\text{Mass} = (\text{volume in mL})(\text{density in g/mL})$$

$$\text{mass } SbCl_5 \text{ added} = (3.5 \text{ mL})(2.336 \text{ g/mL}) = 8.18 \text{ g } SbCl_5$$

$$\text{Mol. wt. } SbCl_5 = 121.75 + 5(35.453) = 299.02 \text{ g/mol}$$

$$\text{No. mol } SbCl_5 = \frac{8.18 \text{ g}}{299.0 \text{ g/mol}} = 2.7\text{x}10^{-2} \text{ mol}$$

No. mol $SbCl_5$ used = 2{No. mol $(C_6H_5)_3P$ used} in the reaction. The $1.00\text{x}10^{-2}$ mol $(C_6H_5)_3P$ can react with $2.00\text{x}10^{-2}$ mol of $SbCl_5$. Since $2.7\text{x}10^{-2}$ mol of $SbCl_5$ have been added, there is excess $SbCl_5$ present. The limiting reagent is the $(C_6H_5)_3P$.

(b) The maximum yield of product is $1.00\text{x}10^{-2}$ mol, since the molar ratio of triphenyl phosphine to product is 1:1.

The molecular weight of $[(C_6H_5)_3PCl][SbCl_6]$ is 632.21 g/mol. The mass of $1.00x10^{-2}$ mol is 6.32 g. The amount of product collected was 5.314g. Hence,

$$\% \text{ yield} = \left(\frac{5.314 \text{ g}}{6.32 \text{ g}}\right)x100 = 84.1\%$$

1.16. (a) $\text{No. mol } H_2O = \frac{1.6862 \text{ g}}{18.0152 \text{ g/mol}} = 9.3599x10^{-2} \text{ mol}$

$\text{No. mol H} = 2(\text{No. mol } H_2O) = 2(9.3599x10^{-2}) = 0.18720 \text{ mol H}$

$\text{mass H} = (\text{No. mol H})(\text{at. wt. H})$

$= (0.18720 \text{ mol})(1.0079 \text{ g/mol}) = 0.18868 \text{ g of H atoms}$

mass C = (0.7791)(4.8102 g) = 3.747_6 g, since 77.91% of the sample is carbon.

mass N = 4.8102 g - 0.18868 g - 3.7476 g = 0.874 g

Because the mass of C is only good to four figures, the mass of N can only be reported to the third decimal place.

(b) In the 4.8102 g sample,

$$\text{No. mol C} = \frac{3.748 \text{ g}}{12.011 \text{ g/mol}} = 3.120x10^{-1} \text{ mol C}$$

No. mol H = 0.18720 mol {calculated in part (a)}

$$\text{No. mol N} = \frac{0.874 \text{ g}}{14.0067 \text{ g/mol}} = 6.24x10^{-2} \text{ mol N}$$

$$\frac{\text{No. moles C}}{\text{No. moles N}} = \frac{0.3120}{0.0624} = 5.00$$

$$\frac{\text{No. moles H}}{\text{No. moles N}} = \frac{0.1872}{0.0624} = 3.00$$

The empirical formula of the compound is $(C_5H_3N)_n$.

(c) The formula weight of C_5H_3N is 77.09.

Thus 77.09n ~ 155, and n is exactly 2. The molecular formula is $C_{10}H_6N_2$, and the exact molecular weight is 154.171 g/mol.

1.17. (a) $C_3H_8(g) + 5\ O_2(g) \rightarrow 3CO_2(g) + 4H_2O(liq)$

(b) Mol. wts.: C_3H_8 44.096, O_2 31.9988, CO_2 44.010

$$\text{No. mol } C_3H_8 = \frac{3.907\ g}{44.096\ g/mol} = 0.08860\ mol$$

$$\text{No. mol } O_2 = \frac{10.848\ g}{31.9988\ g/mol} = 0.33901\ mol$$

For each mole of C_3H_8, five moles of O_2 are needed for complete combustion. Thus 5(0.08860) = 0.4430 mol of O_2 are needed. As there is not enough O_2 present to burn all the propane, the limiting reagent is the O_2.

$$\frac{\text{No. mol } CO_2 \text{ formed}}{\text{No. mol } O_2 \text{ used}} = \frac{3}{5}$$

Thus, $\text{No. mol } CO_2 \text{ formed} = \frac{3}{5}(0.33901\ mol) = 0.20341\ mol$

mass CO_2 formed = (0.20341 mol)(44.010 g/mol) = 8.9520 g

1.18. $4Fe(s) + 3\ O_2(g) \rightarrow Fe_2O_3(s)$

You may find it easier to use an equation without fractional coefficients.

Mol. wt. O_2 = 31.9988 g/mol; At. wt. Fe = 55.847 g/mol

$$\text{No. mol } O_2 \text{ used} = \frac{2.2943\ g}{31.9988\ g/mol} = 0.071700\ mol$$

$$\text{No. mol Fe used} = \frac{4}{3}(0.071700\ mol) = 0.095600\ mol$$

mass Fe rusted = (55.847 g/mol)(0.095600 mol) = 5.33897 g

$$\% \text{ Fe rusted} = \left(\frac{5.33897 \text{ g}}{11.2811 \text{ g}}\right) \times 100 = 47.327\%$$

$$\frac{\text{No. mol } Fe_2O_3 \text{ formed}}{\text{No. mol } O_2 \text{ used}} = \frac{2}{3}$$

Thus, No. mol Fe_2O_3 formed $= \frac{2}{3}(0.071700) = 0.047800$ mol

Mol. wt. Fe_2O_3 = 159.69 g/mol

mass Fe_2O_3 formed = (0.047800 mol)(159.69 g/mol) = 7.6332 g

1.19.

Formula wt. AgI = 107.868 + 126.9045 = 234.772 g/mol

$$\text{No. mol AgI} = \frac{5.8622 \text{ g}}{234.772 \text{ g/mol}} = 2.4970 \times 10^{-2} \text{ mol AgI}$$

Because the mass of iodine is conserved, there was a total of 2.4970×10^{-2} mole of I^- in the original mixture. This is the sum of the number of moles of KI and NaI.

Let x = mass NaI in original mixture, in grams

y = mass KI in original mixture, in grams

Formula wt. NaI = 22.9898 + 126.9045 = 149.8943 g/mol

Formula wt. KI = 39.0983 + 126.9045 = 166.0028 g/mol

$$\text{No. mol NaI} = \frac{x}{149.8943}$$

$$\text{No. mol KI} = \frac{y}{166.0028}$$

We have two unknowns, and we have two equations relating these unknowns.

$$\text{(I)} \qquad x + y = 3.9762\text{g}$$

$$\text{(II)} \qquad \frac{x}{149.8943} + \frac{y}{166.0028} = 2.4970\text{x}10^{-2} \text{ mol}$$

Multiply Eq. (II) by 166.0028. We obtain

$$1.107466x + y = 4.14509$$

Substitute $y = 3.9762 - x$ {from Eq. (I)} into the equation above:

$$1.107466x + 3.9762 - x = 4.14509$$

Hence, $0.107466x = 4.14509 - 3.9762 = 0.1689$

and $x = \dfrac{0.1689}{0.107466} = 1.571_6\text{g} = 1.572\text{g}$ of NaI

$$y = 3.9762 \text{ g} - 1.571_6 \text{ g} = 2.404_6 \text{ g} = 2.405 \text{ g of KI}$$

$$\% \text{ by weight of KI in sample} = \left(\frac{2.4046 \text{ g}}{3.9762 \text{ g}}\right)\text{x}100 = 60.47\%$$

Solutions to Multiple Choice Questions, Chapter 2.

1. **(d)** Carbon tetrabromide, CBr_4, is a molecular compound, composed of two nonmetallic elements. Molecular compounds are poor conductors of electricity. All the other compounds listed are ionic crystalline solids at room temperature. Molten ionic compounds are good conductors of electricity.

2. **(c)** The symbol for tin is Sn, from the Latin stannum. The sulfide ion is S^{2-}, and the tin(II) ion is Sn^{2+}. They must combine in a 1:1 molar ratio to make a neutral compound, so the correct formula is SnS. Ti is the symbol for titanium.

3. **(e)** The symbol for silver is Ag, from the Latin argentum. The perchlorate ion is ClO_4^-. AgCl is silver chloride, and $AgClO_3$ is silver chlorate.

4. **(a)** Methanol (methyl alcohol), CH_3OH, is an organic, molecular compound. Aqueous solutions of an alcohol do not conduct electricity. All the other compounds listed are ionic crystalline solids, whose aqueous solutions are good conductors of electricity.

5. **(d)** Strontium fluoride is an ionic crystalline solid. The other compounds listed are all molecular compounds, composed of two nonmetallic elements, and are gases at room temperature.

6. **(e)** Using Fig. 2.1, starting from element 106 and adding one element under each of the elements of the 6th period, element 117 is directly under astatine.

7. **(d)** The oxide ion is O^{2-}. Dysprosium oxide, Dy_2O_3, contains 3 oxide ions per formula unit, for a total charge of −6. Thus 2 dysprosium ions must carry a total charge of +6 for electrical neutrality of the solid. Each dysprosium ion therefore has a charge of +3. The bromide ion is Br^-, so that dysprosium bromide is $DyBr_3$.

8. **(a)** Sodium oxalate, $Na_2C_2O_4$, is composed of the ions Na^+ and $C_2O_4^{2-}$. The ratio of sodium to carbon atoms is 2:2 = 1:1.

9. **(e)** Selenium and tellurium are both members of the chalcogens, group VIA.

10. **(c)** The carbonate ion is CO_3^{2-}. For electrical neutrality, the molar ratio of Ce^{3+} ions to CO_3^{2-} ions must be 2:3. The formula of cerium(III) carbonate pentahydrate is therefore $Ce_2(CO_3)_3 \cdot 5H_2O$. The equation for the reaction described is

$$Ce_2(CO_3)_3 \cdot 5H_2O(s) \rightarrow Ce_2O_3(s) + 3CO_2(g) + 5H_2O(g)$$

There must be 3 moles of CO_2 on the right-hand side to balance the 3 moles of C atoms in the carbonate on the left-hand side. Decomposing 1.50 mol of $Ce_2(CO_3)_3 \cdot 5H_2O$ therefore produces 3(1.50) = 4.50 mol of CO_2 if the decomposition is complete.

11. **(c)** See the section on naming oxyanions in Table 2.4. The names of the oxyanions of bromine are parallel to those of chlorine.

12. **(b)** Rb is an alkali metal of the 5th period. In each period the alkali metal has the lowest first ionization energy, and the ionization energy decreases within a group as the atomic number increases, because the outer (valence) electrons are further from the nucleus and therefore easier to remove.

13. **(c)** The equation for the reaction between Ga and S is

$$2Ga(s) + 3S(s) \xrightarrow{\text{heat}} Ga_2S_3(s)$$

The sulfur is the limiting reagent in this mixture, because there is not enough sulfur to combine with all the gallium present. Two moles of S will combine with 4/3 mole of Ga to yield 2/3 mole of Ga_2S_3. From the equation you obtain the relation

$$\text{No. mol } Ga_2S_3 \text{ formed} = (1/3)(\text{No. mol S used})$$

$$= (1/3)(2) = 2/3$$

14. **(b)** Yttrium is atomic number 39, and follows Sr in the periodic table. The alkaline earth metals are harder, denser, and have higher melting points than the adjacent alkali metals (See Table 2.1). We therefore expect Y to be a solid metal, with a high melting point.

15. **(b)** Metallic character increases as one goes to the left across a period of the periodic table. The most metallic element in each period is therefore an alkali metal, in group IA. The alkali of the fifth period is rubidium, Rb.

16. **(a)** See the section on naming oxyanions in Table 2.4.

Solutions to Problems, Chapter 2.

2.1. Rubidium hydride, RbH, is an ionic crystalline solid at room temperature. Hydrogen sulfide, $H_2S(g)$, (analogous to H_2O) is molecular. Strontium hydride, $SrH_2(s)$, is ionic. Hydrogen iodide, HI(g), is molecular.

2.2

(a) $Sr(NO_3)_2$ is strontium nitrate.

(b) Ag_2CO_3 is silver carbonate.

(c) $CoCl_2$ is cobalt(II) chloride or cobaltous chloride.

(d) $CoCl_3$ is cobalt(III) chloride or cobaltic chloride.

(e) AuCN is gold(I) cyanide or aurous cyanide.

(f) $(NH_4)_3PO_4$ is ammonium phosphate.

(g) $KHSO_4$ is potassium hydrogen sulfate or potassium bisulfate.

(h) Na_2S is sodium sulfide.

(i) $Ca(HSO_3)_2$ is calcium hydrogen sulfite or calcium bisulfite.

(j) CuBr is copper(I) bromide or curprous bromide.

(k) $Fe_2(SO_4)_3$ is iron(III) sulfate or ferric sulfate.

(l) $FeSO_4$ is iron(II) sulfate or ferrous sulfate.

(m) Na_2SO_3 is sodium sulfite.

(n) $KMnO_4$ is potassium permanganate.

(o) CuI_2 is copper(II) iodide or cupric iodide.

2.3. In general, electrical conductivity is much higher for metals than for nonmetals. Metallic character increases as we move across the periodic table to the left, and as the atomic number increases within a group. Of the 5 elements listed, S and Si are nonmetals, but Si is to the left of S in the 3rd period. Both Si and Sn are in group IVA, but Sn has a greater atomic number, and is in the 5th period. Tl is in group IIIA and in the 6th period. Ca is an alkaline earth, and should have the highest electrical conductivity of the 5 elements listed. We therefore expect the order of increasing electrical conductivities to be

S, Si, Sn, Tl, Ca.

CAUTION! Electrical conductivity cannot be determined solely by position in the periodic table. For the alkali and alkaline earth metals, for example, electrical conductivity is high, but does not increase within a family as the atomic number increases. While Na has a higher electrical conductivity than Li, K has a lower conductivity than Na, and also has a lower conductivity than both Mg and Ca. For the transition metals as well, individual characteristics determine the conductivity, and we cannot predict relative values solely from the position in the periodic table. The metals with the greatest electrical conductivity are Ag, Cu, and Au.

2.4.

(a) CaC_2O_4, calcium oxalate.

(b) $KHCO_3$, potassium bicarbonate.

(c) $Ba(NO_2)_2$, barium nitrite.

(d) NH_4MnO_4, ammonium permanganate.

(e) $LiNO_3$, lithium nitrate.

(f) $Al(ClO_4)_3 \cdot 6H_2O$, aluminum perchlorate hexahydrate.

(g) $Na_2S_2O_3$, sodium thiosulfate.

(h) Rb_2O_2, rubidium peroxide.

(i) Cu_2O, copper(I) oxide.

(j) $Co_2(SO_4)_3$, cobalt(III) sulfate.

(k) Fe_2O_3, iron(III) oxide.

(l) $Sr(OH)_2$, strontium hydroxide.

(m) CrF_2, chromium(II) fluoride.

(n) $CuSeO_4 \cdot 5H_2O$, copper(II) selenate pentahydrate.

2.5. $Rb_2S(s)$, rubidium sulfide, ionic. $H_2Se(g)$, hydrogen selenide, molecular. $NH_3(g)$, ammonia, molecular. Ammonia is such a familiar substance that it has a common, not a systematic name. $CCl_4(\ell)$, carbon tetrachloride, molecular. $BaI_2(s)$, barium iodide, ionic. $OF_2(g)$, oxygen difluoride, molecular. $BrF_5(\ell)$, bromine pentafluoride, molecular. $SrS(s)$, strontium sulfide, ionic. $CO(g)$, carbon monoxide, molecular.

2.6. (a) $2K(s) + 2H_2O \rightarrow 2K^+(aq) + 2OH^-(aq) + H_2(g)$

(b) The reaction between potassium and oxygen yields a mixture of potassium peroxide and potassium superoxide:

$$2K(s) + O_2(g) \rightarrow K_2O_2(s)$$

$$K(s) + O_2(g) \rightarrow KO_2(s)$$

(c) $Sr(s) + 2H_2O \rightarrow Sr^{2+}(aq) + 2\ OH^-(aq) + H_2(g)$

(d) The reaction between strontium and oxygen yields a mixture of strontium oxide and strontium peroxide:

$$Sr(s) + 1/2\ O_2(g) \rightarrow SrO(s)$$

$$Sr(s) + O_2(g) \rightarrow SrO_2(s)$$

2.7. $N_2(g)$, $O_2(g)$, $F_2(g)$, $Ne(g)$, $P_4(s)$, $S_8(s)$, Cl_2, $H_2(g)$, $Ar(g)$, $Br_2(\ell)$, $I_2(s)$, $Kr(g)$.

2.8. (a) The next rare gas will be element 118.

(b) The atomic number of the element directly beneath gold is 111.

(c) Thallium, Tl, atomic number 81, is the element that will have properties most similar to those of element 113. An element in the 7th period has an atomic number exactly 32 greater than the atomic number of the element in the 6th period in the same group.

2.9. (a) These are all elements of Group IVA. Metallic character within one group increases as the atomic number increases. The order of increasing metallic character is therefore C, Si, Ge, Sn, Pb.

(b) These are all elements of the 3rd period. Metallic character increases as we go across a period to the left. The order of increasing metallic character is, therefore, Cl, P, Si, Al, Na.

2.10. (a) $Cl_2(g) + H_2O \rightarrow H^+(aq) + Cl^-(aq) + HOCl(aq)$

(b) $Cl_2(g) + H_2(g) \rightarrow 2HCl(g)$

(c) $Cl_2(g) + Sr(s) \rightarrow SrCl_2(s)$ See Eqs. (2-14) to (2-16).

(d) $H_2(g) + 1/2\ O_2(g) \rightarrow H_2O(\ell)$

2.11. $N_2O_3(g) + BaO(s) \rightarrow Ba(NO_2)_2(s)$ Because there is only a single product, by the conservation of mass, all the atoms in N_2O_3 and BaO must be in the product. The empirical formula of the product is therefore BaN_2O_4. But the product is an ionic crystalline solid. Since barium is an alkaline earth metal, the cation must be Ba^{2+}. The anion must have a molar ratio of N:O = 1:2. The only anion with this molar ratio is NO_2^-. The product is barium nitrite.

2.12. (a) These are the elements of group VA. Nonmetallic character increases as we go upward within the group to elements of lower atomic number. The order of increasing nonmetallic character is therefore Bi, Sb, As, P, N.

(b) These elements are all in the second period. Nonmetallic character increases as we go to the right across the period. The order of increasing nonmetallic character is Li, B, N, O, F.

2.13. The table of calculations of atomic volumes of the alkali and alkaline earth metals is on the following page.

(a) Within one family or group, as the atomic number increases the atomic volume increases. As the number of electrons increases, the volume of the atom increases, and the valence electrons are further from the nucleus.

(b) The atomic volumes of the alkaline earths are smaller than those of the adjacent alkali metals.

element	atomic number	atomic weight $g \cdot mol^{-1}$	density $g \cdot cm^{-3}$	atomic volume $cm^3 mol^{-1}$
Li	3	6.94	0.53	13.
Na	11	22.99	0.97	24.
K	19	39.10	0.86	45.
Rb	37	85.47	1.53	55.9
Cs	55	132.9	1.89	70.3
Be	4	9.01	1.85	4.87
Mg	12	24.31	1.74	14.0
Ca	20	40.08	1.54	26.0
Sr	38	87.62	2.6	34.
Ba	56	137.33	3.5	39.

2.14.

$$Mg(s) + 1/2\ O_2(g) \rightarrow MgO(s)$$

$$3Mg(s) + N_2(g) \rightarrow Mg_3N_2(s)$$

$$Mg(s) + H_2(g) \rightarrow MgH_2(s)$$

$$Mg(s) + Cl_2(g) \rightarrow MgCl_2(s)$$

2.15. $C_2H_6(g)$, ethane, is molecular. $Mg(NO_3)_2(s)$, magnesium nitrate, is ionic. $N_2O_5(s)$, dinitrogen pentoxide, is molecular. $CS_2(\ell)$, carbon disulfide, is molecular. $SiBr_4(\ell)$, silicon tetrabromide, is molecular. $(NH_4)_2SO_4(s)$, ammonium sulfate, is ionic. $NCl_3(\ell)$, nitrogen trichloride, is molecular. $Na_2O_2(s)$, sodium peroxide, is ionic.

2.16.

$$NH_4NO_3(s) \xrightarrow{\text{heat}} 2H_2O(g) + N_2O(g)$$

All the hydrogen of NH_4NO_3 must be in the water vapor, so there must be 2 moles of H_2O per mole of NH_4NO_3. All the nitrogen of NH_4NO_3 must be in the N_2O, so there must be one mole of N_2O per mole of NH_4NO_3. The O atoms are balanced: there are three O atoms on each side of the equation.

2.17. Representative elements: Rb, Al, Sr, P, Li, Sb, Mg, Pb. Transition metals: Cu, Ag, Zn, Fe, Mn, Mo, Pt, Hg. Inner transition metals: U, Gd, Th, Ce.

Solutions to Exercises, Chapter 3

1. Method #1. At 0°C and 1 atm, one mole of any gas occupies a volume ~ 22.4 liters. Convert the volume of the gas to liters.

$$\text{No. of moles of gas} = (0.426\ \text{L})\left(\frac{1\ \text{mol}}{22.4\ \text{L}}\right) = 0.0190\ \text{mol}$$

$$\text{mol. wt.} = \frac{2.929\ \text{g}}{0.0190\ \text{mol}} = 154\ \text{g/mol}$$

Method #2. Use the ideal gas law, PV = nRT. Let M = the molecular weight of the gas. The number of moles of gas, n, can be expressed as n = m/M, where m is the mass of the sample, in grams. In this problem, m = 2.929 g, and n = 2.929/M. The ideal law is therefore

$$(1.00\ \text{atm})(0.426\ \text{L}) = \left(\frac{2.929\ \text{g}}{M}\right)\left(0.082057\ \frac{\text{L}\cdot\text{atm}}{\text{mol}\cdot\text{K}}\right)(273.15\ \text{K})$$

$$\text{and}\quad M = \frac{(2.929)(8.2057\times10^{-2})(2.7315\times10^{2})}{(0.426)} = 154\ \text{g/mol}$$

2. (a) FALSE. Equal volumes of gases contain equal numbers of molecules (and therefore equal numbers of moles) only if the gases are at the same temperature and pressure. The pressures of the two gases are different, so the number of moles of the two gases are different. In fact, for two gases at the same T and V, the number of moles is directly proportional to the pressure, so the number of moles of N_2 is twice the number of moles of C_3H_8.

(b) FALSE. The number of molecules is not the same for the two samples, as the gases are at different pressures. It is impossible to say how many molecules are in either sample, because the volume V is unspecified.

3. The student's error is in using 22.4 L/mol as the molar volume when the gas is not at $0^\circ C$ and 1.00 atm. The most straightforward way of solving this problem is to use the ideal gas law.

$$n = \frac{PV}{RT} = \frac{(1.00 \text{ atm})(0.175 \text{ L})}{\left(0.082057 \frac{\text{L}\cdot\text{atm}}{\text{mol}\cdot\text{K}}\right)(298.15 \text{ K})} = 7.15\text{x}10^{-3} \text{ mol}$$

An alternative method is to calculate the molar volume of an ideal gas at $25^\circ C$ and 1.00 atm. Since the volume is directly proportional to the absolute temperature for constant n (1 mole) and constant P (1.00 atm),

$$\frac{V_{298}}{V_{273}} = \frac{298.15 \text{ K}}{273.15 \text{ K}}, \quad \text{or } V_{298} = 22.4 \text{ L}\left(\frac{298.15}{273.15}\right) = 24.45 \text{ L/mol}$$

and $$\text{No. moles of gas} = \frac{0.175 \text{ L}}{24.45 \text{ L/mol}} = 7.16\text{x}10^{-3} \text{ mol}$$

Using 22.4 L/mol for the molar volume at STP introduces a larger uncertainty in the 3rd significant figure than using the ideal gas law.

4. Since the O_2 and CH_4 are at the same temperature and pressure, the ratio of their volumes is the same as their molar ratios.

$$\frac{\text{No. moles } O_2 \text{ used}}{\text{No. moles } CH_4 \text{ used}} = \frac{2}{1} = \frac{\text{volume } O_2}{\text{volume } CH_4}$$

Hence, volume O_2 = 2(volume CH_4) = 2(3.00 L) = 6.00 L

5. (a) $P \text{ in atm} = (43.7 \text{ cm Hg})\left(\frac{1 \text{ atm}}{76.0 \text{ cm Hg}}\right) = 0.575 \text{ atm}$

(b) $(0.575 \text{ atm})\left(1.0132\text{x}10^5 \frac{\text{Pa}}{\text{atm}}\right) = 0.583\text{x}10^5 \text{ Pa} = 5.83\text{x}10^4 \text{ Pa}$

6. Pressure = $\frac{\text{force}}{\text{area}}$. If V = 1000 cm^3, one side of the cube is 10 cm in length, and the area of one wall is 100 cm^2. If V = 8000 cm^3, one side of the cube is 20 cm in length, and the area of one wall is 400 cm^2. Since force = (pressure)(area), if both gases are at the same pressure, the force on a wall is directly proportional to the area of the wall.

$$\frac{\text{force on wall of larger cube}}{\text{force on wall of smaller cube}} = \frac{400P}{100P} = \frac{4}{1}$$

7. Pressure = (density of fluid)(ht. of column)(g), where g is the acceleration of gravity. At 0°C, 0.500 atm supports a column of mercury 38.0 cm high. Hence,

$$(13.6 \text{ g}\cdot\text{cm}^{-3})(38.0 \text{ cm})(g) = (6.09 \text{ g}\cdot\text{cm}^{-3})(h)(g)$$

where h is the height of the column of gallium that is supported by 0.500 atm.

$$h = \frac{(13.6)(38.0)}{6.09} = 84.9 \text{ cm of gallium}$$

8. Since n and T are constant for this gas sample, $P_1V_1 = P_2V_2$. Thus, $P_1 = (395 \text{ mmHg})\left(\frac{0.074 \text{ cm}^3}{450 \text{ cm}^3}\right) = 0.065 \text{ mmHg}$

In atmospheres, $P_1 = (0.065 \text{ mmHg})\left(\frac{1 \text{ atm}}{760 \text{ mmHg}}\right) = 8.5\text{x}10^{-5}$ atm

9. The relation $P_1V_1 = P_2V_2$ is valid <u>only</u> if n and T are constant. In this problem, the number of moles of He is not constant as another 0.0100 mole has been added. The only variable held constant is the temperature. Thus RT = $P_1V_1/n_1 = P_2V_2/n_2$. Solving for P_2 we obtain

$$P_2 = \left(\frac{n_2}{n_1}\right)\left(\frac{V_1}{V_2}\right)P_1 = \frac{(0.0200)(V)(1.00 \text{ atm})}{(0.0100)(1.60V)} = \frac{2.00}{1.60} = 1.25 \text{ atm}$$

10. Since n and P are constant, $V_1/T_1 = V_2/T_2$. Thus,

$$T_2 = T_1(V_2/V_1) = (297.6 \text{ K})(36.9/39.4) = 278.7 \text{ K} = 5.5°\text{C}$$

11. The variables that are constant in this problem are the volume of the tank and the temperature. Thus,

$$\frac{RT}{V} = \frac{P_1}{n_1} = \frac{P_2}{n_2}$$

The two pressures must be given in the same units. Solving for n_2 we obtain $n_2 = (P_2/P_1)n_1$.

$$P_1 = (703/760) \text{ atm} = 0.925 \text{ atm}$$

$$n_1 = \frac{36.4 \text{ g}}{28.0134 \text{ g/mol}} = 1.30 \text{ mol}$$

Thus,

$$n_2 = (1.30 \text{ mol})\frac{(40.0 \text{ atm})}{(0.925 \text{ atm})} = 56.2 \text{ mol } N_2$$

The mass of gas in the tank when the pressure is 40.0 atm is therefore (56.2 mol)(28.0134 g/mol) = 1574 g of N_2. As the tank already holds 36.4 g of N_2, the amount that can be added is 1538 g. <u>Note</u>: the molecular weight of N_2 cancels out of this problem because $n_2/n_1 = m_2/m_1$, where m is the mass in grams.

12. First calculate the number of moles of H_2 formed in the reaction. $n_{H_2} = \frac{PV}{RT} = \frac{(772/760 \text{ atm})(0.1200 \text{ L})}{\left(0.082057 \frac{\text{L·atm}}{\text{mol·K}}\right)(298.15 \text{ K})}$

$$= 4.98\text{x}10^{-3} \text{ mol}$$

$$\frac{\text{moles Al used}}{\text{moles } H_2 \text{ formed}} = \frac{1}{3/2} = \frac{2}{3}$$

Hence, No. mol Al used $= (2/3)(4.98\text{x}10^{-3}) = 3.32\text{x}10^{-3}$ mol

13. Solving the ideal gas law for the absolute temperature we obtain $T = PV/nR$. The number of moles of O_2 is

$$n_{O_2} = \frac{1.00 \text{ g}}{32.00 \text{ g/mol}} = 3.125\text{x}10^{-2} \text{ mol } O_2$$

Thus,

$$T = \frac{(762/760 \text{ atm})(0.6500 \text{ L})}{\left(0.082057 \frac{\text{L·atm}}{\text{mol·K}}\right)(0.03125 \text{ mol})} = 254 \text{ K} = -19^\circ\text{C}$$

14. The molar volume (volume per mole) is $V/n = RT/P$. At 1.00 atm and 298.15 K,

$$V/n = \frac{(0.082057 \text{ L·atm·mol}^{-1}\text{K}^{-1})(298.15 \text{ K})}{(1.00 \text{ atm})}$$
$$= 24.465 \text{ L/mol} = 24.5 \text{ L/mol}$$

15. Let M = mol. wt. of gas. Then the number of moles of gas is

$$n = \frac{0.9539 \text{ g}}{M} = \frac{PV}{RT} = \frac{(742.1/760 \text{ atm})(0.2800 \text{ L})}{\left(0.082057 \frac{\text{L·atm}}{\text{mol·K}}\right)(393.2 \text{ K})}$$

$$= 8.475\text{x}10^{-3} \text{ mol}$$

Hence, $M = \frac{0.9539 \text{ g}}{8.477\text{x}10^{-3} \text{ mol}} = 112.55 \text{ g/mol} = 112.6 \text{ g/mol}$

16. (a) The density of a gas, δ, is

$$\delta = \frac{\text{mass in g}}{\text{volume in L}} = \frac{m}{V} = \frac{nM}{V}$$

where M is the molecular weight of the gas and n is the number of moles. The mol. wt. of N_2 is 28.0134 g/mol. The quantity n/V is calculated from the ideal gas law:

$$\frac{n}{V} = \frac{P}{RT} = \frac{1.00 \text{ atm}}{\left(0.082057 \frac{\text{L}\cdot\text{atm}}{\text{mol}\cdot\text{K}}\right)(333.15 \text{ K})} = 0.0366 \text{ mol}\cdot\text{L}^{-1}$$

Hence, $\delta = (0.0366 \text{ mol/L})(28.0134 \text{ g/mol}) = 1.02 \text{ g/L}$

Note that the density depends only on the temperature, pressure and molecular weight of the gas, and not on its volume.

(b) The number of moles of N_2 in the container at 60.0°C is

$$(0.0366 \text{ mol}\cdot\text{L}^{-1})(1.50 \text{ L}) = 5.49\text{x}10^{-2} \text{ mol of } N_2$$

At 100.0°C,
$$n = \frac{(1 \text{ atm})(1.50 \text{ L})}{\left(0.082057 \frac{\text{L}\cdot\text{atm}}{\text{mol}\cdot\text{K}}\right)(373.15 \text{ K})} = 4.90\text{x}10^{-2} \text{ mol } N_2$$

Hence to keep the pressure at 1.00 atm, we must remove

$$5.487\text{x}10^{-2} - 4.899\text{x}10^{-2} = 0.588\text{x}10^{-2} = 5.9\text{x}10^{-3} \text{ mol } N_2$$

$$\text{mass } N_2 \text{ to be removed} = (28.0134 \text{ g/mol})(5.88\text{x}10^{-3} \text{ mol}) = 0.16 \text{ g}$$

17. The volume of the tank and the number of moles of gas in the tank are constant. Hence $nR/V = P_1/T_1 = P_2/T_2$. Solving for P_2,

$$P_2 = P_1\left(\frac{T_2}{T_1}\right) = (30.0 \text{ atm})\frac{(398.2 \text{ K})}{(295.5 \text{ K})} = 40.4 \text{ atm}$$

18. Only the number of moles of gas is constant. Thus,

$$\frac{P_1V_1}{T_1} = \frac{P_2V_2}{T_2} \quad \text{and} \quad T_2 = T_1\frac{(P_2V_2)}{(P_1V_1)} = (298.2\text{K})\frac{(1.00\ \text{atm})(3V\ \text{L})}{(2.00\ \text{atm})(V\ \text{L})}$$

$$T_2 = (298.2\text{K})\frac{(3.00)}{(2.00)} = 447\ \text{K} = 174^\circ\text{C}$$

19. First calculate the number of moles of CO_2 produced by the combustion.

$$n_{CO_2} = \frac{PV}{RT} = \frac{(750/760\ \text{atm})(0.1600\ \text{L})}{\left(0.082057\ \frac{\text{L}\cdot\text{atm}}{\text{mol}\cdot\text{K}}\right)(295.2\ \text{K})} = 6.518\text{x}10^{-3}$$

$$\frac{\text{moles } O_2 \text{ used}}{\text{moles } CO_2 \text{ formed}} = \frac{5}{3}, \quad \therefore \text{moles } O_2 \text{ used} = \frac{5}{3}(6.518\text{x}10^{-3})$$

$$= 1.09\text{x}10^{-2}$$

20. Only T is constant. Thus $\frac{P_1V_1}{n_1} = \frac{P_2V_2}{n_2}$ and

$$P_2 = P_1\left(\frac{n_2}{n_1}\right)\left(\frac{V_1}{V_2}\right)$$

Since $n_2/n_1 = 3.60/2.40 = 3/2$, $V_1/V_2 = 1.00/1.50$

$P_2 = (750\ \text{mmHg})(3/2)(1.00/1.50) = 750\ \text{mmHg}$ The final pressure is the same as the original pressure.

21. $P_{total} = P_{N_2} + P_{O_2} + P_{H_2O} = 758.3\ \text{mmHg}$

$$P_{N_2} = \frac{n_{N_2}RT}{V} = \frac{(0.0162\ \text{mol})}{(0.900\ \text{L})}\left(62.36\ \frac{\text{L}\cdot\text{mmHg}}{\text{mol}\cdot\text{K}}\right)(295.6\ \text{K})$$

$$= 331.8\ \text{mmHg}$$

Hence, $P_{O_2} = (758.3 - 331.8 - 20.3)\ \text{mmHg} = 406.2\ \text{mmHg}$

$$n_{O_2} = \frac{P_{O_2}\cdot V}{RT} = \frac{(406.2\ \text{mmHg})(0.900\ \text{L})}{\left(62.36\ \frac{\text{L}\cdot\text{mmHg}}{\text{mol}\cdot\text{K}}\right)(295.6\ \text{K})} = 0.0198\ \text{mol of } O_2$$

22. (a) Consider a 100.00 g sample of this mixture. It contains 38.4 g of N_2 and 61.6 g of CO_2.

$n_{N_2} = \frac{38.4\ g}{28.01\ g/mol} = 1.37\ mol$, $n_{CO_2} = \frac{61.6\ g}{44.01\ g/mol} = 1.40\ mol$

$n_{total} = 1.37 + 1.40 = 2.77\ mol$ $X_{N_2} = \frac{1.37}{2.77} = 0.495 = 49.5\%$

(b) $P_{N_2} = P_{total}X_{N_2} = (1.46\ atm)(0.495) = 0.722\ atm$

23. (a) The equation for the reaction tells us that the number of moles of H_2 formed is equal to the number of moles of Mg used. At. wt. Mg = 24.305 g/mol.

$$\text{No. moles Mg} = \frac{0.8995\ g}{24.305\ g/mol} = 3.701\text{x}10^{-2}$$

(b) $P_{total} = 767.6\ mmHg = P_{H_2} + P_{H_2O} = P_{H_2} + 23.5\ mmHg$

Therefore $P_{H_2} = 744.1\ mmHg$

(c) $V = \frac{n_{H_2}RT}{P_{H_2}} = \frac{(0.03701\ mol)}{(744.1\ mmHg)}\left(62.36\ \frac{L\cdot mmHg}{mol\cdot K}\right)(298.0\ K)$

$= 0.9243\ L$

Solutions to Multiple Choice Questions, Chapter 3

1. (b) The number of moles of gas and the volume are constant. Therefore the pressure is directly proportional to the absolute temperature. Since the gas is cooled, the pressure must decrease. Only (a) and (b) are possible, and as the temperature has changed by only a relatively small amount, (b) is the most likely answer. To calculate the final pressure, use $P_2 = P_1\left(\frac{T_2}{T_1}\right) = (754.2\ mmHg)\left(\frac{293.2\ K}{301.4\ K}\right)$ so $P_2 = 733.7\ mmHg$.

2. __(d)__ Both n and V are constant, so P and T are directly proportional. Thus $T_2 = T_1(P_2/P_1)$.

$$P_1 = (765.3/760)\ \text{atm} = 1.007\ \text{atm}$$

$$T_2 = (297.6\ \text{K})(2.50/1.007) = 738.8\ \text{K} = 465.6^\circ\text{C}$$

3. __(c)__ The molecular weight, M, of the gas is $M = \frac{\delta RT}{P}$.

$$M = \frac{(1.60\ \text{g}\cdot\text{L}^{-1})(62.36\ \text{L}\cdot\text{mmHg}\cdot\text{mol}^{-1}\text{K}^{-1})(299.7\ \text{K})}{(680.2\ \text{mmHg})}$$

$$= 44.01\ \text{g}\cdot\text{mol}^{-1}$$

Of the gases listed, only CO_2 has a molecular weight of 44.01 g/mol.

4. __(a)__ Use Avogadro's law and the conservation of C atoms. Since the gases are at the same temperature and pressure, the volume of each is directly proportional to the number of moles. The molar ratio of CO_2 formed to C_4H_{10} burned is 4:1, by the conservation of mass. Thus the volume of CO_2 formed must be 4 times the volume of C_4H_{10} used, or 4(1.85 L) = 7.40 L.

5. __(e)__ $P_{CO_2} = n_{CO_2}(RT/V)$. The number of moles of CO_2 formed is 12 times the number of moles of sucrose burned, from the equation given. The mol. wt. of $C_{12}H_{22}O_{11}$ = 342.3 g/mol. Thus the number of moles of sucrose is $\frac{0.8763\ \text{g}}{342.3\ \text{g/mol}}$ = 2.560×10^{-3} mol, and

$$\text{No. mol } CO_2 = 12(2.560\times10^{-3}) = 3.072\times10^{-2}$$

$$P_{CO_2} = \frac{(3.072\times10^{-2}\text{mol})}{(3.40\ \text{L})}\left(62.36\ \frac{\text{L}\cdot\text{mmHg}}{\text{mol}\cdot\text{K}}\right)(298.15\ \text{K}) = 168\ \text{mmHg}$$

6. (d) $(13.6\ g\cdot cm^{-3})(200\ mm)(g) = (2.89\ g\cdot cm^{-3})(h)(g)$ where h is the height of the bromoform column, and g is the acceleration of gravity. Thus $h = \frac{13.6}{2.89}(200\ mm) = 941\ mm = 94.1\ cm$

7. (a) Both P and n are constant, so $T_2/T_1 = V_2/V_1$, and $T_2 = (V_2/V_1)T_1 = \left(\frac{3.00\ L}{3.75\ L}\right)(308.15\ K) = 246.52\ K = -26.6^{\circ}C$

8. (b) Since the temperature is above $0^{\circ}C$, one mole must occupy a volume greater than 22.4 L at 1.00 atm, so the number of moles of gas that occupies 22.4 L must be less than 1. Only (a) and (b) are possible answers, and (b) is most likely, as the temperature is not very far above $0^{\circ}C$. To calculate the number of moles of gas, use the ideal gas law. $n = \frac{PV}{RT} = \frac{(1.00\ atm)(22.4\ L)}{\left(0.082057\ \frac{L\cdot atm}{mol\cdot K}\right)(303.2K)} = 0.900\ mol$

9. (c) $P_{total} = 753.2\ mmHg = P_{H_2} + P_{H_2O} = P_{H_2} + 25.8$ Thus $P_{H_2} = 727.4\ mmHg$. Since the number of moles of H_2 is constant, $V_2 = \left(\frac{T_2}{T_1}\right)\left(\frac{P_1}{P_2}\right)V_1 = \left(\frac{293.2\ K}{299.6\ K}\right)\left(\frac{727.4\ mmHg}{760.0\ mmHg}\right)(94.6\ mL)$

$= 88.6\ mL$

10. (b) If we rearrange Eq.(3-34) to solve for the density, we obtain $\delta = MP/RT$. The mol. wt. of $Cl_2(g)$ is 70.91 g/mol. Hence

$$\delta = \frac{(70.91\ g/mol)(1.60\ atm)}{\left(0.082057\ \frac{L\cdot atm}{mol\cdot K}\right)(323.2\ K)} = 4.28\ g\cdot L^{-1}$$

11. (b) $P_{total} = P_{gas} + P_{H_2O} = P_{gas} + 21.7 = 758.3$ mmHg

so $P_{gas} = 736.6$ mmHg

$$M = \frac{(0.4153\ g)}{(0.13\ L)}\left(62.36\ \frac{L\cdot mmHg}{mol\cdot K}\right)\frac{(296.7\ K)}{(736.6\ mmHg)} = 80.2\ g/mol$$

$= 80\ g\cdot mol^{-1}$

12. (c) $M = \delta RT/P$

$$M = \frac{(1.22\ g/L)(0.08206\ L\cdot atm\cdot mol^{-1}K^{-1})(300\ K)}{(1.00\ atm)} = 30.0\ g/mol$$

Of the gases listed, only ethane, C_2H_6, has a molecular weight of 30.

13. (e) If the total number of moles of gas is 5, there are 2 moles of Ar. Hence, $X_{Ar} = 2/5$. $P_{Ar} = P_{total}X_{Ar} = (2/5)P_{total}$.

14. (e) The equation for the reaction tells us that the number of moles of H_2 formed is 3/2(No. mol Al used).

$$n_{Al} = \frac{1.7093\ g}{26.9815\ g/mol} = 6.335x10^{-2}\ mol$$

$$n_{H_2} = (3/2)(6.335x10^{-2}) = 9.503x10^{-2}\ mol$$

$$V = nRT/P = \frac{(9.503x10^{-2}\ mol)}{(738.5\ mmHg)}\left(62.363\ \frac{L\cdot mmHg}{mol\cdot K}\right)(298.0\ K)$$

$= 2.391$ L

15. (e) We know that the molar volume is 22.4 L at 0°C and 1.00 atm. If we halve the pressure, the volume will double to 44.8 L. Increasing the temperature will further increase the molar volume. $V/n = RT/P$. At 40°C and 0.500 atm, $V/n = (0.082057)(313.2)/0.5 = 51.4$ L. Option (b) is ruled out because at a pressure of 0.25 atm and 0°C the molar volume is 4(22.4 L) = 89.6 L.

16. __(c)__ Since all gases are at the same temperature and pressure, the molar ratios are the same as the volume ratios. There is excess ammonia, as only (4/5)(60.0 mL) = 48.0 mL of NH_3 are required to react completely with 60.0 mL of O_2. Thus the O_2 is the limiting reagent, and the volume of $H_2O(g)$ formed is (6/5)(volume O_2 used) = (6/5)(60.0 mL) = 72.0 mL.

17. __(d)__ Mol. wt. SO_2 = 64; mol. wt. O_2 = 32. For 100 g samples of each, n_{O_2} = 3.13 mol; n_{SO_2} = 1.56 mol; n_{total} = 4.69 mol.

$$X_{SO_2} = \frac{1.56}{4.69} = 0.333, \quad \text{and}$$

$$P_{SO_2} = P_{total}X_{SO_2} = (0.333)(600\ \text{mmHg}) = 200\ \text{mmHg}$$

18. __(a)__ Burning 0.20 mol of C_xH_y will yield 0.20x mol of CO_2, by the conservation of C atoms. Since 0.20x = 0.80, x = 4. Burning 0.20 mol of C_xH_y will yield (1/2)(0.20y) mol of H_2O, by the conservation of H atoms, as each H_2O molecule has 2 H atoms. Thus (1/2)(0.20y) = 0.10y = 1.0 mol H_2O, and y = 10. The hydrocarbon is therefore butane, C_4H_{10}.

Solutions to Problems, Chapter 3

3.1. (a) $$\text{No. mol } CO_2 \text{ formed} = \frac{0.8010 \text{ g}}{44.01 \text{ g/mol}} = 1.820\times10^{-2} \text{ mol}$$

No. mol C atoms in CO_2 and in hydrocarbon sample = 1.820×10^{-2} mol

$$\text{mass C} = (12.011 \text{ g/mol})(1.820\times10^{-2} \text{ mol}) = 0.2186 \text{ g of C}$$

$$\text{mass H in sample} = 0.2553 \text{ g} - 0.2186 \text{ g} = 0.0367 \text{ g H atoms}$$

$$\text{No. mol H atoms} = \frac{0.0367 \text{ g}}{1.0079 \text{ g/mol}} = 0.0364 \text{ mol H}$$

$$\frac{\text{No. mol H}}{\text{No. mol C}} = \frac{0.0364}{0.0182} = \frac{2.00}{1.00}$$

The empirical formula of this compound is $(CH_2)_n$.

(b) $$M = \frac{\delta RT}{P} = (1.87\frac{g}{L})\left(0.08206 \frac{L\cdot atm}{mol\cdot K}\right)\frac{(273.2K)}{(1.00 \text{ atm})} = 41.9 \text{ g/mol}$$

The formula weight of CH_2 is 14.027, so the molecular weight of $(CH_2)_n$ is 14.027n. Since 14.027n ~ 41.9, n must be exactly 3. The molecular formula is C_3H_6, and the molecular weight is 42.080 g/mol.

3.2. (a) FALSE. Since both gases have the same V and T, the ratio P/n is the same for both. Since the pressure of C_2H_6 is half the pressure of H_2, the number of moles of C_2H_6 is 1/2 the number of moles of H_2, and therefore the number of molecules of C_2H_6 is half the number of molecules of H_2. But there are 8 atoms per C_2H_6 molecule and only 2 atoms per H_2 molecule. Thus there are twice as many atoms in the ethane sample as there are in the H_2 sample.

(b) FALSE. $\delta = MP/RT$. $M_{C_2H_6} = 30.07$ and $M_{H_2} = 2.016$ Both gases are at the same temperature.

$$\frac{\delta_{C_2H_6}}{\delta_{H_2}} = \frac{(30.07)(340)}{(2.016)(680)} = 7.5$$

The density of the ethane is 7.5 times the density of the H_2 sample.

3.3. $$\frac{n}{V} = \frac{P}{RT} = \frac{1.00\times10^{-6}\ \text{mmHg}}{\left(62.36\ \frac{\text{L}\cdot\text{mmHg}}{\text{mol}\cdot\text{K}}\right)(298.2\ \text{K})} = 5.378\times10^{-11}\ \text{mol/L}$$

$$\left(5.378\times10^{-11}\ \frac{\text{mol}}{\text{L}}\right)\left(\frac{1\ \text{L}}{1000\ \text{cm}^3}\right)\left(6.022\times10^{23}\ \frac{\text{molecules}}{\text{mol}}\right)$$

$$= 3.24\times10^{10}\ \text{molecules}\cdot\text{cm}^{-3}$$

A vacuum is a space empty of all matter. This "vacuum" has 3.24×10^{10} molecules in each cubic centimeter. Although the pressure is very low, and experimentally this is a "good vacuum", there are still a very large number of molecules in one cubic centimeter.

3.4. The equation tells us that the number of moles of H_2 formed is equal to the number of moles of Mg used.

$$\text{No. mol Mg used} = \frac{0.3404\ \text{g}}{24.305\ \text{g/mol}} = 1.4005\times10^{-2}\ \text{mol Mg}$$

$$P_{H_2} = P_{total} - P_{H_2O} = 764.8\ \text{mmHg} - 25.8\ \text{mmHg} = 739.0\ \text{mmHg}$$

$$V = \frac{nRT}{P} = \frac{(1.4005\times10^{-2}\ \text{mol})}{739.0\ \text{mmHg}}\left(62.363\ \frac{\text{L}\cdot\text{mmHg}}{\text{mol}\cdot\text{K}}\right)(299.6\ \text{K})$$

$$= 0.3540\ \text{L} = 354.0\ \text{mL}$$

3.5. $$\text{No. mol } H_2O = \frac{1.1206\ \text{g}}{18.015\ \text{g/mol}} = 6.2204\times10^{-2}\ \text{mol}$$

$$\text{No. mol H} = 2(\text{No. mol } H_2O) = 1.2441\times10^{-1}\ \text{mol H atoms}$$

mass H atoms = (1.0079 g/mol)(1.2441×10^{-1} mol) = 0.1254 g

Since mass is conserved, this is the mass of H atoms in the 1.3704 g sample.

$$\text{mass C} = (0.6542)(1.3704\ \text{g}) = 0.8965\ \text{g}$$

mass N = 1.3704 g - 0.8965 g - 0.1254 g = 0.3485 g N atoms

(b) In this 1.3704 g sample of the compound,

$$\text{No. mol C} = \frac{0.8965\ \text{g}}{12.011\ \text{g/mol}} = 7.464\times10^{-2}\ \text{mol C}$$

$$\text{No. mol N} = \frac{0.3485\ \text{g}}{14.007\ \text{g/mol}} = 2.488\times10^{-2}\ \text{mol N}$$

$$\text{No. mol H} = 1.244\times10^{-1}\ \text{mol H} \quad \text{(from part a)}$$

Divide each by the smallest number of these, which is the number of moles of N.

$$\frac{\text{moles H}}{\text{moles N}} = \frac{0.1244}{0.02488} = \frac{5.00}{1.00}; \qquad \frac{\text{moles C}}{\text{moles N}} = \frac{0.07464}{0.02488} = \frac{3.00}{1.00}$$

The simplest formula is C_3H_7N. The empirical formula is $(C_3H_7N)_n$.

(c) The formula weight of C_3H_7N is 57.095 g/mol. Hence, 57.095n ~ 110, and n = 2. The molecular formula is $C_6H_{14}N_2$, and the exact molecular weight is 114.19 g/mol.

3.6. (a) $$n = \frac{PV}{RT} = \frac{(376\ \text{mmHg})(1.00\ \text{L})}{\left(62.36\ \frac{\text{L}\cdot\text{mmHg}}{\text{mol}\cdot\text{K}}\right)(580\text{K})} = 1.04\times10^{-2}\ \text{mol}$$

$$M = \frac{2.359\ \text{g}}{1.04\times10^{-2}\ \text{mol}} = 227\ \text{g/mol}$$

(b) There cannot be more than 1 Sb atom per molecule, because if there were 2 Sb atoms the molecular weight would have to be greater than 2(121.75) = 243.5 g/mol, and it is only 227 g/mol. Hence there is only 1 Sb atom per molecule, and the rest is Cl.

(c) Of the 227 g/mol, 121.75 g is the mass of the Sb, and 105 g is the mass of the Cl atoms.

$$\text{No. mol Cl} = \frac{105 \text{ g}}{35.45 \text{ g/mol}} = 3 \text{ mol Cl}$$

The formula of the compound is $SbCl_3$.

(d) The exact molecular weight of $SbCl_3$ is 228.11 g/mol.

3.7. If all gases are at the same T and P, volume ratios are the same as molar ratios. The H_2 is the limiting reagent. The complete reaction of 12.00 mL of H_2 consumes 6.00 mL of O_2, and produces 12.00 mL of $H_2O(g)$. There are 14.00 mL of O_2 in excess. The resulting mixture therefore has a volume of 26.00 mL.

3.8. $$P_{H_2} = P_{total} - P_{H_2O} = 746.6 \text{ mmHg} - 23.2 \text{ mmHg}$$
$$= 723.4 \text{ mmHg}$$

$$n_{H_2} = \frac{PV}{RT} = \frac{(723.4 \text{ mmHg})(0.436 \text{ L})}{\left(62.363 \frac{\text{L}\cdot\text{mmHg}}{\text{mol}\cdot\text{K}}\right)(297.8 \text{ K})} = 1.698\times10^{-2} \text{ mol } H_2$$

$$\text{No. mol Al used} = \left(\frac{2}{3}\right)(\text{No. mol } H_2 \text{ formed}) = \left(\frac{2}{3}\right)(1.698\times10^{-2})$$
$$= 1.132\times10^{-2} \text{ mol Al}$$

$$\text{mass Al} = (1.132\times10^{-2} \text{ mol})(26.98 \text{ g/mol}) = 0.3054 \text{ g Al}$$

$$\%\text{ Al by weight} = \left(\frac{0.3054 \text{ g}}{0.415 \text{ g}}\right)\times100 = 73.6\%\text{ Al}$$

3.9. (a) $\%H = 100.00 - 53.28 - 31.07 = 15.65$

In a 100.00 g sample,

$$\text{No. mol C} = \frac{53.28 \text{ g}}{12.011 \text{ g/mol}} = 4.436$$

$$\text{No. mol H} = \frac{15.65 \text{ g}}{1.0079 \text{ g/mol}} = 15.53$$

$$\text{No. mol N} = \frac{31.07 \text{ g}}{14.007 \text{ g/mol}} = 2.218$$

Divide each by the number of moles of N atoms.

$$\frac{\text{moles C}}{\text{moles N}} = \frac{4.436}{2.218} = 2.00; \qquad \frac{\text{moles H}}{\text{moles N}} = \frac{15.53}{2.218} = 7.00$$

The empirical formula is $(C_2H_7N)_n$.

(b) $$M = \frac{\delta RT}{P} = \frac{(1.47 \text{ g/L})}{(0.940 \text{ atm})}\left(0.082057 \frac{\text{L·atm}}{\text{mol·K}}\right)(350 \text{ K})$$
$$= 44.9 \text{ g/mol}$$

The formula weight of C_2H_7N is 45.084 g/mol. Hence, $45.084n \sim 44.9$, and $n = 1$. The correct molecular formula is C_2H_7N, and the exact molecular weight is 45.084 g/mol.

3.10. First calculate how many moles of He atoms are collected in a year.

$$n = \frac{PV}{RT} = \frac{(152.0 \text{ mmHg})(2.37\text{x}10^{-4} \text{ L})}{\left(62.363 \frac{\text{L·mmHg}}{\text{mol·K}}\right)(300 \text{ K})} = 1.93\text{x}10^{-6} \text{ (mol He)/yr}$$

Then calculate the number of α-particles emitted per year.

$$\left(2.23\text{x}10^{12} \frac{\alpha\text{-particles}}{\text{minute}}\right)\left(60 \frac{\text{min}}{\text{hr}}\right)\left(24 \frac{\text{hr}}{\text{da}}\right)\left(365 \frac{\text{da}}{\text{yr}}\right)$$

$$= 1.17\text{x}10^{18} \frac{\alpha\text{-particles}}{\text{yr}}$$

Each α-particle becomes one He atom. Hence the number of atoms in a mole of helium is

$$\frac{1.17\times10^{18} \text{ He atoms per year}}{1.93\times10^{-6} \text{ mol of He per year}} = 6.06\times10^{23} \text{ atoms/mol}$$

3.11. (a) There is a mole of SO_2 formed from each mole of H_2S, and two moles of SO_2 formed from each mole of CS_2. Hence,

$$\text{No. mol } SO_2 \text{ formed} = n_1 + 2n_2$$

$$\text{No. mol } CO_2 \text{ formed} = n_2$$

since there is no carbon in H_2S.

(b) (1) $330.0 \text{ mmHg} = (n_1 + n_2)(RT/V)$

(2) $440.0 \text{ mmHg} = (n_1 + 2n_2 + n_2)(RT/V)$

$$= (n_1 + 3n_2)(RT/V)$$

(c) Divide Eq. (2) by Eq. (1) to cancel the RT/V factor, which cannot be determined.

$$\frac{330.0}{440.0} = \frac{3}{4} = \frac{n_1 + n_2}{n_1 + 3n_2}, \qquad \text{hence} \quad 3n_1 + 9n_2 = 4n_1 + 4n_2$$

Collecting terms, we obtain: $5n_2 = n_1$

The mole fraction of CS_2 in the original mixture is

$X_2 = \dfrac{n_2}{n_1 + n_2}$. Substituting $5n_2$ for n_1, we obtain

$$X_2 = \frac{n_2}{5n_2 + n_2} = \frac{1}{6}$$

The mole fraction of CS_2 is 0.1667, or 16.67 mole%.

3.12. (a) Alex has made two errors. (1) The volume of the gas should be expressed in liters to agree with the volume unit in the value of R chosen. (2) Alex has used the mass of O_2 in grams for the number of moles of O_2.

$$n_{O_2} = \frac{1.20 \text{ g}}{32.00 \text{ g/mol}} = 0.0375 \text{ mol}$$

$$T = \frac{(742.0 \text{ mmHg})(0.900 \text{ L})}{(0.0375 \text{ mol})\left(62.36 \dfrac{\text{L}\cdot\text{mmHg}}{\text{mol}\cdot\text{K}}\right)} = 286 \text{ K} = 13^\circ\text{C}$$

(b) Bonny has made 4 errors. (1) The pressure unit in R is not the same as the unit used for the pressure of the gas. If the value of R used is 0.08206, then P must be in atm. Or, if P is in mmHg, R must be 62.36 $\text{L}\cdot\text{mmHg}\cdot\text{mol}^{-1}\text{K}^{-1}$. (2) The volume should be given in liters to agree with the volume unit in R. (3) The temperature must be in kelvins, not $^\circ$C. (4) Bonny's expression for M is inverted. M = mRT/PV, where m is the mass in grams. The correct expression is

$$M = \frac{(2.08 \text{ g})\left(0.082057 \dfrac{\text{L}\cdot\text{atm}}{\text{mol}\cdot\text{K}}\right)(423 \text{ K})}{(756/760 \text{ atm})(0.350 \text{ L})} = 207 \text{ g/mol}$$

(c) Caspar has forgotten the restrictions that are an essential part of Avogadro's hypothesis. Equal volumes of different gases contain equal numbers of molecules <u>provided</u> that the gases are at the same temperature and pressure.

(d) Dolly has used Boyle's law in a situation where it does not apply, because the number of moles of gas is not constant. In this problem $P_1V_1/n_1 = P_2V_2/n_2$.

$$P_2 = \left(\frac{0.0300}{0.0100}\right)\left(\frac{V}{1.50V}\right)(1.00 \text{ atm}) = 2.00 \text{ atm}$$

(e) Edgar has assumed that n and T are directly proportional, whereas they are inversely proportional. In this problem, P and V are constant. Hence, $PV/R = n_1T_1 = n_2T_2$.

$$n_2 = (0.0600)(300\ K)/(400\ K) = 0.0450\ mol$$

(f) Fanny has made 3 errors. (1) She has inverted the ratio of moles O_2 used to moles CO_2 formed. The ratio is 3/2, and not 2/3. (2) The temperature must be in kelvins, not °C. (3) The pressure unit in the value of R chosen is not the same as the unit used for the pressure of the gas. The correct expression is

$$n_{O_2} = \left(\frac{3}{2}\right)\frac{(745\ mmHg)(0.420\ L)}{\left(62.36\ \frac{L\cdot mmHg}{mol\cdot K}\right)(303\ K)} = 2.48\times10^{-2}\ mol$$

3.13. (a) Only n_{total} is constant.

$$nR = (P_1V_1/T_1) = (P_2V_2/T_2)$$

$$T_2 = \left(\frac{P_2V_2}{P_1V_1}\right)T_1 = \frac{(1.20\ atm)(2.50V)}{(1.80\ atm)\quad(V)}(293.2\ K)$$

$$= 489\ K = 216^\circ C$$

(b) Consider a 100.00 g sample of this mixture. It contains 78.5 g of Ne and 21.5 g of H_2.

$$\text{No. mol Ne} = \frac{78.5\ g}{20.179\ g/mol} = 3.89\ mol\ Ne$$

$$\text{No. mol } H_2 = \frac{21.5\ g}{2.016\ g/mol} = 10.66\ mol\ H_2$$

$$n_{total} = 14.55\ mol \qquad X_{Ne} = \frac{3.89}{14.55} = 0.267$$

$$P_{Ne} = P_{total}X_{Ne} = (1.20\ atm)(0.267) = 0.321\ atm$$

3.14. (a) $$n_{He} = \frac{PV}{RT} = \frac{(187.1\ \text{mmHg})(0.2500\ \text{L})}{\left(62.363\ \frac{\text{L}\cdot\text{mmHg}}{\text{mol}\cdot\text{K}}\right)(300\ \text{K})}$$

$$= 2.500\text{x}10^{-3}\ \text{mol}$$

(b) $$n_{CO_2} = \frac{PV}{RT} = \frac{(561.3\ \text{mmHg})(0.2500\ \text{L})}{\left(62.363\ \frac{\text{L}\cdot\text{mmHg}}{\text{mol}\cdot\text{K}}\right)(300\ \text{K})} = 7.500\text{x}10^{-3}\ \text{mol}$$

(c) The number of moles of C atoms is conserved. Each of these hydrocarbons has 2 C atoms per molecule. The number of moles of C atoms is twice the total number of moles of hydrocarbon. The number of moles of CO_2 formed is therefore also equal to twice the number of moles of hydrocarbon in the original vessel. Hence,

$$\text{no. mol hydrocarbon} = \tfrac{1}{2}(7.500\text{x}10^{-3}\ \text{mol}) = 3.750\text{x}10^{-3}\ \text{mol}$$

(d) $$n_{total} = 3.750\text{x}10^{-3}\ \text{mol hydrocarbon} + 2.500\text{x}10^{-3}\ \text{mol He}$$

$$= 6.250\text{x}10^{-3}\ \text{mol}$$

$$V = \frac{n_{total}RT}{P_{total}} = \frac{(6.250\text{x}10^{-3}\text{mol})}{(680\ \text{mmHg})}\left(62.363\ \frac{\text{L}\cdot\text{mmHg}}{\text{mol}\cdot\text{K}}\right)(300\ \text{K})$$

$$= 0.172\ \text{L} = 172\ \text{mL}$$

(e) $P_{He} = X_{He}P_{total}$. $\quad X_{He} = \frac{2.500\text{x}10^{-3}}{6.250\text{x}10^{-3}} = 0.4000$

Hence, $\quad P_{He} = (0.4000)(680\ \text{mmHg}) = 272\ \text{mmHg}$

3.15. No. mol Ne added $= \frac{8.6787\ \text{g}}{20.179\ \text{g/mol}} = 4.3009\text{x}10^{-1}$ mol

$P_{total} = P_{C_4H_{10}} + P_{Ne}$. Since adding the Ne increased the pressure by 860.0 mmHg,

$$P_{Ne} = 860.0\ \text{mmHg} = \frac{(0.43009\ \text{mol})}{V}\left(62.36\ \frac{\text{L}\cdot\text{mmHg}}{\text{mol}\cdot\text{K}}\right)(298.0\ \text{K})$$

and $$V = \frac{(0.43009)(62.363)(298.0)}{(860.0)} = 9.294\ \text{L}$$

$$n_{C_4H_{10}} = \frac{(560.0\ \text{mmHg})(9.294\ \text{L})}{\left(62.363\ \frac{\text{L}\cdot\text{mmHg}}{\text{mol}\cdot\text{K}}\right)(298.0\ \text{K})} = 0.28006\ \text{mol}$$

$$= 2.801\text{x}10^{-1}\ \text{mol}\ C_4H_{10}$$

$$\text{mass}\ C_4H_{10} = (58.123\ \text{g/mol})(0.28006\ \text{mol}) = 16.28\ \text{g}$$

3.16. (a) $P_{O_2} = P_{total} - P_{H_2O} = 741.5\ \text{mmHg} - 27.1\ \text{mmHg}$

$$= 714.4\ \text{mmHg}$$

$$n_{O_2} = \frac{PV}{RT} = \frac{(714.4\ \text{mmHg})(0.8654\ \text{L})}{\left(62.363\ \frac{\text{L}\cdot\text{mmHg}}{\text{mol}\cdot\text{K}}\right)(300.4\ \text{K})} = 1.6512\text{x}10^{-2}\ \text{mol}\ O_2$$

No. mol $KClO_3$ used = (2/3)(No. mol O_2 formed)

$$= (2/3)(1.6512\text{x}10^{-2}) = 1.1008\text{x}10^{-2} = 1.101\text{x}10^{-2}$$

(b) mass $KClO_3$ = (122.55 g/mol)($1.1008\text{x}10^{-2}$ mol) = 1.349 g

$$\%\ \text{by weight}\ KClO_3 = \left(\frac{1.349\ \text{g}}{7.0950\ \text{g}}\right)\text{x}100 = 19.01\%$$

3.17. $$n_{CO_2} = \frac{(785.50\ \text{mmHg})(2.004\ \text{L})}{\left(62.363\ \frac{\text{L}\cdot\text{mmHg}}{\text{mol}\cdot\text{K}}\right)(297.7\ \text{K})} = 8.4810\text{x}10^{-2}\ \text{mol}$$

One mole of CO_2 is formed per mole of $CaCO_3$ and per mole of $NaHCO_3$. Let n_1 = moles $CaCO_3$, and n_2 = moles $NaHCO_3$. Then,

$$n_1 + n_2 = 0.084810$$

Let x = mass of $CaCO_3$, and y = mass of $NaHCO_3$. The formula weight of $CaCO_3$ is 100.09 g/mol, and of $NaHCO_3$ is 84.007 g/mol. Therefore

$$x + y = 7.8902\text{g},\quad \text{and}\quad x = 7.8902 - y$$

$$n_1 + n_2 = \frac{(7.8902 - y)}{100.09} + \frac{y}{84.007} = 0.084810$$

Multiply by 100.09.

$$7.8902 - y + 1.19145y = 8.48866$$

$$0.19145y = 0.59846$$

$$y = 3.126 \text{ g} = \text{mass } NaHCO_3$$

$$\% \text{ by weight of } NaHCO_3 = \left(\frac{3.1259 \text{ g}}{7.8902 \text{ g}}\right) x100 = 39.62\%$$

Solutions to Exercises, Chapter 4

1. Two gases mix by diffusion more rapidly at lower pressure than at higher pressure. At higher pressures, the gas is more dense, there are more collisions between the molecules per second, and the molecular velocities change more frequently. Consider two bulbs, one containing gas A and one containing gas B. If the stopcock between the bulbs is opened, a molecule of gas A travelling through the opening into the bulb containing gas B is more likely to collide with a B molecule and have its direction reversed if gas B is at higher pressure than if gas B is at lower pressure.

2. As the pressure is increased at constant temperature, the average distance between the molecules decreases, the force of attraction between the molecules increases, and, at sufficiently high pressure, the gas is liquefied. The compressibility of a liquid is very small, and further large increases in pressure produce only very small decreases in volume.

3. The molar volume, V/n, for an ideal gas is RT/P. At 10.0 atm and 320 K,

$$\frac{V}{n} = \frac{RT}{P} = \left(0.082057\ \frac{\text{L·atm}}{\text{mol·K}}\right)\cdot\frac{(320\ \text{K})}{(10.0\ \text{atm})} = 2.63\ \text{L/mol}$$

$$\% \text{ error} = \left(\frac{P_{ideal} - P_{real}}{P_{real}}\right) x100 = \left(\frac{2.63 - 2.52}{2.52}\right) x100$$

$$= \frac{11}{2.52} = 4.4\%$$

At 40.0 atm and 320 K,

$$\frac{V}{n} = \frac{RT}{P} = \left(0.082057 \frac{L \cdot atm}{mol \cdot K}\right) \frac{(320 \text{ K})}{(40.0 \text{ atm})} = 0.657 \text{ L/mol}$$

$$\% \text{ error} = \left(\frac{0.66 - 0.54}{0.54}\right) x100 = \frac{12}{0.54} = 22\%$$

4. At pressures as high as 80 atm, if the product PV increases as P increases (instead of remaining constant, as predicted by Boyle's law), the principal reason is that the molecular diameter is no longer negligible compared to the average distance between molecules. The volume occupied by the molecules themselves is a significant fracion of the volume of the container, and doubling the pressure reduces the volume by a factor less than 1/2.

5. The molecules of a gas are in rapid, random motion (Postulate 3). On the average, there are as many molecules moving in one direction as in any other direction. The x, y, and z directions are all equivalent, so that $\langle u_x^2 \rangle = \langle u_y^2 \rangle = \langle u_z^2 \rangle$.

6. All collisions the molecules make with other molecules and with the walls of the container are elastic (Postulate 6). If collisions are elastic, energy is conserved, that is, the translational kinetic energy is constant.

7. $K.E. = \frac{1}{2}mu^2 = \frac{1}{2}(20.0\times10^{-6}\ kg)(25.0\ m^2s^{-2})$

$= 2.5\times10^{-4}\ J$

8. $E_{trans} = (3/2)nRT$

$$\begin{array}{ccc} \underline{\text{nitrogen}} & & \underline{\text{methane}} \\ \frac{3}{2}(0.80)RT & = & \frac{3}{2}(0.50)R(400.0\ K) \end{array}$$

The 3/2 and R factors cancel.

$$T = \left(\frac{0.50}{0.80}\right)(400.0\ K) = 250\ K$$

Note that it is both time consuming and unnecessary to calculate the translational kinetic energy of 0.50 mol of CH_4 at 400.0 K.

9. $\langle \varepsilon_k \rangle = \frac{3}{2}kT$, and depends only on the temperature. The two samples will have the same average translational kinetic energy at the same temperature, 310.0 K.

10. $$T = \frac{PV}{nR} = \frac{(1.00\ atm)(5.40\ L)}{(0.200\ mol)\left(0.082057\ \frac{L\cdot atm}{mol\cdot K}\right)} = 329\ K$$

$E_{trans} = \frac{3}{2}nRT = \frac{3}{2}(0.200\ mol)(8.3144\ J\cdot mol^{-1}K^{-1})(329\ K)$

$= 821\ J$

$\langle \varepsilon_k \rangle = (3/2)kT = (3/2)(1.38066\times10^{-23}\ J\cdot K^{-1})(329\ K)$

$= 4.54\times10^{-21}\ J$

11. $$\langle u \rangle = \frac{1 + 2 + 3 + 4 + 5}{5} = \frac{15}{5} = 3.00\ m/s$$

$$\langle u^2 \rangle = \frac{1^2 + 2^2 + 3^2 + 4^2 + 5^2}{5} = \frac{1 + 4 + 9 + 16 + 25}{5} = \frac{55}{5}$$

$= 11\ m^2/s^2$

$$u_{rms} = \langle u^2 \rangle^{1/2} = 11^{1/2} = 3.32\ m/s$$

u_{rms} is larger than $\langle u \rangle$. In any sample of gas, u_{rms} is always larger than $\langle u \rangle$.

12. (a) Let the weight of the first bead be w_1, the weight of the second bead be w_2, and so on. Then,

total weight of the four beads $= w_1 + w_2 + w_3 + w_4$

$$\langle w \rangle = \text{average weight of a bead} = \frac{w_1 + w_2 + w_3 + w_4}{4}$$

Thus, $4\langle w \rangle$ = total weight of the four beads, Q.E.D.

(b) Let the mass of the ith object be m_i. Then,

$$\text{total mass} = \sum m_i$$

$$\text{average mass} = \langle m \rangle = \frac{\text{total mass}}{N} = (1/N)\sum m_i$$

Thus, $N\langle m \rangle$ = total mass, Q.E.D.

13. $u_{rms} = (3RT/M)^{1/2}$, and is independent of the volume of the container or the number of moles of gas. $M_{Ne} =$ 20.18; $M_{Cl_2} = 70.906$. The temperature is higher and the molecular weight lower for the neon sample, so u_{rms} is greater for Sample A.

14. No, CH_4 effuses 1.66 times as fast as CO_2.

$$\frac{\text{rate of effusion of } CH_4}{\text{rate of effusion of } CO_2} = \left(\frac{M_{CO_2}}{M_{CH_4}}\right)^{1/2} = \frac{44.01}{16.04}^{1/2} = 1.66$$

15.
$$\frac{\text{rate of effusion at } 398.2 \text{ K}}{\text{rate of effusion at } 298.2 \text{ K}} = \left(\frac{398.2 \text{ K}}{298.2 \text{ K}}\right)^{1/2}$$
$$= (1.335)^{1/2} = 1.16$$

Any gas effuses 1.16 times faster at 125°C (398.2 K) than at 25°C (298.2 K).

16. From Table 4.4 we see that the value of van der Waals' constant b for SO_2 is 0.0564 L/mol, while for H_2O it is 0.0305 L/mol. Thus SO_2 has a larger molecular diameter than H_2O. This is not surprising, as S and O are larger atoms than H.

17. (a)

$$P_{ideal} = \frac{nRT}{V} = \frac{(1.00\ mol)}{(2.52\ L)}\left(0.082057\ \frac{L\cdot atm}{mol\cdot K}\right)(320.0\ K)$$

$$= 10.4\ atm$$

The actual pressure, 10.00 atm, is less than the ideal pressure, 10.4 atm. This indicates that the major cause of deviation from ideality at this temperature and pressure is the non-zero force of attraction between the CO_2 molecules.

(b) $$P_{vderW} = \frac{nRT}{(V - nb)} - \frac{n^2 a}{V^2} = \frac{(0.082057)(320.0)}{2.52 - 0.0427} - \frac{3.592}{(2.52)^2}$$

$$= 10.60 - 0.57 = 10.03\ atm$$

At this temperature and pressure, van der Waals' equation agrees better with experimental observation than does the ideal gas law.

Solutions to Multiple Choice Questions, Chapter 4

1. (d) The average molecular speed is proportional to $(T/M)^{1/2}$. Thus light molecules at high temperatures move fastest. The mean speed is independent of the size of the sample. The lightest molecule of those listed is He, and the highest temperature of those given is 560 K. Hence,

just calculate T/M for choices (a) and (d) for comparison. For (a), M_{N_2} = 28.0, and T/M = 560/28.0 = 20. For (d) M_{He} = 4.0, and T/M = 140/4.0 = 35. Choices (c) and (e) are immediately eliminated as the temperature is lower and the molecular weight greater than the sample of choice (a). For option (b), the molecular weight of Ne is 5 times that of He, but 500 K is less than 5 times 140 K. Thus T/M, and therefore the mean speed, is greatest in sample (d).

2. **(c)** A real gas most closely approaches the behavior of an ideal gas at low pressure and high temperature.

3. **(d)** $$\frac{\text{rate of effusion of } O_2}{\text{rate of effusion of He}} = \left(\frac{4.0}{32.0}\right)^{1/2} = 0.35$$

4. **(b)** At 0.5 atm, P_1V_1 = (0.5 atm)(2.0 L) = 1.0 L·atm

At 100 atm, P_2V_2 = (100 atm)(0.013 L) = 1.3 L·atm

An increase in PV with increasing pressure is due to the fact that the volume of the gas molecules is a significant fraction of the volume of the container. Option (c) is a correct statement, but the increasing force of attraction causes PV to decrease with increasing pressure. Study Figs. 4.10 and 4.11. If the molecules dimerize, the number of moles of gas will decrease, and PV will decrease significantly.

5. **(d)**

$$\frac{\text{effusion rate of } N_2 \text{ at T}}{\text{effusion rate of } SO_2 \text{ at 323 K}} = \left(\frac{(T/28.01)}{(323.2/64.06)}\right)^{1/2} = 1.625$$

Squaring the two terms on the right yields

$$\frac{64.06\ T}{(28.01)(323.2)} = (1.625)^2 = 2.6406$$

$$7.076 \times 10^{-3} T = 2.6406, \quad \text{and } T = 373.2\ K$$

6. **(e)** The first four quantities listed all increase with temperature at constant volume. The density of the gas depends on the number of moles of gas and the volume. As these are both constant, the density does not change.

7. **(c)** The rate of effusion is inversely proportional to the time it takes for the gas to effuse, that is, the less the time, the faster the rate.

$$\frac{\text{rate of effusion of gas X}}{\text{rate of effusion of } H_2} = \left(\frac{2.0}{M_X}\right)^{1/2} = \frac{(1/130)}{(1/26)} = \frac{1}{5}$$

Thus, $\frac{2.0}{M_X} = \frac{1}{25}$ and $M_X = (2.0)(25) = 50$

8. **(e)** $u_{rms} = (3RT/M)^{1/2}$

9. **(a)** $\langle u \rangle$ is proportional to $(T/M)^{1/2}$. Since M is constant, $\langle u \rangle$ is proportional to $T^{1/2}$. Thus,

$$\frac{\langle u \rangle \text{ at } 375\ K}{\langle u \rangle \text{ at } 250\ K} = \left(\frac{375}{250}\right)^{1/2} = 1.22$$

10. **(a)** All the gases are at the same temperature, so that the gas with the highest molecular weight has the lowest mean speed. Of the gases listed, CO_2 has the highest molecular weight, 44.01 g/mol.

11. **(b)** The number of collisions of Ar atoms with the walls of the container depends on the partial pressure of

the Ar. If the temperature decreases at constant volume, the pressure decreases and the number of collisions decreases. If the average K.E. increases, the temperature has increased, and the number of collisions increases. If the volume decreases, the pressure increases, and the number of collisions increases. Adding CO_2 does not change the partial pressure of the Ar, and hence does not affect the number of collisions of Ar atoms with the walls.

12. <u>**(b)**</u> The principal reason that PV for a real gas is less than PV for an ideal gas is the nonzero force of attraction between the molecules. Study Figs. 4.10 and 4.11.

13. <u>**(e)**</u> $$\frac{\text{rate of effusion of } NH_3}{\text{rate of effusion of X}} = \left(\frac{M_X}{17.03}\right)^{1/2} = 3.32$$

Thus, $$\frac{M_X}{17.03} = (3.32)^2 = 11.02$$

$$M_X = (17.03)(11.02) = 187.7 = 188 \text{ g/mol}$$

14. <u>**(b)**</u> As these are monatomic gases, they have only translational kinetic energy. $E_{trans} = \frac{3}{2}RT$, and depends on T only. Gases at the same T have the same molar translational kinetic energy.

15. <u>**(a)**</u> The total translational kinetic energy, E_{trans}, is (3/2)nRT.

$$\underset{\text{helium}}{(3/2)(0.30)RT} = \underset{\text{argon}}{(3/2)(0.40)R(400)}$$

The 3/2 and R factors cancel. $T = \frac{(0.40)}{(0.30)}(400\text{ K}) = 533\text{ K}$

Solutions to Problems, Chapter 4

4.1. (a) Argon is monatomic, therefore all its kinetic energy is translational.

$$E_{trans} = \frac{3}{2}nRT = \frac{3}{2}\left(\frac{1}{3}\ \text{mol}\right)(8.3144\ \text{J}\cdot\text{mol}^{-1}\text{K}^{-1})(400.0\ \text{K})$$

$$= (8.3144)(200.0)\ \text{J} = 1663\ \text{J} = 1.663\ \text{kJ}$$

(b) $\langle\varepsilon_k\rangle = \frac{3}{2}kT$, independent of the size of the sample.

$$\langle\varepsilon_k\rangle = \frac{3}{2}(1.38066\text{x}10^{-23}\ \text{J}\cdot\text{K}^{-1})(400.0\ \text{K}) = 8.284\text{x}10^{-21}\ \text{J}$$

(c) $\Delta E = \frac{3}{2}nR(T_2 - T_1) = \frac{3}{2}\left(\frac{1}{3}\ \text{mol}\right)(8.3144\ \text{J}\cdot\text{mol}^{-1}\text{K}^{-1})(120.0\ \text{K})$

$= (8.3144)(60.00)\ \text{J} = 498.9\ \text{J}$

4.2. $u_{rms} = (3RT/M)^{1/2}$

$$= \left(\frac{(3)(8.3144\ \text{J}\cdot\text{mol}^{-1}\text{K}^{-1})(298.2\ \text{K})}{28.0134\text{x}10^{-3}\ \text{kg}\cdot\text{mol}^{-1}}\right)^{1/2}$$

$= 515.3\ \text{m/s} = 0.5153\ \text{km/s}$

$$(515.3\ \frac{\text{m}}{\text{s}})(3600\ \frac{\text{s}}{\text{h}})(10^{-3}\ \frac{\text{km}}{\text{m}})(0.6214\ \frac{\text{mi}}{\text{km}}) = 1153\ \frac{\text{mi}}{\text{h}}$$

4.3.
$$\frac{u_{rms}\ \text{at}\ 373.2\ \text{K}}{u_{rms}\ \text{at}\ 273.2\ \text{K}} = \left(\frac{373.2}{273.2}\right)^{1/2} = 1.169$$

u_{rms} at 373.2 K = $(1.169)(u_{rms}$ at 273.2 K$) = (1.169)(425)$

$= 497\ \text{m/s}$

4.4. The balloon will expand. Helium effuses faster than Ne, since He has a lower molecular weight than Ne. Helium effuses into the balloon faster than Ne effuses out of the balloon, and as the number of moles of gas in the balloon increases, the balloon expands.

4.5. **(a)**, **(b)**, and **(c)** are on the next page.

4.5. (a), (b), and (c). PV vs V for 1 mol CO_2 at 0°C

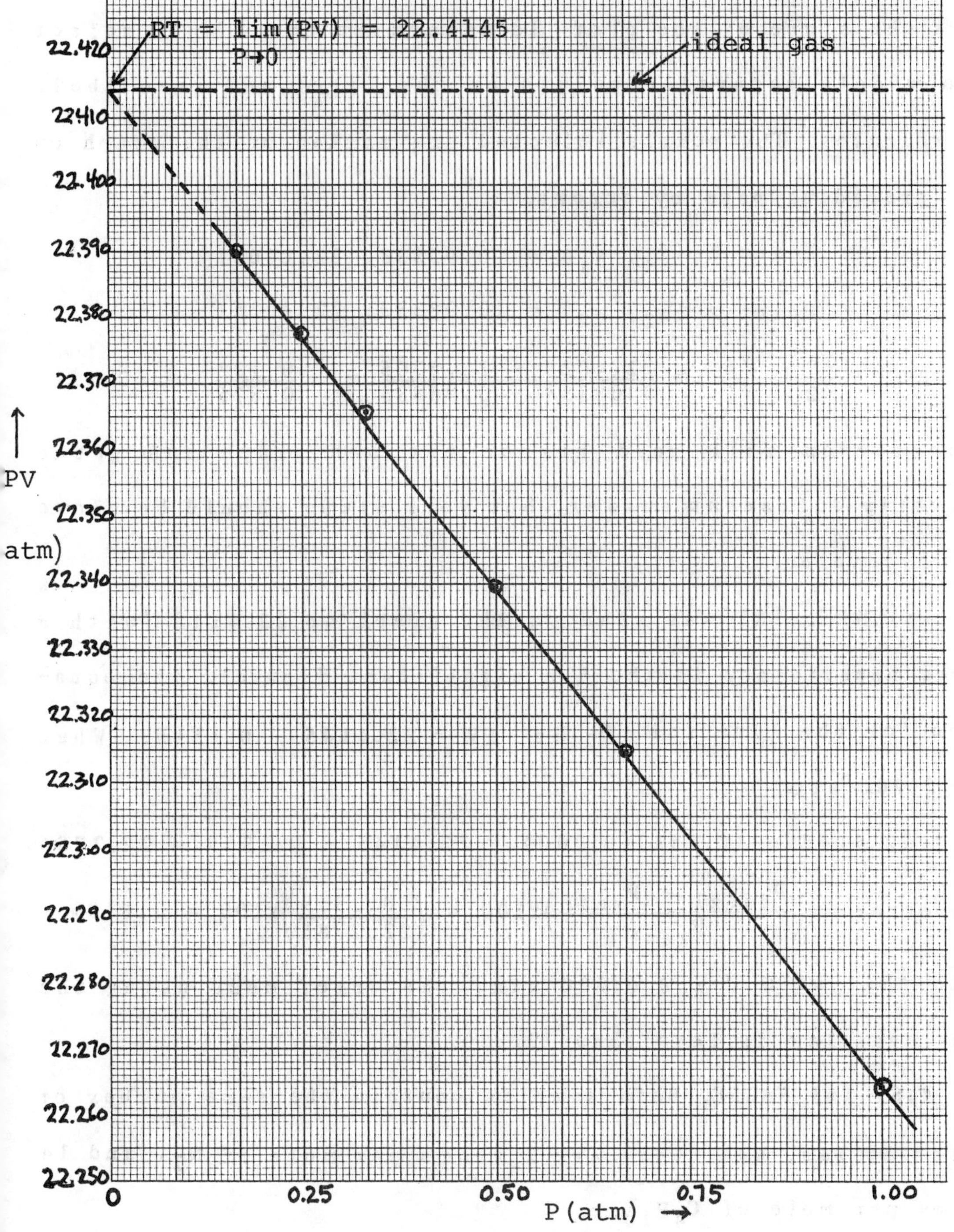

(d) If $PV = RT + BP$, and PV is plotted against P, then B is the slope of the plot. To determine the slope, select two widely separated points on the line, and read their coordinates. The points selected are marked on the graph on the preceding page by arrows.

$$\text{Point 1 } (x_1, y_1) = (0.95833,\ 22.2705)$$

$$\text{Point 2 } (x_2, y_2) = (0.08333,\ 22.4025)$$

$$\text{slope} = \frac{y_2 - y_1}{x_2 - x_1} = \frac{22.4025 - 22.2705}{0.08333 - 0.95833} = -\frac{0.132}{0.875} = -0.151$$

Each person will read his or her own graph and get a slightly different answer, but your slope should be close to this value.

(e) Since RT was read on the graph as 22.4145 (with a large uncertainty in the 6th significant figure), the equation for the line for CO_2 is $PV = 22.4145 - 0.151P$. When $P = 0.900$ atm,

$$PV = 22.4145 - (0.151)(0.900) = 22.4145 - 0.1359 = 22.2786$$

$$\%\ \text{error} = \left(\frac{P_{ideal} - P_{real}}{P_{real}}\right) \text{x}100 = \left(\frac{0.1359}{22.2786}\right) \text{x}100 = 0.610\%$$

Note that at 0°C and 0.900 atm, the error made using the ideal gas law is less than 1%.

4.6. (a) FALSE. Both samples contain the same number of moles of gas, but there are 2 atoms per mole of N_2, and 14 atoms per mole of C_4H_{10}.

(b) FALSE. $u_{rms} = (3RT/M)^{1/2}$. The temperature, T, is the same for both gases, but M = 28.01 for N_2 and 58.12 for C_4H_{10}. Thus the root-mean-square speed is greater for N_2 than for C_4H_{10} at the same temperature.

(c) TRUE. $\langle \varepsilon_k \rangle = (3/2)kT$ and depends only on the temperature.

(d) TRUE. $\delta = MP/RT$. P and T are the same for both samples, but M is less for N_2, and therefore the density, δ, is less for N_2.

(e) TRUE. $E_{trans} = \frac{3}{2}nRT$. Since both gases have the same P, T, and V, they have the same number of moles. If n and T are the same, the total translational kinetic energies are the same.

4.7. (a) Axel has made two errors. (1) He has used the wrong formula. $E_{trans} = \frac{3}{2}nRT$. The molecular weight does not enter into the calculation, and the factor is 3/2 and not 3. (2) He has used the wrong value of R. To obtain an energy in joules, use $R = 8.3144\ J \cdot mol^{-1}K^{-1}$. The correct expression should be

$$E_{trans} = \frac{3}{2}(2.0\ mol)(8.3144\ J \cdot mol^{-1}K^{-1})(300\ K)$$
$$= 7.48 \times 10^3\ J = 7.48\ kJ$$

(b) Beula has made two errors. Both gases must be <u>at the same temperature</u>, and the relative rates of effusion are inversely proportional to <u>the square root of</u> their molecular weights.

(c) Cyril forgot to take the square root of the ratio of the molecular weights of these two gases. $M_{Ne} = 20.179$ and $M_{He} = 4.0026$.

$$\frac{\text{rate of effusion of He}}{\text{rate of effusion of Ne}} = \left(\frac{20.179}{4.0026}\right)^{1/2} = (5.0415)^{1/2} = 2.245$$

He effuses 2.245 times faster than Ne at the same temperature.

(d) Derry has made 3 errors. All terms in the expression for u_{rms} must be in SI units. (1) R should be 8.3144 $J \cdot mol^{-1}K^{-1}$. (2) T should be in kelvins, 373.2 K, not 100.0°C. (3) The molecular weight should be in kg/mol, not g/mol. M = 0.04401 kg/mol.

$$u_{rms} = \left(\frac{(3)(8.3144)(373.2)}{0.04401}\right)^{1/2} = 460 \text{ m/s}$$

4.8. (a) TRUE. Pressure = force/area. Thus the force, f, is PA. Both gases are at the same pressure, P, and the walls of their containers have the same area, A.

(b) FALSE. As He is monatomic, its total kinetic energy is translational kinetic energy. $E_{trans} = \frac{3}{2}nRT$. As both gases are in containers of the same volume, and have the same pressure and temperature, the number of moles of each gas is the same. Thus they have the same total translational kinetic energy. The total K.E. of the C_3H_8 sample is greater than the total K.E. of the He, because C_3H_8 has vibrational and rotational K.E. as well as translational.

(c) FALSE. The He effuses out of its container 3.32 times as fast as the C_3H_8.

$$\frac{\text{rate of effusion of He}}{\text{rate of effusion of } C_3H_8} = \left(\frac{M_{C_3H_8}}{M_{He}}\right)^{1/2} = \left(\frac{44.10}{4.003}\right)^{1/2} = 3.32$$

4.9. $$\frac{\text{rate of effusion of X at 480 K}}{\text{rate of effusion of } SO_2 \text{ at 300 K}} = \left(\frac{480/M_X}{300/64.06}\right)^{1/2}$$

$$= 1.60$$

Squaring both sides, $$\frac{(480)(64.06)}{(300)\quad M_X} = (1.60)^2 = 2.56$$

and $$M_X = \frac{(1.6)(64.06)}{2.56} = 40.0$$

4.10. (a) Let n_1 = No. mol Kr, and n_2 = No. mol CH_4

P_{total} = 160.0 mmHg = $n_{total}(RT/V) = (n_1 + n_2)(RT/3.00)$

Eq.(I): $(3.00)(160.0)\ L\cdot mmHg = n_1RT + n_2RT$

Let V_1 = volume of bulb containing Kr originally, and V_2 = volume of bulb containing CH_4 originally. Then $V_1 + V_2$ = 3.00 L.

200.0 mmHg = $n_1(RT/V_1)$ and 80.0 mmHg = $n_2(RT/V_2)$

Thus, $n_1RT = 200.0V_1\ L\cdot mmHg$ and $n_2RT = 80.0V_2\ L\cdot mmHg$

Substitute these expressions into Eq.(I). Also substitute $(3.00 - V_1)$ for V_2. We obtain

$$(3.00)(160.0) = 200.0V_1 + 80.0(3.00 - V_1)$$

Then, $480.0 = 200.0V_1 + 240.0 - 80.0V_1 = 120.0V_1 + 240.0$

$$120.0V_1 = 240.0, \quad \text{and} \quad V_1 = 2.00\ L$$

The bulb that originally contained the Kr had a volume of 2.00 L.

(b) $E_{trans} = (3/2)n_{total}RT$. We therefore need n_{total} to obtain the translational kinetic energy of the mixture of gases.

$$n_{total} = \frac{P_{total} \cdot V}{RT} = \frac{(160.0\ \text{mmHg})(3.00\ \text{L})}{\left(62.36\ \frac{\text{L} \cdot \text{mmHg}}{\text{mol} \cdot \text{K}}\right)(298\ \text{K})} = 0.0258\ \text{mol}$$

$$E_{trans} = (3/2)(0.0258\ \text{mol})(8.3144\ \text{J} \cdot \text{mol}^{-1}\text{K}^{-1})(298\ \text{K})$$

$$= 96.0\ \text{J}$$

(c) $$\frac{u_{rms}\ \text{of}\ CH_4}{u_{rms}\ \text{of Kr}} = \left(\frac{83.80}{16.04}\right)^{1/2} = (5.224)^{1/2} = 2.29$$

Hence, u_{rms} of CH_4 = (2.29)(298 m/s) = 681 m/s

(d) The ratio is 1.00 exactly. The two average translational kinetic energies are equal, because both gases are at the same temperature, and $\langle \varepsilon_k \rangle = (3/2)kT$.

4.11. (a) $$P_{ideal} = \frac{nRT}{V}$$

$$= \frac{(2.60\ \text{mol})}{(1.40\ \text{L})}\left(0.082057\ \frac{\text{L} \cdot \text{atm}}{\text{mol} \cdot \text{K}}\right)(320.0\ \text{K})$$

$$= 48.8\ \text{atm}$$

(b) For CO_2, the van der Waals' constants are $\underline{a}$ = 3.592 and $\underline{b}$ = 0.0427.

$$P_{vderW} = \frac{nRT}{(V - nb)} - \frac{n^2 a}{V^2}$$

$$P_{vderW} = \frac{(2.60)(0.082057)(320.0)}{1.40 - (2.60)(0.0427)} - \frac{(2.60)^2(3.592)}{(1.40)^2}$$

$$= 52.97 - 12.39 = 40.58\ \text{atm} = 40.6\ \text{atm}$$

(c) Using the ideal law,

$$\% \text{ error} = \left(\frac{48.8 - 40.0}{40.0}\right) \text{x}100 = 22.0\%$$

Using van der Waals' equation,

$$\% \text{ error} = \left(\frac{40.6 - 40.0}{40.0}\right) \text{x}100 = 1.5\%$$

4.12. $$\frac{u_{rms}\ N_2 \text{ at } T}{u_{rms}\ CH_4 \text{ at } 373.2\ K} = \left(\frac{(T/28.0134)}{(373.2/16.04)}\right)^{1/2} = 1.00$$

If the two speeds are equal, their ratio is 1.00 exactly.

Thus, $$\frac{T}{28.0134} = \frac{373.2}{16.04}$$

and $$T = \frac{(28.0134)(373.2\ K)}{16.04} = 651.8\ K = 378.6^{\circ}C$$

4.13. (a) Eq. (3-27) is $\lim_{P \to 0} (PV) = nRT$

The number of moles of gas $n = m/M$, where m is the mass of the sample in grams, and M is the molecular weight in grams per mole. Substitute this into Eq. (3-27). We obtain

$$\lim_{P \to 0} (PV) = \frac{mRT}{M}$$

Divide by m. Since the mass of the sample is constant, it does not change as the pressure changes, and can be incorporated into the limit sign. Thus,

$$\lim_{P \to 0} (PV/m) = RT/M \quad \text{or} \quad \lim_{P \to 0} (P/\delta) = RT/M$$

where we have introduced the definition of density, $\delta = m/V$. If we invert both sides of this equation, we obtain

$$\lim_{P \to 0} (\delta/P) = M/RT, \quad \text{or} \quad M = RT \lim_{P \to 0} (\delta/P)$$

Q.E.D.

(b) We first tabulate the values to be plotted:

P (atm)	1.00000	0.75000	0.50000	0.25000
δ (g/L)	0.71707	0.53745	0.35808	0.17893
δ/P (g/L·atm)	0.71707	0.71660	0.71616	0.71572

A plot of (δ/P) vs P is shown on the next page. This plot is extrapolated back to P = 0, and the value of the intercept, 0.71528, is the $\lim_{P\to 0}(\delta/P)$. Therefore,

$$M = \left(0.082057\ \frac{\text{L·atm}}{\text{mol·K}}\right)(273.15\ \text{K})(0.71528\ \text{g·L}^{-1}\text{atm}^{-1})$$

$$= 16.032\ \text{g/mol}$$

(c) If we use the ideal law, M = RT(δ/P), for the data at 1.0000 atm, we obtain

$$M = (0.082057)(273.15)(0.71707) = 16.072\ \text{g/mol}$$

$$\%\ \text{error} = \left(\frac{16.072 - 16.032}{16.032}\right)\text{x}100 = 0.25\%$$

4.14. Because H_2 is lighter, the mean speed of H_2 is greater than the mean speed of N_2. Each molecule of H_2 therefore makes more collisions with the wall per second than does each molecule of N_2. Since the number of collisions per second is the same for the two gases, there must be more N_2 in the container than H_2.

4.15. The molecular weights of BF_3 and NH_3 are, respectively, 67.81 and 17.03. Since NH_3 is lighter, its mean speed is greater than the mean speed of BF_3. Therefore the NH_3 will travel down the tube faster than the BF_3, and the complex will form on the BF_3 side of the center.

4.13. (b) Plot of δ/P vs P for CH_4 at 0 °C

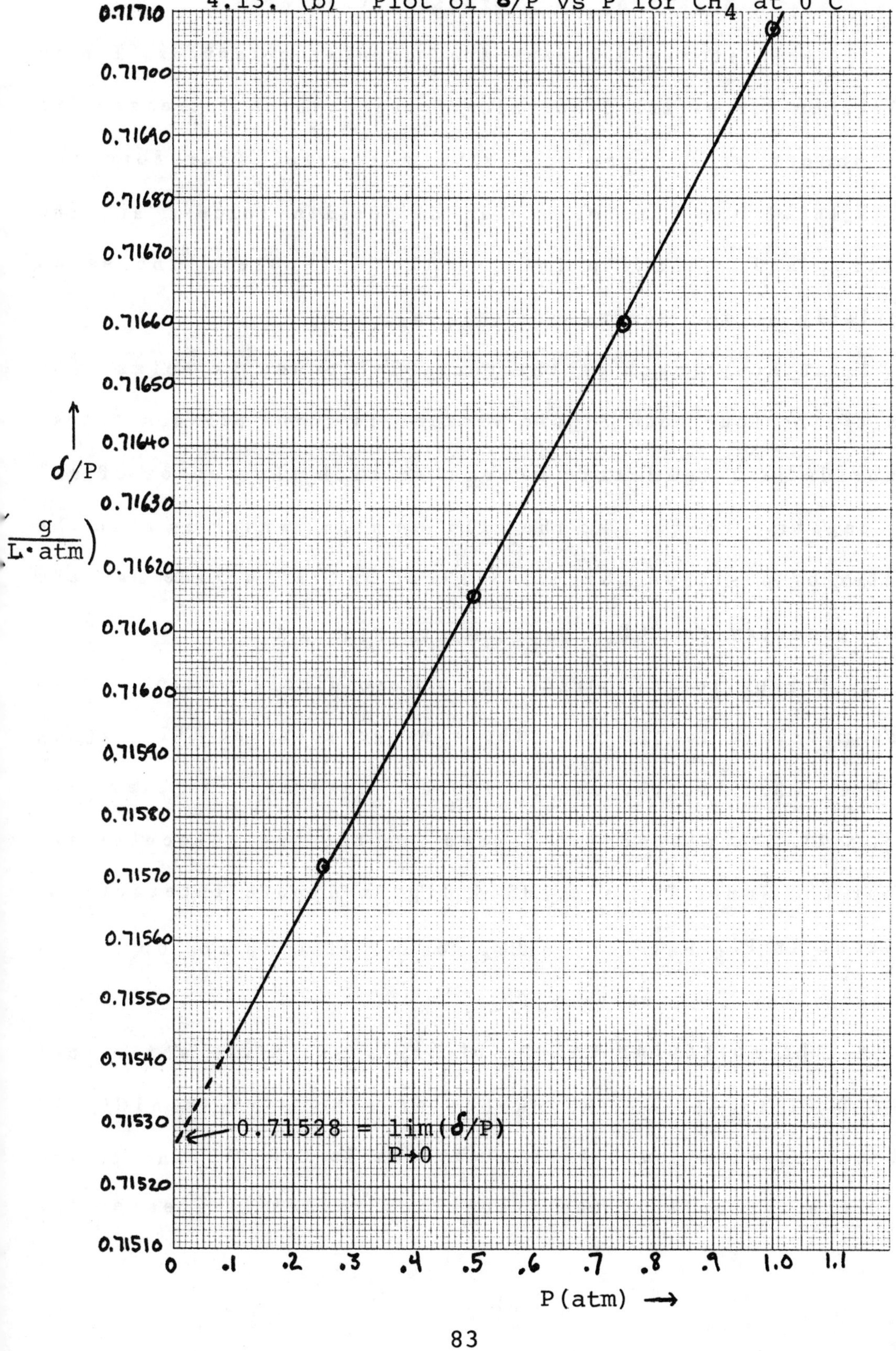

Solutions to Exercises, Chapter 5

1. The diatomic halogens are nonpolar molecules. Intermolecular forces are dispersion forces, which increase with the number of electrons in the molecule. Therefore the strength of the intermolecular dispersion forces, and the melting and boiling points of the molecules, increases regularly in the series F_2, Cl_2, Br_2, I_2.

2. Although each of the four Si-F bonds is polar, the sum of the four bond-dipole vectors is zero. Silicon tetrafluoride is a symmetric molecule, with the center of all the negative charges at the silicon atom, which is also the center of positive charge. Silicon tetrafluoride has the same geometry as CCl_4, depicted in Fig. 5.3.

3. Carbon tetrafluoride has a zero dipole moment. It is a symmetric molecule with the same geometry as CCl_4, shown in Fig. 5.3. Phosphorus trifluoide, however, is polar (see Fig. 5.2). The dispersion forces for the two molecules are about the same, but the added dipole-dipole interaction, present in PF_3 but not in CF_4, causes the mp and bp of PF_3 to be higher than that of CF_4.

4. The molecular weight of $SiCl_4$ is 169.9, while that of SiH_3Cl is 66.56. The number of electrons in $SiCl_4$ is greater than the number of electrons in SiH_3Cl, and therefore the strength of the dispersion forces is greater for

$SiCl_4$ than for SiH_3Cl. Since $SiCl_4$ has a much higher boiling point than SiH_3Cl, we conclude that the dispersion forces in $SiCl_4$ are greater than the combined dispersion forces and dipole-dipole interactions for SiH_3Cl.

5. Carbon dioxide must be linear if its dipole moment is zero. If it were a V-shaped molecules like H_2O or SO_2, it would be polar. It is linear, and the two bond-dipoles $O \leftarrow C \rightarrow O$ sum to zero.

6. The water in the hose froze during the winter. Ice is less dense than liquid water. Ice has an open structure, due to the linear hydrogen bonds between H_2O molecules. When water freezes, the volume of the solid ice is greater than the volume of the liquid water. The expansion in volume of the ice inside the hose caused the hose to crack.

7. In order for hydrogen bonding to occur, the molecule must possess a hydrogen atom bonded to a highly electronegative atom. Molecules with a polar N-H, O-H, or F-H bond can form hydrogen bonds. The only molecules, of those listed, that are capable of hydrogen bonding are (a) NH_3, (d) CH_3OH, and (j) CH_3COOH.

8. Ethanol has an O-H bond, and liquid ethanol is hydrogen-bonded. In dimethyl ether none of the hydrogen atoms is bonded to a highly electronegative atom, and hydrogen bonding cannot occur. Hydrogen bonding causes unusually high melting and boiling points.

9. Lowest: Ne, nonpolar, at. wt. 20.18, bp $-246.0^\circ C$
next: N_2, nonpolar, mol. wt. 28.01, bp $-195.8^\circ C$
next: F_2, nonpolar, mol. wt. 38.0, bp $-188^\circ C$
next: HCl, polar, mol. wt. 36.5, bp $-84.9^\circ C$
next: H_2O, polar, hydrogen-bonded, bp $+100^\circ C$
highest: NaF, ionic crystalline solid, bp $1695^\circ C$

10. The average distance between molecules in the gas phase is many times greater than the average distance between molecules in the liquid phase. Evidence for this is that gas densities are roughly 1000 times smaller than liquid densities. Because of the large average distance between molecules in the gas phase, it is possible to move molecules much closer together. In the liquid phase, however, the molecules cannot be pushed much closer together.

11. The substance is a gas. Liquid and solid densities are of the order of a few grams per mL. Gas densities are of the order of a few grams per liter.

12. $\Delta H^{273}_{subl} = \Delta H^{273}_{fus} + \Delta H^{273}_{vap}$

$$= 6.008\ kJ/mol + 44.86\ kJ/mol = 50.87\ kJ/mol$$

13. Hydrogen fluoride is the only one of these compounds that is hydrogen-bonded in the liquid state. The intermolecular forces are therefore strongest in HF. The order of strength of the intermolecular forces in the other three molecules is greatest for HI and least for HCl, because of the increasing dispersion forces with increasing numbers of electrons. See Fig. 5.9. The order of the heats of vaporization is the same as the order of the boiling points. Thus, in increasing order of ΔH_{vap}: HCl<HBr<HI<HF.

14. As H_2O is heated from 20°C to 100°C, the average kinetic energy of the molecules increases, and some hydrogen bonds are broken, so that intermolecular forces at the higher temperature are not quite as large as at 20°C. Thus the heat of vaporization at 100°C is somewhat less than the heat of vaporization at 20°C.

15. The heat of fusion is used to overcome the forces of attraction between molecules in the solid phase, to increase the average distance between the molecules, and therefore increase the potential energy of the molecules.

16. The increase in the average distance between molecules, and therefore the increase in potential energy, is much greater for the transition from liquid to gas than for the transition from solid to liquid.

17. (a)

compound	M, g/mol	ΔH_{vap} (kJ/mol)	$\Delta H_{vap}/M$ (kJ/g)
CH_4	16.04	8.907	0.5552
NH_3	17.03	23.6	1.39
H_2O	18.02	40.7	2.26
HF	20.01	30.17	1.508
HCl	36.46	15.06	0.413
CH_3OH	32.042	39.23	1.224
CH_3COCH_3	58.08	31.97	0.5504
$HCONH_2$	45.04	65.09	1.445
C_6H_6	78.11	30.8	0.394

(b) The hydrogen-bonded liquids are those with N-H, O-H, or F-H bonds, namely, NH_3, H_2O, HF, CH_3OH, and $HCONH_2$. These five liquids have heats of vaporization per gram ranging from 1224 to 2260 J/g. The nonhydrogen-bonded liquids, CH_4, HCl, CH_3COCH_3, and C_6H_6, have much lower heats of vaporization per gram, ranging from 394 to 555 J/g. The heats of vaporization per gram of the nonhydrogen-bonded liquids are therefore less than half the heats of vaporization of the hydrogen-bonded liquids.

18. The freezing of a liquid is an exothermic process. The potential energy of the system decreases as the transition from liquid to solid occurs, and the difference in energy is released as heat.

19. As there is evaporation from both liquid surfaces, the vapor phase soon contains both radioactive and nonradioactive CH_3I molecules. Once in the vapor, the molecules move randomly and occupy the space above both liquids. In the course of their random motion, some of the radioactive molecules will strike the surface of the liquid in compartment A and become part of the liquid in that compartment. The radioactivity of the liquid in compartment B will decrease with time, and the radioactivity of the liquid in compartment A will increase with time. If there were not continual exchange between the liquid and vapor phases in both compartments, the radioactivity of each liquid phase would be constant with time.

20. Before opening the stopcock, the volume of the gas phase is 0.4000 L. The number of moles of $CHCl_3$ in the gas phase is

$$n = \frac{(159.6\ \text{mmHg})(0.4000\ \text{L})}{\left(62.363\ \frac{\text{L}\cdot\text{mmHg}}{\text{mol}\cdot\text{K}}\right)(293.15\ \text{K})} = 3.492\times10^{-3}\ \text{mol}$$

After opening the stopcock, the volume of the gas is 0.9000 L, and the number of the moles of $CHCl_3$ in the gas phase is

$$n = \frac{(159.6)(0.9000)}{(62.363)(293.15)} = 7.857\times10^{-3}\ \text{mol}$$

The increase in the number of moles of $CHCl_3$ in the gas phase is $(7.857 - 3.492)\times10^{-3} = 4.365\times10^{-3}$ mol. This increase in the gas phase is the decrease in the number of moles of $CHCl_3$ in the liquid. The mass of the liquid phase has decreased by

$$(4.365\times10^{-3}\ \text{mol})(119.38\ \text{g}\cdot\text{mol}^{-1}) = 0.5211\ \text{g}$$

The volume of 0.5211 g of $CHCl_3$ is $\frac{0.5211\ \text{g}}{1.4832\ \text{g/mL}} = 0.3513$ mL. The final volume of the liquid phase is, therefore, $100.0 - 0.35 = 99.6$ mL.

21. The entropy increases. Two moles of gases are formed from one mole of solid. The gas phase is much more disordered than the solid phase, so that there is a large increase in entropy when this reaction takes place.

22. **(a)** $\Delta S_{fus} > 0$ for all substances. There is more disorder in the liquid phase than in the solid phase, and $\Delta S_{fus} = S_{liq} - S_{solid}$.

(b) For any substance, $\Delta S_{vap} > \Delta S_{fus}$. There is a much greater increase in molecular disorder when a liquid vaporizes than when a solid melts.

23. From the plot of Fig. 5.20, if the external pressure is 450 mmHg, chloroform will boil at 46°C. Read the temperature of the intersection of the 450 mmHg horizontal line with the plot of the vp of $CHCl_3$ vs temperature.

24. Reading Fig. 5.20, the vp of H_2O at 94°C is 600 mmHg, or 0.79 atm. Thus, if the atmospheric pressure is only 600 mmHg, water will boil at 94°C.

25. The intermolecular forces in iron pentacarbonyl, $Fe(CO)_5$, are stronger than the intermolecular forces in nickel tetracarbonyl, $Ni(CO)_4$. Dispersion forces are greater for $Fe(CO)_5$ than for $Ni(CO)_4$ because the molecular weight of $Fe(CO)_5$ is larger (195.9) than the molecular weight of $Ni(CO)_4$ (170.7). From the fairly large difference in vapor pressure at the same temperature, we might also predict that the dipole moment of $Fe(CO)_5$ is greater than that of $Ni(CO)_4$. In fact, $Ni(CO)_4$ is nonpolar. It has tetrahedral geometry, like CCl_4, and has a zero dipole moment. $Fe(CO)_5$ has a small dipole moment, 0.63 D.

26. Acetone is considerably more volatile than water. Intermolecular forces are much stronger in water, which is hydrogen-bonded, than in acetone, CH_3COCH_3, which is not hydrogen-bonded. Vaporization is endothermic, and as the acetone evaporates, the heat required for the vaporization comes from the portion of your arm under the acetone, which therefore feels cool.

27. **(a)** At 8 atm and $-60^\circ C$, CO_2 is a solid. As the temperature is increased to ~ $55^\circ C$, the solid melts, forming liquid CO_2. If the temperature is raised further to ~ $-10^\circ C$, the liquid vaporizes. Thus both fusion and vaporization occur as solid CO_2 is heated from $-60^\circ C$ to $+10^\circ C$ at 8 atm.

(b) At $-20^\circ C$ and 1 atm, CO_2 is a gas. As the pressure is increased to 10 atm, the gas is liquefied. The pressure at which liquefaction occurs is greater than 5.2 atm but less than 10 atm.

(c) At $-60^\circ C$ and 1 atm, CO_2 is a gas. As the pressure is increased to 10 atm, the gas is converted into solid CO_2. The pressure at which solidification occurs is below 5.2 atm.

28. (a)

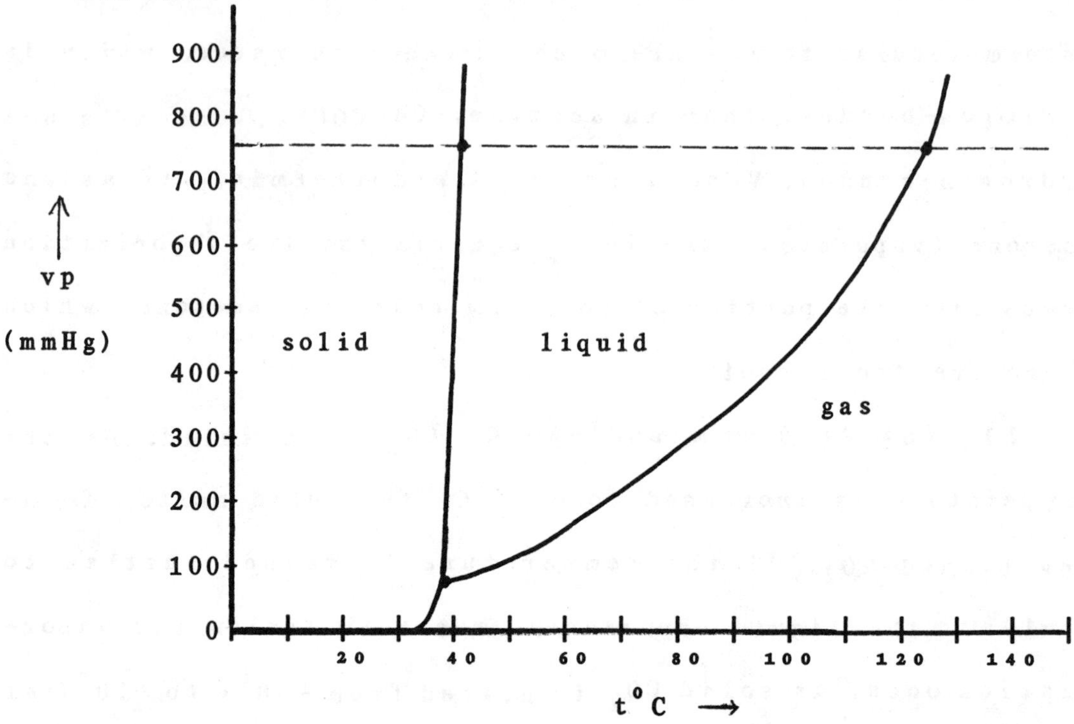

(b) The density of the liquid phase is less than the density of the solid phase. The slope of the solid = liquid curve is positive. At 200 mmHg and 40°C, this compound is a liquid. Increasing the pressure above 1 atm converts the liquid into a solid.

29.

t (°C)	P (atm)	stable phase
-90	1.0	solid
-65	1.0	gas
-65	10.0	solid
-35	2.0	gas
-35	8.0	liquid
-20	10.0	liquid

30. (a) At point A, rhombic, monoclinic, and gaseous S are in equilibrium. At point B, monoclinic, liquid, and

gaseous S are in equilibrium. At point C, rhombic, monoclinic, and liquid S are in equilibrium.

(b) Rhombic S is denser than monoclinic. If you start with monoclinic S and increase the pressure at constant temperature, rhombic S is formed. The stress of added pressure causes a shift to the phase of greater density.

Solutions to Multiple Choice Questions, Chapter 5

1. **(a)** Methanol, CH_3OH, is a hydrogen-bonded liquid, and will have the highest boiling point of these three compounds. Methane, CH_4, boils at a higher temperature than H_2 because dispersion forces are stronger for CH_4, which has a higher molecular weight than H_2.

2. **(b)** The densities of most liquids are roughly 10% lower than the densities of their solid phases.

3. **(c)** Both MgO and LiF are ionic crystalline solids. Of the other three substances, B_2H_6 has by far the lowest molecular weight, and can be expected to have the weakest dispersion forces. In fact, B_2H_6 is a gas at 25°C and 1 atm pressure.

4. **(a)** Magnesium oxide is an ionic crystalline solid, mp 2800°C. The other compounds are molecular. Carbon monoxide is a gas at room temperature and 1 atmosphere, N_2O_5 melts at 30°C, SeO_2 at ~315°C, and B_2O_3 at 460°C.

5. (b) The normal boiling point is the temperature at which the vp of the liquid is 760.0 mmHg.

6. (a) Sublimation is the transition from solid to gas.

7. (b) Fusion is the transition from solid to liquid.

8. (e) The equilibrium vapor pressure depends only on the temperature.

9. (c) The molecular weights of F_2 and Ar are very close, and they are both nonpolar.

10. (d) The equilibrium vapor pressure of a liquid increases as the temperature increases, and depends only on the temperature.

11. (e) The molecular weights of Br_2 and ICl are very close, so the dispersion forces should be roughly the same in the two compounds. As I is much less electronegative than Cl, ICl is polar.

12. (c) The vapor pressure of a liquid depends only on the temperature.

13. (b) These are all similar, molecular compounds. The one with the highest boiling point is the one with the highest molecular weight, CH_2I_2, as it has the strongest dispersion forces of the compounds listed.

14. (a) If the intermolecular forces in A are greater than in B, we can expect A to be less volatile and to have a lower vapor pressure than B at 20°C.

15. **(e)** Gases with the greatest deviation from ideality are polar, large molecules with strong dispersion forces. Of those listed, NF_3 has the largest molecular weight, and is polar.

16. **(c)**

17. **(d)** Both NH_3 and PH_3 are polar, and dispersion forces are higher for PH_3, which has more electrons, but NH_3 is hydrogen bonded, which results in an unusually high boiling point.

18. **(d)** Magnesium fluoride, MgF_2, is an ionic crystalline solid. The other compounds are molecular.

19. **(b)** The number of moles of H_2O in the vapor phase is

$$n = \frac{PV}{RT} = \frac{(31.824\ \text{mmHg})(10.0\ \text{L})}{\left(62.363\ \frac{\text{L}\cdot\text{mmHg}}{\text{mol}\cdot\text{K}}\right)(303.15\ \text{K})} = 1.683\text{x}10^{-2}\ \text{mol}$$

The mass of H_2O in the vapor phase is

$$(1.683\text{x}10^{-2}\ \text{mol})(18.015\ \text{g/mol}) = 0.3032\ \text{g}$$

The mass of H_2O injected into the flask was 2.00 g. Thus the percentage in the gas phase is $\left(\frac{0.3032\ \text{g}}{2.00\ \text{g}}\right)\text{x}100 = 15.2\%$

20. **(d)** If all 2.00 g were gas, the volume would be

$$V = \frac{(2.00/18.015\ \text{mol})\left(62.363\ \frac{\text{L}\cdot\text{mmHg}}{\text{mol}\cdot\text{K}}\right)(303.15\ \text{K})}{(31.824\ \text{mmHg})} = 66.0\ \text{L}$$

Solutions to Exercises, Chapter 6

1. The formula weight of NaOH is 39.9972 $g \cdot mol^{-1}$. A solution that is 0.100 F contains 0.100 mol of NaOH per liter of solution. The mass of 0.100 mol of NaOH is 3.99972 g. To prepare one quarter of a liter (250.0 mL), we need only (1/4)(3.99972 g) or 1.00 g to 3 significant figures.

2. (a) The mol. wt. of glucose is 180.158 $g \cdot mol^{-1}$. The number of moles of glucose in this liter of solution is

$$\frac{33.3295\ g}{180.158\ g/mol} = 0.18500\ mol$$

The molarity of the solution is 0.18500 moles per liter.

(b) The mol. wt. of CO_2 is 44.01 $g \cdot mol^{-1}$. The number of moles of CO_2 in 0.145 g is

$$\frac{0.145\ g}{44.01\ g/mol} = 3.29 \times 10^{-3}\ mol$$

As the volume of the solution is 0.100 L, the molarity is

$$\frac{3.29 \times 10^{-3}\ mol}{0.100\ L} = 3.29 \times 10^{-2}\ M$$

3. (a) The formula weight of $(NH_4)_2SO_4$ is 132.139 $g \cdot mol^{-1}$. The number of moles of $(NH_4)_2SO_4$ in one liter of solution is

$$\frac{45.5880\ g}{132.139\ g/mol} = 0.34500\ mol$$

Thus the solution is 0.34500 F in $(NH_4)_2SO_4$.

(b) The formula weight of $Na_4P_2O_7$ is 289.903 $g \cdot mol^{-1}$. The number of moles in 9.3065 g is

$$\frac{9.3065\ g}{289.903\ g/mol} = 0.032102\ mol$$

The formality is

$$\frac{0.032102\ mol}{0.2500\ L} = 0.1284\ F$$

(c) The formula weight of AgCl is 143.321 $g \cdot mol^{-1}$. In 0.192 mg of AgCl there are

$$\frac{1.92 \times 10^{-4}\ g}{143.32\ g/mol} = 1.34 \times 10^{-6}\ mol$$

The formality is therefore

$$\frac{1.34 \times 10^{-6}\ mol}{0.1000\ L} = 1.34 \times 10^{-5}\ F$$

4. Adding water to a solution decreases the solute concentration but does not change the number of moles of solute. Let x be the formality of K_2CrO_4 after dilution.

No. mmol of K_2CrO_4 = $(10.00\ mL)(0.500\ \frac{mmol}{mL}) = (25.00\ mL)(x)$

Thus x = 5.00/25.00 = 0.200 F.

5. (a) $[NH_4^+] = 0.100\ M$; $[Cl^-] = 0.100\ M$

(b) $[Ba^{2+}] = 0.200\ M$; $[Cl^-] = 0.400\ M$

(c) $[La^{3+}] = 0.180\ M$; $[NO_3^-] = 0.540\ M$

6. (a) $[Cu^{2+}] = \frac{(50.00\ mL)(0.100\ M)}{250.0\ mL} = 0.0200\ M$

$$[SO_4^{2-}] = \frac{(50.00\ mL)(0.100\ M) + (200.0\ mL)(0.040\ M)}{250.0\ mL}$$

$$= \frac{13.0\ mmol}{250.0\ mL} = 0.0520\ M$$

$$[K^+] = \frac{2(0.040\ M)(200.0\ mL)}{250.0\ mL} = \frac{16\ mmol}{250.0\ mL} = 0.064\ M$$

You can check your arithmetic by checking to make sure the

solution is electrically neutral. The total amount of positive charge is

$$2[Cu^{2+}] + [K^+] = 2(0.0200) + 0.064 = 0.104\ M$$

because each Cu^{2+} ion carries two positive charges. The total amount of negative charge is $2[SO_4^{2-}] = 2(0.0520) = 0.104$ M. Since the total amount of negative charge equals the total amount of positive charge, the solution is electrically neutral.

(b) $$[Ba^{2+}] = \frac{(80.00\ mL)(0.200\ M)}{100.00\ mL} = 0.160\ M$$

$$[NO_3^-] = \frac{2(0.200\ M)(80.00\ mL) + (0.500\ M)(20.00\ mL)}{100.00\ mL}$$

$$= \frac{32.0 + 10.0}{100.00\ mL} = 0.420\ M$$

$$[NH_4^+] = \frac{(20.00\ mL)(0.500\ M)}{100.00\ mL} = 0.100\ M$$

7. Consider a solution containing m moles of ethanol and 1000 grams or 1000/18.015 = 55.51 moles of H_2O. Then the mole fraction of ethanol is, by definition,

$$X_{EtOH} = \frac{m}{m + 55.51} = 0.0820$$

Thus,

$$m = 0.0820m + 4.552; \quad 0.9180m = 4.552 \quad \text{and } m = 4.96$$

8. The solution after dilution must contain exactly the same number of moles of HCl as it did before dilution. Let V = the volume, in mL, of 12.0 F HCl to which water will be added in order to make 500.0 mL of 1.00 F HCl. Then,

$$(V)(12.0\ F) = (500.0\ mL)(1.00\ F), \quad \text{and} \quad V = 41.7\ mL$$

To prepare the solution, transfer 41.7 mL of the 12.0 F HCl to a 500 mL volumetric flask. Add distilled water to below the mark. Mix thoroughly. Add distilled water just to the mark, mixing thoroughly after each addition of water.

9. The formula weights of benzoic acid and benzene are, respectively, 122.124 g/mol and 78.114 g/mol. In this solution the mass of C_6H_6 is (300.0 mL)(0.8787 $g \cdot mL^{-1}$) = 263.6 g, or 0.2636 kg. The molality is the number of moles of C_6H_5COOH per kg of C_6H_6, or

$$\frac{19.5392/122.124 \text{ mol}}{0.26361 \text{ kg}} = \frac{0.16000 \text{ mol}}{0.26361 \text{ kg}} = 0.6069 \text{ m}$$

The number of moles of benzene in solution is

$$263.61 \text{ g}/78.114 \text{ g}\cdot\text{mol}^{-1} = 3.3747 \text{ mol} = 3.375 \text{ mol}$$

Hence the mole fraction of C_6H_5COOH is

$$X = \frac{0.16000}{0.16000 + 3.3747} = \frac{0.16000}{3.5347} = 0.04527$$

10. The formula weight of $Ca(OH)_2$ is 74.095 g/mol. A 0.0250 F solution contains (0.0250 mol)(74.095 $g \cdot mol^{-1}$) = 1.85 g in one liter, or 0.185 g in 100.0 mL of solution.

11. Add a known mass of solid NaCl to the solution. Stir. After a few moments, filter the solution and dry the solid material collected. (If no solid is collected the solution was certainly not saturated.) Weigh the collected solid. If the solution was saturated, the mass of solid collected should be the same as the mass of solid added.

12. The formula weight of $K_2Cr_2O_7$ is 294.18 $g{\cdot}mol^{-1}$. We need (0.5000)(29.418 g) or 14.709 g of $K_2Cr_2O_7$ to prepare 0.5000 L of 0.1000 F solution. Transfer 14.709 g of $K_2Cr_2O_7$ to a 500 mL volumetric flask. Add distilled water to below the neck of the flask. Shake thoroughly until all solid has dissolved. Add distilled water to a short distance below the mark. Shake and mix thoroughly. Add distilled water, dropwise, to the mark, mixing after each drop, until the volume of solution is exactly at the mark.

13. Consider exactly 1 L of this solution. It has a mass of 1019.9 g. Of this, 5.0000% or (0.05000)(1019.9 g) = 50.995 g, is levulose. Thus in 1 L of solution there are $\frac{50.995\ g}{180.16\ g/mol} = 0.2831$ mol, and the solution is 0.2831 M.

14. (a) The vapor pressure lowering is 200.0 - 196.4 = 3.6 mmHg. Thus $\Delta P = 3.6 = P_B^o X_Q = 200.0 X_Q$, and $X_Q = 1.8 \times 10^{-2}$

$$X_B = 1 - X_Q = 1 - 0.018 = 0.982$$

(b) The formula weight of C_6H_6 = 78.114 $g{\cdot}mol^{-1}$. The no. of moles of C_6H_6 is $\frac{109.359\ g}{78.114\ g/mol} = 1.4000$ mol.

If n_Q is the number of moles of Q, then

$$X_Q = \frac{n_Q}{n_Q + 1.400} = 0.018$$

Thus, $n_Q = 0.018 n_Q + 0.0252$; $0.982 n_Q = 0.0252$, and n_Q = 0.0257. The mol. wt. of Q is $\frac{3.50\ g}{0.0257\ mol} = 1.4 \times 10^2$. (2 sig. figs. only in 0.018.)

15. To calculate the vapor pressure lowering, ΔP, we need the mole fraction of dextrose, X_D. Consider exactly one liter of this solution. Its mass is 1021.3 g. Of this, 5.5000%, or 56.1715 g is dextrose, and 94.500%, or 965.13 g, is H_2O.

$$n_{H_2O} = \frac{965.13\ g}{18.015\ g/mol} = 53.5736; \quad n_D = \frac{56.1715\ g}{180.16\ g/mol} = 0.31179$$

$$X_D = \frac{0.31179}{0.3118 + 53.5736} = 5.7861\times10^{-3}$$

$$\Delta P = (17.535\ mmHg)(5.7861\times10^{-3}) = 0.10146\ mmHg$$

Thus the vapor pressure will be lowered from 17.535 to 17.434 mmHg. Note that the vapor pressure lowering is quite small.

16. The mol. wt. of C_6H_5OH, phenol, is 94.113 g/mol. There are therefore $\frac{34.09\ g}{94.113\ g/mol} = 0.3622$ mol of C_6H_5OH in 100.0 g of H_2O. The mole fraction of phenol is

$$X_{C_6H_5OH} = \frac{0.3622}{0.3622 + 5.551} = 0.06125$$

$$X_{H_2O} = 1 - X_{C_6H_5OH} = 1 - 0.06125 = 0.93875$$

The vapor pressure of the solution, if it were ideal, would be

$$P_{ideal} = (23.756\ mmHg)(0.93875) = 22.30\ mmHg$$

This solution is not ideal. The real vapor pressure is less than predicted for an ideal solution. There are more solute particles than the number of moles of C_6H_5OH added. This indicates that some dissociation of phenol has occurred.

17. The mol. wt. of $C_{10}H_8$ = 128.17 g/mol. In 0.0800 kg of solvent there are $\frac{2.933\ g}{128.17\ g/mol}$ = 0.02288 mol $C_{10}H_8$. The solution is therefore

$$\frac{0.02288\ mol}{0.08000\ kg} = 0.2860\ molal$$

As $\Delta T_b = 1.50 = K_b m = K_b(0.2860)$, $K_b = 5.24$

18. From Table 6.1, for CCl_4, K_b = 5.03, and the normal boiling point is 76.5°C. Thus ΔT_b = 78.2 - 76.5 = 1.7°. The molality of this solution is therefore $\Delta T_b/K_b$ = 1.7/5.03 = 0.338 molal. Let n be the number of moles of unknown. Then,

$$m = 0.338 = \frac{n\ moles\ unknown}{0.05800\ kg\ CCl_4}$$

and n = (0.05800)(0.338) = 1.96×10^{-2}. The molecular weight of the unknown is therefore $\frac{2.076\ g}{1.96\times10^{-2}\ mol}$ = 106 g/mol = 1.1×10^2 g/mol. It is only known to 2 sig. figs. as ΔT_b and m are only known to 2 sig. figs.

19. We must find the molality of the fructose in order to calculate the boiling point elevation. Consider exactly one liter of solution. It has a mass of 1015.8 g. Of this, 4.000% or 40.63 g are fructose, and 96.000% or 975.17 g are H_2O. There are 40.63/180.16 = 0.2255 moles of fructose in 0.97517 kg of H_2O, so the molality is

$$m = \frac{0.2255}{0.97517} = 0.2313\ molal$$

For H_2O, K_b = 0.51 (Table 6.1), and ΔT_b = (0.51)(0.2313) =

0.12°. As the normal boiling point of H_2O is $100.00^\circ C$, the solution boils at $100.12^\circ C$.

20. K_f for H_2O = 1.86 (from Table 6.2). $\Delta T_f = K_f m$. Hence, $\Delta T_f = (1.86)(0.2313) = 0.430^\circ$. The solution therefore freezes at $-0.430^\circ C$.

21. To calculate the freezing point depression, we need the molality of $C_{14}H_{10}$ in the solution. The formula weight of $C_{14}H_{10}$ is 178.23 g/mol. There are $\frac{5.346\ g}{178.23\ g/mol}$ = 0.2999 mol of $C_{14}H_{10}$ in 0.07500 kg of solvent. The molality is therefore $\frac{0.2999\ mol}{0.07500\ kg}$ = 0.3999. From Table 6.2, K_f for C_6H_6 = 5.1. Thus,

$$\Delta T_f = K_f m = (5.1)(0.3999) = 2.0^\circ$$

As the normal freezing point of C_6H_6 is $5.5^\circ C$, this solution freezes at $3.5^\circ C$.

22. $\Delta T_f = 6.52^\circ - 2.87^\circ = 3.65^\circ$. From Table 6.2, K_f for cyclohexane is 19.2. Thus the molality of solute is 3.65/19.2 = 0.190 m. Let n be the number of moles of solute dissolved in 0.09347 kg of cyclohexane. Then m = 0.190 = n/0.09347, and n = 0.0178 mol. The approximate molecular weight of the solute is therefore $\frac{2.736\ g}{0.0178\ mol}$ = 154 g/mol.

As the formula weight of C_3H_6Cl is 77.534, 77.534n ~ 154, and n must be exactly 2. The molecular formula is $C_6H_{12}Cl_2$, and the exact molecular weight of the unknown is 155.068 g/mol.

23. K_f for H_2O = 1.86; K_b for H_2O = 0.51.

(a) For $NaNO_3$, there are 2 ions per formula unit. Thus

$$\Delta T_f = 2(1.86)(0.050) = 0.186^\circ$$

and

$$\Delta T_b = 2(0.51)(0.050) = 0.051^\circ$$

If the solution were ideal, its freezing point would be $-0.186^\circ C$ and its boiling point would be $100.051^\circ C$.

(b) For $MgBr_2$, there are 3 ions per formula unit. Thus

$$\Delta T_f = 3(1.86)(0.050) = 0.279^\circ$$

and

$$\Delta T_b = 3(0.51)(0.050) = 0.077^\circ$$

If the solution were ideal, its freezing point would be $-0.279^\circ C$ and its boiling point would be $100.077^\circ C$.

(c) For $La(NO_3)_3$, there are 4 ions per formula unit. Thus,

$$\Delta T_f = 4(1.86)(0.050) = 0.372^\circ$$

and

$$\Delta T_b = 4(0.51)(0.050) = 0.102^\circ$$

If the solution were ideal, its freezing point would be $-0.372^\circ C$ and its boiling point would be $100.102^\circ C$.

24. The boiling point increases with an increase in the total number of solute particles. There are 2 ions per formula unit for KBr, 3 for $CaCl_2$, and 2 for $LiNO_3$. Ethanol is a nonelectrolyte. The solution with lowest boiling point is (b) 0.060 M ethanol, then (a) 0.040 F KBr, then (d) 0.060 F $LiNO_3$, and the solution with highest boiling point is (c) 0.050 F $CaCl_2$.

25. Water flows from the more dilute to the more concentrated solution through a semipermeable membrane. To stop the flow, pressure must be applied to the more concentrated solution, which is the 0.250 M glucose solution.

26. The molecular weight of glucose is 324.30 g/mol. The solution contains $\frac{1.841 \text{ g}}{324.30 \text{ g/mol}} = 5.378\text{x}10^{-3}$ mol in 0.5000 L. The osmotic pressure, π, is

$$\pi = \frac{(5.378\text{x}10^{-3} \text{ mol})}{0.5000 \text{ L}}\left(0.08206 \frac{\text{L}\cdot\text{atm}}{\text{mol}\cdot\text{K}}\right)(298.2 \text{ K}) = 0.263 \text{ atm}$$

The van't Hoff equation for π is only approximate, so it is not valid to report the calculated π to more than 3 figures. In mmHg, $\pi = (0.263 \text{ atm})(760 \frac{\text{mmHg}}{\text{atm}}) = 2.00\text{x}10^2$ mmHg.

27. $\pi = (6.3/760 \text{ atm}) = \left(\frac{n \text{ mol}}{0.1000 \text{ L}}\right)\left(0.08206 \frac{\text{L}\cdot\text{atm}}{\text{mol}\cdot\text{K}}\right)(308 \text{ K})$ and $n = 3.28\text{x}10^{-5}$ mol.

Thus $M = \frac{0.283 \text{ g}}{3.28\text{x}10^{-5} \text{ mol}} = 8.6\text{x}10^3$. As π is only known to 2 sig. figs, the molecular weight is only known to 2 figures.

28. As the number of moles of benzene and toluene is the same, $X_B = X_T = 0.500$. $P_B = P_B^0 X_B = (125)(0.500) = 62.5$ mmHg. Similarly, $P_T = P_T^0 X_T = (39.0)(0.500) = 19.5$ mmHg. The vapor pressure of the solution $= P_B + P_T = 82.0$ mmHg.

29. (a) The mol. wts. of C_8H_{18} and C_9H_{20} are, respectively, 114.23 and 128.26 g/mol. Thus,

$$n_{oct} = \frac{200.0 \text{ g}}{114.23 \text{ g/mol}} = 1.751; \quad n_{non} = \frac{300.0 \text{ g}}{128.26 \text{ g/mol}} = 2.339$$

$X_{oct} = \frac{1.751}{1.751 + 2.339} = 0.4281$, and $X_{non} = 1 - X_{oct} = 0.5719$

(b) $P_{oct} = (100.0 \text{ mmHg})(0.4281) = 42.81 \text{ mmHg}$

$P_{non} = (40.0 \text{ mmHg})(0.5719) = 22.88 \text{ mmHg} = 22.9 \text{ mmHg}$

(c) $X_{oct}^{vap} = \frac{P_{oct}}{P_{total}} = \frac{42.81}{65.7} = 0.652$

$X_{non}^{vap} = 1 - 0.652 = 0.348$

30. (a) $P_C^o = 328.0$ mmHg; $P_D^o = 174.6$ mmHg. $X_C^{liq} = 0.048$

$P_C(\text{ideal}) = (328.0 \text{ mmHg})(0.048) = 16 \text{ mmHg} < P_C(\text{real})$, since $P_C(\text{real}) = 18.5$ mmHg.

$P_D(\text{ideal}) = (174.6 \text{ mmHg})(0.952) = 166 \text{ mmHg} = P_D(\text{real}) = 166.3$ mmHg. C does not obey Raoult's law; D obeys Raoult's law within experimental uncertainties.

(b) This system exhibits positive deviations from Raoult's law. Both components must obey Raoult's law for the system to be ideal. Since the real P_C (18.5 mmHg) is greater than the ideal P_C (16 mmHg), there are positive deviations from ideality.

Solutions to Multiple Choice Questions, Chapter 6

1. **(d)** In 0.040 F $Sr(NO_3)_2$,

$[Sr^{2+}] = 0.040$ M; $[NO_3^-] = 0.080$ M

2. **(b)** In 0.10 m $NiCl_2$, the molality of Ni^{2+} is 0.10 m and of Cl^- is 0.20 m, so that the total concentration of all solute particles is 0.30 m. The larger the total con-

centration of all solute particles, the lower the freezing point. Sucrose and glucose are nonelectrolytes, and the number of ions per formula unit for $CuSO_4$ and NH_4NO_3 is 2.

3. __(a)__ Mol. wt. CH_3COCH_3 is 58.08 g/mol. Consider 100.00 g of this solution. It contains 10.00 g of acetone and 90.00 g of H_2O.

$$\text{No. moles acetone} = \frac{10.00\ \text{g}}{58.08\ \text{g/mol}} = 0.1722$$

$$\text{No. moles } H_2O = \frac{90.00\ \text{g}}{18.015\ \text{g/mol}} = 4.996$$

$$X_{acetone} = \frac{0.1722}{0.1722 + 4.996} = \frac{0.1722}{5.168} = 0.03332 \text{ or } 3.332\%$$

4. __(c)__ Consider one liter of this solution. It weighs 986.7 g. Of this, 98.67 g are acetone. The mol. wt. of CH_3COCH_3 is 58.08 g/mol.

$$\begin{array}{c}\text{No. moles acetone}\\ \text{per liter of solution}\end{array} = \frac{98.67\ \text{g}}{58.08\ \text{g/mol}} = 1.699$$

Hence the solution is 1.699 M in acetone.

5. __(c)__ The formula wt. of $CuSO_4{\cdot}5H_2O$ is 249.68 g/mol. The no. of moles of $CuSO_4{\cdot}5H_2O$ is $\frac{10.00\ \text{g}}{249.68\ \text{g/mol}} = 0.04005$ mol, in 0.5000 L.

Thus the molarity is 0.04005 mol/0.5000 L = 0.08010 M.

6. __(e)__ $K_f = 1.86$ for H_2O. $\Delta T_f = K_f m = 0.14 = 1.86m$, so that m is 0.075 molal.

7. __(b)__ We must calculate the mole fraction of benzene to find the vapor pressure of the solution, as $P_B = P_B^0 X_B =$

(93.4 mmHg)X_B. The mol. wt. of C_6H_6 is 78.114 g/mol.

$$\text{No. mol } C_6H_6 = \frac{250.0 \text{ g}}{78.114 \text{ g/mol}} = 3.200 \text{ mol}$$

$$\text{No. mol 1,2-benzanthracene} = \frac{18.2632 \text{ g}}{228.29 \text{ g/mol}} = 0.08000 \text{ mol}$$

$$X_B = \frac{3.200}{3.200 + 0.0800} = 0.9756$$

$$P_B = (93.4 \text{ mmHg})(0.9756) = 91.1 \text{ mmHg}$$

8. __(d)__ The number of mmoles of HNO_3 is the same before and after the dilution. Let V = the final volume of the 0.500 F HNO_3.

$$(25.00 \text{ mL})(6.00 \tfrac{\text{mmol}}{\text{mL}}) = (V)(0.500 \tfrac{\text{mmol}}{\text{mL}})$$

and V = 300 mL. If the volumes are additive, we must add 275 mL of water to 25.00 mL of 6.00 F HNO_3, to prepare 300 mL of 0.500 F HNO_3.

9. __(c)__ There are two NH_4^+ ions per $(NH_4)_2SO_4$ formula unit.

10. __(d)__ The mol. wt. of CH_3CH_2OH is 46.069 g/mol. Consider exactly 100 g of solution. It contains 12.00 g of ethanol and 88.00 g of H_2O.

$$\text{No. mol } CH_3CH_2OH = \frac{12.00 \text{ g}}{46.069 \text{ g/mol}} = 0.2605$$

$$\text{molality} = \frac{0.2605 \text{ mol}}{0.08800 \text{ kg}} = 2.960 \text{ m}$$

11. __(e)__ $\Delta T_f = 5.48 - 4.33 = 1.15^\circ$. For C_6H_6, $K_f = 5.1$ (Table 6.2). Thus m = 1.15/5.1 = 0.2255 = 0.23. Let n be the no. of moles of solute in 0.4000 kg of C_6H_6. Then

$0.2255 = \frac{n \text{ moles solute}}{0.4000 \text{ kg}}$, and n is 0.0902 mole. As the mass of solute is 20.5461 g, the approximate molecular weight of solute is $\frac{20.5461 \text{ g}}{0.0902 \text{ mol}} = 228$ g/mol. The formula weight of C_3H_2 is 38, so 38n ~ 228, and n = 6. Thus the correct molecular formula is $C_{18}H_{12}$.

12. **(d)** For $CaCl_2$, $\nu = 3$ as there are 3 ions per formula unit. If the solution were ideal, $\Delta T_b = \nu K_b m = 3(0.51)(1.00) = 1.53°$. Solutions of electrolytes deviate from ideality more than solutions of nonelectrolytes, and the actual boiling point elevation will be somewhat less than 1.53°.

13. **(b)** Let V be the volume, in mL, of the 0.0500 F solution. Then (V)(0.0500 F) = (500.0 mL)(0.0200 F), and V = 200 mL.

14. **(a)** No. mol $C_6H_6 = \frac{64.05 \text{ g}}{78.11 \text{ g/mol}} = 0.8200$ mol

$$\text{No. mol toluene} = \frac{106.26 \text{ g}}{92.14 \text{ g/mol}} = 1.153 \text{ mol}$$

$$X_T^{liq} = \frac{1.153}{1.973} = 0.5844; \quad X_B^{liq} = 1 - 0.5844 = 0.4156$$

$$P_B = (160.0 \text{ mmHg})(0.4156) = 66.49 \text{ mmHg}$$

$$P_T = (50.0 \text{ mmHg})(0.5844) = 29.2 \text{ mmHg}$$

$$P_{total} = 66.49 + 29.2 = 95.7 \text{ mmHg}. \quad X_T^{vap} = \frac{29.2}{95.7} = 0.305$$

15. **(a)** The formula weight of $KMnO_4$ is 158.034 g/mol. In 1 L we need 0.1000 mol, or 15.8034 g, and in 0.25000 L we need 1/4 of 0.1000 mol, or (15.8034/4) = 3.951 grams.

16. (c) $\pi = cRT = (1.0\times10^{-3}\ \frac{mol}{L})(0.08206\ \frac{L\cdot atm}{mol\cdot K})(298\ K)$

$= 2.44\times10^{-3}\ atm = (2.44\times10^{-3}\ atm)(760\ \frac{mmHg}{atm})$

$= 18.6\ mmHg = 19\ mmHg$

17. (c)

$$[NO_3^-] = \frac{(20.00\ mL)(2)(0.100\ M) + (30.00\ mL)(0.400\ M)}{50.00\ mL}$$

$$= \frac{4.00 + 12.0\ mmol}{50.00\ mL} = 0.320\ M$$

18. (d) The solubility of a compound with a molecular weight of many thousands is usually quite small, so that the vapor pressure lowering, boiling point elevation, and freezing point depression are too small to be measured with sufficient accuracy. Only the osmotic pressure is large enough for an accurate determination of the molecular weight.

19. (e) The formula wts. of KCl and K_2CO_3 are, respectively, 74.551 and 138.204 g/mol.

$$\text{No. mol KCl} = \frac{1.864\ g}{74.551\ g/mol} = 0.02500\ mol$$

$$\text{No. mol } K_2CO_3 = \frac{8.293\ g}{138.204\ g/mol} = 0.06001\ mol$$

There are 2 moles of K^+ ions per mole of K_2CO_3. The final volume of solution is 0.5000 L. Thus,

$$[K^+] = \frac{\{0.02500 + 2(0.06001)\}\ mol}{0.5000\ L} = 0.2900\ M$$

20. (b) $P_{CS_2}(ideal) = (512\ mmHg)(0.25) = 128\ mmHg$

$P_A(ideal) = (344\ mmHg)(0.75) = 258\ mmHg$

Thus, if the solution were ideal, its total vapor pressure would be 128 + 258 = 386 mmHg. As the actual vapor pressure is 600 mmHg, the system exhibits positive deviations from ideality. Options (a) and (d) are only true for ideal solutions, and options (c) and (e) are true for systems that exhibit negative deviations from Raoult's law. Only option (b) is correct for positive deviations.

Solutions to Problems, Chapter 6

6.1. (a) The mol. wts. of n-hexane and n-heptane are, respectively, 86.18 and 100.20 g/mol. Let w = the weight of both n-hexane and n-heptane. Then

$$n_{total} = \frac{w}{86.18} + \frac{w}{100.20} = \frac{186.38w}{(100.20)(86.18)}$$

$$X_{hex} = \frac{(w/86.18)}{\left(\frac{186.38w}{(100.20)(86.18)}\right)} = \frac{100.20}{186.38} = 0.5376$$

Note that the value of w cancels out; the mole fraction of each of the components is the same whatever weight is chosen, as long as the weight of both liquids is the same.

$$X_{hep} = 1 - X_{hex} = 0.4624$$

(b) $P_{hex} = (400.0 \text{ mmHg})(0.5376) = 215.0 \text{ mmHg}$

$P_{hep} = (124 \text{ mmHg})(0.4624) = 57.3 \text{ mmHg}$

$P_{total} = 215.04 + 57.34 = 272.4 \text{ mmHg}$

(c) The composition of the vapor phase in equilibrium with this solution is determined as follows:

$$X_{hex}^{vap} = P_{hex}/P_{total} = 215.04/272.38 = 0.7895$$

$$X_{hep}^{vap} = 1 - X_{hex}^{vap} = 1 - 0.7895 = 0.2105$$

If this vapor is condensed, the new liquid will have the same composition as the vapor. Note that the vapor has a larger mole fraction of n-hexane, and a smaller mole fraction of n-heptane than the original liquid.

(d) If a mixture of n-hexane and n-heptane is distilled, n-hexane will be collected from the top of the distillation column and n-heptane will be the residue in the pot. n-Hexane is the more volatile of the two liquids. Each successive vaporization and condensation produces a liquid richer in n-hexane and poorer in n-heptane than the preceding, and the vapor that reaches the top of the distillation column will be pure n-hexane.

6.2. $\Delta T_b = 83.28^\circ - 80.15^\circ = 3.13^\circ$. For C_6H_6, $K_b = 2.53$ from Table 6.1. Hence,

$$m = \Delta T_b/K_b = 3.13/2.53 = 1.237 = 1.24 \text{ molal}$$

Let n = the no. of moles of limonene dissolved in 0.05000 kg of C_6H_6. Then,

$$m = 1.237 = \frac{n}{0.05000} \quad \text{and} \quad n = 0.0618 \text{ mol}$$

$$M = \frac{8.362 \text{ g}}{0.0618 \text{ mol}} = 135 \text{ g/mol}$$

The empirical formula of limonene is obtained from the elemental analysis. Consider a 100.00 g sample of limonene.

$$\text{No. mol C} = \frac{88.16\ \text{g}}{12.011\ \text{g/mol}} = 7.340\ \text{mol C}$$

$$\text{No. mol H} = \frac{11.84\ \text{g}}{1.008\ \text{g/mol}} = 11.75\ \text{mol H}$$

$$\text{Ratio}\ \frac{\text{No. mol H}}{\text{No. mol C}} = \frac{11.75}{7.340} = \frac{1.60}{1.00} = \frac{8.00}{5.00}$$

The empirical formula of limonene is $(C_5H_8)_n$. The formula weight of C_5H_8 is 68.118 g/mol. Hence $68.118n \sim 135$, and n is exactly 2. The correct molecular formula is $C_{10}H_{16}$, and the correct molecular weight is 136.236 g/mol.

There are two reasons why the value of 135 g/mol from the bp elevation experiment is not the exact molecular weight. (1) There is an experimental uncertainty in the third significant figure of ΔT_b, 3.13°. (2) The equation used, $\Delta T_b = K_b m$, is exact only for ideal solutions, and it is not likely that a solution as concentrated as 1.24 molal is ideal.

6.3. (a) $M = \dfrac{\delta RT}{P}$

$$M = \frac{(0.713\ \frac{g}{L})(0.08206\ \text{L·atm·mol}^{-1}\text{K}^{-1})(423.2\ \text{K})}{(200.0/760\ \text{atm})} = 94.1\ \text{g/mol}$$

(b) $\Delta T_f = 4.32 = 14.4m$, and $m = 4.32/14.4 = 0.300$

Let M = mol. wt. of phenol in bromoform. Then the number of moles of phenol dissolved in 0.1000 kg of solvent is (5.45/M). Hence,

$$m = 0.300 = \frac{(5.45/M)\ \text{mol}}{0.1000\ \text{kg}} \quad \text{and} \quad M = \frac{5.45}{0.0300} = 182\ \text{g/mol}$$

The molecular weight of phenol in bromoform, 182, is nearly twice the molecular weight of gaseous phenol, 94. We conclude that phenol dimerizes in bromoform solution, that is, two molecules combine to form a larger one of twice the molecular weight.

6.4.

$$[NH_4^+] = \frac{2(0.120\ M)(30.00\ mL) + (70.00\ mL)(0.200\ M)}{(200.00\ mL)} = \frac{21.2}{200.0}$$

$$= 0.106\ M$$

$$[SO_4^{2-}] = \frac{(30.00\ mL)(0.120\ M)}{(200.00\ mL)} = \frac{3.60}{200.00} = 0.0180\ M$$

$$[Cl^-] = \frac{(70.00\ mL)(0.200\ M) + (100.00\ mL)(2)(0.080\ M)}{(200.00\ mL)}$$

$$= \frac{30}{200.0} = 0.15\ M$$

$$[Zn^{2+}] = \frac{(100.00\ mL)(0.080\ M)}{200.00\ mL} = 0.040\ M$$

We can check the arithmetic by verifying that the solution is electrically neutral. Electroneutrality requires that

$$[NH_4^+] + 2[Zn^{2+}] = [Cl^-] + 2[SO_4^{2-}]$$

$$0.106 + 0.080 = 0.15 + 0.036$$

$$0.186 = 0.186$$

6.5. (a) The formula wt. of KIO_3 is 214.00 g/mol. The mass of KIO_3 needed is, therefore,

$$(2\ L)(0.0800\ \frac{mol}{L})(214.00\ \frac{g}{mol}) = 34.24\ g$$

Weigh out 34.24 g of KIO_3. Transfer to a 2 L volumetric flask. Add distilled H_2O below the neck of the flask. Mix thoroughly. Be sure all the solid has dissolved. Add distilled water below the mark on the neck. Mix thoroughly. Add water dropwise to the mark, mixing after each drop, until the solution is exactly at the mark.

(b) Let V = the volume, in mL, of the stock solution to be diluted. Then (V)(0.0800 F) = (100.0 mL)(0.0200 F), and V = 25.0 mL. Using a 25 mL volumetric pipet, transfer 25.0 mL of the 0.0800 F KIO_3 to a 100.0 mL volumetric flask. Add distilled water to below the mark. Mix thoroughly. Add water to the mark, dropwise, mixing after each addition.

(c)
$$\frac{\text{No. mmol } Fe^{2+} \text{ used}}{\text{No. mmol } IO_3^- \text{ used}} = \frac{10}{2} = 5$$

$$\text{No. mmol } IO_3^- \text{ used} = (20.00 \text{ mL})(0.0200 \frac{\text{mmol}}{\text{mL}}) = 0.400 \text{ mmol}$$

$$\text{No. mmol } Fe^{2+} \text{ needed} = 5(0.400 \text{ mmol}) = 2.00 \text{ mmol}$$

Let V = volume, in mL, of 0.0500 F $FeSO_4$ needed. Then,

$$(V)(0.0500 \frac{\text{mmol}}{\text{mL}}) = 2.00 \text{ mmol}, \quad \text{and } V = 40.0 \text{ mL}$$

6.6. (a)

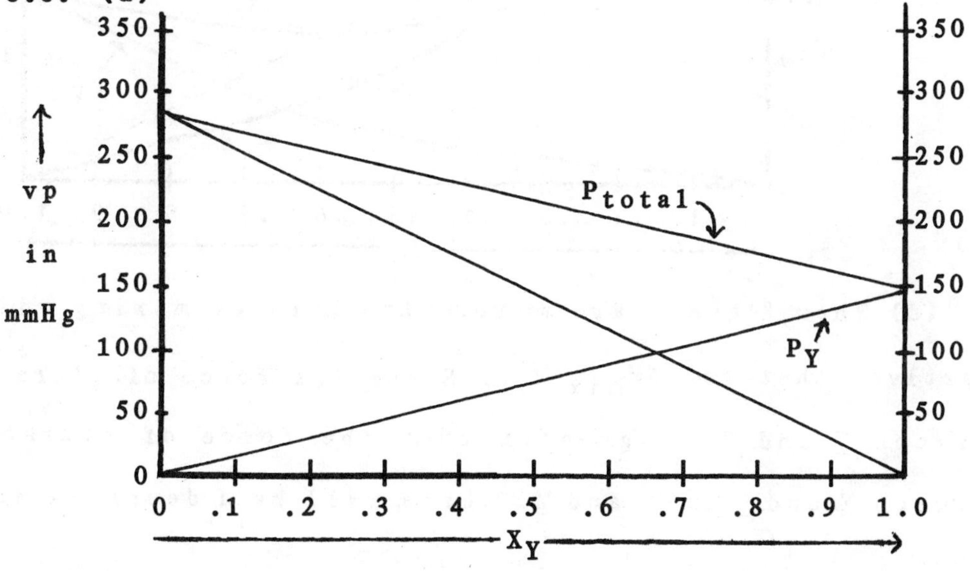

(b) $P_Y(\text{ideal}) = P_Y^{o}X_Y = (148.0\ \text{mmHg})(0.250) = 37.0\ \text{mmHg}$

$P_Z(\text{ideal}) = P_Z^{o}X_Z = (286.0\ \text{mmHg})(0.750) = 214.5\ \text{mmHg}$

$P_Y(\text{real}) = 21.4\ \text{mmHg} < 37.0\ \text{mmHg} = P_Y(\text{ideal})$

$P_Z(\text{real}) = 172.6\ \text{mmHg} < 214.5\ \text{mmHg} = P_Z(\text{ideal})$

This system exhibits negative deviations from ideality. Both partial pressures are less than the values predicted by Raoult's law. Molecules Y and Z are strongly attracted to one another, and it is harder, e.g., for a Y molecule to escape from a mixture of Y and Z than to escape from pure liquid Y.

(c)

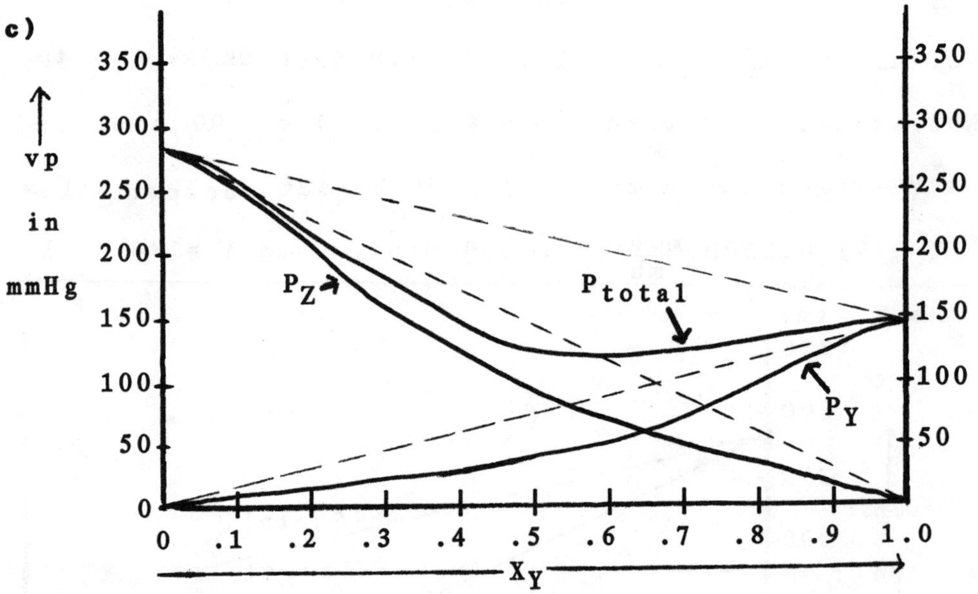

(d) When Y and Z are mixed, the heat of mixing will be negative, that is, $\Delta H_{mix} < 0$. Since the force of attraction between Y and Z is greater than the force of attraction between Y and Y or Z and Z, there will be a decrease in the potential energy when Y and Z are mixed, and the extra energy will be released as heat.

6.7. $\%O = 100.00 - 65.60 - 9.44 = 24.96\%\ O$

Consider a sample of mass 100.00 g. In this sample,

$$\text{No. mol C} = \frac{65.60\ g}{12.011\ g/mol} = 5.462\ \text{mol C}$$

$$\text{No. mol H} = \frac{9.44\ g}{1.0079\ g/mol} = 9.365\ \text{mol H}$$

$$\text{No. mol O} = \frac{24.96\ g}{16.00\ g/mol} = 1.560\ \text{mol O}$$

$$\frac{\text{moles C}}{\text{moles O}} = \frac{5.462}{1.560} = 3.50; \qquad \frac{\text{mcles H}}{\text{moles O}} = \frac{9.365}{1.560} = 6.00$$

molar ratio C:H:O = 3.50:6.00:1.00 = 7.00:12.00:2.00

The empirical formula of this ester is $(C_7H_{12}O_2)_n$.

From Table 6.2, K_f(camphor) = 40. $\Delta T_f = 15.2 = 40m$, so $m = 0.38$, and the solution is 0.38 molal. Let M = mol. wt. of this ester. Then the solution contains (0.785/M) mol of ester in 0.008040 kg of solvent. Thus,

$$m = 0.38 = \frac{(0.785/M)\ \text{mol solute}}{0.008040\ \text{kg solvent}}$$

and $$M = \frac{0.785}{(0.38)(0.008040)} = 257\ g/mol$$

The formula wt. of $C_7H_{12}O_2$ is 128, so that $128n \sim 257$, and n is exactly 2. Thus the molecular formula of the ester is $C_{14}H_{24}O_2$, and its exact molecular weight is 256.34 g/mol.

6.8. The formula wt. of $PbI_2 = 207.2 + 2(126.9) = 461.0$ g/mol. A sample of 0.0701 g contains

$$\frac{0.0701\ g}{461.0\ g/mol} = 1.52 \times 10^{-4}\ \text{mol of } PbI_2$$

$$[Pb^{2+}] = \frac{1.52\times10^{-4} \text{ mol}}{0.1000 \text{ L}} = 1.52\times10^{-3} \text{ M}$$

$$[I^-] = 2(1.52\times10^{-3}) = 3.04\times10^{-3} \text{ M}$$

6.9. (a) $P_A(\text{ideal}) = (343.8 \text{ mmHg})(0.938) = 322.5 \text{ mmHg}$

$P_A(\text{real}) = 331.0 \text{ mmHg} > 322.5 \text{ mmHg} = P_A(\text{ideal})$, so that A does not obey Raoult's law.

(b) $P_{CS_2} = 110.7 \text{ mmHg}$, $P_A = 331.0 \text{ mmHg}$

and $P_{total} = 441.7 \text{ mmHg}$

$$X_A^{gas} = \frac{P_A}{P_{total}} = \frac{331.0}{441.7} = 0.7494, \quad X_{CS_2}^{gas} = \frac{110.7}{441.7} = 0.2506$$

(c) This solution exhibits positive deviations from Raoult's law. The vapor pressure of each component is larger than predicted by Raoult's law.

$$P_{CS_2}(\text{ideal}) = (512.3 \text{ mmHg})(0.062) = 31.8 \text{ mmHg}$$

while the real value of P_{CS_2} is 110.7 mmHg.

(d) The force of attraction between an acetone molecule and a CS_2 molecule is less than that between two acetone molecules. CS_2 is a nonpolar molecule. As CS_2 is linear and symmetric, the center of negative charge coincides with the center of positive charge, right at the C atom. Acetone, CH_3COCH_3, is polar. Generally, the force of attraction between polar and nonpolar molecules is less than the force of attraction between two polar molecules.

(e) When 100.00 mL of A and 100.00 mL of CS_2 are mixed, the volume of the solution will be greater than 200.00 mL.

Because of the weak force of attraction between acetone and CS_2 molecules, these molecules stay further apart from one another than do the like molecules in the pure liquids. Thus the volume expands when acetone and CS_2 are mixed.

6.10. $\pi = 1.24 \text{ atm} = cRT = \frac{n}{V}\left(0.08206 \frac{\text{L·atm}}{\text{mol·K}}\right)(293.2 \text{ K})$ where V is the volume of the solution, and n is the number of moles of solute, thyroxine. The volume of 25.00 g of benzene is $\frac{25.00 \text{ g}}{0.8787 \text{ g/mL}}$ or 28.45 mL. The volume, V, must be in liters with the value of R used.

$$\text{Hence } n = \frac{(1.24 \text{ atm})(0.02845 \text{ L})}{\left(0.08206 \frac{\text{L·atm}}{\text{mol·K}}\right)(293.2 \text{ K})} = 1.47\text{x}10^{-3} \text{ mol}$$

Let M = the molecular weight of thyroxine. Then,

$$\frac{1.138 \text{ g}}{M} = 1.467\text{x}10^{-3} \text{ mol}, \quad \text{and } M = 776 \text{ g/mol}$$

6.11. If the molecular weights of the two compounds are the same, then the weight fraction and the mole fraction of either compound in any solution are identical. To see this, consider the solution for which the weight fraction of isopropyl alcohol is 3/4. That means that if w is the weight of n-propyl alcohol, 3w is the weight of the isopropyl alcohol. Let M be the molecular weight of these compounds. Then the solution contains 3w/M moles of isopropyl alcohol (i) and w/M moles of n-propyl alcohol (n), and

$$X_i = \frac{3w/M}{3w/M + w/M} = \frac{3}{4}$$

Hence, for the two solutions described,

$$88.8 \text{ mmHg} = P_i + P_n = (3/4)P_i^o + (1/4)P_n^o$$

and $$68.3 \text{ mmHg} = (1/3)P_i^o + (2/3)P_n^o$$

Multiply the first equation through by 8, and the second by 3. Then,

$$710.4 \text{ mmHg} = 6P_i^o + 2P_n^o$$

and $$204.9 \text{ mmHg} = P_i^o + 2P_n^o$$

By subtraction, $$505.5 \text{ mmHg} = 5P_i^o$$

so that $P_i^o = 101.1$ mmHg. By substitution into either equation, we find $P_n^o = 51.9$ mmHg.

6.12. (a) $$\text{mol. wt. } C_6H_6O_2 = 110.11 \text{ g/mol}$$

$$\text{No. mol } C_6H_6O_2 = \frac{4.4044 \text{ g}}{110.11 \text{ g/mol}} = 4.0000\text{x}10^{-2} \text{ mol}$$

$$m = \frac{0.040000 \text{ moles solute}}{0.2000 \text{ kg solvent}} = 0.2000 \text{ molal}$$

(b) mol. wt. C_6H_6 = 78.114 g/mol. In 200.0 g of C_6H_6 there are 2.560 mol. Hence the mole fraction of catechol is

$$X_C = \frac{0.04000}{0.04000 + 2.560} = 0.01538$$

(c) From Table 6.1, $K_b(C_6H_6) = 2.53$ and the normal bp is 80.2°C. $\Delta T_b = K_b m = (2.53)(0.2000) = 0.506°$. Hence the boiling point of this solution is 80.2 + 0.506 = 80.7°C.

(d) From Table 6.2, $K_f(C_6H_6) = 5.1$, and the normal fp is 5.5°C. $\Delta T_f = K_f m = (5.1)(0.2000) = 1.02°$. Hence the freezing point of this solution is 5.5 - 1.0 = 4.5°C.

(e) $$P_B = P_B^o X_B = (100.0 \text{ mmHg})(1 - 0.01538)$$

$$= (100.0 \text{ mmHg})(0.98462) = 98.46 \text{ mmHg}$$

6.13. The formula wt. of C_6H_5ONa = 116.095 g/mol. A sample of mass 5.805 g contains 0.05000 mol. The mass of 250.0 mL of water is (250.0 mL)(0.997 g/mL) = 249 g, or 0.249 kg. The molality of the solution is, therefore,

$$0.05000 \text{ mol}/0.249 \text{ kg} = 0.200 \text{ molal}$$

If this compound is a nonelectrolyte, the freezing point depression should be $\Delta T_f = (1.86)(0.200) = 0.372$. The observed ΔT_f is almost twice this, 0.72°. We conclude that this compound dissociates into two particles in aqueous solution. (The ions formed are Na^+ and $C_6H_5O^-$).

6.14. (a) $P_{total} = P_Y + P_Z = 300.0$ mmHg

$X_Y^{gas} = 0.650 = P_Y/P_{total} = P_Y/300.0$ mmHg; $P_Y = 195$ mmHg

$X_Z^{gas} = 0.350 = P_Z/P_{total} = P_Z/300.0$ mmHg; $P_Z = 105$ mmHg

(b) $P_Y = 195$ mmHg $= P_Y^o X_Y^{liq} = P_Y^o(0.300)$; $P_Y^o = 650$ mmHg

$P_Z = 105$ mmHg $= P_Z^o X_Z^{liq} = P_Z^o(0.700)$; $P_Z^o = 150$ mmHg

(c)

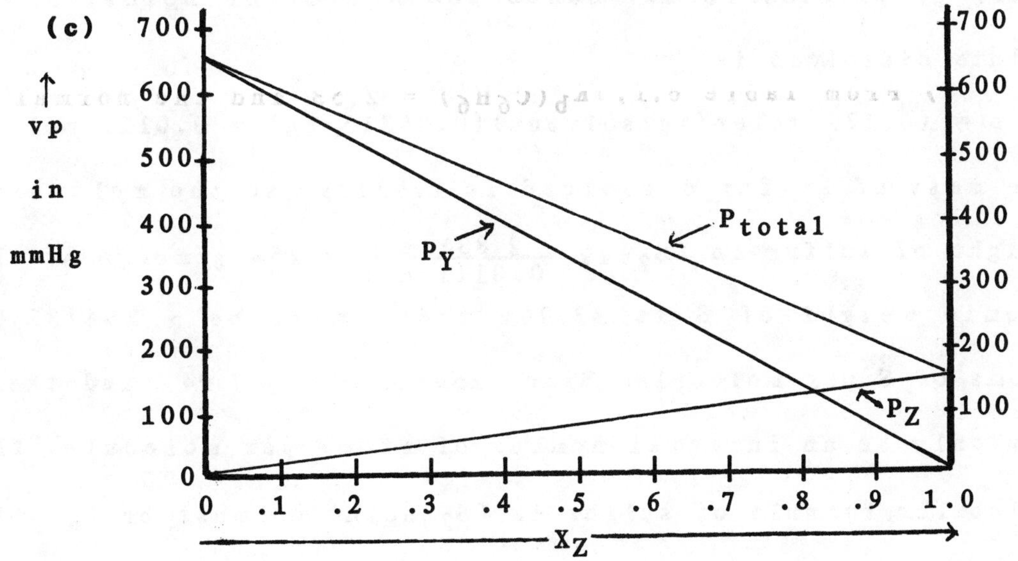

6.15. Consider exactly 1 L of this solution. It has a mass of 1500 g, of which 47.3% or (0.473)(1500) = 709.5 g is HI, and 790.5 g is therefore H_2O. As the formula weight of HI is 127.91, the number of moles of HI in a liter of solution is $\frac{709.5\text{ g}}{127.91\text{ g/mol}} = 5.547$ mol. The molarity, therefore, is 5.55 M.

Since there are 5.547 moles of HI in 0.7905 kg of H_2O, the molality of the solution is $\frac{5.547\text{ moles HI}}{0.7905\text{ kg }H_2O} = 7.02$ m.

The mol. wt. of H_2O = 18.015 g/mol. In 790.5 g of H_2O there are 43.88 moles of H_2O. Hence the mole fraction of HI is

$$X_{HI} = \frac{5.547}{5.547 + 43.88} = 0.112$$

6.16. $\Delta T_b = 0.412 = K_b m = 2.34m$, and m = 0.176 molal The mass of 50.00 mL of CS_2 = (50.00 mL)(1.263 g/mL) = 63.15 g, or 0.06315 kg. Hence the number of moles, n, of solute dissolved is

$$n = (0.176\text{ moles/kg solvent})(0.06315\text{ kg}) = 0.0111\text{ mol}$$

The mass of sulfur dissolved is 2.831 g, so the molecular weight of sulfur in CS_2 is $\frac{2.831\text{ g}}{0.0111\text{ mol}} = 254$ g/mol. As the atomic weight of S is 32.06, there must be ~ 254/32.06 atoms of S per molecule. Since 254/32.06 is 7.94, and there can only be an integral number of atoms per molecule, the molecular formula of sulfur in CS_2 solution must be S_8, and the molecular weight must be 256.48 g/mol.

6.17. (a) There are $(0.5000 \text{ L})(4.73 \frac{\text{mol}}{\text{L}}) = 2.365$ mol HCl in this solution. Assuming HCl is an ideal gas,

$$V = \frac{nRT}{P} = \frac{(2.365 \text{ mol})(62.363 \text{ L}\cdot\text{mmHg}\cdot\text{mol}^{-1}\text{K}^{-1})(299.6 \text{ K})}{748 \text{ mmHg}}$$

$$= 59.1 \text{ L}$$

(b) The mol. wt. of HCl is 36.461. The mass of 4.73 mol is (4.73 mol)(36.461 g/mol) = 172.5 g. Since a liter of solution has a mass of 1080 g, there are 172.5 g of HCl and 907.5 g of H_2O per liter. The mol. wt. of H_2O is 18.015 g/mol, so there are $\frac{907.5}{18.015} = 50.38$ mol of H_2O per liter of solution.

Assuming 100% dissociation, there are 4.73 moles of H^+, 4.73 moles of Cl^- and 50.38 moles of H_2O per liter.

$$X_{H_2O} = \frac{50.38}{50.38 + 4.73 + 4.73} = \frac{50.38}{59.84} = 0.842$$

The mole fraction is only known to 3 significant figures as the mass of HCl and the mass of H_2O are only known to 3 figures, since they are calculated from the 4.73 F HCl.

6.18. An explanation of the apparent molecular weight of 100 is that a significant fraction of the acetic acid molecules have dimerized in benzene solution. If some of the molecules are dimers (mol. wt. 120 g/mol) and others are monomers (mol. wt. 60 g/mol), the mol. wt. calculated using $\Delta T_f = K_f m$ will be between 60 and 120.

6.19. Consider one liter of concentrated HNO_3. It weighs 1410 g. Of this, 69% or (0.69)(1410 g) = 972.9 g is HNO_3. The formula weight of HNO_3 is 63.013 g/mol. Therefore, the number of moles of HNO_3 in a liter of solution is $\frac{972.9 \text{ g}}{63.013 \text{ g/mol}}$ = 15.4 moles, and the solution is 15.4 F.

Let V = volume, in mL, of the concentrated HNO_3 solution. Then,

$$(V)(15.4 \text{ F}) = (250.0 \text{ mL})(2.0 \text{ F})$$

and V = 32 mL. To prepare 250.0 mL of 2.0 F HNO_3 from concentrated HNO_3, measure out 32 mL of the concentrated acid, and add distilled H_2O until the volume of the thoroughly mixed solution is 250.0 mL.

Solutions to Exercises, Chapter 7

1. The work required to separate two ions of opposite charge is directly proportional to the force of attraction between them, which is given by Coulomb's Law, Eq. (7-3). We therefore need to compare those factors involved in Coulomb's Law, namely the product of the charges, the distance between the charges, and the dielectric constant of the medium in which the charges are immersed. Since this question specifies that the ions are to be separated to an equal extent, the distance between the charges is the same for both pairs of ions.

(a) As the ions are the same, the charges are the same, and the difference in the dielectric constants of the two solvents is the only factor that is different for the two pairs of ions. The work required is inversely proportional to the dielectric constant of the liquid (see Table 7.2).

$$\frac{\text{work required in } H_2O}{\text{work required in acetone}} = \frac{D(\text{acetone})}{D(H_2O)} = \frac{20.7}{78.54} = 0.264$$

Thus the work required to separate a given pair of ions to an equal extent at 25°C in H_2O is only 26.4% of the work required in acetone.

(b) The product of the charges, q_1q_2, is 4 times larger for Mg^{2+} and SO_4^{2-}, than for K^+ and Cl^-, so 4 times as much work must be done to separate Mg^{2+} and SO_4^{2-} as to separate K^+ and Cl^- in the same solvent, to an equal extent.

2. The dipole moment is a property of an individual molecule. An acetone molecule is more polar than a methanol molecule, because the $\geq C=O$ bond in $CH_3\overset{O}{\overset{\|}{C}}CH_3$ is more polar than the C–O bond in CH_3OH (H_3C-OH). The dielectric constant is a bulk property of the solvent. Methanol is extensively hydrogen bonded, but acetone is not. Hydrogen bonding in methanol results in a large network of CH_3OH molecules, and allows for a separation of charge over large distances.

3. Tetrabromomethane is a nonpolar, tetrahedral molecule. Each of the four C–Br bonds is polar, but the bond-dipole vectors sum to zero, and the centers of positive and negative charge coincide at the carbon atom. Water molecules, however, are polar. The force of attraction between two polar molecules is considerably larger than the force of attraction between a polar and a nonpolar molecule. In general, nonpolar solutes do not dissolve in water, but dissolve only in nonpolar solvents such as benzene and hexane.

4. (a) For electrolytes the terms strong and weak refer to the percentage of ions (in contrast to molecules) that are found in aqueous solution. A strong electrolyte exists as 100% ions in dilute aqueous solution. The terms concentrated and dilute refer to the amount of material that

dissolves, regardless of whether the solute particles are ions or molecules. A concentrated solution is one in which the solute concentration is large.

(b) Silver bromide is a strong electrolyte. 100% of the dissolved solid exists as ions, Ag^+ and Br^-, in aqueous solution. A saturated solution of AgBr is, however, dilute because very little solid AgBr (7.1×10^{-7} moles per liter) dissolves in H_2O. The concentrations of the ions are very low, but the percentage of the dissolved solid material that exists in solution as ions is 100%.

(c) An 8.0 M solution is concentrated. Ammonia, NH_3, is a weak electrolyte. The percentage of solute particles that are ions (NH_4^+ and OH^- ions) is very small, less than 2%. Most of the solute particles are NH_3 molecules.

5.

substance	category	electrolyte	cation	anion
(a) $NiBr_2$	salt	strong	Ni^{2+}	Br^-
(b) CH_3NH_2	base	weak	$CH_3NH_3^+$	OH^-
(c) K_2SO_3	salt	strong	K^+	SO_3^{2-}
(d) CH_3OH	nonelectrolyte	—	—	—
(e) $Na_2C_2O_4$	salt	strong	Na^+	$C_2O_4^{2-}$
(f) HNO_2	acid	weak	H_3O^+	NO_2^-
(g) $(NH_4)_2CO_3$	salt	strong	NH_4^+	CO_3^{2-}
(h) H_3PO_4	acid	weak	H_3O^+	$H_2PO_4^-$, HPO_4^{2-}, PO_4^{3-}

substance	category	electrolyte	cation	anion
(i) $Sr(OH)_2$	base	strong	Sr^{2+}	OH^-
(j) $Co(NO_3)_2$	salt	strong	Co^{2+}	NO_3^-
(k) $LiClO_4$	salt	strong	Li^+	ClO_4^-
(l) C_6H_6	nonelectrolyte	——	——	——
(m) $H_2C_2O_4$	acid	weak	H_3O^+	$HC_2O_4^-$ and $C_2O_4^{2-}$
(n) CH_3CH_2COOH	acid	weak	H_3O^+	$CH_3CH_2COO^-$
(o) ZnI_2	salt	strong	Zn^{2+}	I^-

6. Put a drop of an aqueous solution of phenol on both pink and blue litmus paper. The spot will remain pink on the pink litmus, and will turn pink on the blue litmus paper. Phenol is a weak acid, also called carbolic acid. Any kind of pH paper may be used. The pH can also be measured with a pH meter.

7. $$HBr(g) + H_2O \xrightarrow{100\%} H_3O^+ + Br^-$$

8. Propionic acid has only one acidic hydrogen, the one bonded to an oxygen atom, circled below:

$$CH_3CH_2COO\textcircled{H}$$

9.

	p^+ acceptor	+	p^+ donor	⇌	p^+ donor	+	p^+ acceptor
(a)	OH^-	+	NH_4^+	⇌	H_2O	+	NH_3
(b)	S^{2-}	+	H_2O	⇌	HS^-	+	OH^-
(c)	NH_3	+	HSO_4^-	⇌	NH_4^+	+	SO_4^{2-}

10. There are several possibilities, of which two are described here. Method 1. Measure the freezing point of aqueous dilute solutions of the two acids having identical concentrations. The freezing point of the nitric acid solution will be lower than the freezing point of the nitrous acid solution, because there will be approximately twice as many solute particles (H_3O^+ and NO_3^- ions) in the nitric acid as in the nitrous acid (mostly HNO_2 molecules). The freezing point depression, ΔT_f, will be almost twice as large for HNO_3 as for HNO_2.

Method 2. Use the apparatus of Fig. 7.6, with a solution of each of the two acids having identical concentrations. The bulb will shine very brightly when the nitric acid solution is used because ions conduct electricity. The bulb will be quite dim when the nitrous acid solution is used because the ionic concentrations in HNO_2 are low.

11. $$HNO_2 + H_2O \rightleftharpoons NO_2^- + H_3O^+$$

The anion formed is nitrite ion, also written as ONO^-. Nitrous acid may be written as HONO.

12. Since the freezing point of pure H_2O is exactly 0°C, the freezing point depression of this solution is 0.000 - (-0.098) = +0.098. The dissociation of formic acid is due to the proton-transfer reaction

$$HCOOH + H_2O \rightleftharpoons HCOO^- + H_3O^+$$

If α is the percentage of formic acid that exists as ions in this solution, then

molality of formate ions ($HCOO^-$) = $\alpha(0.0500)$ m

molality of hydronium ions (H_3O^+) = $\alpha(0.0500)$ m

molality of formic acid (HCOOH) = $(1 - \alpha)(0.0500)$ m

total molality of all 3 solutes = $(1 + \alpha)(0.0500)$ m

The freezing point depression depends on the total molality of all 3 solutes and is, therefore,

$$\Delta T_f = +0.098 = K_f(1 + \alpha)(0.0500) = 1.86(1 + \alpha)(0.0500)$$

$$0.098 = 0.093(1 + \alpha) \quad \text{so that } (1 + \alpha) = 1.0538$$

and $$\alpha = 0.0538 \text{ or } 5.4\%$$

13.

Soluble	Insoluble
$(NH_4)_3PO_4$	$Cr(OH)_3$
$NaHCO_3$	NiS
HNO_2	Hg_2Br_2
$Al(NO_3)_3$	$SrSO_3$
HI	$ZnCO_3$
$(NH_4)_2S$	$PbCrO_4$
$H_2C_2O_4$	AgI
	Ag_2CrO_4

14.

(a) $Ca^{2+}(aq) + CO_3^{2-}(aq) \rightleftharpoons CaCO_3\downarrow$

(b) $NH_4^+(aq) + OH^-(aq) \rightleftharpoons NH_3 + H_2O$

(c) NR

(d) $Zn^{2+}(aq) + S^{2-}(aq) \rightleftharpoons ZnS\downarrow$

(e) $OH^-(aq) + H^+(aq) \rightleftharpoons H_2O$

(f) $2Ag^+(aq) + CrO_4^{2-}(aq) \rightleftharpoons Ag_2CrO_4\downarrow$

(g) $CH_3COOH + NH_3 \rightleftharpoons CH_3COO^-(aq) + NH_4^+(aq)$

(h) $Sr^{2+}(aq) + SO_4^{2-}(aq) \rightleftharpoons SrSO_4\downarrow$ (i) NR

(j) $Ba^{2+}(aq) + SO_3^{2-}(aq) \rightleftharpoons BaSO_3\downarrow$

(k) $H_2S + Cu^{2+}(aq) \rightleftharpoons CuS\downarrow + 2H^+(aq)$

(l) $Ni^{2+}(aq) + 2OH^-(aq) \rightleftharpoons Ni(OH)_2\downarrow$

15.

(a)

OH^-	+	$HONO$	$\rightleftharpoons$	H_2O	+	ONO^-
p^+ acceptor		p^+ donor		p^+ donor		p^+ acceptor

(b)

OH^-	+	H_3O^+	$\rightleftharpoons$	$2H_2O$
p^+ acceptor		p^+ donor		p^+ donor and acceptor

(c) $Pb^{2+}(aq) + SO_4^{2-}(aq) \rightleftharpoons PbSO_4\downarrow$

(d)

CN^-	+	$HCOOH$	$\rightleftharpoons$	HCN	+	$HCOO^-$
p^+ acceptor		p^+ donor		p^+ donor		p^+ acceptor

(e) $3S^{2-}(aq) + 2Fe^{3+}(aq) \rightleftharpoons Fe_2S_3\downarrow$

Note: In addition to the reaction given above, two other reactions occur. Sulfide ion reacts with water in a proton-transfer reaction:

$$S^{2-}(aq) + H_2O \rightleftharpoons HS^-(aq) + OH^-$$

and the OH^- ions formed combine with Fe^{3+} ions to precipitate $Fe(OH)_3$:

$$Fe^{3+}(aq) + 3OH^-(aq) \rightleftharpoons Fe(OH)_3\downarrow$$

(f)

$2OH^-(aq)$	+	H_2S	$\rightleftharpoons$	$2H_2O$	+	$S^{2-}(aq)$
p^+ acceptor		p^+ donor		p^+ donor		p^+ acceptor

16.

(a) $MnS(s) + 2H^+(aq) \rightleftharpoons H_2S + Mn^{2+}(aq)$

(b) $2AgCl(s) + CO_3^{2-}(aq) \rightleftharpoons Ag_2CO_3\downarrow + 2Cl^-(aq)$

(c) $BaCO_3(s) + 2H^+(aq) \rightleftharpoons Ba^{2+} + CO_2\uparrow + H_2O$

(d) $Sr^{2+}(aq) + H_2SO_3 \rightleftharpoons SrSO_3\downarrow + 2H^+(aq)$

(e) $Zn(OH)_2(s) + 2CH_3COOH \rightleftharpoons Zn^{2+} + 2CH_3COO^- + 2H_2O$

(f) $2Fe^{3+} + 3SO_4^{2-} + 3Ba^{2+} + 6OH^- \rightleftharpoons 3BaSO_4\downarrow + 2Fe(OH)_3\downarrow$

17. The four species in solution are K^+, Ba^{2+}, Br^-, and NO_3^- ions, in a total volume of 50.00 mL.

$$[K^+] = \frac{(10.00\ mL)(0.100\ M) + (20.00\ mL)(0.120\ M)}{50.00\ mL}$$

$$= 6.80x10^{-2}\ M$$

$$[Br^-] = \frac{(10.00\ mL)(0.100\ M)}{50.00\ mL} = 2.00x10^{-2}\ M$$

$$[Ba^{2+}] = \frac{(20.00\ mL)(0.0850M)}{50.00\ mL} = 3.40x10^{-2}\ M$$

$$[NO_3^-] = \frac{(20.00\ mL)(2)(0.0850\ M) + (20.00\ mL)(0.120\ M)}{50.00\ mL}$$

$$= 0.116\ M$$

To check your arithmetic, use the electroneutrality condition. The sum of all positive charges must equal the sum of all negative charges. The concentration of any doubly charged ion must be multiplied by 2 to calculate the amount of charge, as each ion carries two charges:

$$\begin{array}{ccccc} [K^+] & + & 2[Ba^{2+}] & = & [Br^-] + [NO_3^-] \\ 0.0680 & & 0.0680 & = & 0.0200 + 0.116 \end{array}$$

As there are 0.136 moles per liter of both positive and negative charge, the solution is electrically neutral and our arithmetic is correct.

18.

No. mmol K^+ added = (40.00 mL)(0.0850 M) = 3.40 mmol

No. mmol Cl^- added = (40.00 mL)(0.0850 M) = 3.40 mmol

No. mmol Ag^+ added = (20.00 mL)(0.110 M) = 2.20 mmol

No. mmol NO_3^- added = (20.00 mL)(0.110 M) = 2.20 mmol

The final volume of the solution is 60.00 mL. 2.20 mmol of Ag^+ ions combine with 2.20 mmol Cl^- ions to precipitate 2.20 mmol of solid white AgCl, leaving 1.20 mmol Cl^- in excess in solution. The principal ions in solution after reaction are K^+, Cl^-, and NO_3^- ions.

$$[K^+] = \frac{3.40 \text{ mmol}}{60.00 \text{ mL}} = 0.05666 \text{ M} = 0.0567 \text{ M}$$

$$[Cl^-] = \frac{1.20 \text{ mmol}}{60.00 \text{ mL}} = 0.0200 \text{ M}$$

$$[NO_3^-] = \frac{2.20 \text{ mmol}}{60.00 \text{ mL}} = 0.03666 \text{ M} = 0.0367 \text{ M}$$

19. Formula weight of $CaCO_3$ = 100.09 $g \cdot mol^{-1}$

$$\text{mass of } CaCO_3 \text{ dissolved} = \frac{0.6506 \text{ g}}{100.09 \text{ g/mol}} = 6.500\text{x}10^{-3} \text{ mol}$$

reaction occurring: $CaCO_3(s) + 2H^+(aq) \rightarrow CO_2\uparrow + Ca^{2+} + H_2O$

Since the $CaCO_3$ dissolved completely, $6.500\text{x}10^{-3}$ mol of Ca^{2+} ions were formed. The volume is still 80.00 mL. Thus,

$$[Ca^{2+}] = \frac{6.500\text{x}10^{-3} \text{ mol}}{80.00\text{x}10^{-3} \text{ L}} = 8.125\text{x}10^{-2} \text{ M}$$

The reaction does not involve nitrate ions, so the $[NO_3^-]$ remains constant at 0.2000 M.

The reaction uses up $H^+(aq)$ ions. We must find how many mmol of H^+ ions are left after reaction.

No. mmol $H^+(aq)$ added = (80.00 mL)(0.200 M) = 16.00 mmol

No. mmol $H^+(aq)$ reacted = 2(No. mmol $CaCO_3$ dissolved)

= 2(6.500 mmol) = 13.00 mmol

No. mmol $H^+(aq)$ in excess = 16.00 - 13.00 = 3.00 mmol

$$[H^+(aq)] = \frac{3.00\ \text{mmol}}{80.00\ \text{mL}} = 0.0375\ \text{M}$$

Check your arithmetic by making sure the solution is electrically neutral:

$$2[Ca^{2+}(aq)] + [H^+(aq)] = [NO_3^-]$$
$$2(0.08125)\ \text{M} + 0.0375\ \text{M} = 0.2000\ \text{M}$$

20. The dissolution reaction is

$$2H^+(aq) + Mg(OH)_2(s) \rightarrow Mg^{2+} + 2H_2O$$

No. mmol $H^+(aq)$ added = (100.00 mL)(0.100 M) = 10.0 mmol

No. mmol $Mg(OH)_2$ reacted = (1/2){No. mmol $H^+(aq)$ added}
= 5.00 mmol

Formula weight of $Mg(OH)_2$ = 58.320 g/mol. Hence the mass of $Mg(OH)_2$ reacted is

$$(5.00\times10^{-3}\ \text{mol})(58.320\ \text{g/mol}) = 0.2916\ \text{g} = 0.292\ \text{g}$$

21. The net ionic equation for the reaction is

$$Ba^{2+}(aq) + SO_4^{2-}(aq) \rightarrow BaSO_4\downarrow$$

The NO_3^- and K^+ ions take no part in the reaction. Their concentrations are halved because the volume of solution is doubled.

$$[NO_3^-] = (1/2)(2)(0.0750\ \text{M}) = 0.0750\ \text{M}$$
$$[K^+] = (1/2)(2)(0.1200\ \text{M}) = 0.1200\ \text{M}$$

Let V = volume, in mL, of each solution added.

No. mmol Ba^{2+} added = (V mL)(0.0750 M) = 0.0750V mmol

No. mmol SO_4^{2-} added = (V ml)(0.1200 M) = 0.1200V mmol

0.0750V mmol Ba^{2+} ions react with 0.0750V mmol SO_4^{2-} ions to precipitate 0.0750V mmol of solid white $BaSO_4$ leaving

$(0.1200V - 0.0750V) = 0.0450V$ mmol of SO_4^{2-} ions in solution. The volume of the mixture is 2V mL. Thus

$$[SO_4^{2-}] = \frac{0.0450V\ \text{mmol}}{2V\ \text{mL}} = 0.0225\ \text{M}$$

Solutions to Multiple Choice Questions, Chapter 7

1. **(c)**

No. mmol Pb^{2+} added = $(20.00\ \text{mL})(0.1000\ \frac{\text{mmol}}{\text{mL}}) = 2.000$ mmol

No. mmol SO_4^{2-} added = $(30.00\ \text{mL})(0.1000\ \frac{\text{mmol}}{\text{mL}}) = 3.000$ mmol

Since Pb^{2+} and SO_4^{2-} ions react in a 1:1 molar ratio to form $PbSO_4$, 2.000 mmol Pb^{2+} ions react with 2.000 mmol SO_4^{2-} ions to precipitate 2.000 mmol $PbSO_4$, leaving 1.000 mmol SO_4^{2-} ions in excess. The formula weight of $PbSO_4$ is 303.26 $g \cdot mol^{-1}$. The maximum mass of $PbSO_4$ that can be precipitated is, therefore,

$$(2.000 \times 10^{-3}\ \text{mol})(303.26\ \text{g/mol}) = 0.6065\ \text{g}$$

2. **(d)**

$$[Na^+] = \frac{(30.00\ \text{mL})(0.120\ \text{M}) + (70.00\ \text{mL})(0.150\ \text{M})(2)}{100.00\ \text{mL}}$$

$$= 0.246\ \text{M}$$

3. **(a)** Acetic acid, CH_3COOH, is a weak electrolyte. Cesium hydroxide, CsOH, calcium hydroxide, $Ca(OH)_2$, and potassium hydroxide, KOH, are all strong bases. Methyl alcohol, CH_3OH, is a nonelectrolyte.

4. **(d)** The formula weight of Ag_2SO_4 is 311.79 g/mol. Thus the number of moles of dissolved Ag_2SO_4 is

$$\frac{0.57\ g}{311.79\ g/mol} = 1.83\times10^{-3}\ mol = 1.8\times10^{-3}\ mol \text{ in } 100.00\ mL$$

Ten times as much can be dissolved in 1 L as in 100.00 mL, so 1.83×10^{-2} mol of Ag_2SO_4 dissolve per liter.

$$\frac{\text{moles } Ag^+ \text{ ion in solution}}{\text{moles } Ag_2SO_4 \text{ dissolved}} = \frac{2}{1}$$

The number of moles of Ag^+ ions per liter is $2(1.83\times10^{-2})$, and

$$[Ag^+] = 0.037\ M$$

5. **(b)** Benzene, C_6H_6, is a nonpolar organic molecule that cannot hydrogen bond to water. Because it is nonpolar, the force of attraction between two H_2O molecules is very much greater than the force of attraction between C_6H_6 and H_2O, and C_6H_6 does not mix with H_2O. Ammonium dichromate, $(NH_4)_2Cr_2O_7$, is a salt, a soluble, strong electrolyte. Ethanol, CH_3CH_2OH, hydrogen bonds to H_2O, and mixes with it in all proportions. Methylamine, CH_3NH_2, is a weak base that is very soluble in water, and oxalic acid, $H_2C_2O_4$, is also very soluble in water.

6. **(d)**

$$\text{No. mmol } OH^- = (2)(0.1080\ \frac{mmol}{mL})(25.00\ mL) = 5.400\ mmol$$

Remember that $Ba(OH)_2$ is a strong base, and that there are 2 OH^- ions per $Ba(OH)_2$ formula unit. The net ionic equation for the reaction is $H^+(aq) + OH^- \longrightarrow H_2O$. The NO_3^- and Ba^{2+}

ions take no part in the reaction, they are only spectator ions. Since H^+ and OH^- ions react in a 1:1 molar ratio, we need 5.400 mmol of H^+ ions for the reaction.

$$\text{volume } HNO_3 \text{ required} = \frac{5.400 \text{ mmol}}{0.1250 \text{ mmol/mL}} = 43.20 \text{ mL}$$

7. <u>(e)</u> Sodium chloride, NaCl, is an ionic crystalline solid. It is not soluble in nonpolar liquids. The only nonpolar liquid of those listed is carbon tetrachloride.

8. <u>(c)</u> The reaction that occurs when these two solutions are mixed is

$$H^+(aq) + OH^-(aq) \rightleftharpoons H_2O$$

No. mmol H^+ added = (80.00 mL)(0.200 M) = 16.0 mmol

No. mmol OH^- added = (120.00 mL)(0.150 M) = 18.0 mmol

As H^+ and OH^- react in a 1:1 molar ratio, there are 2.00 mmol of OH^- in excess. The solution contains 16.0 mmol Cl^-, 18.0 mmol K^+, and 2.00 mmol OH^- in a total volume of 200.00 mL. Thus, $[Cl^-]$ = 16.0 mmol/200.00 mL = 0.0800 M; $[K^+]$ = 0.0900 M; and $[OH^-]$ = 0.0100 M. This is identical with a solution that is 0.0800 F KCl and 0.0100 F KOH.

9. <u>(b)</u> Let V = volume, in mL, of each solution used. Then the volume of the final solution is 2V mL.

No. mmol Ba^{2+} added = $(V \text{ mL})(0.200 \frac{\text{mmol}}{\text{mL}})$ = 0.200V mmol

No. mmol $CrO_4{}^{2-}$ added = $(V \text{ ml})(0.120 \frac{\text{mmol}}{\text{mL}})$ = 0.120V mmol

Since Ba^{2+} and $CrO_4{}^{2-}$ must react in a 1:1 molar ratio to produce an electrically neutral compound, there are

0.080V mmol Ba^{2+} in excess, in 2V mL.

$$[Ba^{2+}] = \frac{0.080V \text{ mmol}}{2V \quad \text{mL}} = 0.040 \text{ M}$$

10. **(d)** The reaction is $Pb^{2+}(aq) + 2Cl^-(aq) \rightleftharpoons PbCl_2\downarrow$

No. mmol Pb^{2+} added = (40.00 mL)(0.100 M) = 4.00 mmol

No. mmol Cl^- added = (60.00 mL)(0.300 M) = 18.0 mmol

The limiting reagent is Pb^{2+}, as only 8.00 mmol of Cl^- are needed to precipitate completely the 4.00 mmol of Pb^{2+}. Thus a maximum of 4.00 mmol of $PbCl_2$ could be precipitated. The formula weight of $PbCl_2$ is 278.1 g/mol. The maximum mass of $PbCl_2$ that could be precipitated is therefore

$$(4.00\text{x}10^{-3} \text{ mol})(278.1 \text{ g/mol}) = 1.112 \text{ g}$$

$$\text{Percentage yield} = \frac{\text{actual yield}}{\text{maximum yield}} = \left(\frac{1.068 \text{ g}}{1.112 \text{ g}}\right)\text{x}100 = 96.0\%$$

11. **(c)** Of the 5 solutions listed, the only one containing a cation that reacts with Cl^- to form an insoluble precipitate is mercury(I) nitrate. The reaction that occurs is

$$Hg_2{}^{2+} + 2Cl^- \rightleftharpoons Hg_2Cl_2\downarrow$$

12. **(e)** Many weak and nonelectrolytes are very soluble in water. While a large number of strong electrolytes are very soluble in water, there are a significant number of insoluble salts.

13. **(b)** The reaction that occurs is

$$H^+(aq) + OH^-(aq) \rightleftharpoons H_2O$$

As the volumes are equal and the concentration of KOH is twice the concentration of HCl, there will be OH^- in excess, and only options (b) and (c) need to be considered. These two options differ only in $[K^+]$ given, so focus on that. Mixing equal volumes doubles the volume. Since K^+ ions take no part in the reaction that occurs, the concentration of K^+ must be halved when the volume is doubled. As $[K^+]$ is 0.400 M initially, it must be 0.200 M in the final solution.

14. <u>(c)</u> The reaction that occurs is

$$Fe^{3+}(aq) + 3OH^-(aq) \rightleftharpoons Fe(OH)_3\downarrow$$

Thus Fe^{3+} and OH^- react in a 1:3 molar ratio. In (a) there is excess OH^- and only 1.00 mmol of $Fe(OH)_3$ can be precipitated, as there is only 1.00 mmol of Fe^{3+} added. In (b) there is excess OH^- and only 2.00 mmol of $Fe(OH)_3$ can be precipitated. In (c) the solutions are mixed in a 1:3 molar ratio, neither reagent is in excess, and 2.5 mmol of $Fe(OH)_3$ can be precipitated. In (d) and (e) the limiting reagent is OH^-. The maximum number of moles of $Fe(OH)_3$ that can be precipitated is 1/3 the number of moles of OH^- added, or 1.80 mmol for (d) and 1.20 mmol for (e).

15. <u>(a)</u> Strontium hydroxide and sulfuric acid react in a 1:1 molar ratio. The net ionic equation for the reaction is

$$Sr^{2+} + 2OH^- + H^+(aq) + HSO_4^- \rightleftharpoons SrSO_4\downarrow + 2H_2O$$

No. mmol H_2SO_4 added = (34.57 mL)(0.0452 $\frac{mmol}{mL}$) = 1.563 mmol

Let x = formality of the $Sr(OH)_2$ solution. Then,

No. mmol $Sr(OH)_2$ added = 50.00x = (34.57 mL)(0.0452 F)

and x = 0.0313 F

16. <u>(a)</u> $2La^{3+}(aq) + 3C_2O_4^{2-}(aq) \rightleftharpoons La_2(C_2O_4)_3\downarrow$

No. mmol La^{3+} added = (30.00 mL)(0.0860 M) = 2.58 mmol

No. mmol $C_2O_4^{2-}$ added = (20.00 mL)(0.114 M) = 2.28 mmol

The limiting reagent is the $C_2O_4^{2-}$. There is excess La^{3+} present, as only (2/3)(2.28 mmol) of La^{3+} are needed to precipitate all the $C_2O_4^{2-}$.

$$\frac{\text{No. mol } La_2(C_2O_4)_3 \text{ precipitated}}{\text{No. mol } C_2O_4^{2-} \text{ added}} = \frac{1}{3}$$

The maximum amount of $La_2(C_2O_4)_3$ precipitate is therefore

(1/3)(2.28 mmol) = 0.760 mmol

17. <u>(e)</u> Barium carbonate, $BaCO_3$, precipitates when $BaCl_2$ and Na_2CO_3 are mixed. Silver chloride, AgCl, precipitates when $BaCl_2$ and $AgNO_3$ are mixed. Barium sulfate, $BaSO_4$, precipitates when $BaCl_2$ and $(NH_4)_2SO_4$ are mixed. Lead chloride, $PbCl_2$, precipitates when $BaCl_2$ and $Pb(NO_3)_2$ are mixed.

18. <u>(b)</u> Precipitates of $PbCl_2$, $PbBr_2$, and PbI_2 will form when HCl, HBr, and HI, respectively, are added to $Pb(OH)_2$. Precipitates of $SrSO_4$ and $PbSO_4$ will form when H_2SO_4 is added to $Sr(OH)_2$ or $Pb(OH)_2$. Nitrates are soluble.

Solutions to Problems, Chapter 7

7.1.

Substance	Formula	Soluble or Insoluble	Strong or Weak
Silver chloride	$AgCl$	insoluble	strong
Ammonia	NH_3	soluble	weak
Barium sulfite	$BaSO_3$	insoluble	strong
Potassium permanganate	$KMnO_4$	soluble	strong
Ammonium sulfide	$(NH_4)_2S$	soluble	strong
Mercurous iodide	Hg_2I_2	insoluble	strong
Lithium hydroxide	$LiOH$	soluble	strong
Sodium acetate	CH_3COONa	soluble	strong
Hydrogen sulfide	H_2S	soluble	weak
Silver chromate	Ag_2CrO_4	insoluble	strong
Oxalic acid	$H_2C_2O_4$	soluble	weak
Dimethylamine	$(CH_3)_2NH$	soluble	weak
Iron(II) carbonate	$FeCO_3$	insoluble	strong
Perchloric acid	$HClO_4$	soluble	strong
Potassium chlorate	$KClO_3$	soluble	strong
Lead sulfate	$PbSO_4$	insoluble	strong
Hydrocyanic acid	HCN	soluble	weak

7.2.

(a) $Zn(OH)_2(s) + 2CH_3COOH \rightleftharpoons Zn^{2+}(aq) + 2CH_3COO^-(aq) + 2H_2O$

(b) $MgCO_3(s) + 2H^+(aq) \rightleftharpoons CO_2\uparrow + Mg^{2+}(aq) + H_2O$

(c) $Fe(OH)_3 + 3H^+(aq) \rightleftharpoons Fe^{3+}(aq) + 3H_2O$

(d) $BaSO_3(s) + 2H^+(aq) \rightleftharpoons Ba^{2+}(aq) + H_2O + SO_2\uparrow$

(e) $CuCO_3(s) + 2CH_3COOH \rightleftharpoons Cu^{2+}(aq) + H_2O + CO_2\uparrow + 2CH_3COO^-$

7.3.

(a) $Pb(OH)_2(s) + 2H^+(aq) + 2I^-(aq) \rightleftharpoons PbI_2\downarrow + 2H_2O$

(b) $H_2S + Mn^{2+}(aq) \rightleftharpoons MnS\downarrow + 2H^+(aq)$

(c) $Ba^{2+}(aq) + 2I^-(aq) + Ag_2SO_4(s) \rightleftharpoons 2AgI\downarrow + BaSO_4\downarrow$

(d) $\underset{p^+ \text{ acceptor}}{NH_3} + \underset{p^+ \text{ donor}}{HCN} \rightleftharpoons \underset{p^+ \text{ donor}}{NH_4^+(aq)} + \underset{p^+ \text{ acceptor}}{CN^-(aq)}$

(e) $SrCO_3(s) + 2H^+(aq) + SO_4^{2-}(aq) \rightleftharpoons SrSO_4\downarrow + H_2O + CO_2\uparrow$

(f) $MgCO_3(s) + 2H^+(aq) \rightleftharpoons Mg^{2+}(aq) + H_2O + CO_2\uparrow$

(g) $H_2SO_3 + Zn^{2+}(aq) \rightleftharpoons ZnSO_3\downarrow + 2H^+(aq)$

(h) $Ba^{2+} + 2CH_3COO^- + 2H^+(aq) + SO_4^{2-} \rightleftharpoons BaSO_4\downarrow + 2CH_3COOH$

(i) $Ag_2CO_3(s) + 2H^+(aq) + 2Cl^-(aq) \rightleftharpoons 2AgCl\downarrow + H_2O + CO_2\uparrow$

(j) $Ba^{2+} + \underset{p^+ \text{ acptor}}{2OH^-(aq)} + \underset{\text{donor}}{2NH_4^+} + CO_3^{2-} \rightleftharpoons BaCO_3\uparrow + \underset{\text{donor}}{2H_2O} + \underset{\text{acptor}}{2NH_3}$

7.4. The reaction that occurs is

$$Hg_2^{2+} + 2CH_3COO^- + 2H^+(aq) + 2Cl^- \rightleftharpoons Hg_2Cl_2\downarrow + 2CH_3COOH$$

No. mmol Hg_2^{2+} added = (30.00 mL)(0.0240 M) = 0.720 mmol

No. mmol Cl^- added = (50.00 mL)(0.100 M) = 5.00 mmol

The limiting reagent is the Hg_2^{2+} and the number of millimoles of Hg_2Cl_2 precipitated is 0.720 mmol.

No. mmol Cl^- used in reaction = 2(0.720 mmol) = 1.44 mmol

No. mmol Cl^- in excess = 5.00 - 1.44 = 3.56 mmol

The final volume of solution is 80.00 mL. Hence,

$$[Cl^-] = \frac{3.56 \text{ mmol}}{80.00 \text{ mL}} = 0.0445 \text{ M}$$

The formula weight of Hg_2Cl_2 is 472.09 g/mol. Therefore

mass Hg_2Cl_2 precipitated = $(7.20\times10^{-4}$ mol)(472.09 g/mol)

= 0.3399 g = 0.340 g

7.5. (a) Formula weight of $CaC_2O_4 \cdot H_2O$ = 146.11 g/mol

$$\text{No. mol } CaC_2O_4 \cdot H_2O = \frac{0.8212 \text{ g}}{146.11 \text{ g/mol}} = 5.620\times10^{-3} \text{ mol}$$

Because of conservation of mass of oxalate ion, $C_2O_4^{2-}$,

No. mmol $H_2C_2O_4$ = No. mmol $CaC_2O_4 \cdot H_2O$ = 5.620 mmol

Let x = formality of the oxalic acid solution. Then,

(40.00 mL)(x) = 5.620 mmol, and x = 0.1405 F

(b) The net ionic equation for the reaction is

$$H_2C_2O_4 + Ca^{2+} + 2NH_3 + H_2O \rightleftharpoons CaC_2O_4 \cdot H_2O + 2NH_4^+$$

No. mmol NH_4^+ formed = 2(No. mmol $CaC_2O_4 \cdot H_2O$) = 11.24 mmol

7.6.

No. mmol BrO_3^- used = (42.80 mL)(0.0200 M) = 0.856 mmol

No. mmol N_2H_4 titrated = (3/2)(No. mmol BrO_3^- used)

= (3/2)(0.856 mmol) = 1.284 mmol

Let x = molarity of N_2H_4 solution. Then,

No. mmol N_2H_4 titrated = (20.00 mL)(x) = 1.284 mmol

x = 0.0642 M

7.7. (a)

No. mmol MnO_4^- used = (40.05 mL)(0.04120 M) = 1.650 mmol

No. mmol $H_2C_2O_4$ titrated = (5/2)(No. mmol MnO_4^- used)

= 4.125 mmol

Therefore 4.125×10^{-3} mol $H_2C_2O_4$ were titrated.

(b) By conservation of mass of the oxalate ion, $C_2O_4^{2-}$,

No. mol $H_2C_2O_4$ = No. mol CaC_2O_4 precipitated = 4.125×10^{-3}

By conservation of mass of calcium,

No. mol $CaCl_2$ = No. mol CaC_2O_4 = 4.125×10^{-3} mol. Thus there was 4.125×10^{-3} mol $CaCl_2$ in the original sample.

(c) The formula weight of $CaCl_2$ is 110.99 g/mol. The mass of $CaCl_2$ in the original sample was therefore

$$(4.125 \times 10^{-3} \text{ mol})(110.99 \text{ g/mol}) = 0.4578 \text{ g}$$

$$\text{Percentage of } CaCl_2 \text{ in sample} = \left(\frac{0.4578 \text{ g}}{0.7075 \text{ g}}\right) \times 100 = 64.71\%$$

7.8. The formula weight of HgO is 216.59 g/mol.

$$\text{No. mol HgO used} = \frac{0.7000 \text{ g}}{216.59 \text{ g/mol}} = 3.232 \times 10^{-3} \text{ mol}$$

No. mol OH^- produced = 2(No. mol HgO used) = 6.464×10^{-3} mol

Since $H^+(aq)$ and $OH^-(aq)$ react in a 1:1 molar ratio,

No. mmol H^+ used = No. mmol OH^- used = 6.464 mmol

Let x = formality of Karla's HCl solution. Then

$$31.73x = 6.464 \quad \text{and } x = 0.2037 \text{ M}$$

7.9. The reaction that occurs is

$$2H^+(aq) + 2Cl^-(aq) + Ag_2CO_3(s) \rightarrow 2AgCl(s) + H_2O + CO_2\uparrow$$

No. mmol H_3O^+ initially = No. mmol Cl^- initially

= (50.00 mL)(0.3020 M) = 15.10 mmol

The formula weight of Ag_2CO_3 = 275.745 g/mol. Thus,

$$\text{No. mol } Ag_2CO_3 \text{ used} = \frac{1.3683 \text{ g}}{275.745 \text{ g/mol}} = 4.9622 \times 10^{-3} \text{ mol}$$

As the number of millimoles of Cl^- and H_3O^+ used is twice the number of millimoles of Ag_2CO_3 used, or 2(4.9622 mmol),

$$\text{No. mmol } H_3O^+ \text{ and } Cl^- \text{ in excess} = (15.10 - 9.9244) \text{ mmol}$$

$$= 5.176 \text{ mmol} = 5.18 \text{ mmol}$$

$$[H_3O^+] = [Cl^-] = \frac{5.176 \text{ mmol}}{50.00 \text{ mL}} = 0.1035 \text{ M} = 0.104 \text{ M}$$

(b) No. mol AgCl precipitated = No. mol Cl^- used

$$= 9.9244 \times 10^{-3} \text{ mol}$$

The formula weight of AgCl is 143.321 g/mol. Therefore,

$$\text{mass AgCl precipitated} = (9.9244 \times 10^{-3} \text{ mol})(143.321 \text{ g/mol})$$

$$= 1.4224 \text{ g}$$

(c) No. mol CO_2 evolved = No. mol Ag_2CO_3 used

$$= 4.9622 \times 10^{-3} \text{ mol}$$

$$V = \frac{nRT}{P} = \frac{(4.9622 \times 10^{-3} \text{ mol})}{(752 \text{ mmHg})}\left(62.363 \frac{\text{L} \cdot \text{mmHg}}{\text{mol} \cdot \text{K}}\right)(298.15 \text{ K})$$

$$= 0.1227 \text{ L} = 123 \text{ mL}$$

7.10.

No. mmol Pb^{2+} ions added = (25.00 mL)(0.0812 M) = 2.03 mmol

No. mmol NO_3^- ions added = 2(2.03 mmol) = 4.06 mmol

No. mmol K^+ ions added = No. mmol IO_3^- ions added

$$= (25.00 \text{ mL})(0.1024 \text{ M}) = 2.560 \text{ mmol}$$

The reaction that occurs is $Pb^{2+} + 2IO_3^- \rightleftharpoons Pb(IO_3)_2\downarrow$

The limiting reagent is IO_3^-. Only 1.280 mmol Pb^{2+} are required to precipitate completely 2.560 mmol of IO_3^-, forming 1.280 mmol of $Pb(IO_3)_2$. Thus,

No. mmol Pb^{2+} in excess = 2.03 − 1.280 = 0.75 mmol

$$[Pb^{2+}] = \frac{0.750 \text{ mmol}}{50.00 \text{ mL}} = 0.0150 \text{ M}$$

$$[K^+] = \frac{2.540 \text{ mmol}}{50.00 \text{ mL}} = 0.05120 \text{ M}$$

$$[NO_3^-] = \frac{4.06 \text{ mmol}}{50.00 \text{ mL}} = 0.0812 \text{ M}$$

The formula weight of $Pb(IO_3)_2$ is 557.0 g/mol. Therefore,

mass of $Pb(IO_3)_2$ formed = (557.0 g/mol)($1.280\text{x}10^{-3}$ mol)

= 0.7130 g

7.11. (a) No. mmol $S_2O_3^{2-}$ used = (38.40 mL)(0.1250 M)

= 4.800 mmol

No. mmol I_2 titrated = (1/2)(No. mmol $S_2O_3^{2-}$) = 2.400 mmol

(b) No. mmol IO_3^- reacted = (1/3)(No. mmol I_2) = 0.8000 mmol

Let x = formality of the KIO_3 solution. Then,

(25.00 mL)(x) = 0.8000 mmol and x = 0.03200 F

7.12. No. mmol $Cr_2O_7^{2-}$ used = (41.55 mL)(0.04000 M)

= 1.662 mmol

No. mmol Fe^{2+} titrated = 6(1.662 mmol) = 9.972 mmol

No. mol Fe in sample = No. mol Fe^{2+} titrated = $9.972\text{x}10^{-3}$

The atomic weight of Fe is 55.847 g/mol. Therefore,

mass Fe in sample = ($9.972\text{x}10^{-3}$ mol)(55.847 g/mol)

= 0.5569 g

$$\text{Percentage of Fe} = \left(\frac{0.5569 \text{ g}}{3.6831 \text{ g}}\right)\text{x}100 = 15.12\%$$

7.13. To a weighed sample of pure solid $BiCl_3$ add exactly 100.00 mL of distilled H_2O. Filter the precipitate formed, Titrate a 25.00 mL portion of the resulting acidic solution with 0.2000 F NaOH to determine the [$H^+(aq)$] in the solution. From the concentration of H^+ determine the number of moles of H^+ in the 100.00 mL of solution, and from that calculate the molar ratio

$$\frac{\text{No. mol } H^+(aq) \text{ formed}}{\text{No. mol } BiCl_3 \text{ used}}$$

If this ratio is 2:1, reactions (b) and (c) are eliminated, but (a) is possible, although not proved with certainty. If this ratio is 3:1, reactions (a) and (c) are eliminated, but (b) is possible. If this ratio is 1:1, reactions (a) and (b) are eliminated, but (c) is possible.

7.14. $\Delta T_f = 0.000 - (-0.345) = +0.345^\circ$

The proton transfer reaction that occurs is

$$HSO_4^- + H_2O \rightleftharpoons H_3O^+ + SO_4^{2-}$$

Let α = percentage HSO_4^- dissociated

Then, $(1 - \alpha)$ = percentage HSO_4^- not dissociated

molality Na^+ = 0.0800 m

molality HSO_4^- = $(1 - \alpha)(0.0800)$ m

molality H_3O^+ = $\alpha(0.0800)$ m

molality SO_4^{2-} = $\alpha(0.0800)$ m

Total molality of all solutes = $(2 + \alpha)(0.0800 \text{ m})$ Hence,

$$\Delta T_f = +0.345^\circ = K_f(2+\alpha)(0.0800) = 1.86(0.0800)(2+\alpha)$$

$$2+\alpha = 2.319 \text{ and } \alpha = 0.319 \text{ or } 32\% \text{ dissociated}$$

As K_f is only good to 3 figs, α is only known to 2 figs.

7.15. The reaction with acid is

$$\{CuCl_2 \cdot xCu(OH)_2\} + 2xH^+(aq) \rightleftharpoons 2xH_2O + (1+x)Cu^{2+} + 2Cl^-$$

No. mmol $H^+(aq)$ used = (45.05 mL)(0.5089 M) = 22.93 mmol

The formula weight of atacamite is 134.452 + 97.5606x

$$\text{No. mol atacamite dissolved} = \frac{1.6320\ \text{g}}{(134.452 + 97.5606x)\ \text{g/mol}}$$

$$\frac{\text{No. mol } H^+(aq) \text{ used}}{\text{No. mol atacamite dissolved}} = 2x$$

Therefore,

$$\text{No. mol } H^+(aq) \text{ used} = \frac{(2x)(1.6320)}{(134.452 + 97.5606x)} = 22.93\text{x}10^{-3}$$

Multiplying this out yields

$$3.2640x = 3.0824 + 2.2362x$$

$$1.0278x = 3.0824 \text{ and } x = 3.00$$

Solutions to Exercises, Chapter 8

1.

(a) $K_{eq} = K_{sp} = [Ag^+]^2[CO_3^{2-}]$

(b) $K_{eq} = P_{O_2}^{1/2}/[H_2O_2]$

(c) $K_{eq} = K_b = \dfrac{[NH_4^+][OH^-]}{[NH_3]}$

(d) $K_{eq} = K_a = \dfrac{[H_3O^+][PO_4^{3-}]}{[HPO_4^{2-}]}$

(e) $K_{eq} = P_{CHCl_3}$ This equilibrium constant is the vapor pressure of pure liquid chloroform.

(f) $K_{eq} = K_p = P_{CO_2}/P_{O_2}^2P_{CH_4}$

(g) $K_{eq} = [Cu(NH_3)_4^{2+}]/[NH_3]^4[Cu^{2+}]$

(h) $K_{eq} = P_{H_2}^{3/2}[Al^{3+}]/[H^+(aq)]^3$

(i) $K_{eq} = P_{NO}^2[Pb^{2+}]^3/[NO_3^-]^2[H^+(aq)]^8$

(j) $K_{eq} = P_{CO_2}$ Note that the pressure of CO_2 in equilibrium with both $CaCO_3(s)$ and $CaO(s)$ is a constant.

(k) $K_{eq} = [SO_4^{2-}]/[CO_3^{2-}]$

2.

(a) $K_{eq} = K_{sp} = [OH^-]^3[Fe^{3+}]$ units are M^4 or $(mol/L)^4$

(b) $K_{eq} = K_{sp} = [Pb^{2+}][I^-]^2$ units are M^3 or $(mol/L)^3$

(c) $K_{eq} = K_a = \dfrac{[SO_3^{2-}][H_3O^+]}{[HSO_3^-]}$ units are M

(d) $K_{eq} = K_p = P_{N_2O}/P_{N_2}P_{O_2}^{1/2}$ units are $atm^{-1/2}$

(e) $K_{eq} = P_{CH_3OH}$ This equilibrium constant is the vapor pressure of pure methanol, in atm.

(f) $K_{eq} = K_p = P_{NO_2}^2/P_{O_2}^2P_{N_2}$ units are atm^{-1}

(g) $K_{eq} = P_{H_2}[Mg^{2+}]/[H^+(aq)]^2$ units are atm/M or $\dfrac{L\cdot atm}{mol}$

(h) $K_{eq} = P_{SO_2}$ units are atm

3.
$$K_p = P_{O_2}P^2_{SO_2}/P^2_{SO_3} \text{ atm} = 1.80\text{x}10^{-5} \text{ atm}$$

$$P_{O_2} = [O_2]RT; \quad P^2_{SO_2} = [SO_2]^2(RT)^2; \quad P^2_{SO_3} = [SO_3]^2(RT)^2$$

$$K_p = \frac{[O_2][SO_2]^2(RT)^3}{[SO_3]^2 \quad (RT)^2} = K_c(RT)$$

Note that $\Delta n_{gas} = 2+1-2 = 1$, so that Eq. (8-8) yields $K_p = K_c(RT)$ immediately. By substitution,

$$1.80\text{x}10^{-5} \text{ atm} = K_c\left(8.2057\text{x}10^{-2} \frac{L\cdot atm}{mol\cdot K}\right)(700 \text{ K})$$

$$K_c = \frac{1.80\text{x}10^{-5} \text{ atm}}{57.44 \text{ L}\cdot\text{atm}\cdot\text{mol}^{-1}} = 3.13\text{x}10^{-7} \text{ mol/L or M}$$

4. The general relation is given by Eq. (8-8). Only when $\Delta n_{gas} = 0$ will K_p and K_c be numerically equal, that is, only when the number of moles of gas is the same on both sides of the equation. That is true for reactions (c) and (e), which have 2 moles of gas on each side of the equation. The value of $\Delta n_{gas} = -1/2$ for (a), -1 for (b), and -2 for (d).

5. The order of decreasing acid strength is the same as the order of decreasing K_a value.

strongest ↑	HSO_4^-	$K_a = 1.2\text{x}10^{-2}$
	HONO	$4.5\text{x}10^{-4}$
	HCOOH	$1.8\text{x}10^{-4}$
	C_6H_5COOH	$6.3\text{x}10^{-5}$
	CH_3COOH	$1.8\text{x}10^{-5}$
weakest	HCN	$4.0\text{x}10^{-10}$

6. $$K_p = P^2_{HI}/P_{H_2} = 0.35 \text{ atm}$$

(a) $$Q = \frac{(0.90)^2 \text{ atm}^2}{(0.10) \text{ atm}} = \frac{81\text{x}10^{-2}}{1\text{x}10^{-1}} \text{ atm} = 8.1 \text{ atm}$$

Since Q > K_{eq}, the reaction proceeds to the left. Some HI will decompose to form $H_2(g)$ and $I_2(s)$.

(b) $$Q = \frac{(0.44)^2}{(0.55)} \text{ atm} = 0.35 \text{ atm}$$

Since Q = K_{eq} this system is at equilibrium and no net reaction will occur.

(c) $$Q = \frac{(1.5\text{x}10^{-1})^2 \text{ atm}^2}{2.5 \text{ atm}} = 9.0\text{x}10^{-3} \text{ atm}$$

Since Q < K_{eq} the reaction will proceed to the right. Some $H_2(g)$ and $I_2(s)$ will combine to make more HI(g).

7. $$K_p = P_{NH_3}P_{H_2S} \text{ atm}^2$$

$$P_{total} = P_{NH_3} + P_{H_2S} = 0.659 \text{ atm}$$

Let $x = P_{NH_3} = P_{H_2S}$ The pressures of these two gases are equal because they are formed in a 1:1 molar ratio by the decomposition of $NH_4HS(s)$. Therefore,

$$2x = 0.659 \text{ atm} \quad \text{and } x = 0.329_5 \text{ atm}$$

$$K_p = x^2 = (0.329_5)^2 \text{ atm}^2 = 0.109 \text{ atm}^2$$

8. $$K_{eq} = \frac{1}{P_{NH_3}P_{HCl}} = 17.8 \text{ atm}^{-2}$$

(a) $$Q = \frac{1}{\left(\frac{684}{760}\right)\left(\frac{912}{760}\right)} = \frac{(760)^2}{(684)(912)} = 0.926 \text{ atm}^{-2}$$

Since Q < K_{eq}, the reaction must proceed to the right to reach equilibrium. Yes, some solid NH_4Cl will form.

(b) $Q = \dfrac{1}{\left(\frac{30.4}{760}\right)\left(\frac{22.8}{760}\right)} = \dfrac{(760)^2}{(30.4)(22.8)}\ atm^{-2} = 833\ atm^{-2}$

Since $Q > K_{eq}$, the reaction would have to proceed to the left to attain equilibrium. No solid NH_4Cl will form. If there were any solid NH_4Cl present, it would decompose to produce more NH_3 and HCl gas. As there is none, nothing will happen.

9. $Q = [Ag^+][BrO_3^-]\ M^2$

(a) $Q = (1.0x10^{-3}\ M)(2.0x10^{-3}\ M) = 2.0x10^{-6}\ M^2$ at the instant of mixing. Since $Q<K_{sp}$, no solid $AgBrO_3$ will form.

(b) $Q = (1.0x10^{-1}\ M)(5.0x10^{-1}\ M) = 5.0x10^{-2}\ M^2$ at the instant of mixing. Since $Q>K_{sp}$, some $AgBrO_3(s)$ will form.

10. $K_p = P_{SO_3}/P_{SO_2}P_{O_2}^{1/2} = 1.84x10^{12}\ atm^{-1/2}$

$$Q = \frac{3.00}{(1x10^{-1})(4x10^{-2})^{1/2}}\ atm^{-1/2} = \frac{30}{2x10^{-1}} = 150\ atm^{-1/2}$$

Since $Q < K_p$, the reaction must proceed to the right to achieve equilibrium. There will be more SO_3 in the container at equilibrium than there was at the instant of mixing.

11. (a) The pressure of HBr in the vessel will decrease. $K_p = P_{NH_3}P_{HBr}$ is a constant at constant temperature. If P_{NH_3} is increased, P_{HBr} must decrease to keep K_p constant. In terms of Le Chatelier's Principle, to counter the stress of added NH_3, the reaction shifts to the left, using up some HBr as well as some of the added NH_3, so that P_{HBr} decreases.

12. Since sulfurous acid, H_2SO_3, is a weak acid, while sulfuric acid, H_2SO_4, is a strong acid, the reaction of the salt with H_3O^+ proceeds much further to the right for $SrSO_3$ than it does for $SrSO_4$. Strontium sulfite, $SrSO_3$, reacts with H_3O^+ to produce H_2SO_3, which decomposes to H_2O and $SO_2(g)$. As a gas is formed, the reaction goes to completion to the right. The net ionic equation for the reaction is

$$SrSO_3(s) + 2H^+(aq) \rightarrow H_2O + SO_2\uparrow + Sr^{2+}$$

Strontium sulfate, $SrSO_4$, is only slightly more soluble in HCl than it is in H_2O, because HSO_4^- is a moderately strong acid and H_2SO_4 is a strong acid, 100% dissociated in dilute solution. The net ionic equation for the reaction is

$$SrSO_4(s) + H^+(aq) \rightleftharpoons HSO_4^- + Sr^{2+}(aq)$$

This reaction does not proceed very far to the right.

13. (a) Adding another 20 mL of water increases the volume of solution, and thereby decreases the concentrations of both Ag^+ and $CO_3{}^{2-}$ ions. The reaction shifts to the right, and a little more Ag_2CO_3 dissolves, to increase both $[Ag^+]$ and $[CO_3{}^{2-}]$ and restore equilibrium.

(b) The addition of Ag^+ ions drives the equilibrium to the left. More Ag_2CO_3 precipitates. This is the common ion effect. As the $[Ag^+]$ has increased, the $[CO_3{}^{2-}]$ must decrease to restore equilibrium. In order to decrease $[CO_3{}^{2-}]$ and use up some of the added Ag^+, more Ag_2CO_3 precipitates.

(c) Adding H_3O^+ from the strong acid decreases the $[CO_3{}^{2-}]$, as H_3O^+ and $CO_3{}^{2-}$ ions combine to form the weak acid, H_2CO_3, which decomposes to form H_2O and $CO_2(g)$. To counter the stress of decreased $[CO_3{}^{2-}]$, the equilibrium shifts to the right, and silver carbonate dissolves. The equation for the reaction is

$$Ag_2CO_3(s) + 2H^+(aq) \rightarrow H_2O + CO_2\uparrow + 2Ag^+$$

(d) The addition of $CO_3{}^{2-}$ ions drives the equilibrium to the left, and more Ag_2CO_3 precipitates. This is the common ion effect.

(e) Adding more Ag_2CO_3 has no effect on the equilibrium. Note that there is no term in solid silver carbonate in the expression for the equilibrium constant, which is $[Ag^+]^2[CO_3{}^{2-}]$. Only changes that affect the concentrations appearing in K_{eq} will affect the equilibrium.

14. (a) The equilibrium constant, K_p, will remain the same. An equilibrium constant is a constant (invariant) as long as the temperature is constant.

(b) The equilibrium constant expression is

$$K_p = \frac{P^2_{HCl}}{P_{H_2}P_{Cl_2}}$$

At the instant of adding more $Cl_2(g)$, P_{Cl_2} increases and $Q<K_p$. The reaction shifts to the right, forming more HCl and using up some H_2 and some Cl_2 until $Q = K_p$ again. The amount of HCl therefore increases.

15. $Cu(OH)_2(s) + 2H^+(aq) \rightleftharpoons Cu^{2+}(aq) + 2H_2O$

$ZnCO_3(s) + 2H^+(aq) \rightarrow H_2O + CO_2\uparrow + Zn^{2+}(aq)$

$Ca_3(PO_4)_2(s) + 6H^+(aq) \rightleftharpoons 2H_3PO_4 + 3Ca^{2+}(aq)$

$BaC_2O_4(s) + 2H^+(aq) \rightleftharpoons H_2C_2O_4 + Ba^{2+}(aq)$

16. (a) This is an exothermic reaction, which means that the products of the reaction are at a lower energy than the reactants. The tendency for reactions to proceed in the direction that minimizes the energy therefore favors the right-hand side, the products of the reaction.

(b) As the left-hand side has 3 moles of gases, while the right-hand side has only 2 moles of gases, there is more molecular disorder on the left, and the tendency to proceed in the direction that maximizes entropy favors the left-hand side of this reaction, namely NO(g) and $O_2(g)$.

(c) This reaction is exothermic: $\Delta H = -113$ kJ. If the temperature is raised, the reaction shifts in the direction that uses up (absorbs) heat, that is, to the left.

17. Raising the temperature from 25°C to 100°C will shift the equilibrium to the side that absorbs heat, that is, to the right, as this is an endothermic reaction. The solubility of lead nitrate at 100°C will be greater than it is at 25°C.

18. (a) Doubling the volume halves the pressure of CO_2. At the instant of doubling the volume, $Q = (1/2)P_{CO_2} =$

$(1/2)K_p$, and the reaction must shift to the right to restore equilibrium. Thus the number of moles of CO_2 in the vessel increases. Note, however, that P_{CO_2} remains constant. The volume is doubled, and the number of moles of CO_2 is doubled, so that $K_{eq} = P_{CO_2}$ remains unchanged when equilibrium is restored.

19. (a) The amount of CO will decrease. To counter the stress of increased pressure, the reaction shifts to the side with fewer moles of gas, that is, to the left, using up some CO(g) and Cl_2(g) and forming more $COCl_2$(g).

(b) The equilibrium constant, K_p, remains the same as long as the temperature is constant.

(c) The partial pressure of $COCl_2$ increases as the reaction shifts to the left and more moles of $COCl_2$ are formed. [See answer to part (a)]

20.

$$K_{overall} = \frac{[C_2O_4^{2-}][H_3O^+]^2}{[H_2C_2O_4]} = K_1K_2$$

$$= \frac{[H_3O^+]\cancel{[HC_2O_4^-]}}{[H_2C_2O_4]} \cdot \frac{[H_3O^+][C_2O_4^{2-}]}{\cancel{[HC_2O_4^-]}}$$

$$= (5.9\times10^{-2})(6.4\times10^{-5}) = 3.8\times10^{-6}$$

21.

$$\frac{[HCOO^-][HCN]}{[HCOOH][CN^-]} = 4.5\times10^5 \qquad \text{Thus,}$$

$$\frac{[HCOOH][CN^-]}{[HCOO^-][HCN]} = \frac{1}{4.5\times10^5} = 0.22\times10^{-5} = 2.2\times10^{-6}$$

22. (a) $K_p = P_{NO_2}/P_{NO}P_{O_2}^{1/2} = (1.62\text{x}10^{12}\ \text{atm}^{-1})^{1/2}$

$= 1.27\text{x}10^{6}\ \text{atm}^{-1/2}$

(b)

$$K_p = \frac{P_{O_2}^{1/2}P_{NO}}{P_{NO_2}} = \left(\frac{1}{1.62\text{x}10^{12}\ \text{atm}^{-1}}\right)^{1/2} = 7.86\text{x}10^{-7}\ \text{atm}^{1/2}$$

23. $K_1 = P_{PCl_3}/P_{Cl_2}^{3/2} = 8.3\text{x}10^{46}\ \text{atm}^{-1/2}$

$K_2 = P_{PCl_5}/P_{Cl_2}P_{PCl_3} = 3.4\text{x}10^{6}\ \text{atm}^{-1}$

The desired equilibrium constant is

$$K_{eq} = P_{PCl_5}/P_{Cl_2}^{5/2} = K_1K_2 = (8.3\text{x}10^{46})(3.4\text{x}10^{6})$$

$$= 28.2\text{x}10^{52} = 2.8\text{x}10^{53}\ \text{atm}^{-3/2}$$

24. $K_1 = \dfrac{[Ag(NH_3)^+]}{[NH_3][Ag^+]}$ and $K_2 = \dfrac{[Ag(NH_3)_2{}^+]}{[Ag(NH_3)^+][NH_3]}$

Thus, $K_1K_2 = \dfrac{[Ag(NH_3)_2{}^+]}{[NH_3]^2[Ag^+]}$

which is K_{eq} for $Ag^+(aq) + 2NH_3 \rightleftharpoons Ag(NH_3)_2{}^+(aq)$

25. $K_p = P_{PCl_5}/P_{PCl_3}P_{Cl_2}$

$$P_{total} = 1.295\ \text{atm} = P_{PCl_5} + P_{PCl_3} + P_{Cl_2}$$

Let x = decrease in partial pressure of Cl_2 and PCl_3 when reaction has come to equilibrium. Since they react in a 1:1 molar ratio, each partial pressure is decreased by the same amount.

	P_{Cl_2}	P_{PCl_3}	P_{PCl_5}
initial	0.820	0.640	0
change	x	x	x
final	0.0820-x	0.640-x	x

$$P_{total} = 0.820\text{-x} + 0.640\text{-x} + \text{x} = 1.460 - \text{x} = 1.295$$

Therefore, $\text{x} = 1.460 - 1.295 = 0.165\ \text{atm}$

At equilibrium $P_{Cl_2} = 0.655$ atm, $P_{PCl_3} = 0.475$ atm, and

P_{PCl_5} = 0.165 atm. Hence,

$$K_p = \frac{0.165}{(0.475)(0.655)} = 0.530\ \text{atm}^{-1}$$

26. $$2HBr(g) \rightleftharpoons H_2(g) + Br_2(g)$$

For this reaction $K_p = P_{H_2}P_{Br_2}/P^2_{HBr}$, which is dimensionless, that is, K_p and K_c have the same numerical value.

To form 0.104 mol of H_2 and Br_2, 0.208 mol of HBr must be lost, since

$$\frac{\text{No. mol } H_2 \text{ formed}}{\text{No. mol HBr used}} = \frac{1}{2}$$

Thus the number of moles of HBr left at equilibrium is 0.600 - 0.208 = 0.392 Let V = volume of the container. Then,

$$K_c = \left(\frac{n_{H_2}}{V}\right)\left(\frac{n_{Br_2}}{V}\right)\Bigg/\left(\frac{n_{HBr}}{V}\right)^2$$

All the V's cancel, and $K_c = \dfrac{(0.104)(0.104)}{(0.392)^2} = 7.04\text{x}10^{-2}$

Thus, $$K_p = K_c = 7.04\text{x}10^{-2}$$

27. (a) If there is no dissociation, the number of moles of SO_3 remains constant, and since the volume of the flask is constant,

$$\frac{P_1}{T_1} = \frac{P_2}{T_2} = \frac{1.00\ \text{atm}}{298.0\ \text{K}} = \frac{P_2}{900.0\ \text{K}}$$

$$P_2 = \frac{900.0}{298.0} = 3.020\ \text{atm}$$

If there were no dissociation of the SO_3, the pressure in the flask would have been 3.020 atm. It is higher than this because O_2 and SO_2 have been formed as SO_3 dissociated.

(b) Let $x = P_{O_2}$ in the flask at equilibrium

Then, $2x = P_{SO_2}$ in the flask at equilibrium

$$\frac{\text{No. mol } SO_3 \text{ used}}{\text{No. mol } O_2 \text{ formed}} = \frac{2}{1}$$

The decrease in the partial pressure of SO_3 is therefore twice the pressure of the O_2 formed, since the pressure of each gas is directly proportional to the number of moles of each gas. Thus the partial pressure of SO_3 is less than 3.020 atm by the amount 2x:

$$P_{SO_3} = 3.020 - 2x$$

$$P_{total} = 3.020 - 2x + x + 2x = 3.020 + x = 3.346 \text{ atm}$$

Hence, $x = 3.346 - 3.020 = 0.326$ atm

and $P_{O_2} = 0.326$ atm, $P_{SO_2} = 0.652$ atm

$$P_{SO_3} = 3.020 - 0.652 = 2.368 \text{ atm}$$

Thus,
$$K_p = \frac{P_{O_2} P_{SO_2}^2}{P_{SO_3}^2} = \frac{(0.326)(0.652)^2}{(0.2368)^2} \text{ atm} = 2.47\text{x}10^{-2} \text{ atm}$$

28. (a) The molecular weight of SO_2Cl_2 = 134.96 g/mol

$$\text{No. mol } SO_2Cl_2 = \frac{3.509 \text{ g}}{134.96 \text{ g/mol}} = 2.600\text{x}10^{-2} \text{ mol}$$

If no dissociation occurred,

$$P_{SO_2Cl_2} = \frac{(2.600\text{x}10^{-2} \text{ mol})\left(0.082057 \frac{\text{L}\cdot\text{atm}}{\text{mol}\cdot\text{K}}\right)(375 \text{ K})}{1.00 \text{ L}}$$
$$= 0.800 \text{ atm}$$

If there were no dissociation of SO_2Cl_2, $P_{SO_2Cl_2}$ would be 0.800 atm.

(b) $P_{total} = P_{SO_2Cl_2} + P_{SO_2} + P_{Cl_2} = 1.43$ atm

Let $P_{SO_2} = P_{Cl_2} = x$, as SO_2 and Cl_2 are formed in a 1:1 molar ratio. To form SO_2 and Cl_2, SO_2Cl_2 must decompose, that is, be used up. The decrease in the pressure of SO_2Cl_2 is also x, as

$$\frac{\text{No. mol } SO_2Cl_2 \text{ used}}{\text{No. mol } SO_2 \text{ formed}} = \frac{1}{1}$$

Hence, at equilibrium $P_{SO_2Cl_2} = 0.800 - x$, $P_{Cl_2} = x$, and $P_{SO_2} = x$.

$$P_{total} = 0.800 + x = 1.43 \text{ atm} \quad \text{and} \quad x = 0.63 \text{ atm}$$

Thus $P_{Cl_2} = P_{SO_2} = 0.63$ atm, and $P_{SO_2Cl_2} = 0.800 - 0.63 = 0.17$ atm.

(c) $$K_p = \frac{P_{Cl_2}P_{SO_2}}{P_{SO_2Cl_2}} = \frac{(0.63)^2}{(0.17)} \text{ atm} = 2.3 \text{ atm}$$

Solutions to Multiple Choice Questions, Chapter 8

1. (b) A solubility product is the equilibrium constant for the equilibrium between a very slightly soluble electrolyte and the saturated aqueous solution of that solid. The solid is always written on the left side of the equation, and the ions of which the solid is composed are on the right side. No other species but the solid and its ions appear in thè equation. The equilibrium constant for the reaction given in (c) is the inverse of K_{sp} for AgCl.

2. (c) Only if $\Delta n_{gas} = 0$ does $K_p = K_c$. For (a), $\Delta n_{gas} = 2+1-2 = 1$. For (b) $\Delta n_{gas} = 2-1-3 = -2$. For (c) $\Delta n_{gas} = 2-1-1 = 0$. For (d) $\Delta n_{gas} = 2-1 = 1$. Note that the iodine,

I_2, is a solid in (d). Pure solids do not appear in K_{eq} expressions. For (e) $\Delta n_{gas} = 1+1-1 = 1$.

3. <u>(e)</u> $K_p = P_{CO_2}$ The pressure of CO_2 is a constant at constant temperature, independent of the amount of either solid, as long as both solids are present.

4. <u>(d)</u> The equilibrium constant for $PCl_3 + Cl_2 \rightleftharpoons PCl_5$ is the inverse of K_{eq} for $PCl_5 \rightleftharpoons PCl_3 + Cl_2$. Thus

$$K_p = \frac{1}{0.0024} = 4.2\text{x}10^2$$

5. <u>(a)</u> Generally, the reaction quotient is evaluated when the system is not at equilibrium and Q and K_{eq} have different numerical values. The reaction quotient is zero when none of the products of the reaction are present, but there are reactants present.

6. <u>(e)</u> Doubling the volume means halving each pressure. The reaction will shift to the side with more moles of gas to restore equilibrium. Only in (e) are there more moles of gas on the right than on the left.

7. <u>(d)</u> An equilibrium constant is a constant (invariant) at constant temperature.

8. <u>(c)</u> An acidity constant is the equilibrium constant for the proton-transfer reaction between a weak acid and <u>water</u>.

9. <u>(c)</u> As each pressure is halved, the reaction shifts to the side with more moles of gas, that is, to the left. More Cl_2 is formed.

10. <u>(a)</u> In (a), $\Delta n_{gas} = 0$. Both sides have the same number of moles of gas. Decreasing the volume increases each pressure by the same factor, but as K_p is dimensionless, Q is unaffected if each pressure increases by the same factor. Thus Q remains equal to K_p and no shift occurs.

11. <u>(e)</u> Only increasing the temperature increases K_p for the decomposition reaction. Increasing the temperature for any endothermic reaction drives the reaction to the right, to absorb heat.

12. <u>(d)</u>

$$K_c = \frac{[H_2O][CO]}{[CO_2][H_2]} = 3.24$$

Let $x = [H_2O] = [CO]$ at equilibrium. Then $[H_2] = [CO_2] = 0.800 - x$, as the volume is 1.00 L. As the reaction proceeds to form H_2 and CO, both H_2 and CO_2 are used up. Thus

$$\frac{x^2}{(0.800 - x)^2} = 3.24$$

Take the square root of both sides of this equation.

$$\frac{x}{0.800 - x} = 1.80$$

Thus $\quad x = (1.80)(0.800) - 1.80x \quad$ or $\quad 2.80x = 1.44$

and $\quad x = 0.514$ mol of $H_2O(g)$ and $CO(g)$ formed

13. (c) $K_c = [C]^2/[B]^2$

$[C] = \dfrac{0.40\ \text{mol}}{2.00\ \text{L}} = 0.20\ M \qquad [B] = \dfrac{0.80\ \text{mol}}{2.00\ \text{L}} = 0.40\ M$

Thus, $K_c = \dfrac{(0.20)^2}{(0.40)^2} = (1/2)^2 = 1/4 = 0.25$

14. (b) $[NO_2] = \dfrac{0.120\ \text{mol}}{4.00\ \text{L}} = 3.00\text{x}10^{-2}\ M$

$[O_2] = \dfrac{0.640\ \text{mol}}{4.00\ \text{L}} = 1.6\text{x}10^{-1}\ M$

$[NO] = \dfrac{0.080\ \text{mol}}{4.00\ \text{L}} = 2.0\text{x}10^{-2}\ M$

$$K_c = \frac{[NO_2]^2}{[O_2][NO]^2} = \frac{(3.00\text{x}10^{-2}\ M)^2}{(1.60\text{x}10^{-1}\ M)(2.0\text{x}10^{-2}\ M)^2} = \frac{9.00\text{x}10^{-4}}{6.4\text{x}10^{-5}}\ M^{-1}$$

$= 1.4\text{x}10\ M^{-1} = 14\ \text{L/mol}$

15. (c)

$$K_p = \frac{P_{HI}^2}{P_{H_2}P_{I_2}} = 9.0$$

For each gas, $P = n\left(\frac{RT}{V}\right)$ As K_p has no units, the (RT/V) factors all cancel, and

$$K_p = \frac{n_{HI}^2}{n_{H_2}n_{I_2}} = \frac{(0.060)^2}{(0.40)(x)}$$

Thus, $$x = \frac{(0.60)^2}{(9.0)(0.40)} = 1.0\text{x}10^{-1} = 0.10$$

Solutions to Problems, Chapter 8

8.1. $$K_1 = \frac{[Ag(NH_3)_2{}^+]}{[NH_3]^2[Ag^+]} = 1.8\text{x}10^7$$

$$K_2 = \frac{1}{[Ag^+][Cl^-]} = 5.6\text{x}10^9$$

$$K_{eq} = \frac{[Ag(NH_3)_2{}^+][Cl^-]}{[NH_3]^2}$$

$$K_{eq} = \frac{K_1}{K_2} = \frac{[Ag(NH_3)_2^+]}{[NH_3]^2 \cancel{[Ag^+]}} \cdot \cancel{[Ag^+]}[Cl^-] = \frac{1.8x10^7}{5.6x10^9} = 3.2x10^{-3}$$

8.2. (a)

$$K = \frac{[CO_2]}{P_{CO_2}}$$

(b) An increase in the pressure of CO_2 above the solution causes a shift to the right to use up some of the gaseous CO_2. A shift to the right means an increase in the $[CO_2]$. Since the ratio of $[CO_2]$ to P_{CO_2} is a constant, if P_{CO_2} is increased, $[CO_2]$ must also increase, in direct proportion.

8.3. The molecular weight of PCl_5 is 208.239 g/mol. The number of moles of PCl_5 used is, therefore,

$$\frac{2.4156 \text{ g}}{208.239 \text{ g/mol}} = 1.1600x10^{-2} \text{ mol}$$

The initial partial pressure of PCl_5, before any decomposition, is given by the ideal gas law:

$$P_{PCl_5} = \frac{(1.1600x10^{-2} \text{ mol})}{(2.00 \text{ L})}\left(0.082057 \frac{\text{L}\cdot\text{atm}}{\text{mol}\cdot\text{K}}\right)(523.2 \text{ K})$$

$$= 0.249 \text{ atm}$$

Let x = decrease in P_{PCl_5} on decomposition. Then

$$P_{PCl_5} = 0.249 - x \quad \text{and} \quad P_{Cl_2} = P_{PCl_3} = x$$

since Cl_2 and PCl_3 are formed in a 1:1 molar ratio when PCl_5 decomposes.

$$P_{total} = P_{PCl_5} + P_{PCl_3} + P_{Cl_2} = 0.249 - x + x + x = 0.249 + x$$

Since the 0.249 is in atm, we must give P_{total} in atm also. (Alternatively, we could have calculated the initial partial pressure of PCl_5 in mmHg). P_{total} = 358.7 mmHg = 0.4720 atm. Thus,

$$0.249 + x = 0.4720 \quad \text{and} \quad x = 0.223 \text{ atm}$$

$$P_{PCl_5} = 0.249 - x = 0.249 - 0.223 = 0.026 \text{ atm}$$

$$K_p = \frac{P_{Cl_2} P_{PCl_3}}{P_{PCl_5}} = \frac{(0.223)^2 \text{ atm}^2}{(0.026 \text{ atm})} = 1.9 \text{ atm}$$

8.4. $K_p = K_c(RT)^{\Delta n_{gas}}$ and $\Delta n_{gas} = 2 - 3 - 1 = -2$

$$RT = (8.2057\text{x}10^{-2})(773)\ \frac{\text{L·atm}}{\text{mol}} = 63.43\ \frac{\text{L·atm}}{\text{mol}}$$

$$K_c = 6.00\text{x}10^{-2}\ \text{M}^{-2} = 6.00\text{x}10^{-2}\ \text{L}^2\text{mol}^{-2}$$

$$K_p = \frac{K_c}{(RT)^2} = \frac{6.00\text{x}10^{-2}\ \text{L}^2\text{mol}^{-2}}{(63.43)^2\ \frac{\text{L}^2\text{atm}^2}{\text{mol}^2}} = 1.49\text{x}10^{-5}\ \text{atm}^{-2}$$

8.5. **(a)** At the instant of mixing,

$$Q = \frac{P_{NOCl}}{P_{Cl_2}^{1/2} \cdot P_{NO}} = \frac{1.00}{(0.040)^{1/2}(0.200)} = 25\ \text{atm}^{-1/2}$$

(b) Since $Q < K_p$ the reaction must go to the right to increase Q in order to attain equilibrium. More NOCl is formed. The amount of NOCl at equilibrium is more than there was at the instant of mixing.

(c)

$$P_{NO} = 0.200 - x$$

$$P_{Cl_2} = 0.040 - (1/2)x$$

$$P_{NOCl} = 1.00 + x$$

8.6. **(a)** Increasing the temperature from 308 K (35°C) to 675 K decreases the value of K_p. The reaction is exothermic, therefore the forward reaction releases heat and the reverse reaction absorbs heat. Adding heat causes the reaction to shift to the left, to absorb heat, and the value of K_p decreases.

(b) In order to form SO_3, SO_2 must be used up, and

$$\frac{\text{No. mol } SO_3 \text{ formed}}{\text{No. mol } SO_2 \text{ used}} = \frac{1}{1}$$

As the pressure of each gas is directly proportional to the number of moles of that gas, if $P_{SO_3} = 0.980$ atm at equilibrium, $P_{SO_2} = 1.00 - 0.980 = 0.02$ atm. The decrease in pressure of O_2 is only half the decrease in the pressure of SO_2. Thus,

$$P_{O_2} = 0.500 - (1/2)(0.980) = 0.500 - 0.490 = 0.010 \text{ atm}$$

$$K_p = \frac{0.980}{(0.020)(0.010)^{1/2}} \text{ atm}^{-1/2} = 0.490\text{x}10^3 = 490 \text{ atm}^{-1/2}$$

8.7. $$Ag_3PO_4(s) \rightleftharpoons 3Ag^+(aq) + PO_4^{3-}(aq)$$

$$Ag_2CO_3(s) \rightleftharpoons 2Ag^+(aq) + CO_3^{2-}(aq)$$

The anions CO_3^{2-} and PO_4^{3-} combine with H_3O^+ to form weak acids, H_2CO_3 and H_3PO_4, respectively. Therefore adding H_3O^+ ions reduces the $[CO_3^{2-}]$ and $[PO_4^{3-}]$, and drives the dissolution reactions of Ag_2CO_3 and Ag_3PO_4 to the right.

$$AgCl(s) \rightleftharpoons Ag^+(aq) + Cl^-(aq)$$

The anion Cl^- has essentially no tendency to combine with H_3O^+ in dilute solution, because HCl is a strong acid, existing 100% as separate H_3O^+ and Cl^- ions. The weaker the acid formed when H_3O^+ ions are added, the more soluble the insoluble electrolyte will be in strong acid. The net ionic equations for the dissolution reactions in excess dilute acid are

$$Ag_2CO_3(s) + 2H^+(aq) \rightarrow H_2O + CO_2\uparrow + 2Ag^+(aq)$$

$$Ag_3PO_4(s) + 3H^+(aq) \rightleftharpoons H_3PO_4 + 3Ag^+(aq)$$

Carbonic acid, H_2CO_3, decomposes to H_2O and CO_2, and as the CO_2 gas escapes into the atmosphere, the dissolution reaction is driven to completion to the right. There is no reaction between AgCl and dilute HNO_3.

8.8 (a) Since the pressure of NH_3 is directly proportional to the number of moles of NH_3, when NH_3 is added, P_{NH_3} increases. The reaction then shifts to the left to counter the stress of added NH_3, and some of the additional NH_3 is used up, but not all. When the reaction shifts to the left, H_2S is also used up. At equilibrium P_{NH_3} is larger than before the NH_3 was added, P_{H_2S} is less than it was originally, and $K_p = P_{NH_3}P_{H_2S}$ is the same.

(b) The pressure of NH_3 decreases when H_2S is added. The reaction shifts to the left, using up some of the NH_3 originally present.

(c) Adding solid NH_4HS does not affect the equilibrium. The P_{NH_3} and P_{H_2S} both remain the same.

(d) The pressure of NH_3 increases. This is an endothermic reaction. Adding heat shifts the reaction to the right, to absorb heat, producing more NH_3 and H_2S, and using up some solid NH_4HS.

(e) If the volume is doubled, each pressure is halved, and the reaction shifts to the right to produce more NH_3 and H_2S. If P_{NH_3} and P_{H_2S} were equal before the volume was doubled, they will be equal when the system comes to equilibrium again, because the two gases are produced in a 1:1 molar ratio. In this case, each pressure will be exactly the same as it was originally. The <u>increase</u> in the number of moles of NH_3 and in the number of moles of H_2S is the same. If P_{NH_3} was larger than P_{H_2S} originally, and they both increase by the same amount, then the increase is a smaller percentage of the P_{NH_3} than of the P_{H_2S}, and P_{NH_3} is less than it was originally. On the other hand, if P_{NH_3} was smaller than P_{H_2S} originally, the same increase in the amount of both gases will cause P_{NH_3} to be greater than it was originally. This is difficult to see without trying some real values.

8.9 (a) $$K_{eq} = K_{sp} = [Al^{3+}][OH^-]^3 \ M^4$$

(b) Adding HNO_3 will greatly increaase the solubility of $Al(OH)_3$. The added H_3O^+ ions decrease the $[OH^-]$, so the $[Al^{3+}]$ must increase to keep K_{sp} constant. The only way to increase the $[Al^{3+}]$ is to dissolve $Al(OH)_3$. If excess nitric acid is added, all the $Al(OH)_3$ can be dissolved.

(c) Adding excess Al^{3+} from $Al(NO_3)_3$ shifts the equilibrium $Al(OH)_3(s) \rightleftharpoons Al^{3+} + 3OH^-$ to the left, precipitating more $Al(OH)_3$ and decreasing the solubility of $Al(OH)_3$. This is the common ion effect.

8.10. $K_{P_I} = P_{NO}^2/P_{N_2}\cdot P_{O_2} = 4.23\times10^{-31}$ unitless

(a) $K_{P_{II}} = P_{N_2}^{1/2}\cdot P_{O_2}^{1/2}/P_{NO} = (1/K_{P_I})^{1/2}$ unitless

$= \{1/(4.23\times10^{-31})\}^{1/2} = 1.54\times10^{15}$

(b) The increase in the number of moles of NO in the container is 0.016 mol, as there was no NO present originally. The decrease in the number of moles of N_2 and O_2 is 1/2 the increase in the number of moles of NO, or 0.0080 mol. Thus, at equilibrium

No. mol N_2 = No. mol O_2 = 1.500 - 0.008 = 1.492 mol

To find the concentrations of each gas, we divide the number of moles of each by the volume of the container, 10.00 L. However, since this is a unitless equilibrium constant, all the 10.00 L factors will cancel out, and

$$K_{C_I} \text{ at } 1800\text{ K} = \frac{(1.60\times10^{-2})^2}{(1.492)(1.492)} = 1.15\times10^{-4}$$

(c) This is an endothermic reaction. Heat energy must be added to form the product, NO. Thus 2 moles of NO are at a higher energy than a mole of N_2 plus a mole of O_2. The tendency for reactions to proceed to the state of minimum energy therefore favors the reactants, N_2 and O_2, and drives this reaction to the left.

(d) The value of K_c for reaction (I) at 1800 K is very much larger than the value at 298 K (25°C), 1.15×10^{-4} and 4.23×10^{-31}, respectively. Reaction (I) is endothermic. Raising the temperature (adding heat) drives the reaction to the right, and increases the equilibrium constant.

8.11. (a) The number of moles of gas is the same on both sides of this equation. Therefore K_p and K_c have the same numerical value, and are unitless.

$$K_p = P_{H_2}/P_{H_2S} = 8 \times 10^{-6} \quad \text{and} \quad K_c = [H_2]/[H_2S] = 8 \times 10^{-6}$$

Note that the sulfur is a pure solid, in a separate phase from the gases, and no term involving sulfur appears in either K_{eq} expression.

(b) If the number of moles of both gases is the same, then their pressures are equal, and their concentrations are equal. Thus, at the instant of mixing, Q = 1. Since Q is considerably larger than K_{eq}, the reaction must proceed to the left to decrease Q in order to reach equilibrium. Some $H_2(g)$ will react with some of the solid sulfur present, and more H_2S will be formed, until $Q = K_{eq}$.

(c) If the system is at equilibrium, and the volume of the container is doubled, each pressure will be halved, but the ratio P_{H_2}/P_{H_2S} will remain exactly the same, at the value 8×10^{-6}. There is no shift of the equilibrium and the total amount of H_2S remains the same. Note that only for reactions for which $\Delta n_{gas} = 0$ is there no shift in the equilibrium when the volume is changed.

8.12. $$K_p = P_{IBr}^2/P_{I_2}P_{Br_2} = 280 \text{ unitless}$$

Since I_2 and Br_2 are formed in a 1:1 molar ratio when IBr decomposes, their partial pressures must be equal.

$$\text{Let } x = P_{I_2} = P_{Br_2} \text{ at equilibrium}$$

Then, $$\frac{(0.46)^2}{x^2} = 280$$

Take the square root of both sides of this equation. We obtain $0.46/x = 16.73$, and $x = 2.749\text{x}10^{-2}$ atm = 0.027 atm.

8.13. (a) $$K_p = P_{NH_3}P_{H_2S} \text{ atm}^2$$

$$P_{total} = P_{NH_3} + P_{H_2S} = 0.659 \text{ atm}$$

Hence $$P_{NH_3} = P_{H_2S} = 0.329_5 \text{ atm}$$

and $$K_p = (0.329_5)^2 = 1.09\text{x}10^{-1} \text{ atm}^2$$

(b) We can calculate the number of moles of NH_3 or H_2S in the flask using the ideal gas law:

$$n_{NH_3} = \frac{(0.3295 \text{ atm})(3.00 \text{ L})}{\left(8.2057\text{x}10^{-2} \frac{\text{L}\cdot\text{atm}}{\text{mol}\cdot\text{K}}\right)(298.2 \text{ K})} = 4.04\text{x}10^{-2} \text{ mol}$$

No. mol NH_3 formed = No. mol NH_4HS decomposed = $4.04\text{x}10^{-2}$

The formula weight of NH_4HS is 51.11 g·mol^{-1}. Thus,

mass NH_4HS used up = $(4.04\text{x}10^{-2}$ mol$)(51.11$ g/mol$)$ = 2.065 g

$$\text{Percent } NH_4HS \text{ decomposed} = \left(\frac{2.065 \text{ g}}{5.2589 \text{ g}}\right)\text{x}100 = 39.3\%$$

(c) If the volume is halved, P_{NH_3} and P_{H_2S} are each doubled, and the reaction shifts to the left to decrease the pressure and restore equilibrium. The number of moles of solid NH_4HS increases.

(d) The concentration of NH_4HS in moles per liter remains the same. It is a fixed quantity, essentially the density of NH_4HS in other units (convert grams to moles and milliliters to liters). The concentration of a pure solid or liquid (not a constituent of a solution or a mixture) is a constant, independent of the amount of solid present. The mass of one liter of pure solid NH_4HS is fixed, and thus the number of moles of NH_4HS in 1 L of pure NH_4HS is fixed.

8.14. (a) $$K_p = P_{NH_3}P_{HCl} = 5.67\times10^{-2}\ \text{atm}^2$$

$$P_{total} = P_{NH_3} + P_{HCl} = 1.086\ \text{atm} \quad \text{so} \quad P_{NH_3} = 1.086 - P_{HCl}$$

$$\text{Let } P_{HCl} = x \quad \text{then } P_{NH_3} = 1.086 - x \quad \text{and}$$

$$K_p = (1.086 - x)(x) = 5.67\times10^{-2}\ \text{atm}^2$$

Multiply this out and bring all terms to the left side. We obtain

$$1.086x - x^2 - 0.0567 = 0$$

This equation can be solved in a straightforward manner by using the quadratic formula (see Appendix B). Written as

$$x^2 - 1.086x + 0.0567 = 0$$

we find

$$x = \frac{1.086 \pm \sqrt{(1.086)^2 - (4)(0.0567)}}{2} = \frac{1.086 \pm 0.976}{2}$$

There are two roots to this equation, but as there is more NH_3 in the bulb than HCl, only the smaller root is possible for P_{HCl}. Thus,

$$P_{HCl} = x = (1/2)(1.086 - 0.976) = 0.0550 \text{ atm}$$

$$P_{NH_3} = 1.086 - 0.055 = 1.031 \text{ atm}$$

(b) If the initial partial pressure of HCl was 0.600 atm, and the equilibrium partial pressure is 0.055 atm, then the change in P_{HCl} = 0.600 - 0.055 = 0.545 atm. The nunmber of moles of HCl that has been used up can therefore be calculated from the ideal gas law:

$$n_{HCl} \text{ used up} = \frac{(0.545 \text{ atm})(2.00 \text{ L})}{\left(0.082057 \frac{\text{L}\cdot\text{atm}}{\text{mol}\cdot\text{K}}\right)(573.2 \text{ K})} = 2.318\text{x}10^{-2} \text{ mol}$$

No. mol NH_4Cl formed = No. mol HCl used = $2.318\text{x}10^{-2}$ mol

The formula weight of NH_4Cl is 53.492 g/mol. Thus,

$$\text{mass of } NH_4Cl = (2.318\text{x}10^{-2} \text{ mol})(53.492 \text{ g/mol}) = 1.24 \text{ g}$$

8.15. At the instant of mixing

$$Q = [F^-]^2/[CO_3^{2-}] = (0.24)^2/0.12 = 0.48 \text{ M}$$

Since $Q<K_{eq}$, the reaction must go to the right to increase Q in order to attain equilibrium. Yes, $BaCO_3$ will form.

8.16. The reaction is $H_2(g) + I_2(g) \rightleftharpoons 2HI(g)$

$$K_p = \frac{P_{HI}^2}{P_{H_2}P_{I_2}} = \frac{(0.2024)^2}{(0.02745)^2} = 54.37$$

After the addition of HI the equilibrium shifts to the left to use up some of the added HI and form more H_2 and I_2. Let x = increase in P_{H_2} and P_{I_2} when the system returns to equilibrium. Then 2x = decrease in P_{HI} because

$$\frac{\text{No. mol HI used}}{\text{No. mol } H_2 \text{ formed}} = \frac{2}{1}$$

Thus, at the new position of equilibrium

$$P_{HI} = 0.8000 - 2x \quad \text{and} \quad P_{H_2} = P_{I_2} = 0.02745 + x$$

The equilibrium constant expression is now

$$\frac{(0.8000 - 2x)^2}{(0.02745 + x)^2} = 54.37$$

Take the square root of both sides of this equation. We obtain

$$\frac{0.8000 - 2x}{0.02745 + x} = (54.37)^{1/2} = 7.373$$

Thus $$0.8000 - 2x = 0.2024 + 7.373x$$

or $$0.5976 = 9.373x \quad \text{and} \quad x = 0.06376 \text{ atm}$$

$$P_{H_2} = P_{I_2} = 0.02745 + 0.06376 = 0.09121 \text{ atm}$$

$$P_{HI} = 0.8000 - 2(0.06376) = 0.6725 \text{ atm}$$

Solutions to Exercises, Chapter 9

1. (a) Perchloric acid, $HClO_4$, is a strong acid. Thus

$$[H_3O^+] = 0.250 \text{ M in } 0.250 \text{ F } HClO_4$$

$$[OH^-] = K_w/[H_3O^+] = 1.00x10^{-14}/0.250 = 4.00x10^{-14} \text{ M}$$

(b) Potassium hydroxide, KOH, is a strong base. Thus

$$[OH^-] = 0.160 \text{ M in } 0.160 \text{ F KOH}$$

$$[H_3O^+] = K_w/[OH^-] = 1.00x10^{-14}/0.160 = 6.25x10^{-14} \text{ M}$$

2. (a) Hydrobromic acid, HBr, is a strong acid. Thus

$$[H_3O^+] = 1.40 \text{ M in } 1.40 \text{ F HBr}$$

$$pH = -\log[H_3O^+] = -\log(1.40) = -0.146 = -0.15$$

Note that if $[H_3O^+] > 1.0$ M, $pH < 0$, that is, the pH is negative. Report the pH to two decimal places only.

(b) Nitric acid, HNO_3, is a strong acid. Thus

$$[H_3O^+] = 0.30 \text{ M in } 0.30 \text{ F } HNO_3$$

$$pH = -\log[H_3O^+] = -\log(0.30) = 0.52$$

(c) Perchloric acid, $HClO_4$, is a strong acid. Thus

$$[H_3O^+] = 4.58x10^{-3} \text{ M in } 4.58x10^{-3} \text{ F } HClO_4$$

$$pH = -\log[H_3O^+] = -\log(4.58x10^{-3}) = 3 - \log(4.58) = 2.34$$

3. (a) Sodium hydroxide, NaOH, is a strong base. Thus

$$[OH^-] = 1.25 \text{ M in } 1.25 \text{ F NaOH}$$

$$pOH = -\log[OH^-] = -\log(1.25) = -0.097$$

$$pH = 14.00 - pOH = 14.00 + 0.097 = 14.10$$

Alternatively, one could calculate the $[H_3O^+]$ as

$$[H_3O^+] = K_w/[OH^-] = 1.00x10^{-14}/1.25 = 8.00x10^{-15} \text{ M}$$

$$pH = -\log(8.00\times10^{-15}) = 15 - \log 8.00 = 15 - 0.90 = 14.10$$

The first method requires less arithmetic, and there is no need to calculate the $[H_3O^+]$ if only the pH is asked for.

(b) Potassium hydroxide, KOH, is a strong base.

$$[OH^-] = 0.37\ M \qquad pOH = -\log(0.37) = 0.43$$

$$pH = 14.00 - pOH = 14.00 - 0.43 = 13.57$$

(c) $[OH^-] = 6.10\times10^{-4}\ M \qquad pOH = -\log(6.10\times10^{-4}) = 3.21$

$$pH = 14.00 - pOH = 14.00 - 3.21 = 10.79$$

(d) Barium hydroxide, $Ba(OH)_2$, is a strong base.

$$[OH^-] = 0.090\ M \text{ in } 0.045\ F\ Ba(OH)_2$$

since the molar ratio of OH^- ions to $Ba(OH)_2$ formula units is 2:1. The $pOH = -\log(0.090) = 1.05$

$$pH = 14.00 - pOH = 14.00 - 1.05 = 12.95$$

4. **(a)** $[H_3O^+] = 1.12\ M$ in $1.12\ F$ HCl

$pH = -\log(1.12) = -0.05 \qquad pOH = 14.00 - pH = 14.05$

(b) $[OH^-] = 4.74\times10^{-3}\ M$ in $4.74\times10^{-3}\ F$ KOH

$$pOH = -\log(4.74\times10^{-3}) = 3 - \log 4.74 = 2.32$$

$$pH = 14.00 - pOH = 14.00 - 2.32 = 11.68$$

(c) $[OH^-] = 0.625\ M \qquad pOH = -\log(0.625) = 0.20$

$$pH = 14.00 - pOH = 14.00 - 0.20 = 13.80$$

5. If $pH = 2.32$, $\log[H_3O^+] = -2.32 = -3 + 0.68$

$$[H_3O^+] = \text{antilog}(-2.32) = 10^{-2.32} = 4.8\times10^{-3}\ M$$

As there are two significant figures in the mantissa of the logarithm (0.68), the antilog should be reported to two significant figures.

$[OH^-] = K_w/[H_3O^+] = 1.00x10^{-14}/(4.8x10^{-3}) = 2.1x10^{-12}$ M

6. If pH = 11.54, $\log[H_3O^+] = -11.54 = -12 + 0.46$

$[H_3O^+] = \text{antilog}(-11.54) = 10^{-11.54} = 2.9x10^{-12}$ M

$[OH^-] = K_w/[H_3O^+] = 1.00x10^{-14}/(2.9x10^{-12}) = 3.5x10^{-3}$ M

7. (a) If pH = 4.7, pOH = 14.00 - 4.7 = 9.3

$[H_3O^+] = \text{antilog}(-4.7) = 10^{-4.7} = 2x10^{-5}$ M

(b) If pH = 11.22, pOH = 14.00 - 11.22 = 2.78

$[H_3O^+] = \text{antilog}(-11.22) = 10^{-11.22} = 6.0x10^{-12}$ M

(c) If pH = -0.30, pOH = 14.00 - (-0.30) = 14.30

$[H_3O^+] = \text{antilog}(+0.30) = 10^{0.30} = 2.0$ M

8. (a) $C_6H_5COOH + H_2O \rightleftharpoons C_6H_5COO^-(aq) + H_3O^+(aq)$

(b) $CH_3NH_2 + H_2O \rightleftharpoons CH_3NH_3{}^+(aq) + OH^-(aq)$

(c) $H_2C_2O_4 + H_2O \rightleftharpoons HC_2O_4^-(aq) + H_3O^+(aq)$

(d) $HSO_3^- + H_2O \rightleftharpoons SO_3{}^{2-}(aq) + H_3O^+(aq)$

(e) $OCl^-(aq) + H_2O \rightleftharpoons HOCl + OH^-(aq)$

9. $CH_3COOH + H_2O \rightleftharpoons CH_3COO^-(aq) + H_3O^+(aq)$

$$K_a = 1.8x10^{-5} = \frac{[CH_3COO^-][H_3O^+]}{[CH_3COOH]}$$

$$[CH_3COO^-] = [H_3O^+]$$

since these ions are produced in a 1:1 molar ratio by the proton-transfer reaction between CH_3COOH and H_2O.

Let $x = [CH_3COO^-] = [H_3O^+]$

Then $[CH_3COOH] = 0.250 - x$

Note that the $[CH_3COOH]$ is less than its initial value

because the proton-transfer reaction uses up some of the CH_3COOH molecules. Substitution of these expressions into the equation for the acidity constant yields

$$K_a(HOAc) = 1.8x10^{-5} = \frac{x^2}{0.250 - x}$$

Assume x < 10% of 0.250 M. Then, 0.250 - x ~ 0.250 and the equilibrium constant equation becomes

$$1.8x10^{-5} = \frac{x^2}{0.250}$$

$$x^2 = (1.8x10^{-5})(0.250) = 0.45x10^{-5} = 4.5x10^{-6}$$

and $$x = 2.1x10^{-3}\ M$$

Check: Is $2.1x10^{-3} < 10\%$ of 0.250 ? Yes, $2.1x10^{-3} < 2.5x10^{-2}$

Since the assumption we made was valid,

$$[H_3O^+] = [CH_3COO^-] = 2.1x10^{-3}\ M$$

$$pH = -log(2.1x10^{-3}) = 3-log(2.1) = 2.68$$

10. $$NH_3 + H_2O \rightleftharpoons NH_4^+(aq) + OH^-(aq)$$

$$K_b(NH_3) = \frac{[NH_4^+][OH^-]}{[NH_3]} = 1.8x10^{-5}$$

Let $x = [NH_4^+] = [OH^-]$

Then $[NH_3] = 0.370 - x$

$$K_b(NH_3) = 1.8x10^{-5} = \frac{x^2}{0.370 - x}$$

Assume x < 10% of 0.370 M. Then 0.370 - x ~ 0.370 and the equilibrium constant equation is

$$1.8x10^{-5} = \frac{x^2}{0.370}$$

$$x^2 = (0.370)(1.8\times10^{-5}) = 0.666\times10^{-5} = 6.66\times10^{-6}$$

$$x = 2.58\times10^{-3}\ M = 2.6\times10^{-3}\ M$$

Check: Is $2.6\times10^{-3} < 10\%$ of 0.370? Yes, $2.6\times10^{-3} < 3.7\times10^{-2}$

Therefore $[NH_4^+] = [OH^-] = 2.6\times10^{-3}\ M$

$$[H_3O^+] = K_w/[OH^-] = 1.00\times10^{-14}/(2.58\times10^{-3}) = 3.9\times10^{-12}\ M$$

11. $CH_3NH_2 + H_2O \rightleftharpoons CH_3NH_3^+(aq) + OH^-(aq)$

$$K_b(CH_3NH_2) = \frac{[CH_3NH_3^+][OH^-]}{[CH_3NH_2]} = 4.2\times10^{-4}$$

The value of $K_b(CH_3NH_2)$ is given in Table 9.7.

Let $x = [CH_3NH_3^+] = [OH^-]$ at equilibrium

Then $[CH_3NH_2] = 0.45 - x$

$$K_b = 4.2\times10^{-4} = \frac{x^2}{0.45 - x}$$

Assume $x < 10\%$ of 0.45 Then $0.45 - x \sim 0.45$ and

$$4.2\times10^{-4} = \frac{x^2}{0.45}$$

$$x^2 = (0.45)(4.2\times10^{-4}) = 1.89\times10^{-4}$$

$$x = 1.37\times10^{-2}\ M = 1.4\times10^{-2}\ M$$

Check: Is $1.4\times10^{-2} < 10\%$ of 0.45? Yes, $1.4\times10^{-2} < 4.5\times10^{-2}$

Then the assumption made is valid, and

$$[CH_3NH_3^+] = [OH^-] = 1.4\times10^{-2}\ M$$

$$pOH = -\log(1.37\times10^{-2}) = 1.86$$

$$pH = 14.00 - pOH = 14.00 - 1.86 = 12.14$$

12. $HCN + H_2O \rightleftharpoons CN^-(aq) + H_3O^+(aq)$

$$K_a(HCN) = \frac{[CN^-][H_3O^+]}{[HCN]} = 4.0\times10^{-10}$$

Let $x = [CN^-] = [H_3O^+]$ at equilibrium

Then $[HCN] = 0.520 - x$ and

$$4.0\text{x}10^{-10} = \frac{x^2}{0.520 - x}$$

Assume $x < 10\%$ of 0.520 M. Then $0.520 - x \sim 0.520$ and

$$4.0\text{x}10^{-10} = \frac{x^2}{0.520}$$

$$x^2 = (0.520)(4.0\text{x}10^{-10}) = 2.08\text{x}10^{-10}$$

$$x = 1.44\text{x}10^{-5}\text{ M} = 1.4\text{x}10^{-5}\text{ M}$$

Check: Is $1.4\text{x}10^{-5} < 10\%$ of 0.520? Yes, $1.4\text{x}10^{-5} < 5.20\text{x}10^{-2}$ M

Hence $[H_3O^+] = [CN^-] = 1.4\text{x}10^{-5}$ M

$$[OH^-] = K_w/[H_3O^+] = 1.00\text{x}10^{-14}/(1.44\text{x}10^{-5}) = 6.9\text{x}10^{-10}\text{ M}$$

13. $$C_6H_5COOH + H_2O \rightleftharpoons C_6H_5COO^-(aq) + H_3O^+(aq)$$

By definition, α = fraction dissociated $= \dfrac{[H_3O^+]}{0.038}$

Thus, $[H_3O^+] = [C_6H_5COO^-] = 0.038\alpha$

The fraction of C_6H_5COOH molecules that is <u>not</u> dissociated is $(1 - \alpha)$. Hence,

$$[C_6H_5COOH] = (1 - \alpha)(0.038)$$

$$K_a(C_6H_5COOH) = \frac{[C_6H_5COO^-][H_3O^+]}{[C_6H_5COOH]} = \frac{(0.038\alpha)(0.038\alpha)}{(1 - \alpha)(0.038)}$$

$$= \frac{0.038\ \alpha^2}{(1 - \alpha)} = 6.3\text{x}10^{-5}$$

Assume $\alpha < 10\%$ of 1. Then $1 - \alpha \sim 1$, and

$$0.038\alpha^2 = 6.3\text{x}10^{-5} \quad\text{and}\quad \alpha^2 = 1.66\text{x}10^{-3} = 16.6\text{x}10^{-4}$$

$$\alpha = 4.1\text{x}10^{-2} = 4.1\%$$

Check: Is $4.1\text{x}10^{-2} < 10\%$ of 1? Yes, $4.1\text{x}10^{-2} < 1\text{x}10^{-1}$

14. **(a)** The conjugate base of H_3O^+ is water, H_2O.

(b) The conjugate base of HSO_4^- is sulfate ion, SO_4^{2-}.

(c) The conjugate base of NH_4^+ is ammonia, NH_3.

(d) The conjugate base of HF is fluoride ion, F^-.

(e) The conjugate base of H_3PO_4 is dihydrogen phosphate ion, $H_2PO_4^-$.

15. **(a)** The conjugate acid of OH^- is water, H_2O.

(b) The conjugate acid of HPO_4^{2-} is dihydrogen phosphate ion, $H_2PO_4^-$.

(c) The conjugate acid of CH_3NH_2 is methylammonium ion, $CH_3NH_3^+$.

(d) The conjugate acid of CO_3^{2-} is hydrogen carbonate ion, also called bicarbonate ion, HCO_3^-.

(e) The conjugate acid of HS^- is hydrogen sulfide, H_2S.

16. **(a)** $$CN^-(aq) + H_2O \rightleftharpoons HCN + OH^-(aq)$$

$$K_b(CN^-) = \frac{[HCN][OH^-]}{[CN^-]} = \frac{K_w}{K_a(HCN)} = \frac{1.0\times10^{-14}}{4.0\times10^{-10}} = 2.5\times10^{-5}$$

(b) $$CH_3COO^-(aq) + H_2O \rightleftharpoons CH_3COOH + OH^-(aq)$$

$$K_b(OAc^-) = \frac{[CH_3COOH][OH^-]}{[CH_3COO^-]} = \frac{K_w}{K_a(HOAc)} = \frac{1.0\times10^{-14}}{1.8\times10^{-5}} = 5.6\times10^{-10}$$

(c) $$CH_3NH_2 + H_2O \rightleftharpoons CH_3NH_3^+(aq) + OH^-(aq)$$

$$K_b(CH_3NH_2) = \frac{[CH_3NH_3^+][OH^-]}{[CH_3NH_2]} = \frac{K_w}{K_a(CH_3NH_3^+)} = \frac{1.0\times10^{-14}}{2.4\times10^{-11}}$$

$$= 0.42\times10^{-3} = 4.2\times10^{-4}$$

(d) $$PO_4^{3-}(aq) + H_2O \rightleftharpoons HPO_4^{2-}(aq) + OH^-(aq)$$

$$K_b(PO_4^{3-}) = \frac{[HPO_4^{2-}][OH^-]}{[PO_4^{3-}]} = \frac{K_w}{K_a(HPO_4^{2-})} = \frac{1.0\times10^{-14}}{4\times10^{-13}}$$

$$= 0.25\times10^{-1} = 2.5\times10^{-2} = 2\times10^{-2}$$

17. The order of decreasing acid strength is the same as the order of decreasing K_a values, for weak acids.

strongest acid ↓	HI	strong acid
	$H_2C_2O_4$	$K_a = 5.9\times10^{-2}$
	HF	$K_a = 7.2\times10^{-4}$
	HCOOH	$K_a = 1.8\times10^{-4}$
weakest acid	C_6H_5COOH	$K_a = 6.3\times10^{-5}$

18. The order of decreasing base strength is the same as the order of decreasing K_b values for weak bases.

strongest base ↓	S^{2-}	$K_b = 7.7\times10^{-2}$	$= K_w/K_a(HS^-)$
	CN^-	$K_b = 2.5\times10^{-5}$	$= K_w/K_a(HCN)$
	NH_3	$K_b = 1.8\times10^{-5}$	$= K_w/K_a(NH_4^+)$
	CH_3COO^-	$K_b = 5.6\times10^{-10}$	$= K_w/K_a(CH_3COOH)$
weakest base	F^-	$K_b = 1.4\times10^{-11}$	$= K_w/K_a(HF)$

19. (a)

$$K_{overall} = \frac{[C_2O_4^{2-}][H_3O^+]^2}{[H_2C_2O_4]} = K_a(H_2C_2O_4)\cdot K_a(HC_2O_4^-) = K_1K_2$$

$$= (5.9\times10^{-2})(6.4\times10^{-5}) = 37.8\times10^{-7} = 3.8\times10^{-8}$$

(b)

$$K_{overall} = \frac{[H_3O^+]^2[SO_3^{2-}]}{[H_2SO_3]} = K_a(H_2SO_3)\cdot K_a(HSO_3^-) = K_1K_2$$

$K_{overall} = (1.2x10^{-2})(6.2x10^{-8}) = 7.4x10^{-10}$

20. If pH = 1.0, $[H_3O^+] = 1.0x10^{-1}$ M. In a saturated solution of H_2S at 25°C, $[H_2S] = 0.10$ M.

$$K_{overall} = \frac{[H_3O^+]^2[S^{2-}]}{[H_2S]} = K_a(H_2S)\cdot K_a(HS^-) = K_1K_2$$

$$= (1.0x10^{-7})(1.3x10^{-13}) = 1.3x10^{-20}$$

Substitution of the numerical values into $K_{overall}$ yields

$$1.3x10^{-20} = \frac{(0.10)^2[S^{2-}]}{(0.10)} \quad \text{and} \quad [S^{2-}] = 1.3x10^{-19} \text{ M}$$

21. $H_3C_6H_5O_7 + H_2O \rightleftharpoons H_2C_6H_5O_7^-(aq) + H_3O^+(aq)$

$H_2C_6H_5O_7^-(aq) + H_2O \rightleftharpoons HC_6H_5O_7^{2-}(aq) + H_3O^+(aq)$

$HC_6H_5O_7^{2-}(aq) + H_2O \rightleftharpoons C_6H_5O_7^{3-}(aq) + H_3O^+(aq)$

22. (a) Ammonium chloride, NH_4Cl, is an acidic salt. The cation, NH_4^+, is a proton donor, the conjugate acid of the weak base, NH_3.

(b) Potassium cyanide, KCN, is a basic salt. The anion, CN^-, is a proton acceptor, the conjugate base of the weak acid, HCN.

(c) Sodium sulfide, Na_2S, is a basic salt. The anion, S^{2-}, is a proton acceptor, the conjugate base of HS^-.

(d) Sodium nitrate, $NaNO_3$, is a neutral salt. Neither Na^+ nor NO_3^- is a proton donor or a proton acceptor in dilute aqueous solution.

(e) Sodium nitrite, $NaNO_2$, is a basic salt. The anion, NO_2^-, is a proton acceptor, the conjugate base of the weak acid

HNO_2 (or HONO), nitrous acid.

(f) Methylammonium bromide, CH_3NH_3Br, is an acidic salt. The cation, $CH_3NH_3^+$, methylammonium ion, is a proton donor, and the conjugate acid of the weak base CH_3NH_2, methylamine.

(g) Lithium chloride, LiCl, is a neutral salt. Neither Li^+ nor Cl^- is a proton donor or a proton acceptor in dilute aqueous solution.

(h) Sodium carbonate, Na_2CO_3, is a basic salt. The anion, CO_3^{2-}, is a proton acceptor, the conjugate base of HCO_3^-.

(i) Potassium iodide, KI, is a neutral salt. Neither K^+ nor I^- is a proton donor or a proton acceptor in dilute aqueous solution.

(j) Ammonium nitrate, NH_4NO_3, is an acidic salt. The cation, NH_4^+, is a proton donor, the conjugate acid of the weak base, NH_3.

23. (a) Oxalate ion, $C_2O_4^{2-}$, is a base, a proton acceptor:

$$C_2O_4^{2-}(aq) + H_2O \rightleftharpoons H_2C_2O_4 + OH^-(aq)$$

(b) Ammonium ion, NH_4^+, is an acid, a proton donor:

$$NH_4^+(aq) + H_2O \rightleftharpoons NH_3 + H_3O^+(aq)$$

(c) Phosphate ion, PO_4^{3-}, is a base, a proton acceptor:

$$PO_4^{3-}(aq) + H_2O \rightleftharpoons HPO_4^{2-}(aq) + OH^-(aq)$$

(d) Hydrogen sulfite ion, HSO_3^-, is an ampholyte.

As an acid: $HSO_3^-(aq) + H_2O \rightleftharpoons SO_3^{2-}(aq) + H_3O^+(aq)$

As a base: $HSO_3^-(aq) + H_2O \rightleftharpoons H_2SO_3 + OH^-(aq)$

(e) Dihydrogen phosphate ion, $H_2PO_4^-$ is an ampholyte.

As an acid: $H_2PO_4^-(aq) + H_2O \rightleftharpoons HPO_4^{2-}(aq) + H_3O^+(aq)$

As a base: $H_2PO_4^-(aq) + H_2O \rightleftharpoons H_3PO_4 + OH^-(aq)$

(f) Fluoride ion, F^-, is a base, a proton acceptor:

$$F^-(aq) + H_2O \rightleftharpoons HF + OH^-(aq)$$

(g) Methylammonium ion, $CH_3NH_3^+$, is an acid, a proton donor:

$$CH_3NH_3{}^+(aq) + H_2O \rightleftharpoons CH_3NH_2 + H_3O^+(aq)$$

(h) Nitrite ion, $NO_2{}^-$, is a base, a proton acceptor:

$$NO_2^-(aq) + H_2O \rightleftharpoons HNO_2 + OH^-(aq)$$

24. (a) Strontium oxide, SrO, is basic.

$$SrO(s) + H_2O \rightleftharpoons Sr^{2+}(aq) + 2OH^-(aq)$$

(b) Selenium trioxide, SeO_3, is acidic.

$$SeO_3(s) + H_2O \rightleftharpoons H_2SeO_4 \rightleftharpoons HSeO_4^- + H_3O^+$$

(c) Potassium oxide, K_2O, is basic.

$$K_2O(s) + H_2O \rightleftharpoons 2K^+(aq) + 2OH^-(aq)$$

(d) Arsenic pentoxide, As_2O_5, is acidic.

$$As_2O_5(s) + 3H_2O \rightleftharpoons 2H_3AsO_4$$

25. There are two acidic solutions, HBr and NH_4Br. HBr is a strong acid, and $NH_4{}^+$ is a weak acid. Potassium bromide, KBr, is a neutral salt. Both NaOAc and NaCN are basic. To find out which is more basic, we must calculate the K_b values of their anion bases. The one with larger K_b

(CN^-) is the more basic. The lowest pH is the most acidic, HBr. The order of increasing pH (increasing basicity) is

lowest pH ↓	(b)	HBr	strong acid
	(e)	NH_4Br	$K_a(NH_4^+) = 5.6x10^{-10}$
	(d)	KBr	neutral salt
	(c)	NaOAc	$K_b(OAc^-) = K_w/K_a(HOAc) = 5.6x10^{-10}$
highest pH	(a)	NaCN	$K_b(CN^-) = K_w/K_a(HCN) = 2.5x10^{-5}$

26. The anion, HSO_3^-, is an ampholyte.

As an acid: $HSO_3^-(aq) + H_2O \rightleftharpoons SO_3^{2-}(aq) + H_3O^+$

$$K_a(HSO_3^-) = 6.2x10^{-8}$$

As a base: $HSO_3^-(aq) + H_2O \rightleftharpoons H_2SO_3 + OH^-(aq)$

$$K_b(HSO_3^-) = \frac{K_w}{K_a(H_2SO_3)} = \frac{1.0x10^{-14}}{1.2x10^{-2}} = 8.3x10^{-13}$$

Since $K_a(HSO_3^-) > K_b(HSO_3^-)$, solutions of $NaHSO_3$ are acidic. The cation, Na^+, is neither a proton donor nor a proton acceptor.

27. Any acid stronger than H_3O^+ reacts with water to form H_3O^+. Any base stronger than OH^- reacts with water to form OH^-. Thus water levels acids stronger than H_3O^+ to H_3O^+, and levels bases stronger than OH^- to OH^-. $HClO_4$ is a stronger acid than H_3O^+, and NH_2^- is a stronger base than OH^-.

$$HClO_4 + H_2O \xrightarrow{100\%} H_3O^+(aq) + ClO_4^-(aq)$$

$$NaNH_2(s) + H_2O \xrightarrow{100\%} Na^+(aq) + NH_3 + OH^-(aq)$$

Solutions to Multiple Choice Questions, Chapter 9

1. (c) Reading Table E1 we see that of the five acids listed only sulfurous acid, H_2SO_3, has an acidity constant larger than 1.8×10^{-4}, the K_a of formic acid, HCOOH.

2. (e) The reaction between amide ion, NH_2^-, and H_2O goes to completion:

$$NH_2^- + H_2O \xrightarrow{100\%} NH_3 + OH^-$$

Ammonia, NH_3, and nitrite ion, NO_2^-, are weak bases and undergo proton-transfer reactions with H_2O that proceed to the right only to a slight extent. Ammonium ion, NH_4^+, is a weak acid, and the proton-transfer reaction with H_2O also proceeds only to a slight extent. The nitrate ion, NO_3^-, does not react with water in dilute solution.

3. (d) The pH increases when a base is added. The only basic substance of the 5 choices is K_2CO_3, a basic salt. The carbonate ion, CO_3^{2-}, is a base and reacts with acetic acid as follows:

$$CO_3^{2-}(aq) + CH_3COOH \rightleftharpoons HCO_3^-(aq) + CH_3COO^-(aq)$$

4. (e) If pH = 10.82 then pOH = 14.00 - 10.82 = 3.18

$$[OH^-] = \text{antilog}(-3.18) = 10^{-3.18} = 6.6 \times 10^{-4} \text{ M}$$

5. (b) The conjugate base of H_3O^+ is H_2O. The conjugate acid of OH^- is H_2O.

6. (b) Water can act either as a proton donor or as a proton acceptor. The two anions, acetate ion, CH_3COO^-, and

sulfide ion, S^{2-}, are bases. Ammonium ion, NH_4^+, and benzoic acid, C_6H_5COOH, are both acids.

7. **(b)** $[H_3O^+] = [A^-] = \text{antilog}(-5.35) = 4.47\times10^{-6}$ M

$[HA] = 0.050 - 4.47\times10^{-6} = 0.050$ M

$$K_a = \frac{[H_3O^+][A^-]}{[HA]} = \frac{(4.47\times10^{-6})^2}{5.0\times10^{-2}} = 4.0\times10^{-10}$$

8. **(d)** Formic acid, HCOOH, is a weak acid and must be written in molecular form. Potassium hydroxide, KOH, is a strong base, 100% ions in dilute aqueous solution. The potassium ion is a spectator ion and takes no part in the proton-transfer reaction between the proton donor, HCOOH, and the proton acceptor, OH^-.

9. **(b)** Acidity and basicity constants always apply to the proton-transfer reaction with H_2O. The basicity constant for HS^-, $K_b(HS^-)$, is the equilibrium constant for the reaction in which HS^- accepts a proton from H_2O.

10. **(c)** The acidity constant for HS^-, $K_a(HS^-)$, is the equilibrium constant for the reaction in which HS^- donates a proton to water.

11. **(d)** The solution having the highest pH is the most basic. The solutions listed in (a), (b), (c), and (e) are all acidic. Solutions of NaCl are neutral, pH = 7.

12. **(a)** The solution having the lowest pH is the most acidic. Both perchloric acid, $HClO_4$, and hydrochloric acid, are strong acids, but the $[H_3O^+]$ = 2.0 M in (a) and only

0.020 M in (c).

13. <u>(e)</u> Potassium oxide, K_2O, reacts with H_2O to form OH^-

$$K_2O(s) + H_2O \xrightarrow{100\%} 2K^+(aq) + 2OH^-(aq)$$

14. <u>(a)</u> Acetic acid, CH_3COOH, is a weak acid and must be written in molecular form. Sodium carbonate is a salt, a strong electrolyte, 100% ions in aqueous solution. A proton-transfer reaction between the donor, CH_3COOH, and the acceptor, $CO_3{}^{2-}$, occurs. The sodium ions are bystander (spectator) ions and do not appear in the equation.

15. <u>(a)</u> If $[OH^-] = 4.8\text{x}10^{-3}$, $pOH = -\log(4.8\text{x}10^{-3}) = 2.32$ Thus, $pH = 14.00 - pOH = 14.00 - 2.32 = 11.68$

16. <u>(b)</u>

$$K_a(HCOOH) = 1.8\text{x}10^{-4} = \frac{[H_3O^+][HCOO^-]}{[HCOOH]}$$

$$\text{Let } x = [H_3O^+] = [HCOO^-]$$

since these two ions are formed in a 1:1 molar ratio by the proton-transfer reaction between HCOOH and H_2O. Then the concentration of HCOOH molecules is less than the initial value by the amount x:

$$[HCOOH] = 0.20 - x$$

Assume $x < 10\%$ of 0.20. Then $0.20 - x \sim 0.20$ and

$$1.8\text{x}10^{-4} = \frac{x^2}{0.20}$$

$$x^2 = 3.6\text{x}10^{-5} = 36\text{x}10^{-6} \quad \text{and} \quad x = 6.0\text{x}10^{-3}$$

Check: Is $6.0\text{x}10^{-3} < 10\%$ of 0.20? Yes, $6.0\text{x}10^{-3} < 2.0\text{x}10^{-2}$

Hence, $[H_3O^+] = 6.0x10^{-3}$ M and pH = $-\log(6.0x10^{-3}) = 2.22$

17. (a) The $[H_3O^+]$ in a solution containing both a strong acid and a weak acid is essentially just the value contributed by the strong acid. The proton-transfer reaction between H_2S and H_2O proceeds to only a very slight extent, and is repressed by the H_3O^+ ions from the HCl. Thus, $[H_3O^+] = 0.500$ M, and pH = $-\log(0.500) = 0.30$

18. (e) The highest pH means the most basic. Ammonium chloride, NH_4Cl, is an acidic salt, and KNO_3 is a neutral salt. The other three solutions are all basic. To determine the most basic, we must compare the K_b values of the bases.

$$K_b(CN^-) = K_w/K_a(HCN) = 1.00x10^{-14}/4x10^{-10} = 2.5x10^{-5}$$

$$K_b(OAc^-) = K_w/K_a(HOAc) = 1.00x10^{-14}/1.8x10^{-5} = 5.6x10^{-10}$$

$$K_b(CH_3NH_2) = K_w/K_a(CH_3NH_3^+) = 1.00x10^{-14}/2.4x10^{-11}$$

$$= 4.2x10^{-4}$$

Thus methylamine has the largest basicity constant of these three bases, and solution (e) has the highest pH.

19. (c) Since we are only asked about α, the degree of dissociation, use the Ostwald dilution law.

$$K_a = \frac{\alpha^2 C}{(1-\alpha)} = \frac{\alpha^2(0.048)}{(1-\alpha)} = 6.3x10^{-5}$$

Assume $\alpha < 10\%$ of 1. Then $(1-\alpha) \sim 1$, and

$$\alpha^2(0.048) = 6.3x10^{-5} \quad \text{or} \quad \alpha^2 = 1.3x10^{-3} = 13x10^{-4}$$

$$\alpha = 3.6x10^{-2} = 3.6\%$$

Check: Is $3.6 \times 10^{-2} < 10\%$ of 1? Yes, $3.6 \times 10^{-2} < 1.0 \times 10^{-1}$

Thus the degree of dissociation of 0.048 F C_6H_5COOH is 3.6%

20. (c) $CH_3COOH + H_2O \rightleftharpoons CH_3COO^-(aq) + H_3O^+(aq)$

$$K_a = \frac{[H_3O^+][CH_3COO^-]}{[CH_3COOH]} = 1.8 \times 10^{-5}$$

Let $x = [CH_3COO^-] = [H_3O^+]$

Then $[CH_3COOH] = 0.080 - x$

The equilibrium constant equation is

$$1.8 \times 10^{-5} = \frac{x^2}{0.080 - x}$$

Assume $x < 10\%$ of 0.080 Then $0.080 - x \sim 0.080$, and

$$x^2 = (0.080)(1.8 \times 10^{-5}) = 1.44 \times 10^{-6}$$

$$x = 1.2 \times 10^{-3}$$

Check: Is $1.2 \times 10^{-3} < 10\%$ of 0.080? Yes, $1.2 \times 10^{-3} < 8.0 \times 10^{-3}$

Thus $[H_3O^+] = 1.2 \times 10^{-3}$ and $pH = -\log(1.2 \times 10^{-3}) = 2.92$

21. (c) Both NaI and $NaNO_3$ solutions are neutral. The other three solutions are all basic, as their anions are bases. The most basic solution is the one for which K_b for the anion base is the largest. Since $K_b = K_w/K_a$, where K_a is the acidity constant of the conjugate acid, the most basic anion is the one whose conjugate acid has the smallest K_a value. The three conjugate acids of F^-, CN^-, and OAc^-, are, respectively, HF, HCN, and HOAc. Of these, the one with the smallest K_a is HCN. Thus CN^- is the strongest base of the three, and the most basic solution is the NaCN.

22. **(b)** This solution contains both a strong base and a weak base. The total $[OH^-]$ in the solution is essentially just that contributed by the strong base, NaOH. The proton-transfer reaction between NH_3 and H_2O proceeds to only a small extent, and is repressed by the OH^- from the NaOH. Thus, $[OH^-] = 0.100$ M, pOH = 1 and pH = 14 - 1 = 13.

23. **(e)** $K_a(HONO) = 4.5 \times 10^{-4}$

$pK_a = -\log(4.5 \times 10^{-4}) = 4 - \log(4.5) = 4 - 0.65 = 3.35$

24. **(b)** Methanol, CH_3OH, is an extremely weak acid. If the proton bonded to the O atom is lost, the anion remaining is CH_3O^-, methoxide ion, a very strong base.

25. **(a)** An equilibrium constant that is very much larger than 1, as this one is, indicates that the position of equilibrium is far to the right. This means that CN^- has a greater tendency to accept a proton than ONO^- does, so that CN^- is a stronger base than ONO^-. It also means that HCN is a weaker acid than HONO, so that statement (b) is false. Statements (c) and (d) are correct, but the magnitude of the equilibrium constant for the reaction shown has nothing to do with either of those statements. The conjugate base of HONO and the conjugate acid of CN^- are known from the definitions of those quantities. There is no way to tell whether HONO will react with F^- solely from the magnitude of K_{eq} for the reaction given.

Solutions to Problems, Chapter 9

9.1. $C_6H_5COOH + H_2O \rightleftharpoons C_6H_5COO^-(aq) + H_3O^+(aq)$

$$K_a = 6.3\times10^{-5} = \frac{[C_6H_5COO^-][H_3O^+]}{[C_6H_5COOH]}$$

Let $x = [C_6H_5COO^-] = [H_3O^+]$

Then $[C_6H_5COOH] = 0.020 - x$

and $$K_a = 6.3\times10^{-5} = \frac{x^2}{0.020 - x}$$

Assume $x < 10\%$ of 0.020. Then $0.020 - x \sim 0.020$, and

$$x^2 = (2.0\times10^{-2})(6.3\times10^{-5}) = 1.26\times10^{-6}$$

$$x = 1.12\times10^{-3} = 1.1\times10^{-3}$$

Check: Is $1.1\times10^{-3} < 10\%$ of 0.020? Yes, $1.1\times10^{-3} < 2.0\times10^{-3}$

Hence $[H_3O^+] = [C_6H_5COO^-] = 1.1\times10^{-3}$ M

$$[C_6H_5COOH] = 0.020 - 0.001 = 0.019 \text{ M}$$

$$[OH^-] = K_w/[H_3O^+] = 1.00\times10^{-14}/(1.12\times10^{-3}) = 8.9\times10^{-12} \text{ M}$$

$$pH = -\log(1.12\times10^{-3}) = 2.95$$

9.2. The formula weight of sodium acetate, CH_3COONa, is 82.034 g/mol. Thus the number of moles of NaOAc added is 0.1000 mol, and the formality of the solution is

$$0.1000 \text{ mol}/(0.5000 \text{ L}) = 0.2000 \text{ F NaOAc}$$

$$CH_3COO^- + H_2O \rightleftharpoons CH_3COOH + OH^-$$

$$K_b(OAc^-) = K_w/K_a(HOAc) = 1.00\times10^{-14}/(1.8\times10^{-5}) = 5.6\times10^{-10}$$

$$K_b = \frac{[CH_3COOH][OH^-]}{[CH_3COO^-]} = 5.6\times10^{-10}$$

Let $x = [CH_3COOH] = [OH^-]$

Then $[CH_3COO^-] = 0.2000 - x$

and $$K_b = 5.6\times10^{-10} = \frac{x^2}{0.2000 - x}$$

Assume x < 10% of 0.2000. Then 0.2000 - x ~ 0.2000, and

$$x^2 = (0.2000)(5.6\times10^{-10}) = 1.12\times10^{-10}$$

$$x = 1.06\times10^{-5} = 1.1\times10^{-5}\ M$$

Check: Is 1.1×10^{-5} < 10% of 0.2000? Yes, $1.1\times10^{-5} < 2.0\times10^{-2}$

Thus, $$[CH_3COOH] = [OH^-] = 1.1\times10^{-5}\ M$$

$$[CH_3COO^-] = 0.2000 - 1.1\times10^{-5} = 0.2000\ M$$

$$[H_3O^+] = K_w/[OH^-] = 1.00\times10^{-14}/(1.06\times10^{-5}) = 9.4\times10^{-10}\ M$$

9.3. (a) $$HONO + H_2O \rightleftharpoons ONO^-(aq) + H_3O^+(aq)$$

By definition, $$\alpha = [H_3O^+]/C = [ONO^-]/C$$

when C = 1.00 M, α = 0.0226 or 2.26% Hence,

$$[ONO^-] = [H_3O^+] = \alpha C = (0.0226)(1.00) = 0.0226\ M$$

$$pH = -\log[H_3O^+] = -\log(0.0226) = 1.65$$

(b) There are two equivalent methods for determining K_a

Method 1: $$K_a = \frac{\alpha^2 C}{1-\alpha} = \frac{(0.0226)^2(1.00)}{1 - 0.0226} = \frac{5.108\times10^{-4}}{0.9774}$$

$$= 5.226\times10^{-4} = 5.23\times10^{-4}$$

Method 2: $$K_a = \frac{[ONO^-][H_3O^+]}{[HONO]}$$

$$[HONO] = 1.00 - [ONO^-] = 1.00 - 0.0226 = 0.977\ M$$

$$K_a = \frac{(0.0226)^2}{0.977} = 5.23\times10^{-4}$$

(c) $$5.23\times10^{-4} = \frac{\alpha^2(0.250)}{1 - \alpha}$$

Hence $$\frac{\alpha^2}{1-\alpha} = 20.92\times10^{-4}$$

Assume $\alpha < 10\%$ of 1. Then $1 - \alpha \sim 1$ and

$$\alpha^2 = 20.92 \times 10^{-4} \qquad \alpha = 4.57 \times 10^{-2} = 4.57\%$$

Check: Is $4.57 \times 10^{-2} < 10\%$ of 1? Yes, $4.57 \times 10^{-2} < 1.0 \times 10^{-1}$

Hence 0.250 F HONO is 4.57% ionized. Note that when the formality of HONO decreased from 1.00 to 0.250 the percent ionized increased from 2.26% to 4.57%.

9.4. $$HOAc + H_2O \rightleftharpoons OAc^-(aq) + H_3O^+(aq)$$

The proton-transfer reaction between acetic acid and water uses up HOAc molecules and produces H_3O^+ and OAc^- ions. The reaction is the only source of OAc^- ions in the solution. There are two sources of H_3O^+ ions, namely, from the HCl and from the proton-transfer reaction given above. Hence,

$$\text{Let} \quad [OAc^-] = x$$

Then, $[H_3O^+] = 0.080 + x$ and $[HOAc] = 0.150 - x$

$$K_a = \frac{[OAc^-][H_3O^+]}{[HOAc]} = \frac{(x)(0.080 + x)}{(0.150 - x)} = 1.78 \times 10^{-5}$$

Assume $x < 10\%$ of 0.080 Then,

$$0.080 + x \sim 0.080 \quad \text{and} \quad 0.150 - x \sim 0.150$$

and

$$1.78 \times 10^{-5} = \frac{0.080x}{0.150}$$

$$x = \frac{0.150}{0.080}(1.78 \times 10^{-5}) = 3.34 \times 10^{-5}$$

Check: Is $3.34 \times 10^{-5} < 10\%$ of 0.080? Yes, $3.34 \times 10^{-5} < 8.0 \times 10^{-3}$

Hence $$[OAc^-] = 3.34 \times 10^{-5} \text{ M}$$

$$[HOAc] = 0.150 - 3.34 \times 10^{-5} = 0.150 \text{ M}$$

$$[H_3O^+] = 0.080 + 3.34x10^{-5} = 0.080\ M$$

$$pH = -\log(0.080) = 1.10$$

$$[OH^-] = K_w/[H_3O^+] = 1.00x10^{-14}/(0.080) = 1.25x10^{-13}$$
$$= 1.2x10^{-13}$$

Note that in this solution, which contains both a strong acid and a weak acid, the $[H_3O^+]$ is essentially just that contributed by the strong acid.

9.5. (a) $$NH_4^+(aq) + OH^-(aq) \rightleftharpoons NH_3 + H_2O$$

(b) The principal constituent of the solution is H_2O. The Na^+ ions added when the NaOH dissolves are spectator ions and take no part in any reaction. So $[Na^+] = 0.300$ M. The NO_3^- ions from the NH_4NO_3 are also spectator ions. Thus $[NO_3^-] = 0.124$ M.

Because NH_3 is a weak base, the net ionic equation written in (a) goes virtually to completion. Thus 0.124 mol of NH_4^+ ions combines with 0.124 mol of OH^-, producing 0.124 mol of NH_3 and leaving (0.300 - 0.124) = 0.176 mol of OH^- in excess.

The five chemical species with concentrations greater than 0.10 M, arranged in decreasing order of concentration, are therefore

$$H_2O,\ Na^+,\ OH^-,\ NO_3^-,\ \text{and}\ NH_3$$

The concentrations of NO_3^- and NH_3 are both 0.124 M, but as the net ionic equation given in (a) does not proceed 100% to the right (just slightly less), the $[NO_3^-]$ is just slightly larger than the $[NH_3]$.

(c) Choose as the unknown quantity a concentration known to be very small {consider the discussion of part (b)}, so that it will be possible to make simplifying assumptions.

$$\text{Let} \quad x = [NH_4^+]$$

Then $[NH_3] = 0.124 - x$ and $[OH^-] = 0.176 + x$

For every NH_4^+ ion that is not used up in the reaction shown in (a), there is also an OH^- ion that is not used up, and an NH_3 molecule not formed. So the $[NH_3]$ is slightly less than 0.124 M, the value it would be if the reaction in (a) went to completion. Similarly, the $[OH^-]$ is slightly more than 0.176 M.

$$K_b(NH_3) = \frac{[NH_4^+][OH^-]}{[NH_3]} = \frac{(x)(0.176+x)}{(0.124-x)} = 1.8\text{x}10^{-5}$$

Assume x < 10% of 0.124. Then,

$$0.124 - x \sim 0.124 \quad \text{and} \quad 0.176 + x \sim 0.176$$

$$\frac{(x)(0.176)}{(0.124)} = 1.8\text{x}10^{-5}$$

$$x = \frac{0.124}{0.176}(1.8\text{x}10^{-5}) = 1.27\text{x}10^{-5} = 1.3\text{x}10^{-5}\ \text{M}$$

Check: Is $1.3\text{x}10^{-5}$ < 10% of 0.124? Yes, $1.3\text{x}10^{-5} < 1.24\text{x}10^{-2}$

Hence, $[NH_4^+] = 1.3\text{x}10^{-5}$ M

$$[NH_3] = 0.124 - 1.3\text{x}10^{-5} = 0.124\ \text{M}$$

$$[OH^-] = 0.176 + 1.3\text{x}10^{-5} = 0.176\ \text{M}$$

pOH = -log(0.176) = +0.75 and pH = 14.00 - 0.75 = 13.25

9.6. (a) If pH = 10.74, pOH = 14.00 - 10.74 = 3.26

$$[OH^-] = \text{antilog}(-3.26) = 10^{-3.26} = 5.5\text{x}10^{-4}\ M$$

<u>Method 1</u>: By definition, $\alpha = [OH^-]/C$, where α is the fraction ionized or the degree of dissociation. Thus

$$\alpha = 5.5\text{x}10^{-4}/0.10 = 5.5\text{x}10^{-3} = 0.55\%$$

$$K_b = \frac{\alpha^2 C}{1-\alpha} = \frac{(5.5\text{x}10^{-3})^2(0.10)}{1 - 0.0055} = \frac{3.025\text{x}10^{-6}}{0.9945} = 3.0\text{x}10^{-6}$$

<u>Method 2</u>: If the base is denoted B, the proton-transfer reaction between base and H_2O is

$$B + H_2O \rightleftharpoons BH^+(aq) + OH^-(aq)$$

$$K_b = \frac{[BH^+][OH^-]}{[B]}$$

$$[BH^+] = [OH^-] = 5.5\text{x}10^{-4}\ M$$

$$[B] = 0.10 - 5.5\text{x}10^{-4} = 0.10$$

$$K_b = \frac{(5.5\text{x}10^{-4})^2}{0.10} = \frac{30.25\text{x}10^{-8}}{0.10} = 3.0\text{x}10^{-6}$$

(b) pH = 10.36 so that pOH = 14.00 - 10.36 = 3.64

$$[OH^-] = [BH^+] = \text{antilog}(-3.64) = 2.29\text{x}10^{-4}\ M$$

If C is the formality of the solution, then

$$[B] = C - 2.29\text{x}10^{-4}\ M$$

Assume $2.29\text{x}10^{-4} < 10\%$ of C, so that $C - 2.29\text{x}10^{-4} \sim C$

Then $$K_b = 3.0\text{x}10^{-6} = \frac{(2.29\text{x}10^{-4})^2}{C}$$

$$C = \frac{5.25\text{x}10^{-8}}{3.0\text{x}10^{-6}} = 1.7\text{x}10^{-2}$$

Check: Is $2.29\text{x}10^{-4} < 10\%$ of $1.7\text{x}10^{-2}$? Yes, $2.29\text{x}10^{-4}$ is less than 1.7×10^{-3}, so that a 0.017 F solution of this base has a pH = 10.36.

9.7. Let pivalic acid be denoted HA. If the pH = 3.00, then $[H_3O^+] = 1.00\times10^{-3}$. In 0.100 F HA

$$[H_3O^+] = [A^-] = 1.00\times10^{-3} \text{ M}$$

$$[HA] = 0.100 - 0.001 = 0.099 \text{ M}$$

$$K_a = \frac{(1.00\times10^{-3})^2}{0.099} = 10.1\times10^{-6} = 1.01\times10^{-5}$$

The pivalate ion, A^-, is the conjugate base of pivalic acid, HA. Hence,

$$K_b(A^-) = 1.00\times10^{-14}/K_a(HA) = 1.00\times10^{-14}/(1.01\times10^{-5})$$

$$= 9.9\times10^{-10}$$

In a solution of sodium pivalate, the reaction

$$A^-(aq) + H_2O \rightleftharpoons HA + OH^-(aq)$$

occurs. Let $x = [HA] = [OH^-]$

Then $[A^-] = 0.100 - x$

$$K_b = \frac{x^2}{0.100 - x} = 9.9\times10^{-10}$$

Assume x < 10% of 0.100. Then 0.100 - x ~ 0.100, and

$$x^2 = 9.9\times10^{-11} = 99\times10^{-12}$$

$$x = 9.9\times10^{-6} \text{ M}$$

Check: Is 9.9×10^{-6} < 10% of 0.100? Yes, $9.9\times10^{-6} < 1.00\times10^{-2}$

Then $[OH^-] = 9.9\times10^{-6}$ and $pOH = -\log(9.9\times10^{-6}) = 5.00$

$$pH = 14.00 - pOH = 9.00$$

9.8. (a) $\alpha = 0.032$ and $C = 0.086$

$$K_a = \frac{\alpha^2 C}{1-\alpha} = \frac{(0.032)^2(0.086)}{1 - 0.032} = \frac{8.8\times10^{-5}}{0.968} = 9.1\times10^{-5}$$

Alternatively, $[A^-] = [H_3O^+] = \alpha C = 2.75\times10^{-3} = 2.8\times10^{-3}$

$$[HA] = 0.086 - 2.8\times10^{-3} = 0.083\ M$$

$$K_a = \frac{[A^-][H_3O^+]}{[HA]} = \frac{(2.75\times10^{-3})^2}{0.083} = 9.1\times10^{-5}$$

(b) If pH = 2.48, $[H_3O^+] = \text{antilog}(-2.48) = 3.3\times10^{-3}$ M

The proton-transfer reaction between HA and H_2O is

$$HA + H_2O \rightleftharpoons A^-(aq) + H_3O^+(aq)$$

Thus, $[A^-] = [H_3O^+] = 3.3\times10^{-3}$ M

$$[HA] = C - 3.3\times10^{-3}$$

where C is the formality of the solution. Assume 3.3×10^{-3} is less than 10% of C, because HA is a weak acid. Then,

$$C - 3.3\times10^{-3} \sim C$$

and $$K_a = 9.1\times10^{-5} = \frac{(3.3\times10^{-3})^2}{C}$$

Thus $$C = \frac{(3.3\times10^{-3})^2}{9.1\times10^{-5}} = 0.12\ F$$

Check: Is $3.3\times10^{-3} < 10\%$ of 0.12? Yes, $3.3\times10^{-3} < 1.2\times10^{-2}$

Hence a 0.12F solution of HA has a pH = 2.48.

9.9. The formula weight of aniline is 93.128 g·mol^{-1}. If 3.9 g of aniline dissolve per 100.0 mL of solution, then 39 g dissolve in 1.000 L of solution.

$$\text{No. mol aniline in 1.000 L} = \frac{39\ g}{93.128\ g/mol} = 0.419$$

and the molarity of a saturated aqueous solution of aniline

is 0.419 M = 0.42 M.

$$C_6H_5NH_2 + H_2O \rightleftharpoons C_6H_5NH_3^+(aq) + OH^-(aq)$$

Let $x = [C_6H_5NH_3^+] = [OH^-]$

Then $[C_6H_5NH_2] = 0.419 - x$

$$\frac{x^2}{0.419 - x} = 3.8x10^{-10}$$

Assume x < 10% of 0.419. Then $0.419 - x \sim 0.419$, and

$$x^2 = (0.419)(3.8x10^{-10}) = 1.59x10^{-10}$$

$$x = 1.26x10^{-5} = 1.3x10^{-5}$$

Check: Is $1.3x10^{-5}$ < 10% of 0.419? Yes, $1.3x10^{-5} < 4.19x10^{-2}$

Hence $[OH^-] = [C_6H_5NH_3^+] = 1.3x10^{-5}$ M

$$pOH = -\log(1.26x10^{-5}) = 4.90$$

$$pH = 14.00 - pOH = 9.10$$

9.10. (a) Note that the hypobromite ion can be written either as BrO^- or OBr^-. The proton-transfer reaction between BrO^-, a weak base, and water is

$$BrO^-(aq) + H_2O \rightleftharpoons HOBr + OH^-(aq)$$

$$K_b(OBr^-) = \frac{[HOBr][OH^-]}{[BrO^-]}$$

(b) If pH = 10.85, pOH = 14.00 - 10.85 = 3.15

$[OH^-]$ = antilog(-3.15) = $10^{-3.15}$ = $7.08x10^{-4}$ = $7.1x10^{-4}$ M

In a solution of OBr^- in water,

$$[HOBr] = [OH^-] = 7.1x10^{-4} \text{ M}$$

$$[OBr^-] = 0.100 - 7.08x10^{-4} = 0.0993 \text{ M} = 0.099 \text{ M}$$

$$K_b = (7.08x10^{-4})^2/0.0993 = 5.05x10^{-6} = 5.0x10^{-6}$$

(c) $K_a(HOBr) = K_w/K_b(OBr^-) = \frac{1.00x10^{-14}}{5.05x10^{-6}} = 2.0x10^{-9}$

9.11. $$K_a(HOAc) = \frac{[CH_3COO^-][H_3O^+]}{[CH_3COOH]} = 1.8x10^{-5}$$

$$[H_3O^+] = (1.8x10^{-5})\frac{[CH_3COOH]}{[CH_3COO^-]} \qquad \text{Eq. (I)}$$

(a) Method 1: If $[CH_3COO^-]/[CH_3COOH] = 4:1$, then

$$[CH_3COOH]/[CH_3COO^-] = 1:4 = 1/4$$

$$[H_3O^+] = 1.8x10^{-5}\left(\frac{1}{4}\right) = 0.45x10^{-5} = 4.5x10^{-6}$$

$$pH = -log(4.5x10^{-6}) = 5.35$$

Method 2: Since we are only asked for the pH, we really do not need to find $[H_3O^+]$. Take the log of Eq. (I) and solve for the pH. This is accomplished as follows:

$$log[H_3O^+] = log(1.8x10^{-5}) + log\frac{[CH_3COOH]}{[CH_3COO^-]}$$

$$log[H_3O^+] = -4.745 + log\frac{[CH_3COOH]}{[CH_3COO^-]}$$

Multiply by -1.

$$-log[H_3O^+] = pH = 4.745 - log\frac{[CH_3COOH]}{[CH_3COO^-]}$$

$$pH = 4.745 + log\frac{[CH_3COO^-]}{[CH_3COOH]} \qquad \text{Eq. (II)}$$

In writing Eq. (II) we have used the property of logs that

$$log(a/b) = -log(b/a)$$

Using Eq. (II) we obtain

$$pH = 4.745 + log(4) = 4.745 + 0.602 = 5.35$$

(b) Once we have obtained Eq. (II) we can use it to find

the pH for any given ratio of $[CH_3COO^-]/[CH_3COOH]$.

$$pH = 4.745 + \log(2) = 4.745 + 0.301 = 5.05$$

(c) $pH = 4.745 + \log(1/3) = 4.745 - \log(3) = 4.27$

(d) $pH = 4.745 + \log(1.6) = 4.745 - \log(6) = 3.97$

Note that $pK_a = -\log K_a = 4.74_5$. If $[CH_3COO^-]/[CH_3COOH]$ is greater than 1, as in (a) and (b), then the solution has a pH greater than 4.74 (is more basic than pH = 4.74). If the ratio $[CH_3COO^-]/[CH_3COOH]$ is less than 1, as in (c) and (d), then the solution has a pH less than 4.74 (is more acidic than pH = 4.74).

9.12. Perchloric acid, $HClO_4$, is a strong acid, so that if all solutions are equimolar, the $[H_3O^+]$ will be largest in the perchloric acid solution. Both HSO_4^- and $CH_3NH_3^+$ are weak acids, but HSO_4^- is only moderately weak, $K_a(HSO_4^-) = 1.2\times10^{-2}$, while methylammonium ion, $CH_3NH_3^+$, is very weak, $K_a(CH_3NH_3^+) = 2.4\times10^{-11}$. The HCO_3^- ion is an ampholyte, but solutions of $NaHCO_3$ are basic, since $K_b(HCO_3^-) = 2.3\times10^{-8}$ and $K_a(HCO_3^-) = 4.7\times10^{-11}$. The value of $K_b(HCO_3^-)$ is obtained in the text in Section 9.5, page 327. Solutions of Na_2O are identical with solutions of the strong base NaOH:

$$Na_2O(s) + H_2O \xrightarrow{100\%} 2Na^+(aq) + 2OH^-(aq)$$

The order of increasing pH is the order of increasing basicity. Therefore,

lowest pH, most acidic $HClO_4$
$KHSO_4$
CH_3NH_3Br
$NaHCO_3$
highest pH, most basic Na_2O

9.13. (a) The cation of $(NH_4)_2S$ is a weak acid:

$$NH_4{}^+(aq) + H_2O \rightleftharpoons NH_3 + H_3O^+(aq)$$

but the anion is a weak base:

$$S^{2-}(aq) + H_2O \rightleftharpoons HS^-(aq) + OH^-(aq)$$

To determine whether a solution of $(NH_4)_2S$ is acidic or basic we must compare $K_a(NH_4{}^+)$ with $K_b(S^{2-})$. From Table E1 we find $K_a(NH_4{}^+) = 5.7x10^{-10}$

$K_b(S^{2-}) = K_w/K_a(HS^-) = 1.00x10^{-14}/(1.3x10^{-13}) = 7.7x10^{-2}$

Because $K_b(S^{2-}) \gg K_a(NH_4{}^+)$ solutions of $(NH_4)_2S$ are basic.

(b) The anion HSO_3^- is an ampholyte. The Na^+ is neither a proton donor nor acceptor. We must compare K_a and K_b for the HSO_3^- ion. $K_a(HSO_3^-) = 6.2x10^{-8}$. The conjugate acid of HSO_3^- is H_2SO_3. Hence,

$K_b(HSO_3^-) = K_w/K_a(H_2SO_3) = 1.00x10^{-14}/(1.2x10^{-2}) = 8.3x10^{-13}$

Because $K_a(HSO_3^-) > K_b(HSO_3^-)$ solutions of $NaHSO_3$ are acidic.

(c) Solutions of barium acetate are basic because the anion, CH_3COO^-, is a weak base, the conjugate base of acetic acid.

$$OAc^-(aq) + H_2O \rightleftharpoons HOAc + OH^-(aq)$$

(d) Solutions of CaI_2 are neutral. Since HI is a strong acid, I^- has virtually no tendency to accept a proton from H_2O in dilute aqueous solution. The cation, Ca^{2+}, is neither a proton donor nor acceptor.

(e) The anion, CO_3^{2-}, is a weak base:

$$CO_3^{2-}(aq) + H_2O \rightleftharpoons HCO_3^-(aq) + OH^-(aq)$$

$$K_b(CO_3^{2-}) = K_w/K_a(HCO_3^-) = 1.00\times10^{-14}/(4.7\times10^{-11}) = 2.1\times10^{-4}$$

The cation, methylammonium ion, is a weak acid:

$$CH_3NH_3^+(aq) + H_2O \rightleftharpoons CH_3NH_2 + H_3O^+(aq)$$

$$K_a(CH_3NH_3^+) = 2.4\times10^{-11}$$

Since $K_b(CO_3^{2-}) \gg K_a(CH_3NH_3^+)$ solutions of methylammonium carbonate are basic.

9.14. (a) $\alpha = 0.0229 \quad C = 0.120$ M

By definition, $\alpha = [OH^-]/C = [(CH_3)_3NH^+]/C$

Hence, $[OH^-] = [(CH_3)_3NH^+] = \alpha C = (0.0229)(0.120)$

$= 2.75\times10^{-3}$

The fraction <u>not</u> ionized is $(1-\alpha) = 0.9771$ or 97.71%. Thus

$$[(CH_3)_3N] = (1-\alpha)C = (0.9771)(0.120) = 0.117 \text{ M}$$

Alternatively, $[(CH_3)_3N] = 0.120 - [(CH_3)_3NH^+]$

$= 0.120 - 2.75\times10^{-3} = 0.117$ M

$$[H_3O^+] = K_w/[OH^-] = 1.00\times10^{-14}/(2.75\times10^{-3}) = 3.64\times10^{-12} \text{ M}$$

$$pH = -\log(3.64\times10^{-12}) = 11.44$$

(b) $K_b\{(CH_3)_3N\} = [OH^-][(CH_3)_3NH^+]/[(CH_3)_3N]$

$$= \frac{(2.75\times10^{-3})^2}{0.1173} = 6.45\times10^{-5}$$

Alternatively, $K_b = \dfrac{\alpha^2 C}{1-\alpha} = \dfrac{(0.0229)^2(0.120)}{1 - 0.0229} = \dfrac{6.29\times10^{-5}}{0.9771}$

$= 6.44\times10^{-5}$

(c) $K_a = 6.44\text{x}10^{-5}$ $C = 0.096$

$$K_a = \frac{\alpha^2 C}{1-\alpha} = \frac{\alpha^2(0.096)}{1-\alpha} = 6.44\text{x}10^{-5}$$

Thus $$\frac{\alpha^2}{1-\alpha} = 6.709\text{x}10^{-4} = 6.71\text{x}10^{-4}$$

Assume $\alpha < 10\%$ of 1. Then $1 - \alpha \sim 1$, and

$$\alpha^2 = 6.709\text{x}10^{-4}, \quad \alpha = 2.59\text{x}10^{-2} = 2.6\text{x}10^{-2} = 2.6\%$$

Check: Is $2.6\text{x}10^{-2} < 10\%$ of 1? Yes, $2.6\text{x}10^{-2} < 1.0\text{x}10^{-1}$

Hence a 0.096 F solution of trimethylamine is 2.6% ionized. The degree of dissociation increases from 2.29% to 2.6% when the concentration decreases from 0.120 F to 0.096 F. In a more dilute solution, the average distance between ions is greater, and the force of attraction between oppositely charged ions is less, by Coulomb's Law. The degree of dissociation is therefore greater in a more dilute solution. Since $\alpha \ll 1$, $K_a \sim \alpha^2 C$, and as C decreases, α must increase.

9.15.

(a) $CH_3COOH + OH^-(aq) \rightleftharpoons CH_3COO^-(aq) + H_2O$

(b) $CH_3COOH + NH_3 \rightleftharpoons CH_3COO^-(aq) + NH_4^+(aq)$

(c) $H_3O^+(aq) + NH_3 \rightleftharpoons NH_4^+(aq) + H_2O$

(d) $H_3O^+(aq) + CO_3^{2-}(aq) \rightleftharpoons HCO_3^-(aq) + H_2O$

<u>or</u> $2H_3O^+(aq) + CO_3^{2-}(aq) \rightleftharpoons 3H_2O + CO_2\uparrow$

(e) $NH_4^+(aq) + CN^-(aq) \rightleftharpoons NH_3 + HCN$

(f) $NH_4^+(aq) + OH^-(aq) \rightleftharpoons NH_3 + H_2O$

(g) $S^{2-}(aq) + HCOOH \rightleftharpoons HCOO^-(aq) + HS^-(aq)$

(h) $OAc^-(aq) + H_3O^+(aq) \rightleftharpoons HOAc + H_2O$

9.16. (a) $C = 0.0650\ M \quad K_a = 3.2x10^{-8}$

$$K_a = \frac{\alpha^2 C}{1-\alpha} = \frac{\alpha^2}{1-\alpha}(0.065) = 3.2x10^{-8}$$

$$\frac{\alpha^2}{1-\alpha} = 49.2x10^{-8} = 4.9x10^{-7}$$

Assume α < 10% of 1. Then $1 - \alpha \sim 1$ and

$$\alpha^2 = 49.2x10^{-8} \qquad \alpha = 7.0x10^{-4}$$

Check: Is $7.0x10^{-4}$ < 10% of 1? Yes, $7.0x10^{-4} < 1.0x10^{-1}$

Hence a 0.0650 F HOCl solution is 0.070% ionized.

$$[H_3O^+] = [OCl^-] = \alpha C = (7.0x10^{-4})(0.0650) = 4.56x10^{-5}$$

$$= 4.6x10^{-5}\ M$$

$$pH = -\log(4.56x10^{-5}) = 5 - \log(4.56) = 4.34$$

(b) $$K_b = \frac{[HOCl][OH^-]}{[OCl^-]} = \frac{K_w}{K_a(HOCl)} = \frac{1.00x10^{-14}}{3.2x10^{-8}}$$

$$= 3.1x10^{-7}$$

(c) Let $x = [OH^-] = [HOCl]$ in 0.040 F NaOCl

Then $[OCl^-] = 0.040 - x$

$$\frac{x^2}{0.040 - x} = 3.1x10^{-7}$$

Assume x < 10% of 0.040. Then $0.040 - x \sim 0.040$ and

$$x^2 = (3.1x10^{-7})(0.040) = 1.2x10^{-10}$$

$$x = 1.1x10^{-5}\ M$$

Check: Is $1.1x10^{-5}$ < 10% of 0.040? Yes, $1.1x10^{-5} < 4.0x10^{-3}$

Hence $[OH^-] = 1.1x10^{-5}$ M and $pOH = -\log(1.1x10^{-5}) = 4.95$

(d) From the equation we see that HOCl and H_3O^+ are produced in a 1:1 molar ratio. Therefore, when [HOCl] = 0.0650 M, $[H_3O^+]$ = 0.0650 M, and pH = -log(0.0650) = 1.19.

9.17. $HCOOH + H_2O \rightleftharpoons H_3O^+(aq) + HCOO^-(aq)$

$$\text{Let } x = [H_3O^+] = [HCOO^-]$$

$$\text{Then } [HCOOH] = 0.082 - x$$

$$K_a = \frac{x^2}{0.082 - x} = 1.8\text{x}10^{-4}$$

Assume x < 10% of 0.082. Then 0.082 - x ~ 0.082 and

$$x^2 = (0.082)(1.8\text{x}10^{-4}) = 1.48\text{x}10^{-5} = 14.8\text{x}10^{-6}$$

$$x = 3.84\text{x}10^{-3} = 3.8\text{x}10^{-3}$$

Check: Is $3.8\text{x}10^{-3}$ < 10% of 0.082? Yes, $3.8\text{x}10^{-3} < 8.2\text{x}10^{-3}$

As $3.8\text{x}10^{-3}$ is fairly close to $8.2\text{x}10^{-3}$ (same power of 10), we can get a better value by making a second approximation.

2nd approximation: 0.082 - x = 0.082 - 0.0038 = 0.078

Then $x^2 = (0.078)(1.8\text{x}10^{-4}) = 14.0\text{x}10^{-6}$

$$x = 3.747\text{x}10^{-3} = 3.7\text{x}10^{-3}\text{ M}$$

3rd approximation: 0.082 - x = 0.0037 = 0.078

As this is the same value obtained from the 2nd approximation, we have the correct answer to 2 significant figures.

$$[H_3O^+] = [HCOO^-] = 3.7\text{x}10^{-3}\text{ M}$$

$$[HCOOH] = 0.082 - 3.7\text{x}10^{-3} = 0.078\text{ M}$$

$$pH = -\log(3.7\text{x}10^{-3}) = 3 - \log 3.7 = 2.43$$

$$[OH^-] + K_w/[H_3O^+] = 1.00\text{x}10^{-14}/(3.75\text{x}10^{-3}) = 2.7\text{x}10^{-12}\text{ M}$$

$$\alpha = [H_3O^+]/C = 3.75\text{x}10^{-3}/(0.082) = 0.0457 = 4.6\%$$

9.18. The initial concentrations of OH^- and NH_3 are

$$[OH^-] = \frac{0.060 \text{ mol}}{0.5000 \text{ L}} = 0.120 \text{ M}, \quad [NH_3] = \frac{0.045 \text{ mol}}{0.5000 \text{ L}} = 0.090 \text{ M}$$

$$NH_3 + H_2O \rightleftharpoons NH_4^+(aq) + OH^-(aq)$$

$$\text{Let} \quad x = [NH_4^+]$$

Then $[OH^-] = 0.120 + x$ and $[NH_3] = 0.090 - x$

$$K_b(NH_3) = \frac{K_w}{K_a(NH_4^+)} = 1.8\text{x}10^{-5} = \frac{(x)(0.120 + x)}{(0.090 - x)}$$

Assume x < 10% of 0.090. Then $0.090 - x \sim 0.090$ and $0.120 + x \sim 0.120$. The expression for K_b then becomes

$$1.8\text{x}10^{-5} = \frac{(x)(0.120)}{0.090}$$

$$x = \left(\frac{3}{4}\right)(1.8\text{x}10^{-5}) = 1.35\text{x}10^{-5} = 1.4\text{x}10^{-5}$$

Check: Is $1.35\text{x}10^{-5}$ < 10% of 0.090? Yes, $1.35\text{x}10^{-5} < 9.0\text{x}10^{-3}$

Hence, $$[NH_4^+] = 1.4\text{x}10^{-5} \text{ M}$$

$$[OH^-] = 0.12 + 1.4\text{x}10^{-5} = 0.12 \text{ M}$$

$$[NH_3] = 0.090 - 1.4\text{x}10^{-5} = 0.090 \text{ M}$$

$$[H_3O^+] = K_w/[OH^-] = \frac{1.00\text{x}10^{-14}}{0.12} = 8.3\text{x}10^{-14} \text{ M}$$

$$pH = -\log(8.3\text{x}10^{-14}) = 14 - \log 8.3 = 13.08$$

9.19. Sulfuric acid is a strong acid, 100% dissociated into H_3O^+ and HSO_4^- ions. But HSO_4^- is a moderately weak acid:

$$HSO_4^-(aq) + H_2O \rightleftharpoons SO_4^{2-}(aq) + H_3O^+(aq)$$

$$\text{Let} \quad x = [SO_4^{2-}]$$

Then $[H_3O^+] = 0.100 + x$ and $[HSO_4^-] = 0.100 - x$

$$K_a = 1.2\times10^{-2} = \frac{(0.100 + x)(x)}{(0.100 - x)}$$

Assume $x < 10\%$ of 0.100. Then $0.100 + x \sim 0.100$ and $0.100 - x \sim 0.100$, so that $x = 1.2\times10^{-2}$.

Check: Is $1.2\times10^{-2} < 10\%$ of 0.100? No, $1.2\times10^{-2} > 1.0\times10^{-2}$

Hence we must use the method of successive approximations. Use the answer obtained from the first approximation to evaluate $0.100 + x$ and $0.100 - x$.

2nd approximation: $0.100 + x = 0.100 + 0.012 = 0.112$ M

$0.100 - x = 0.100 - 0.012 = 0.088$ M

$$\left(\frac{0.112}{0.088}\right)x = 1.2\times10^{-2}$$

$$x = \left(\frac{88}{112}\right)(1.2\times10^{-2}) = \left(\frac{11}{14}\right)(1.2\times10^{-2}) = 9.4\times10^{-3}\ \text{M}$$

3rd approximation: $0.100 + x = 0.100 + 0.0094 = 0.109$ M

$0.100 - x = 0.100 - 0.0094 = 0.091$ M

$$\left(\frac{0.1094}{0.0906}\right)x = 1.2\times10^{-2}$$

$$x = \left(\frac{0.0906}{0.1094}\right)(1.2\times10^{-2}) = 9.9\times10^{-3}\ \text{M}$$

4th approximation: $0.100 + x = 0.100 + 0.0099 = 0.110$ M

$0.100 - x = 0.100 - 0.0099 = 0.090$ M

$$x = \left(\frac{0.090}{0.110}\right)(1.2\times10^{-2}) = 9.8\times10^{-3}\ \text{M}$$

5th approximation: $0.100 + x = 0.100 + 0.0098 = 0.110$ M

$0.100 - x = 0.100 - 0.0098 = 0.090$ M

Since the 4th and 5th approximations are the same to the

number of significant figures to which we are entitled, we have obtained the correct answer.

$$[SO_4^{2-}] = x = 9.8x10^{-3} \text{ M}$$

$$[H_3O^+] = 0.110 \text{ M} \quad \text{and} \quad [HSO_4^-] = 0.090 \text{ M}$$

$$[OH^-] = K_w/[H_3O^+] = 1.00x10^{-14}/(0.110) = 9.1x10^{-14} \text{ M}$$

$$pH = -\log(0.110) = 0.96$$

1. $$NH_3 + H_2O \rightleftharpoons OH^-(aq) + NH_4^+(aq)$$

$$\text{Let } x = [OH^-]$$

Then $[NH_4^+] = 0.250 + x$ and $[NH_3] = 0.150 - x$

since the volume of solution is 1.00 L.

$$K_b(NH_3) = \frac{K_w}{K_a(NH_4^+)} = \frac{1.00\text{x}10^{-14}}{5.7\text{x}10^{-10}} = 1.8\text{x}10^{-5} = \frac{[NH_4^+][OH^-]}{[NH_3]}$$

Therefore $$\frac{(0.250 + x)(x)}{(0.150 - x)} = 1.8\text{x}10^{-5}$$

Assume x < 10% of 0.150. Then $0.150 - x \sim 0.150$ and $0.250 + x \sim 0.250$, so that

$$1.8\text{x}10^{-5} = \frac{(x)(25)}{(15)} = \frac{5}{3}x$$

and $$x = \left(\frac{3}{5}\right)(1.8\text{x}10^{-5}) = 1.08\text{x}10^{-5} = 1.1\text{x}10^{-5}$$

Check: Is $1.1\text{x}10^{-5}$ < 10% of 0.150? Yes, $1.1\text{x}10^{-5} < 1.50\text{x}10^{-2}$

Hence $$[OH^-] = 1.1\text{x}10^{-5}\ M$$

$$pOH = -\log(1.1\text{x}10^{-5}) = 5 - \log(1.1) = 4.96$$

$$pH = 14.00 - pOH = 14.00 - 4.96 = 9.04$$

2. The formula weight of benzoic acid is 122.123 g/mol and of sodium benzoate is 144.105 g/mol.

$$\text{No. mol } C_6H_5COOH \text{ added} = \frac{6.106\ g}{122.123\ g/mol} = 5.000\text{x}10^{-2}\ mol$$

$$\text{No. mol } C_6H_5COONa \text{ added} = \frac{14.411\ g}{144.105\ g/mol} = 0.10000\ mol$$

As the volume of solution is 0.50000 L the initial concentrations of C_6H_5COOH and C_6H_5COONa are, respectively,

0.1000 F and 0.2000 F.

$$C_6H_5COOH + H_2O \rightleftharpoons C_6H_5COO^-(aq) + H_3O^+(aq)$$

$$\text{Let} \quad x = [H_3O^+]$$

Then $[C_6H_5COO^-] = 0.2000 + x$ and $[C_6H_5COOH] = 0.1000 - x$

$$K_a = \frac{[C_6H_5COO^-][H_3O^+]}{[C_6H_5COOH]} = 6.3\times10^{-5} = \frac{(0.2000 + x)(x)}{(0.1000 - x)}$$

Assume $x < 10\%$ of 0.1000. Then $0.1000 - x \sim 0.1000$ and $0.2000 + x \sim 0.2000$, so that

$$\left(\frac{0.2000}{0.1000}\right)x = 2x = 6.3\times10^{-5} \quad \text{and} \quad x = 3.1_5\times10^{-5}$$

Check: Is $3.2\times10^{-5} < 10\%$ of 0.100? Yes, $3.2\times10^{-5} < 1.00\times10^{-2}$

Hence $$[H_3O^+] = 3.2\times10^{-5}\ M$$

$$pH = -\log(3.15\times10^{-5}) = 4.50$$

3. $$CH_3COOH + H_2O \rightleftharpoons CH_3COO^-(aq) + H_3O^+(aq)$$

$$K_a(HOAc) = \frac{[H_3O^+][CH_3COO^-]}{[CH_3COOH]} = 1.8\times10^{-5}$$

If $pH = 4.32$, $[H_3O^+] = \text{antilog}(-4.32) = 4.79\times10^{-5}$

$$1.8\times10^{-5} = 4.79\times10^{-5}\ \frac{[CH_3COO^-]}{[CH_3COOH]}$$

$$\frac{[CH_3COOH]}{[CH_3COO^-]} = \frac{4.79}{1.8} = 2.66 = 2.7$$

The molar ratio of acetic acid to sodium acetate must be 2.7:1 to make a buffer with pH = 4.32.

4. No. mmol OH^- added = (20.00 mL)(0.500 M) = 10.00

No. mmol HOAc added = (80.00 mL)(0.500 M) = 40.00

$$OH^-(aq) + HOAc \rightleftharpoons H_2O + OAc^-(aq)$$

This reaction goes virtually to completion because OAc^- is a weaker base than OH^- and H_2O is a weaker acid than HOAc. Thus 10.00 mmol OH^- react with 10.00 mmol HOAc to produce 10.00 mmol OAc^-, leaving (40.00 - 10.00) = 30.00 mmol HOAc in excess. The volume of solution is 100.00 mL (20.00 ml + 80.00 mL). This solution is identical to one prepared by adding 30.00 mmol HOAc and 10.00 mmol OAc^- ions to enough water to make the volume of solution 100.00 mL.

$$\text{Initial [HOAc]} = \frac{30.00 \text{ mmol}}{100.00 \text{ mL}} = 0.3000 \text{ F}$$

$$\text{Initial } [OAc^-] = \frac{10.00 \text{ mmol}}{100.00 \text{ mL}} = 0.1000 \text{ M}$$

$$HOAc + H_2O \rightleftharpoons OAc^-(aq) + H_3O^+(aq)$$

Let $x = [H_3O^+]$ at equilibrium

Then $[OAc^-] = 0.1000 + x$ and $[HOAc] = 0.3000 - x$

$$K_a = 1.8\text{x}10^{-5} = \frac{[H_3O^+][OAc^-]}{[HOAc]} = \frac{(x)(0.1000 + x)}{(0.3000 - x)}$$

Assume $x < 10\%$ of 0.1000. Then $0.1000 + x \sim 0.1000$ and $0.3000 - x \sim 0.3000$.

$$1.8\text{x}10^{-5} = \frac{x}{3} \quad \text{so that} \quad x = 5.4\text{x}10^{-5}$$

Check: Is $5.4\text{x}10^{-5} < 10\%$ of 0.1000? Yes, $5.4\text{x}10^{-5} < 1.0\text{x}10^{-2}$

Hence $[H_3O^+] = 5.4\text{x}10^{-5}$ M

$$pH = -\log(5.4\text{x}10^{-5}) = 4.27$$

5. $CH_3COOH + H_2O \rightleftharpoons CH_3COO^-(aq) + H_3O^+(aq)$

Since this is a solution of CH_3COOH in water, the reaction above is the only source of CH_3COO^- ions.

$$\text{Let } x = [H_3O^+] = [CH_3COO^-]$$

$$\text{Then } [CH_3COOH] = 0.100 - x$$

$$K_a(HOAc) = \frac{[H_3O^+][CH_3COO^-]}{[CH_3COOH]} = \frac{x^2}{0.100 - x} = 1.8x10^{-5}$$

Assume $x < 10\%$ of 0.100. Then $0.100 - x \sim 0.100$ and

$$x^2 = (0.100)(1.8x10^{-5}) = 1.8x10^{-6}$$

$$x = 1.3x10^{-3} \text{ M}$$

Check: Is $1.3x10^{-3} < 10\%$ of 0.100? Yes, $1.3x10^{-3} < 1.00x10^{-2}$

Hence $[CH_3COO^-] = 1.3x10^{-3}$ M

$$[CH_3COOH] = 0.100 - x = 0.100 - 1.3x10^{-3} = 0.099 \text{ M}$$

The ratio $[CH_3COO^-]/[CH_3COOH] = 1.3x10^{-3}/0.099 = 0.013$ is too small for this to be an effective buffer solution. A solution in which the $[CH_3COO^-]/[CH_3COOH]$ ratio is less than 1/10 will not be efficient at keeping the pH approximately constant when small additions of either strong acid or strong base are made. In essence, although there are CH_3COO^- ions present, the $[CH_3COO^-]$ is not sufficiently large for the solution to be an effective buffer.

6. $$HCOOH + OH^-(aq) \rightleftharpoons HCOO^-(aq) + H_2O$$

This reaction goes virtually to completion because formate ion is a much weaker base than OH^- and H_2O is a much weaker acid than formic acid.

No. mmol OH^- added = (40.00 mL)(0.400 M) = 16.00 mmol

No. mmol HCOOH added = (80.00 mL)(0.500 M) = 40.00 mmol

Since HCOOH and OH^- react in a 1:1 molar ratio, there is excess HCOOH present. Thus, 16.00 mmol of OH^- react with 16.00 mmol of HCOOH to produce 16.00 mmol $HCOO^-$, leaving (40.00 - 16.00) = 24.00 mmol HCOOH in excess in a total volume of 120.00 mL. This solution is identical to one in which sufficient water has been added to 16.00 mmol of $HCOO^-$ ions and 24.00 mmol HCOOH to make 120.00 mL of solution.

$$\text{Initial [HCOOH]} = \frac{24.00\ \text{mmol}}{120.00\ \text{mL}} = 0.2000\ \text{M}$$

$$\text{Initial } [HCOO^-] = \frac{16.00\ \text{mmol}}{120.00\ \text{mL}} = 0.1333\ \text{M}$$

$$HCOOH + H_2O \rightleftharpoons HCOO^-(aq) + H_3O^+(aq)$$

Let $x = [H_3O^+]$ at equililbrium

Then [HCOOH] = 0.2000 - x and $[HCOO^-]$ = 0.1333 + x

Note that there are two sources of $HCOO^-$ ions in this solution: (1) from the reaction between HCOOH and OH^-, and (2) from the reaction between HCOOH and H_2O. The first reaction goes virtually to completion, the second proceeds to a slight extent.

$$K_a(HCOOH) = 1.8\text{x}10^{-4} = \frac{(x)(0.1333 + x)}{(0.2000 - x)}$$

Assume x < 10% of 0.1333. Then 0.1333 + x ~ 0.1333 and 0.2000 - x ~ 0.2000, so that

$$K_a(HCOOH) = 1.8\text{x}10^{-4} = \frac{(x)(0.1333)}{(0.2000)} = \frac{1.333x}{2.000}$$

$$x = (2/1.33)(1.8\text{x}10^{-4}) = (1.5)(1.8\text{x}10^{-4}) = 2.7\text{x}10^{-4}$$

Check: Is 2.7×10^{-4} < 10% of 0.1333? Yes, $2.7\times10^{-4} < 1.33\times10^{-2}$

Hence $$[H_3O^+] = 2.7\times10^{-4}\ M$$

$$pH = -\log(2.7\times10^{-4}) = 4 - \log(2.7) = 3.57$$

7. $$HCOO^-(aq) + H_3O^+(aq) \rightleftharpoons HCOOH + H_2O$$

No. mmol $HCOO^-$ added = (60.00 mL)(0.400 M) = 24.00 mmol

No. mmol H_3O^+ added = (40.00 mL)(0.360 M) = 14.40 mmol

The reaction between formate ions and hydronium ions goes virtually to completion because formic acid is a weak acid. Therefore 14.40 mmol H_3O^+ react with 14.40 mmol of $HCOO^-$ producing 14.40 mmol HCOOH and leaving (24.00 - 14.40) = 9.60 mmol $HCOO^-$ in excess, in a total volume of 100.00 mL.

$$\text{Initial } [HCOO^-] = \frac{9.60\ \text{mmol}}{100.00\ \text{mL}} = 0.0960\ M$$

$$\text{Initial } [HCOOH] = \frac{14.40\ \text{mmol}}{100.00\ \text{mL}} = 0.1440\ M$$

$$HCOOH + H_2O \rightleftharpoons HCOO^-(aq) + H_3O^+(aq)$$

This reaction proceeds to a very slight extent since K_a for formic acid is 1.8×10^{-4}.

Let $x = [H_3O^+]$ at equilibrium

Then $[HCOO^-] = 0.0960 + x$ and $[HCOOH] = 0.1440 - x$

$$K_a = \frac{[H_3O^+][HCOO^-]}{[HCOOH]} = 1.8\times10^{-4} = \frac{(x)(0.0960 + x)}{(0.1440 - x)}$$

Assume x < 10% of 0.0960. Then $0.0960 + x \sim 0.0960$ and $0.1440 - x \sim 0.1440$. Thus

$$1.8\times10^{-4} = x\left(\frac{0.0960}{0.1440}\right)$$

and $$x = \left(\frac{14.40}{9.60}\right)(1.8\text{x}10^{-4}) = 2.7\text{x}10^{-4}$$

Check: Is $2.7\text{x}10^{-4}$ < 10% of 0.0960? Yes, $2.7\text{x}10^{-4} < 9.60\text{x}10^{-3}$

Hence $$[H_3O^+] = 2.7\text{x}10^{-4}\ M$$

$$pH = -\log(2.7\text{x}10^{-4}) = 4 - \log(2.7) = 3.57$$

Note that the buffers prepared in Exercises 6 and 7 are identical. These exercises describe two alternate procedures for preparing a $HCOOH/HCOO^-$ buffer with pH = 3.57.

8. No. mmol NH_3 added = (80.00 mL)(1.00 M) = 80.00 mmol

No. mmol H_3O^+ added = (40.00 mL)(1.00 M) = 40.00 mmol

$$NH_3 + H_3O^+(aq) \rightleftharpoons NH_4^+(aq) + H_2O$$

This reaction goes virtually to completion because NH_4^+ is a very weak acid and H_2O is a weaker base than NH_3. Therefore 40.00 mmol H_3O^+ react with 40.00 mmol NH_3 to produce 40.00 mmol NH_4^+ leaving (80.00 - 40.00) = 40.00 mmol NH_3 in excess, in a total volume of 120.00 mL. This solution is an NH_3/NH_4^+ buffer.

$$\text{Initial } [NH_4^+] = \frac{40.00 \text{ mmol}}{120.00 \text{ mL}} = 0.3333\ M$$

$$\text{Initial } [NH_3] = \frac{40.00 \text{ mmol}}{120.00 \text{ mL}} = 0.3333\ M$$

$$NH_3 + H_2O \rightleftharpoons NH_4^+(aq) + OH^-(aq)$$

Let $x = [OH^-]$ at equilibrium

Then $[NH_4^+] = 0.3333 + x$ and $[NH_3] = 0.3333 - x$

$$K_b(NH_3) = 1.8\text{x}10^{-5} = \frac{[NH_4^+][OH^-]}{[NH_3]} = \frac{(0.3333 + x)(x)}{(0.3333 - x)}$$

Assume $x < 10\%$ of 0.3333. Then $0.3333 \pm x \sim 0.3333$ and

$$1.8\text{x}10^{-5} = \frac{0.3333}{0.3333}x = x$$

Check: Is $1.8\text{x}10^{-5} < 10\%$ of 0.3333? Yes, $1.8\text{x}10^{-5} < 3.33\text{x}10^{-2}$

Hence $$[OH^-] = 1.8\text{x}10^{-5}\ M$$

$$pOH = -\log(1.8\text{x}10^{-5}) = 4.745 = 4.74$$

$$pH = 14.00 - pOH = 9.255 = 9.26$$

Note: If instead of using only 2 figures for $K_b(NH_3)$, you keep 3 figures when calculating $K_w/K_a(NH_4^+) = 1.75\text{x}10^{-5}$, you will calculate the pH as 9.24. The uncertainty in the second decimal place is such that there is no significant difference between 9.24 and 9.26.

9.

No. mmol NH_4^+ added = (50.00 mL)(0.200 M) = 10.0 mmol

No. mmol OH^- added = (25.00 mL)(0.200 M) = 5.00 mmol

$$NH_4^+(aq) + OH^-(aq) \rightleftharpoons NH_3 + H_2O$$

This reaction goes virtually to completion to the right as NH_3 is a weak base. Therefore 5.00 mmol OH^- react with 5.00 mmol NH_4^+ to produce 5.00 mmol NH_3, leaving 5.00 mmol NH_4^+ in excess, in a total volume of 75.00 mL. This is therefore an NH_3/NH_4^+ buffer.

$$\text{Initial } [NH_4^+] = \frac{5.00 \text{ mmol}}{75.00 \text{ mL}} = 0.0667\ M$$

$$\text{Initial } [NH_3] = \frac{5.00 \text{ mmol}}{75.00 \text{ mL}} = 0.0667\ M$$

$$NH_3 + H_2O \rightleftharpoons NH_4^+(aq) + OH^-(aq)$$

This reaction proceeds only to a very slight extent to the right as $K_b(NH_3) = 1.8 \times 10^{-5}$.

$$\text{Let } x = [OH^-] \text{ at equilibrium}$$

$$\text{Then } [NH_4^+] = 0.0667 + x \quad \text{and} \quad [NH_3] = 0.0667 - x$$

$$K_b = 1.8 \times 10^{-5} = \frac{[NH_4^+][OH^-]}{[NH_3]} = \frac{(0.0667 + x)(x)}{(0.0667 - x)}$$

Assume x < 10% of 0.0667. Then $0.0667 \pm x \sim 0.0667$, and

$$x = 1.8 \times 10^{-5} \text{ M}$$

Check: Is 1.8×10^{-5} < 10% of 0.0667? Yes, $1.8 \times 10^{-5} < 6.67 \times 10^{-3}$

Hence $$[OH^-] = 1.8 \times 10^{-5} \text{ M}$$

$$pOH = -\log(1.8 \times 10^{-5}) = 4.74 \text{ and } pH = 14.00 - 4.74 = 9.26$$

Note that the buffers prepared in Exercises 8 and 9 are identical. These exercises describe two procedures for preparing an NH_3/NH_4^+ buffer with pH = 9.26.

10. The [weak base]/[conjugate weak acid] ratio must be no smaller than 1/10 and no larger than 10, for a buffer to be effective. Using the Henderson-Hasselbalch equation, Eq. (10-7), the pH of an NH_3/NH_4^+ buffer is given by

$$pH = pK_a(NH_4^+) + \log \frac{[NH_3]}{[NH_4^+]}$$

$K_a(NH_4^+) = 5.7 \times 10^{-10}$ and $pK_a = -\log(5.7 \times 10^{-10}) = 9.24$, so that

$$pH = 9.24 + \log \frac{[NH_3]}{[NH_4^+]}$$

The smallest value the ratio $[NH_3]/[NH_4^+]$ can have is 1/10, if the buffer is to be effective. For that ratio

$$pH = 9.24 + \log(1/10) = 9.24 - 1 = 8.24$$

Since 6.5 is well below this value, it is not possible to make a buffer with pH = 6.5 using a mixture of NH_3 and an ammonium salt.

11. No. mmol OH^- used = (42.50 mL)(0.100 M) = 4.25 mmol

Therefore, No. mmol H_3O^+ titrated = 4.25 mmol. Let c_A be the molarity of the H_3O^+ in the solution of the strong acid HBr. Then,

$$(50.00\ \text{mL})(c_A) = 4.25\ \text{mmol}$$

and
$$c_A = \frac{4.25\ \text{mmol}}{50.00\ \text{mL}} = 0.0850\ \text{M}$$

12. No. mmol OH^- used = (34.75 mL)(0.200 M) = 6.95 mmol

Each H_2SO_4 formula unit has 2 titratable H_3O^+ ions. If c_A is the formality of the sulfuric acid,

$$\text{No. mmol } H_3O^+ \text{ titrated} = (25.00\ \text{mL})(2c_A\ \frac{\text{mmol}}{\text{mL}})$$

Therefore
$$6.95\ \text{mmol} = (25.00\ \text{mL})(2c_a)$$

and
$$c_A = \frac{6.95\ \text{mmol}}{50.00\ \text{mL}} = 0.139\ \text{F}$$

13.

No. mmol H_3O^+ in sample = (20.00 mL)(0.100 M) = 2.00 mmol

When 19.50 mL base have been added,

No. mmol OH^- added = (19.50 mL)(0.100 M) = 1.95 mmol

No. mmol H_3O^+ not yet titrated = 2.00 - 1.95 = 0.05 mmol

Volume of solution at this point = 39.50 mL

$$[H_3O^+] = \frac{0.05\ \text{mmol}}{39.50\ \text{mL}} = 1.27\text{x}10^{-3}\ \text{M}$$

$$\text{pH} = -\log(1.27\text{x}10^{-3}) = 3 - \log(1.27) = 2.90$$

When 20.50 mL base have been added,

No. mmol OH^- added = (20.50 mL)(0.100 M) = 2.05 mmol

No. mmol OH^- in excess = 2.05 - 2.00 = 0.05 mmol

Volume of solution at this point = 40.50 mL

$$[OH^-] = \frac{0.05\ \text{mmol}}{40.50\ \text{mL}} = 1.23\text{x}10^{-3}\ \text{M}$$

pOH = $-\log(1.23\text{x}10^{-3})$ = 2.91 and pH = 14.00 - 2.91 = 11.09

Note that there is a very steep rise in pH, from 2.90 to 11.09, as the volume of base added increases from 19.50 to 20.50 mL. The equivalence point in this titration occurs when 20.00 mL base have been added.

14.

No. mmol H_3O^+ added = (31.83 mL)(0.1000 M) = 3.183 mmol

Let c_B = concentration of the NaOH solution. Then

(25.00 mL)(c_B) = 3.183 mmol and c_B = 0.1273 F

15. Let c_A = concentration of the student's original acid solution. Then

No. mmol H_3O^+ in sample = (40.00 mL)(c_A)

After overtitrating

No. mmol H_3O^+ added = (5.00 mL)(0.100 M) = 0.500 mmol

Total mmol H_3O^+ titrated = ($40.00c_A$ + 0.500) mmol

No. mmol OH^- added = (46.72 mL)(0.100 M) = 4.672 mmol

Hence $40.00c_A + 0.500 = 4.672$

$40.00c_A = 4.172$ and $c_A = 0.1043$ F

16. $$K_a = 1.6\text{x}10^{-9} = \frac{[H_3O^+][In^-]}{[HIn]}$$

$$pK_a = -\log(1.6\text{x}10^{-9}) = 8.80 = pH - \log([In^-]/[HIn])$$

Therefore $$pH = 8.80 + \log([In^-]/[HIn])$$

(a) When pH = 6.5, $\log([In^-]/[HIn]) = -2.3$ and

$$[In^-]/[HIn] = \text{antilog}(-2.3) = 10^{-2.3} = 5.0\text{x}10^{-3}$$

Since $5.0\text{x}10^{-3} < 1/10$, we will see the acid color, yellow.

(b) When pH = 7.5, $\log([In^-]/[HIn] = 7.5 - 8.8 = -1.3$ and

$$[In^-]/[HIn] = \text{antilog}(-1.3) = 10^{-1.3} = 5.0\text{x}10^{-2}$$

Since $5.0\text{x}10^{-2} < 1/10$, we will see the acid color, yellow.

(c) When pH = 8.5, $\log([In^-]/[HIn]) = 8.5 - 8.8 = -0.3$ and

$$[In^-]/[HIn] = \text{antilog}(-0.3) = 10^{-0.3} = 0.50$$

Since 0.50 is between 1/10 and 10, we will see a mixture of the yellow and blue color of the acid and base forms, i.e., the solution will be green.

(d) When pH = 9.5, $\log([In^-]/[HIn]) = 9.5 - 8.8 = 1.3$ and

$$[In^-]/[HIn] = \text{antilog}(1.3) = 10^{1.3} = 20$$

Since 20 is larger than 10, we will see the color of the base In^-, i.e., blue.

17. The equivalence point occurs when 50.00 mL of base have been added, in each case. We must calculate the pH at 0.05 mL before and after the equivalence point.

(a) No. mmol H_3O^+ in sample = (50.00 mL)(0.500 M) = 25.00

When 49.95 mL base have been added,

No. mmol OH^- added = (49.95 mL)(0.500 M) = 24.975 mmol

No. mmol H_3O^+ not titrated = 25.000 - 24.975 = 0.025 mmol

The volume of solution is 99.95 mL at this point in the titration. Hence,

$$[H_3O^+] = \frac{0.025 \text{ mmol}}{99.95 \text{ mL}} = 2.5\text{x}10^{-4} \text{ M}$$

$$\text{pH} = -\log(2.5\text{x}10^{-4}) = 3.60$$

When 50.05 mL base have been added,

No. mmol OH^- added = (50.05 mL)(0.500 M) = 25.025 mmol

No. mmol OH^- in excess = 25.025 - 25.000 = 0.025 mmol

Volume of solution = 100.05 mL

$$[OH^-] = \frac{0.025 \text{ mmol}}{100.05 \text{ mL}} = 2.5\text{x}10^{-4} \text{ M}$$

$$\text{pOH} = 3.60 \text{ and pH} = 14.00 - \text{pOH} = 10.40$$

Any indicator that changes color between pH = 3.60 and 10.40 is suitable for this titration, which includes every indicator listed in Table 10.2.

(b) No. mmol H_3O^+ in sample = (50.00 mL)(0.050 F) = 2.5

When 49.95 mL base have been added

No. mmol OH^- added = (49.95 mL)(0.050 M) = 2.4975

No. mmol H_3O^+ not titrated = 2.5000 - 2.4975 = 0.0025

Volume of solution = 99.95 mL

$$[H_3O^+] = \frac{2.50\text{x}10^{-3} \text{ mmol}}{99.95 \text{ mL}} = 2.5\text{x}10^{-5} \text{ M}$$

$$\text{pH} = -\log(2.5\text{x}10^{-5}) = 4.6$$

When 50.05 mL base have been added

$$\text{No. mmol } OH^- \text{ added} = (50.05 \text{ mL})(0.050 \text{ M}) = 2.5025$$

$$\text{No. mmol } OH^- \text{ in excess} = 2.5025 - 2.5000 = 2.5\text{x}10^{-3}$$

$$\text{Volume of solution} = 100.05 \text{ mL}$$

$$[OH^-] = \frac{2.5\text{x}10^{-3} \text{ mmol}}{100.05 \text{ mL}} = 2.5\text{x}10^{-5} \text{ M}$$

$$pOH = 4.6 \quad \text{and} \quad pH = 14.00 - pOH = 9.4$$

The indicators listed in Table 10.2 that change color between pH = 4.6 and 9.4 are bromcresol green, methyl red, chlorophenol red, bromthymol blue, phenol red and phenolphthalein. Any of these six is suitable for this titration.

(c) No. mmol H_3O^+ in sample = (50.00 mL)(0.0050 M) = 0.250

When 49.95 mL base have been added

$$\text{No. mmol } OH^- \text{ added} = (49.95 \text{ mL})(0.0050 \text{ M}) = 0.24975$$

$$\text{No. mmol } H_3O^+ \text{ not titrated} = 0.25000 - 0.24975 = 2.5\text{x}10^{-4}$$

$$\text{Volume of solution} = 99.95 \text{ mL}$$

$$[H_3O^+] = \frac{2.5\text{x}10^{-4} \text{ mmol}}{99.95 \text{ mL}} = 2.5\text{x}10^{-6}$$

$$pH = -\log(2.5\text{x}10^{-6}) = 5.6$$

When 50.05 mL base have been added

$$\text{No. mmol } OH^- \text{ added} = (50.05 \text{ mL})(0.0050 \text{ M}) = 0.25025$$

$$\text{No. mmol } OH^- \text{ in excess} = 2.5\text{x}10^{-4}$$

$$\text{Volume of solution} = 100.05 \text{ mL}$$

$$[OH^-] = \frac{2.5\text{x}10^{-4} \text{ mmol}}{100.05 \text{ mL}} = 2.5\text{x}10^{-6}$$

$$pOH = 5.6 \text{ and } pH = 14.00 - 5.6 = 8.4$$

Those indicators listed in Table 10.2 that change color

between pH = 5.6 and 8.4 are chlorophenol red, bromthymol blue, and phenol red. Any of these three indicators is suitable for this titration.

Note that the number of indicators suitable for a titration of a strong acid versus a strong base is quite limited when the solutions are dilute.

18. (a) $C_6H_5COOH + OH^-(aq) \rightleftharpoons C_6H_5COO^-(aq) + H_2O$

(b) $NH_3 + H_3O^+(aq) \rightleftharpoons NH_4^+(aq) + H_2O$

(c) $HCOOH + OH^-(aq) \rightleftharpoons HCOO^-(aq) + H_2O$

(d) $C_6H_5NH_2 + H_3O^+(aq) \rightleftharpoons C_6H_5NH_3^+(aq) + H_2O$

19. $C_6H_5COOH + OH^-(aq) \rightleftharpoons C_6H_5COO^-(aq) + H_2O$

No. mmol C_6H_5COOH originally = (50.00 mL)(0.0200 F) = 1.00

In the titration 1.00 mmol C_6H_5COOH reacts with 1.00 mmol OH^- to produce 1.00 mmol $C_6H_5COO^-$ ions. The volume of solution is 100.00 mL at the equivalence point, so that the solution is identical with 0.0100 F sodium benzoate.

$$C_6H_5COO^-(aq) + H_2O \rightleftharpoons C_6H_5COOH + OH^-(aq)$$

$$K_b(C_6H_5COO^-) = \frac{K_w}{K_a(C_6H_5COOH)} = \frac{1.00\times10^{-14}}{6.3\times10^{-5}} = 1.59\times10^{-10}$$

Let $x = [C_6H_5COOH] = [OH^-]$ at the equivalence point

$$\text{Then} \quad [C_6H_5COO^-] = 0.0100 - x$$

$$K_b = \frac{[C_6H_5COOH][OH^-]}{[C_6H_5COO^-]} = \frac{x^2}{0.0100 - x} = 1.59\times10^{-10}$$

Assume $x < 10\%$ of 0.0100. Then $0.0100 - x \sim 0.0100$, and

$$x^2 = 1.59\times10^{-12} \qquad x = 1.26\times10^{-6} = 1.3\times10^{-3}$$

Check: Is $1.3 \times 10^{-6} < 10\%$ of 0.010? Yes, $1.3 \times 10^{-6} < 1.0 \times 10^{-3}$

Hence $$[OH^-] = 1.3 \times 10^{-6}\ M$$

$$pOH = -\log(1.26 \times 10^{-6}) = 5.90, \quad pH = 14.00 - 5.90 = 8.10$$

The pH at the equivalence point in the titration of 50.00 mL of 0.0200 F benzoic acid with 0.0200 F NaOH is 8.1.

20. $$HCOOH + OH^-(aq) \rightleftharpoons HCOO^-(aq) + H_2O$$

No. mmol HCOOH originally = (25.00 mL)(0.200 F) = 5.00 mmol

In the titration 5.00 mmol HCOOH reacts with 5.00 mmol OH^- to produce 5.00 mmol $HCOO^-$ in a total volume of 50.00 mL. The solution at the equivalence point is identical with 0.100 F sodium formate, HCOONa.

$$HCOO^-(aq) + H_2O \rightleftharpoons HCOOH + OH^-(aq)$$

$$K_b(HCOO^-) = \frac{K_w}{K_a(HCOOH)} = \frac{1.0 \times 10^{-14}}{1.8 \times 10^{-4}} = 5.6 \times 10^{-11}$$

Let $x = [HCOOH] = [OH^-]$ at the equivalence point

Then $[HCOO^-] = 0.100 - x$

$$K_b = \frac{[HCOOH][OH^-]}{[HCOOH]} = \frac{x^2}{0.100 - x} = 5.6 \times 10^{-11}$$

Assume $x < 10\%$ of 0.100. Then $0.100 - x \sim 0.100$, and

$$x^2 = 5.6 \times 10^{-12} \quad \text{and} \quad x = 2.36 \times 10^{-6} = 2.4 \times 10^{-6}$$

Check: Is $2.4 \times 10^{-6} < 10\%$ of 0.100? Yes, $2.4 \times 10^{-6} < 1.0 \times 10^{-2}$

Hence $$[OH^-] = 2.4 \times 10^{-6}\ M$$

$$pOH = -\log(2.4 \times 10^{-6}) = 6 - \log(2.4) = 5.63$$

$$pH = 14.00 - pOH = 14.00 - 5.63 = 8.37$$

21.

No. mmol HOAc initially = (20.00 mL)(0.500 F) = 10.0

(a) Before the titration begins the solution is 0.500 F HOAc.

$$HOAc + H_2O \rightleftharpoons H_3O^+ + OAc^-$$

$$\text{Let} \quad x = [H_3O^+] = [OAc^-]$$

$$\text{Then} \quad [HOAc] = 0.500 - x$$

$$K_a = \frac{[H_3O^+][OAc^-]}{[HOAc]} = \frac{x^2}{0.500 - x} = 1.8\text{x}10^{-5}$$

Assume x < 10% of 0.500. Then $0.500 - x \sim 0.500$, and

$$x^2 = (0.500)(1.8\text{x}10^{-5}) = 0.90\text{x}10^{-5} = 9.0\text{x}10^{-6}$$

$$x = 3.0\text{x}10^{-3}$$

Check: Is $3.0\text{x}10^{-3}$ < 10% of 0.500? Yes, $3.0\text{x}10^{-3} < 5.0\text{x}10^{-2}$

Thus

$$[H_3O^+] = 3.0\text{x}10^{-3}\ M$$

$$pH = -\log(3.0\text{x}10^{-3}) = 2.52$$

(b) When 10.00 mL base have been added the titration is at the halfway point since it requires 20.00 mL base to reach the equivalence point. The titration reaction is

$$OH^- + HOAc \rightleftharpoons OAc^- + H_2O$$

No. mmol OH^- added = (10.00 mL)(0.500 M) = 5.00 mmol

At this point in the titration 5.00 mmol OH^- have reacted with 5.00 mmol HOAc to produce 5.00 mmol OAc^-, leaving (10.00 - 5.00) = 5.00 mmol HOAc untitrated. The solution is now a 1:1 buffer containing 5.00 mmol each of HOAc and OAc^- ions in a volume of 30.00 mL.

$$\frac{[HOAc]}{[OAc^-]} = \frac{\text{No. mmol HOAc untitrated}}{\text{No. mmol OAc}^- \text{ formed}} = \frac{5.00}{5.00} = 1.00$$

$$[H_3O^+] = K_a \cdot \frac{[HOAc]}{[OAc^-]} = K_a = 1.8\times10^{-5}$$

$$pH = pK_a = -\log(1.8\times10^{-5}) = 4.74$$

Note that at the halfway point in the titration of a monoprotic weak acid with a strong base, pH = pK_a.

(c) When 19.80 mL base have been added,

No. mmol OH^- added = No. mmol OAc^- formed

$$= (19.80 \text{ mL})(0.500 \text{ M}) = 9.90 \text{ mmol}$$

No. mmol HOAc untitrated = 10.00 - 9.90 = 0.10 mmol

$$\frac{[HOAc]}{[OAc^-]} = \frac{\text{No. mmol HOAc untitrated}}{\text{No. mmol OAc}^- \text{ formed}} = \frac{0.10}{9.90} = 1.01\times10^{-2}$$

$$[H_3O^+] = K_a \frac{[HOAc]}{[OAc^-]} = (1.8\times10^{-5})(1.01\times10^{-2}) = 1.8\times10^{-7}$$

$$pH = -\log(1.8\times10^{-7}) = 6.74$$

(d) At the equivalence point all 10.00 mmol of the original HOAc have been titrated, and there are 10.00 mmol of OAc^- ions in a total volume of 40.00 mL. The solution is identical with 0.250 F sodium acetate, CH_3COONa.

$$CH_3COO^-(aq) + H_2O \rightleftharpoons CH_3COOH + OH^-(aq)$$

$$K_b(OAc^-) = \frac{[HOAc][OH^-]}{[OAc^-]} = \frac{K_w}{K_a(HOAc)} = \frac{1.0\times10^{-14}}{1.8\times10^{-5}} = 5.6\times10^{-10}$$

Let $x = [CH_3COOH] = [OH^-]$ at the equivalence point

Then $[CH_3COO^-] = 0.250 - x$

$$5.6\times10^{-10} = \frac{x^2}{0.250 - x}$$

Assume x < 10% of 0.250. Then 0.250 - x ~ 0.250, and

$$x^2 = (0.250)(5.6\times10^{-10}) = 1.4\times10^{-10}$$

$$x = 1.2\times10^{-5}$$

Check: Is 1.2×10^{-5} < 10% of 0.250? Yes, $1.2\times10^{-5} < 2.5\times10^{-2}$

Hence $$[OH^-] = 1.2\times10^{-5}\ M$$

$$pOH = -\log(1.2\times10^{-5}) = 4.92$$

$$pH = 14.00 - pOH = 14.00 - 4.92 = 9.08$$

(e) When 20.20 mL base have been added

No. mmol OH^- added = (20.20 mL)(0.500 M) = 10.10 mmol

No. mmol OH^- in excess = (10.10 - 10.00) = 0.10 mmol

Volume of solution = 40.20 mL

$$[OH^-] = \frac{0.10\ \text{mmol}}{40.20\ \text{mL}} = 2.49\times10^{-3}\ M$$

$$pOH = -\log(2.49\times10^{-3}) = 2.60$$

$$pH = 14.00 - pOH = 14.00 - 2.60 = 11.40$$

22. Nitrous acid, HNO_2, is a weak acid. The titration reaction is

$$HNO_2 + OH^- \rightleftharpoons NO_2^- + H_2O$$

No. mmol HNO_2 initially = No. mmol NO_2^- formed in titration

= (40.00 mL)(0.100 F) = 4.00 mmol

The volume of solution is 80.00 mL at the equivalence point. The solution is identical with 0.0500 F $NaNO_2$.

$$NO_2^-(aq) + H_2O \rightleftharpoons HNO_2 + OH^-(aq)$$

Let $x = [HNO_2] = [OH^-]$ at the equivalence point

Then $[NO_2^-] = 0.0500 - x$

$$K_b = \frac{K_w}{K_a(HNO_2)} = \frac{1.00\times10^{-14}}{4.5\times10^{-4}} = 2.22\times10^{-11} = \frac{[HNO_2][OH^-]}{[NO_2^-]}$$

$$2.22\times10^{-11} = \frac{x^2}{0.0500 - x}$$

Assume $x < 10\%$ of 0.0500. Then $0.0500 - x \sim 0.0500$ and

$$x^2 = (0.0500)(2.22\times10^{-11}) = 1.11\times10^{-12}$$

$$x = 1.05\times10^{-6} = 1.1\times10^{-6}$$

Check: Is $1.1\times10^{-6} < 10\%$ of 0.0500? Yes, $1.1\times10^{-6} < 5.0\times10^{-3}$

Hence $$[OH^-] = 1.1\times10^{-6}\ M$$

$$pOH = -\log(1.05\times10^{-6}) = 5.98$$

$$pH = 14.00 - pOH = 14.00 - 5.98 = 8.02$$

Of the indicators listed in Table 10.2, phenolphthalein is the best. The orange color of phenol red would be seen just a little before the equivalence point, at a pH of about 7.3 (the middle of the range listed), whereas the first pink color of phenolphthalein would be seen right at or immediately after the equivalence point, at about pH = 8.1.

23.

No. mmol aniline initially = (50.00 mL)(0.100 F) = 5.00

The titration reaction is

$$C_6H_5NH_2 + H_3O^+ \rightleftharpoons C_6H_5NH_3^+ + H_2O$$

In the titration 5.00 mmol of H_3O^+ react with 5.00 mmol of $C_6H_5NH_2$ to produce 5.00 mmol of anilinium ion, $C_6H_5NH_3^+$ in a total volume of 100.00 mL. The solution at the equivalence point is therefore identical with 0.0500 F anilinium chloride.

$$C_6H_5NH_3^+ + H_2O \rightleftharpoons C_6H_5NH_2 + H_3O^+$$

Let $x = [C_6H_5NH_2] = [H_3O^+]$ at the equivalence point

Then $[C_6H_5NH_3^+] = 0.0500 - x$

$$K_a = 2.4x10^{-5} = \frac{[C_6H_5NH_2][H_3O^+]}{[C_6H_5NH_3^+]} = \frac{x^2}{0.0500 - x}$$

Assume $x < 10\%$ of 0.0500. Then $0.0500 - x \sim 0.0500$ and

$$x^2 = (0.0500)(2.4x10^{-5}) = 1.2x10^{-6}$$

$$x = 1.1x10^{-3}$$

Check: Is $1.1x10^{-3} < 10\%$ of 0.0500? Yes, $1.1x10^{-3} < 5.0x10^{-3}$

Hence $$[H_3O^+] = 1.1x10^{-3}\ M$$

$$pH = -\log(1.1x10^{-3}) = 2.96$$

None of the indicators listed in Table 10.2 is ideal for this titration. The best would be either methyl orange or bromphenol blue, but the midpoint of their color change range occurs at a slightly higher pH than the equivalence point pH.

24. If it requires 29.64 mL of base to reach the equivalence point, the titration is at the halfway point when 14.82 mL of titrant have been added. At the halfway point, $pH = pK_a$, so that pK_a for this titration is 4.87.

$$K_a = \text{antilog}(-4.87) = 1.3x10^{-5}$$

If c_A is the concentration of the original acid solution,

$$(29.64\ mL)(0.1022\ M) = (20.00\ mL)c_A$$

and $$c_A = 0.1515\ F$$

25. (a) $H_2C_2O_4 + OH^-(aq) \rightleftharpoons HC_2O_4^-(aq) + H_2O$

(b) $HC_2O_4^-(aq) + OH^-(aq) \rightleftharpoons C_2O_4^{2-}(aq) + H_2O$

(c) $H_2C_2O_4 + 2OH^-(aq) \rightleftharpoons C_2O_4^{2-}(aq) + 2H_2O$

26. (a) The molecular weight of CO_2 is 44.01 $g{\cdot}mol^{-1}$ A liter of solution contains 1.45 g of CO_2, since 100 mL contains 0.145 g. Therefore

$$[CO_2] = \frac{1.45\ g/L}{44.01\ g/mol} = 3.29_5x10^{-2}\ mol/L = 3.29x10^{-2}\ M$$

(b) The Henry's Law constant, K, for CO_2 is 29.7 atm/M {see Eq. 10-30b)}. Therefore

$$P_{CO_2} = K[CO_2] = (29.7)(3.29_5x10^{-2}) = 0.979\ atm$$

(c) $$CO_2 + 2H_2O \rightleftharpoons H_3O^+ + HCO_3^-$$

Let $x = [H_3O^+] = [HCO_3^-]$ in a saturated solution of CO_2

$$K_a = 4.3x10^{-7} = \frac{[H_3O^+][HCO_3^-]}{[CO_2]} = \frac{x^2}{3.295x10^{-2}}$$

and $$x^2 = (4.3x10^{-7})(3.295x10^{-2}) = 1.4x10^{-8}$$

$$x = 1.2x10^{-4}\ M = [H_3O^+]$$

$$pH = -\log(1.2x10^{-4}) = 4 - \log(1.2) = 3.92$$

27. The pH of a solution of KHP (a common abbreviation for potassium hydrogen phthalate) is given, to a good approximation, by

$$pH = \tfrac{1}{2}(pK_1 + pK_2) = \tfrac{1}{2}(3.10 + 5.40) = 4.25$$

Eq. (10-47c) is valid here because K_1 is smaller than 10^{-2}, K_2 is larger than 10^{-13} and C = 0.100 M is larger than K_2.

28. (a) The solution at the first equivalence point is a solution of the salt NaHA, where A stands for the anion that is formed when ascorbic acid loses two protons. Thus

$$[H_3O^+]^2 = K_1K_2 = (6.76x10^{-5})(2.69x10^{-12}) = 1.82x10^{-16}$$

$$[H_3O^+] = 1.35x10^{-8}\ M \quad \text{and} \quad pH = -\log(1.35x10^{-8}) = 7.87$$

As pH = 7.87 is in the middle of the color change range of phenol red, it would be the best indicator of those in Table 10.2 to signal the first equivalence point.

(b) No. mmol H_2A initially = (50.00 mL)(0.0600 F) = 3.00

The titration reaction to the first equivalence point is

$$H_2A + OH^- \rightleftharpoons HA^- + H_2O$$

Thus 3.00 mmol of OH^- must be added to reach the first equivalence point. Let V = volume of base containing 3.00 mmol OH^-. Then

$$(V)(0.100\ M) = 3.00\ \text{mmol} \quad \text{and} \quad V = 30.0\ \text{mL}$$

(c) To reach the second equivalence point another 3.00 mmol of OH^- are required, as the titration reaction between the first and second equivalence points is

$$HA^- + OH^- \rightleftharpoons A^{2-} + H_2O$$

Therefore, another 30.0 mL are required, and a total of 60.0 mL of base is needed to reach the second equivalence point in this titration.

29.

$$K_{eq} = \frac{[H_2C_2O_4][C_2O_4^{2-}]}{[HC_2O_4^-]^2} = \frac{[C_2O_4^{2-}]\cancel{[H_3O^+]}}{[HC_2O_4^-]} \cdot \frac{[H_2C_2O_4]}{[HC_2O_4^-]\cancel{[H_3O^+]}}$$

$$\frac{K_2}{K_1} = \frac{6.4\times10^{-5}}{5.9\times10^{-2}} = 1.1\times10^{-3} = K_{eq}$$

30. The substances present are H_2O, Na^+, S^{2-}, HS^-, H_2S, H_3O^+, and OH^-. The electroneutrality equation is

$$[Na^+] + [H_3O^+] = [OH^-] + [HS^-] + 2[S^{2-}]$$

The material balance equation is

$$C = 0.100\ M = [S^{2-}] + [HS^-] + [H_2S]$$

31. The substances present are H_2O, Na^+, S^{2-}, HS^-, H_2S, H_3O^+, and OH^-. The electroneutrality equation is

$$[Na^+] + [H_3O^+] = [OH^-] + [HS^-] + 2[S^{2-}]$$

The material balance equation is

$$C = 0.100\ M = [S^{2-}] + [HS^-] + [H_2S]$$

32. $C_2O_4^{2-}(aq) + H_2O \rightleftharpoons HC_2O_4^-(aq) + OH^-(aq)$

$$K_b(C_2O_4^{2-}) = \frac{K_w}{K_a(HC_2O_4^-)} = \frac{1.00\times10^{-14}}{6.4\times10^{-5}} = 1.56\times10^{-10} = 1.6\times10^{-10}$$

Since $K_b(HC_2O_4^-) = K_w/K_a(H_2C_2O_4) = 1.7\times10^{-13}$ is much smaller than $K_b(C_2O_4^{2-})$, we can assume the basicity reaction for $C_2O_4^{2-}$ is the principal source of $[OH^-]$ in this solution.

$$\text{Let}\quad x = [OH^-] = [HC_2O_4^-]$$

Then $$[C_2O_4^{2-}] = 0.100 - x$$

$$\frac{x^2}{0.100 - x} = 1.56\times10^{-10}$$

Assume $x < 10\%$ of 0.100. Then $0.100 - x \sim 0.100$, and

$$x^2 = 1.56\times10^{-11} = 15.6\times10^{-12}$$

$$x = 3.95\times10^{-6} = 4.0\times10^{-6}$$

Check: Is $4.0\times10^{-6} < 10\%$ of 0.10? Yes, $4.0\times10^{-6} < 1.0\times10^{-2}$

Hence $[OH^-] = 4.0x10^{-6}$ M

pOH = $-\log(4.0x10^{-6}) = 5.40$ and pH = $14.00 - 5.40 = 8.60$

33. As the K^+ ions take no part in any reaction, $[K^+]$ = 0.200 M. The principal reaction in this solution is

$$CO_3^{2-} + H_2O \rightleftharpoons HCO_3^- + OH^-$$

$$K_b(CO_3^{2-}) = \frac{K_w}{K_a(HCO_3^-)} = \frac{1.00x10^{-14}}{4.7x10^{-11}} = 2.1x10^{-4}$$

The basicity constant for HCO_3^- is $2.3x10^{-8}$ (See Example 10.12) and is so much smaller than $2.1x10^{-4}$ that we can neglect the basicity of HCO_3^- compared to the basicity of CO_3^{2-}. Therefore,

$$\text{Let } x = [HCO_3^-] = [OH^-]$$

The material balance equation for this solution is

$$0.100 \text{ M} = [CO_3^-] + [HCO_3^-] + [CO_2]$$

If we neglect the $[CO_2]$ as small compared to the other two terms on the right-hand side of this equation, then

$$[CO_3^{2-}] = 0.100 - x$$

and

$$2.1x10^{-4} = \frac{x^2}{0.100 - x}$$

Assume x < 10% of 0.100. Then $0.100 - x \sim 0.100$, and

$$x^2 = 2.1x10^{-5} = 21x10^{-6}$$

$$x = 4.58x10^{-3} = 4.6x10^{-3}$$

Check: Is $4.6x10^{-3}$ < 10% of 0.100 M? Yes, $4.6x10^{-3} < 1.0x10^{-2}$

Thus $[OH^-] = [HCO_3^-] = 4.6x10^{-3}$ M

$$[CO_3^{2-}] = 0.100 - 4.6x10^{-3} = 0.100 - 0.0046 = 0.095 \text{ M}$$

$$[H_3O^+] = K_w/[OH^-] = 1.0\times10^{-14}/(4.6\times10^{-3}) = 2.2\times10^{-12}\ M$$

We can obtain the $[CO_2]$ from the first ionization constant of carbonic acid.

$$4.3\times10^{-7} = \frac{[H_3O^+][HCO_3^-]}{[CO_2]} = \frac{(2.2\times10^{-12})(4.6\times10^{-3})}{[CO_2]}$$

$$[CO_2] = \frac{1.0\times10^{-14}}{4.3\times10^{-7}} = 2.3\times10^{-8}\ M$$

Since $2.3\times10^{-8} \ll [HCO_3^-]$ it was valid to neglect $[CO_2]$ in the material balance equation.

34. As K^+ ions take no part in any reaction, $[K^+]$ = 0.0800 M. The bicarbonate ion, HCO_3^-, is an ampholyte.

As an acid: $HCO_3^- + H_2O \rightleftharpoons CO_3^{2-} + H_3O^+$ $K_a = 4.7\times10^{-11}$

As a base: $HCO_3^- + H_2O \rightleftharpoons H_2CO_3 + OH^-$ $K_b = 2.3\times10^{-8}$

The sum of these reactions is the principal reaction in solution:

$$2HCO_3^- \rightleftharpoons CO_3^{2-} + H_2CO_3$$

because $H_3O^+ + OH^-$ on the right-hand side sum to $2H_2O$. Since the H_2CO_3 decomposes to $H_2O + CO_2$ we can write this as

$$2HCO_3^- \rightleftharpoons CO_3^{2-} + H_2O + CO_2$$

From this overall reaction we make the approximation that

$$[CO_3^{2-}] = [CO_2]$$

If that approximation is valid, then the $[H_3O^+]$ is given by Eq. (10-47a), and

$$[H_3O^+]^2 = K_1K_2 = (4.3\times10^{-7})(4.7\times10^{-11}) = 20\times10^{-18}$$

$$[H_3O^+] = 4.5\times10^{-9}\ M$$

The material balance equation is

$$0.0800\ M = [HCO_3^-] + [CO_3{}^{2-}] + [CO_2]$$

$$\text{Let}\quad x = [CO_3{}^{2-}] = [CO_2]\ .$$

$$\text{Then}\quad [HCO_3^-] = 0.0800 - 2x$$

The equilibrium constant for the principal (overall) reaction in the solution is

$$\frac{[CO_3^{2-}][CO_2]}{[HCO_3^-]^2} = \frac{[CO_3^{2-}]\cancel{[H_3O^+]}}{[HCO_3^-]} \cdot \frac{[CO_2]}{[HCO_3^-]\cancel{[H_3O^+]}} = \frac{K_2}{K_1} = \frac{4.7\text{x}10^{-11}}{4.3\text{x}10^{-7}}$$

$$= 1.1\text{x}10^{-4}$$

Thus
$$\frac{x^2}{(0.0800 - 2x)^2} = 1.1\text{x}10^{-4}$$

Take the square root of both sides of this equation.

$$1.05\text{x}10^{-2} = \frac{x}{0.0800 - 2x}$$

Multiplying this out we obtain

$$8.4\text{x}10^{-4} - (2.1\text{x}10^{-2})x = x$$

$$1.02x = 8.4\text{x}10^{-4} \quad \text{and} \quad x = 8.2\text{x}10^{-4}\ M$$

Thus
$$[CO_2] = [CO_3{}^{2-}] = 8.2\text{x}10^{-4}\ M$$

$$[HCO_3^-] = 0.0800 - 2(8.2\text{x}10^{-4}) = 0.0800 - 0.00164 = 0.0784\ M$$

$$[OH^-] = K_w/[H_3O^+] = 1.0\text{x}10^{-14}/(4.5\text{x}10^{-9}) = 2.2\text{x}10^{-6}\ M$$

Since both $[H_3O^+]$ and $[OH^-]$ are much less than $8.2\text{x}10^{-4}$, the approximation made that $[CO_2] = [CO_3{}^{2-}]$ is valid.

Solutions to Multiple Choice Questions, Chapter 10

1. **(d)** The pK_a of the weak acid should be within ± 1 of 3.4. This is true only for HNO_2 of the options given.

2. <u>(a)</u> Of the weak acids in the options given, only NH_4^+ has a pK_a close to 9.0; $pK_a(NH_4^+) = 9.2$.

3. <u>(e)</u> The titration reaction produces $HCOO^-$ ions. Equal volumes of acid and base are mixed, doubling the volume, so the $[HCOO^-]$ is 1/2 of 0.100 M.

4. <u>(b)</u> $pH = pK_a + \log(\text{ratio})$ $5.24 = 4.74 + \log(\text{ratio})$

Hence $\log(\text{ratio}) = 0.50$ and $(\text{ratio}) = 3$ or 3:1

5. <u>(d)</u>

No. mmol OH^- added = (29.38 mL)(0.1025 M) = 3.011

No. mmol C_6H_5COOH originally = 3.011 = No. mmol $C_6H_5COO^-$ formed during the titration. The final volume of solution is 69.38 mL. Hence

$$[C_6H_5COO^-] = \frac{3.011 \text{ mmol}}{69.38 \text{ mL}} = 0.04340 \text{ M}$$

6. <u>(e)</u> Nitrous acid is a weak acid and must be written in molecular form. Potassium hydroxide is a strong electrolyte and is 100% ions.

7. <u>(a)</u> No. mmol OH^- at start = (50.00 mL)(0.0100 M)(2)

= 1.00 mmol

We therefore need 1.00 mmol of H_3O^+, or 100.00 mL of 0.0100 F HCl. The volume at the equivalence point is 150.00 mL, and the solution contains 0.500 mmol Ba^{2+} and 1.00 mmol Cl^- so that its formality is $\frac{0.500 \text{ mmol}}{150.00 \text{ mL}} = 3.33 \times 10^{-3}$ F $BaCl_2$.

8. **(b)** Only a 1:1 HOAc/OAc^- buffer has pH = 4.75, since 4.75 = pK_a for acetic acid. The flask contains 10.0 mmol of acetic acid as (100.00 mL)(0.100 F) = 10.0. Thus we must add 10.0 mmol of OAc^- ions. Option (b) provides 10.0 mmol of OAc^- ions as (25.00 mL)(0.200 F){2 OAc^- ions/$Ba(OAc)_2$}.

9. **(c)** One-half of 38.62 mL is 19.31 mL, so that the halfway point in the titration occurs when 19.31 mL of base have been added. At the halfway point pH = pK_a, and pK_a for acetic acid is 4.7.

10. **(b)** The solution must have both the weak base, NH_3, and its conjugate weak acid, NH_4^+, to be a buffer. Option (a) mixes 5.00 mmol OH^- with 5.00 mmol NH_4^+. They react to produce 5.00 mmol NH_3, and there is no excess NH_4^+ remaining after the reaction with OH^-. In option (b) only 2.50 mmol OH^- are added to 5.00 mmol NH_4^+. The reaction produces 2.50 mmol NH_3 and there are 2.50 mmol NH_4^+ in excess. This is therefore a 1:1 NH_3/NH_4^+ buffer. In the solutions of options (c) and (d) there is no NH_3 at all, just the weak acid NH_4^+ and a strong acid, H_3O^+. In option (e) there is excess OH^- after the reaction with NH_4^+, and the solution contains NH_3 and OH^-, with virtually no NH_4^+ left.

11. **(c)** This is a $C_6H_5COO^-/C_6H_5COOH$ buffer. The pK_a of benzoic acid is 4.20 = $-\log(6.3\times10^{-5})$. For this buffer

$$pH = pK_a + \log \frac{[C_6H_5COO^-]}{[C_6H_5COOH]} = 4.20 + \log \frac{2}{1} = 4.50$$

12. <u>**(d)**</u> We have mixed 10.0 mmol OH^- with 20.0 mmol of HCOOH. The reaction $OH^- + HCOOH \rightleftharpoons H_2O + HCOO^-$ produces 10.0 mmol of $HCOO^-$ ions, and uses up 10.0 mmol of HCOOH, leaving 10.0 mmol HCOOH in excess. This is therefore a 1:1 $HCOO^-/HCOOH$ buffer, with pH = pK_a of HCOOH, or 3.75. K_a of HCOOH = 1.8×10^{-4} and $pK_a = -\log(1.8 \times 10^{-4}) = 3.75$.

13. <u>**(e)**</u> The titration reaction is

$$CH_3NH_2 + H_3O^+ \rightleftharpoons CH_3NH_3^+ + H_2O$$

No. mmol H_3O^+ added = No. mmol $CH_3NH_3^+$ formed

$$= (39.26 \text{ mL})(0.150 \text{ M}) = 5.889 \text{ mmol}$$

Volume of solution at the equivalence point = 79.26 mL

$$CH_3NH_3^+ + H_2O \rightleftharpoons CH_3NH_2 + H_3O^+$$

Let $x = [CH_3NH_2] = [H_3O^+]$ at the equivalence point

$$\text{Then } [CH_3NH_3^+] = \frac{5.889 \text{ mmol}}{79.26 \text{ mL}} - x = 0.07430 - x$$

$K_a(CH_3NH_3^+) = 2.4 \times 10^{-11}$ (listed in Table E1 or calculated from K_w/K_b). Thus

$$\frac{x^2}{0.07430 - x} = 2.4 \times 10^{-11}$$

Assume $x <$ 10% of 0.07430. Then $0.07430 - x \sim 0.07430$ and

$$x^2 = (2.4 \times 10^{-11})(7.430 \times 10^{-2}) = 1.78 \times 10^{-12}$$

$$x = [H_3O^+] = 1.34 \times 10^{-6} \text{ M}$$

Check: Is $1.34 \times 10^{-6} <$ 10% of 7.43×10^{-2}? Yes, $1.34 \times 10^{-6} < 7.430 \times 10^{-3}$. The pH is therefore $-\log(1.34 \times 10^{-6}) = 5.87$

14. __(d)__ No. mmol H_3O^+ added = 7.50

No. mmol OH^- added = 4.50

Excess H_3O^+ = 3.00 mmol in a volume of 120.00 mL

$$[H_3O^+] = \frac{3.00 \text{ mmol}}{120.00 \text{ mL}} = 0.025 \text{ M} \quad \text{and} \quad pH = -\log(0.025) = 1.60$$

15. __(b)__ A solution of CO_2 in water is carbonic acid, for which $K_a = 4.3\text{x}10^{-7}$

$$CO_2 + 2H_2O \rightleftharpoons H_3O^+ + HCO_3^-$$

Let $x = [H_3O^+] = [HCO_3^-]$

Then $x^2/0.050 = 4.3\text{x}10^{-7}$ or $x^2 = 2.15\text{x}10^{-8}$

$x = 1.47\text{x}10^{-4} = [H_3O^+]$ and $pH = -\log(1.47\text{x}10^{-4}) = 3.83$

16. __(e)__ A buffer must contain a weak base and its conjugate weak acid. Aniline is a weak base; its conjugate weak acid is anilinium ion. Aniline reacts with H_3O^+ to produce anilinium ion. In option (e) 0.100 mol H_3O^+ from the HCl reacts with 0.100 mol aniline to produce 0.100 mol anilinium ion, leaving 0.100 mol aniline in excess. The solution of option (e) is therefore a 1:1 buffer. In (a) there is no excess aniline after the reaction. In (b) there is no anilinium ion, two bases have been added. In (c) and (d) there is no weak base or weak acid.

17. __(a)__ Since the pH is greater than 7 in the titration of a weak acid versus a strong base, only options (a) and (b) are possible. The titration of HA versus OH^- produces the weak base A^-. For this weak base, $K_b = K_w/K_a = 2.5\text{x}10^{-9}$

No. mmol A^- formed = (28.54 mL)(0.1016 M) = 2.900 mmol

Volume of solution at the equivalence point = 53.54 mL

Let $x = [HA] = [OH^-]$ at the equivalence point

$$\text{Then} \quad [A^-] = \frac{2.900 \text{ mmol}}{53.54 \text{ mL}} - x = 0.05416 - x$$

$$K_b = 2.5\text{x}10^{-9} = \frac{x^2}{0.05416 - x}$$

Assume x < 10% of 0.05416. Then $0.05416 - x \sim 0.05416$ and

$$x^2 = (0.05416)(2.5\text{x}10^{-9}) = 1.35\text{x}10^{-10}$$

$$x = 1.16\text{x}10^{-5} = 1.2\text{x}10^{-5}$$

Check: Is $1.2\text{x}10^{-5}$ < 10% of 0.05416? Yes, $1.2\text{x}10^{-5} < 5.4\text{x}10^{-3}$

Hence $[OH^-] = 1.2\text{x}10^{-5}$ M

$pOH = -\log(1.16\text{x}10^{-5}) = 4.93$ and $pH = 14.00 - 4.93 = 9.07$

Thymolphthalein does not change color until after the equivalence point in this titration, so that phenolphthalein is the only suitable indicator.

18. <u>**(c)**</u> $B + H_2O \rightleftharpoons BH^+ + OH^-$

$$K_b = 2\text{x}10^{-5} = \frac{[BH^+][OH^-]}{[B]}$$

If $[B] = [BH^+]$ then $[OH^-] = 2\text{x}10^{-5}$ and $[H_3O^+] = 5\text{x}10^{-10}$

$$pH = -\log(5\text{x}10^{-10}) = 9.3$$

19. <u>**(a)**</u> Barium hydroxide and sulfuric acid are soluble, strong electrolytes and are written in ionic form. There are two products, H_2O and insoluble $BaSO_4$, both of which are written in molecular form.

20. (e)

No. mmol H_2X at start = (20.00 mL)(0.200 F) = 4.00

No. mmol OH^- to reach second equivalence point = 8.00

The volume of base required, V_b, in mL, is therefore

$$V_b = \frac{8.00 \text{ mmol}}{0.250 \text{ M}} = 32.0 \text{ mL}$$

Volume of solution at equivalence point = 52.00 mL

As the titration reaction produces 4.00 mmol of X^{2-} from the original 4.00 mmol of H_2X,

$$[X^{2-}] = \frac{4.00 \text{ mmol}}{52.00 \text{ mL}} = 0.0769 \text{ M}$$

21. (c) $$H_2S + H_2O \rightleftharpoons HS^- + H_3O^+$$

Since K_2 for H_2S is so much smaller than K_1 we can neglect the second stage of ionization relative to the first, and

Let $x = [H_3O^+] = [HS^-]$ in a saturated solution of H_2S

$$K_a(H_2S) = 1\text{x}10^{-7} = \frac{[H_3O^+][HS^-]}{[H_2S]} = \frac{x^2}{0.10}$$

$$x^2 = 1.0\text{x}10^{-8} \quad \text{and} \quad x = 1.0\text{x}10^{-4} \text{ M}$$

22. (c) From the preceding question we have

$[H_3O^+] = [HS^-] = 1\text{x}10^{-4}$ M in a saturated H_2S solution,

so that $$pH = -\log(1.0\text{x}10^{-4}) = 4.0$$

23. (b) We can obtain the $[S^{2-}]$ in a saturated solution of H_2S by using the second ionization constant.

$$K_2 = \frac{[H_3O^+][S^{2-}]}{[HS^-]} = 1.3\text{x}10^{-13}$$

Since $[HS^-] = [H_3O^+]$, $[S^{2-}] = K_2 = 1.3\text{x}10^{-13}$ M

24. (d) $$H_3O^+ + OAc^- \rightleftharpoons HOAc + H_2O$$

Since HOAc is a weak acid, this reaction goes virtually to completion. We have added 60.0 mmol of OAc^- ions and 20.0 mmol of H_3O^+. As they react in a 1:1 molar ratio, 20.0 mmol OAc^- react with 20.0 mmol H_3O^+ to produce 20.0 mmol HOAc, leaving 40.0 mmol OAc^- in excess. Thus the $[HOAc]/[OAc^-]$ ratio is 20.0/40.0 = 1/2.

$$K_a(HOAc) = 1.8\text{x}10^{-5} = \frac{[H_3O^+][OAc^-]}{[HOAc]}$$

and $$[H_3O^+] = (1.8\text{x}10^{-5})(1/2) = 9.0\text{x}10^{-6}\ M$$

25. (b) The weak acid of the conjugate pair used to prepare a buffer must have a pK_a within ±1 pH unit of the desired pH. The only weak acid of those given that has a pK_a within ±1 of 3.2 is formic acid, for which $pK_a = 3.75$.

26. (a) A mixture of KCl and HCl has neither a weak base nor a weak acid and is not a buffer, but it is acidic.

27. (e) There are two weak bases in this solution, CO_3^{2-} and CH_3COO^- ions, but no weak acid. It is not a buffer, but it is basic, with pH > 7.

28. (b) This is a 1:2 $HOAc/OAc^-$ buffer. Since pK_a of HOAc is 4.75, the pH of this buffer is between 4 and 7.

29. (e) This solution contains a strong base and a weak base, but no weak acid, so it is not a buffer.

30. (c) H_3O^+ and OH^- have been mixed in a 1:1 molar ratio. They react to form H_2O, and the solution has pH = 7.

31. <u>**(a)**</u> $H_3O^+ + OAc^- \rightleftharpoons HOAc + H_2O$

This reaction goes virtually to completion as HOAc is a weak acid. We have added 25.0 mmol OAc^- ions and 50.0 mmol H_3O^+ ions. Thus 25.0 mmol OAc^- react with 25.0 mmol H_3O^+ to produce 25.0 mmol HOAc, leaving 25.0 mmol H_3O^+ in excess. The solution contains a strong acid, H_3O^+, and a weak acid, HOAc; but no weak base, and is therefore not a buffer. It is however, acidic, with pH < 7.

<u>Solutions to Problems, Chapter 10</u>

10.1. (a) The number of moles of potassium hydrogen phthalate (hereafter abbreviated KHP) used is

$$\frac{0.8097\ g}{204.23\ g/mol} = 3.9646x10^{-3}\ mol = 3.9646\ mmol$$

The titration reaction between the biphthalate ion, HP^-, and OH^- is $HP^- + OH^- \rightleftharpoons H_2O + P^{2-}$

Therefore 3.9646 mmol of OH^- must be used to reach the equivalence point. Let c_B = formality of the NaOH solution.

Then $(40.25\ mL)(c_B) = 3.9646\ mmol$

and $c_B = 9.850x10^{-2}\ M$

(b) The titration reaction for the unknown weak acid, HX, is $X + OH^- \rightleftharpoons H_2O + X^-$

Let c_A = concentration of solution of HX

Then $(28.02\ mL)(9.850x10^{-2}\ M) = (25.00\ mL)(c_A)$

and $c_A = 1.1208x10^{-1} = 0.1121\ F$

If there are 0.1121 mol of HX per liter, then there are 1.121×10^{-2} mol of HX in the 100.00 mL solution that was prepared. Therefore 1.8694 g of HX is 1.1208×10^{-2} mol, and the molecular weight of HX is

$$\frac{1.8694 \text{ g}}{1.1208 \times 10^{-2} \text{ mol}} = 166.8 \text{ g/mol}$$

10.2. The titration reaction is

$$C_5H_5N + H_3O^+ \rightleftharpoons C_5H_5NH^+ + H_2O$$

No. mmol C_5H_5N at start = (50.00 mL)(0.0450 F) = 2.25 mmol

Let V_A = volume HCl needed to reach the equivalence point.

Then $V_A(0.0650 \text{ M}) = 2.25$ mmol and $V_A = 34.62$ mL

Volume of solution at the equivalence point = 84.62 mL

The solution at the equivalence point contains 2.25 mmol of Cl^- ions and 2.25 mmol of $C_5H_5NH^+$ ions in 84.62 mL. It is therefore identical with a solution of anilinium chloride.

$$[Cl^-] = \frac{2.25 \text{ mmol}}{84.62 \text{ mL}} = 2.66 \times 10^{-2} \text{ M}$$

$$C_5H_5NH^+ + H_2O \rightleftharpoons C_5H_5N + H_3O^+$$

Let $x = [C_5H_5N] = [H_3O^+]$ at the equivalence point

Then $$[C_5H_5NH^+] = 2.66 \times 10^{-2} - x$$

$$K_a = \text{antilog}(-5.17) = 6.76 \times 10^{-6} = 6.8 \times 10^{-6}$$

$$\frac{[C_5H_5N][H_3O^+]}{[C_5H_5NH^+]} = \frac{x^2}{2.66 \times 10^{-2} - x} = 6.76 \times 10^{-6}$$

Assume x < 10% of 0.0266. Then 0.0266 - x ~ 0.0266, and

$$x^2 = (0.0266)(6.76 \times 10^{-6}) = 18.0 \times 10^{-8}$$

$$x = 4.2x10^{-4}$$

Check: Is $4.2x10^{-4} < 10\%$ of 0.0266? Yes, $4.2x10^{-4} < 2.66x10^{-3}$

Then $$[C_5H_5N] = [H_3O^+] = 4.2x10^{-4}\ M$$

$$[C_5H_5NH^+] = 0.0266 - 0.00042 = 0.0262\ M$$

$$[OH^-] = K_w/[H_3O^+] = 1.00x10^{-14}/(4.24x10^{-4}) = 2.4x10^{-11}\ M$$

10.3. We observe that $K_2 << K_1$, so that we can neglect the second stage of ionization relative to the first. The proton-transfer reaction of glycinium ion and water can be symbolized as

$$GH_2^+ + H_2O \rightleftharpoons GH + H_3O^+$$

Let $x = [GH] = [H_3O^+]$ in 0.0500 F GH_2^+

Then $$[GH_2^+] = 0.0500 - x$$

$$4.47x10^{-3} = \frac{[GH][H_3O^+]}{[GH_2^+]} = \frac{x^2}{0.0500 - x}$$

Assume $x < 10\%$ of 0.0500. Then $0.0500 - x \sim 0.0500$, and

$$x^2 = (5.00x10^{-2})(4.47x10^{-3}) = 2.235x10^{-4}$$

$$x = 1.5x10^{-2}$$

Check: Is $1.5x10^{-2} < 10\%$ of $5.0x10^{-2}$? No, $1.5x10^{-2} > 5.0x10^{-3}$

Therefore we must make further approximations.

<u>Second approximation</u>:

Assume $0.0500 - x = 0.0500 - 0.0150 = 0.0350$

Then $x^2 = (0.0350)(4.47x10^{-3}) = 1.568x10^{-4}$

$$x = 1.25x10^{-2}$$

<u>Third approximation</u>:

Assume $0.0500 - x = 0.0500 - 0.0125 = 0.0375$

$$\text{Then } x^2 = (0.0375)(4.47\times10^{-3}) = 1.68\times10^{-4}$$

$$x = 1.29\times10^{-2}$$

<u>Fourth approximation</u>:

$$\text{Assume } 0.0500 - x = 0.0500 - 0.0129 = 0.0371$$

$$\text{Then } x^2 = (0.0371)(4.47\times10^{-3}) = 1.66\times10^{-4}$$

$$x = 1.29\times10^{-2}$$

Since the third and fourth approximations agree to 3 significant figures, the correct answer is $x = 1.29\times10^{-2}$ M.

$$[GH] = [H_3O^+] = 1.29\times10^{-2}\ M$$

$$pH = -\log(1.29\times10^{-2}) = 1.89$$

10.4. (a) $NH_4^+ + OH^- \rightleftharpoons NH_3 + H_2O$

This reaction goes virtually to completion as NH_3 is a weak base. Thus 0.100 mol of OH^- reacts with 0.100 mol of NH_4^+ to produce 0.100 mol of NH_3, leaving (0.250 - 0.100) = 0.150 mol NH_4^+ in excess, in a volume of 500.00 mL.

$$K_b(NH_3) = \frac{[NH_4^+][OH^-]}{[NH_3]} = 1.8\times10^{-5}$$

$$\text{Let } x = [OH^-] \text{ at equilibrium}$$

$$\text{Then } [NH_4^+] = \frac{0.150 \text{ mol}}{0.5000 \text{ mL}} + x = 0.300 + x$$

$$\text{and } [NH_3] = \frac{0.100 \text{ mol}}{0.5000 \text{ mL}} - x = 0.200 - x$$

Assume x < 10% of 0.200. Then $0.200 - x \sim 0.200$ and $0.300 - x \sim 0.300$, and

$$K_b = \frac{0.300x}{0.200} = 1.8\times10^{-5}$$

$$x = (2/3)(1.8\text{x}10^{-5}) = 1.2\text{x}10^{-5}$$

Check: Is $1.2\text{x}10^{-5}$ < 10% of 0.200? Yes, $1.2\text{x}10^{-5} < 2.00\text{x}10^{-2}$

Therefore $[OH^-] = 1.2\text{x}10^{-5}$ M

$$[NH_4^+] = 0.300 + 1.2\text{x}10^{-5} = 0.300 \text{ M}$$

$$[NH_3] = 0.200 - 1.2\text{x}10^{-5} = 0.200 \text{ M}$$

$$[H_3O^+] = K_w/[OH^-] = 1.0\text{x}10^{-14}/(1.2\text{x}10^{-5}) = 8.3\text{x}10^{-10} \text{ M}$$

$$[Cl^-] = \frac{0.250 \text{ mol}}{0.50000 \text{ L}} = 0.500 \text{ M}$$

$$[Na^+] = \frac{0.100 \text{ mol}}{0.50000 \text{ L}} = 0.200 \text{ M}$$

(b) The $[NH_3]/[NH_4^+]$ ratio in this solution is 2:3. Since 2/3 is larger than 1/10 but smaller than 10, this is an effective buffer solution.

10.5. Let propionic acid be denoted HOPr.

No. mmol HOPr at start = (50.00 mL)(0.100 M) = 5.00 mmol

<u>Before the titration begins</u> the solution is 0.100 F HOPr.

$$HOPr + H_2O \rightleftharpoons OPr^- + H_3O^+$$

Let $x = [OPr^-] = [H_3O^+]$

Then $[HOPr] = 0.100 - x$

$$K_a = 1.3\text{x}10^{-5} = \frac{[OPr^-][H_3O^+]}{[HOPr]} = \frac{x^2}{0.100 - x}$$

Assume x < 10% of 0.100. Then $0.100 - x \sim 0.100$, and

$$x^2 = 1.3\text{x}10^{-6} \quad \text{and} \quad x = 1.1\text{x}10^{-3}$$

Check: Is $1.1\text{x}10^{-3}$ < 10% of 0.100? Yes, $1.1\text{x}10^{-3} < 1.0\text{x}10^{-2}$

Therefore $[H_3O^+] = 1.1\text{x}10^{-3}$ M and pH = 2.94

$$[OH^-] = K_w/[H_3O^+] = 1.0\text{x}10^{-14}/(1.14\text{x}10^{-3}) = 8.8\text{x}10^{-12} \text{ M}$$

When 5.00 mL base have been added

No. mmol OH^- added = (5.00 mL)(0.100 M) = 0.500 mmol

The titration reaction is $OH^- + HOPr \rightleftharpoons OPr^- + H_2O$. Thus 0.500 mmol OH^- reacts with 0.500 mmol HOPr to produce 0.500 mmol OPr^- ions, leaving 5.00 - 0.500 = 4.50 mmol HOPr in excess (untitrated) in a volume of 55.00 mL.

$$K_a = \frac{[H_3O^+][OPr^-]}{[HOPr]} = 1.3\times10^{-5}$$

$$\frac{\text{No. mmol HOPr untitrated}}{\text{No. mmol OPr}^- \text{ formed}} = \frac{4.50}{0.500} = \frac{[HOPr]}{[OPr^-]} = 9.00$$

$$[H_3O^+] = K_a \frac{[HOPr]}{[OPr^-]} = (1.3\times10^{-5})(9.00) = 1.17\times10^{-4}$$

$$pH = -\log(1.17\times10^{-4}) = 3.93$$

$$[OH^-] = K_w/[H_3O^+] = 1.00\times10^{-14}/(1.17\times10^{-4}) = 8.5\times10^{-11}$$

When 10.00 mL base have been added

No. mmol OH^- added = No. mmol OPr^- formed

= (10.00 mL)(0.100 M) = 1.00 mmol

No. mmol HOPr untitrated = 5.00 - 1.00 = 4.00 mmol

$$\frac{[HOPr]}{[OPr^-]} = \frac{4.00}{1.00} = 4.00$$

$$[H_3O^+] = K_a(4.00) = (1.3\times10^{-5})(4.00) = 5.2\times10^{-5}\text{ M}$$

$$pH = -\log(5.2\times10^{-5}) = 4.28$$

$$[OH^-] = K_w/[H_3O^+] = 1.9\times10^{-10}$$

Note: All the entries for the table before the equivalence point, that is, before 50.00 mL of base have been added are calculated in the same way as the two previous examples.

__At the equivalence point__ the solution is identical with 0.050 F sodium propionate, NaOPr. The 5.00 mmol of HOPr have been used up (titrated) and 5.00 mmol of OPr^- ions have been formed, in a total volume of 100.00 mL.

$$OPr^- + H_2O \rightleftharpoons HOPr + OH^-$$

Let $y = [HOPr] = [OH^-]$ at the equivalence point

Then $[OPr^-] = 0.0500 - y$

$$K_b = \frac{[HOPr][OH^-]}{[OPr^-]} = \frac{K_w}{K_a(HOPr)} = \frac{1.0\times10^{-14}}{1.3\times10^{-5}} = \frac{y^2}{0.0500 - y}$$

Assume $y < 10\%$ of 0.0500. Then $0.0500 - y \sim 0.0500$, and

$$7.7\times10^{-10} = \frac{y^2}{0.0500}$$

$$y^2 = (5.00\times10^{-2})(7.7\times10^{-10}) = 38.5\times10^{-12}$$

$$y = 6.2\times10^{-6}$$

Check: Is $6.2\times10^{-6} < 10\%$ of 0.0500? Yes, $6.2\times10^{-6} < 5.0\times10^{-3}$

$[OH^-] = 6.2\times10^{-6}$ and $[H_3O^+] = K_w/[OH^-] = 1.6\times10^{-9}$

$$pH = -\log(1.6\times10^{-9}) = 8.79$$

Note that the solution is basic at the equivalence point of this titration of a weak acid versus a strong base.

__When 51.00 mL base have been added__

No. mmol OH^- added = (51.00 mL)(0.100 M) = 5.10

No. mmol OH^- in excess = 5.10 - 5.00 = 0.10

Volume of solution = 101.00 mL

$$[OH^-] = \frac{0.10 \text{ mmol}}{101.00 \text{ mL}} = 9.9\times10^{-4} \text{ M}$$

$[H_3O^+] = K_w/[OH^-] = 1.01\times10^{-11}$ and pH = 11.00

When 60.00 mL base have been added

$$\text{No. mmol OH}^- \text{ added} = (60.00 \text{ mL})(0.100 \text{ M}) = 6.00$$

$$\text{No. mmol OH}^- \text{ in excess} = 6.00 - 5.00 = 1.00$$

$$\text{Volume of solution} = 110.00 \text{ mL}$$

$$[\text{OH}^-] = \frac{1.00 \text{ mmol}}{110.00 \text{ mL}} = 9.09\text{x}10^{-3}$$

$$[\text{H}_3\text{O}^+] = K_w/[\text{OH}^-] = 1.1\text{x}10^{-12} \quad \text{and} \quad \text{pH} = 11.96$$

mL NaOH added	Total volume(mL)	$[H_3O^+]$	$[OH^-]$	pH
0.00	50.00	$1.1\text{x}10^{-3}$	$8.8\text{x}10^{-12}$	2.94
5.00	55.00	$1.2\text{x}10^{-4}$	$8.5\text{x}10^{-11}$	3.93
10.00	60.00	$5.2\text{x}10^{-5}$	$1.9\text{x}10^{-10}$	4.28
20.00	70.00	$2.0\text{x}10^{-5}$	$5.1\text{x}10^{-10}$	4.71
25.00	75.00	$1.3\text{x}10^{-5}$	$7.7\text{x}10^{-10}$	4.89
35.00	85.00	$5.6\text{x}10^{-6}$	$1.8\text{x}10^{-9}$	5.25
45.00	95.00	$1.4\text{x}10^{-6}$	$6.9\text{x}10^{-9}$	5.84
49.00	99.00	$2.7\text{x}10^{-7}$	$3.8\text{x}10^{-8}$	6.58
50.00	100.00	$1.6\text{x}10^{-9}$	$6.2\text{x}10^{-6}$	8.79
51.00	101.00	$1.0\text{x}10^{-11}$	$9.9\text{x}10^{-4}$	11.00
60.00	110.00	$1.1\text{x}10^{-12}$	$9.1\text{x}10^{-3}$	11.96

Note that the halfway point in this titration occurs when 25.00 mL of base have been added, and at that point the $[H_3O^+] = K_a = 1.3\text{x}10^{-5}$, so that pH = pK_a = 4.89.

Phenolphthalein is the only indicator in Table 10.2 that is suitable for this titration. The pH at the equivalence point, 8.97, is in the middle of the color change range for phenolphthalein.

The plot of pH versus mL of base added for this titration appears on the following page.

Problem 10.5. Titration curve for the titration of 50.00 mL of 0.100 F propionic acid versus 0.100 F NaOH.

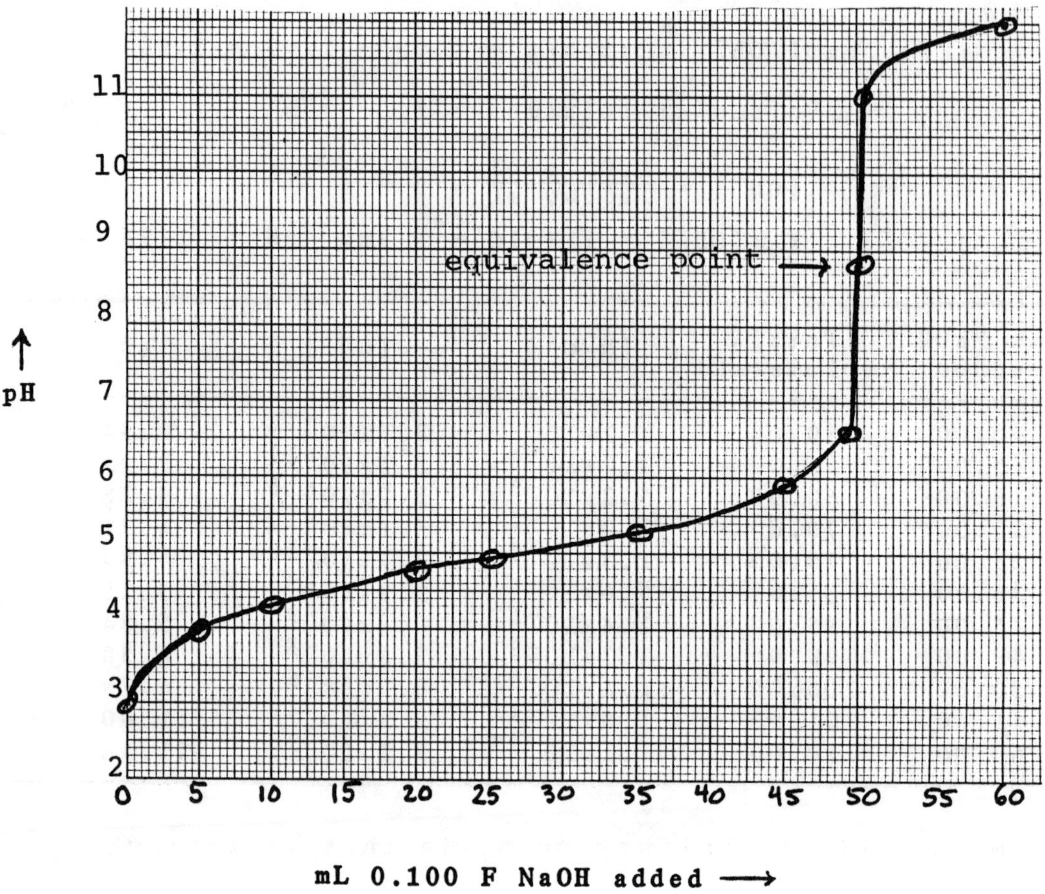

10.6. $$pH = pK_a + \log \frac{[NH_3]}{[NH_4^+]}$$

This is an NH_4^+/NH_3 buffer. $K_a(NH_4^+) = 5.7 \times 10^{-10}$ and pK_a = 9.24. We must prepare a buffer with pH = 9, so that we must make the $[NH_3]/[NH_4^+]$ ratio satisfy the relation

$$9.00 = 9.24 + \log \frac{[NH_3]}{[NH_4^+]}$$

$\log [NH_3]/[NH_4^+] = -0.24$ and $[NH_3]/[NH_4^+] = 10^{-0.24} = 0.575$
The reaction between NH_3 and H_3O^+ produces the NH_4^+ needed

for this buffer: $NH_3 + H_3O^+ \rightleftharpoons NH_4^+ + H_2O$ Let V be the volume, in mL, of 6.00 F strong acid that must be added to 1.00 mol of NH_3 to produce sufficient NH_4^+ ions so that the $[NH_3]/[NH_4^+]$ ratio is 0.575.

$$\text{No. mmol } H_3O^+ \text{ added} = \text{No. mmol } NH_4^+ \text{ formed} = 6.00V$$

$$\text{No. mmol } NH_3 \text{ in excess} = 1000 - 6.00V$$

We have 1.00 mol NH_3 to use, or 1000 mmol, and the reaction with H_3O^+ uses up 6.00V mmol. Since both the NH_3 and NH_4^+ are in the same volume,

$$\frac{[NH_3]}{[NH_4^+]} = \frac{1000 - 6.00V}{6.00V} = 0.575$$

Multiplying out we obtain $1000 - 6.00V = 3.45V$ or

$$9.45V = 1000 \quad \text{and} \quad V = 105.8 \text{ mL} = 106 \text{ mL}$$

Directions: Dissolve the 1.00 mol NH_3 in water, making the total volume significantly less than 800 mL. Add 105.8 mL of 6.00 F HCl or other strong monoprotic acid. Mix thoroughly. Add water until the volume is slightly less than 1.00 L. Mix thoroughly. Add water until the volume is 1.00 L.

10.7. Before the titration begins we have a solution of 0.200 F $C_6H_5NH_2$.

$$C_6H_5NH_2 + H_2O \rightleftharpoons C_6H_5NH_3^+ + OH^-$$

$$\text{Let} \quad z = [C_6H_5NH_3^+] = [OH^-]$$

$$\text{Then} \quad [C_6H_5NH_2] = 0.200 - z$$

$$K_b = 4.2\times10^{-10} = \frac{[C_6H_5NH_3^+][OH^-]}{[C_6H_5NH_2]} = \frac{z^2}{0.200 - z}$$

Assume $z < 10\%$ of 0.200. Then $0.200 - z \sim 0.200$ and

$$z^2 = 8.4\times10^{-11} = 84\times10^{-12}$$

$$z = 9.2\times10^{-6}$$

Check: Is $9.2\times10^{-6} < 10\%$ of 0.200? Yes, $9.2\times10^{-6} < 2.0\times10^{-2}$

Hence $[OH^-] = 9.2\times10^{-6}$ M

$$pOH = -\log(9.2\times10^{-6}) = 5.04 \text{ and } pH = 14.00 - 5.04 = 8.96$$

<u>When 5.00 mL acid have been added</u>

The titration reaction is

$$C_6H_5NH_2 + H_3O^+ \rightleftharpoons C_6H_5NH_3^+ + H_2O$$

No. mmol aniline at start = (40.00 mL)(0.200 M) = 8.00 mmol

No. mmol H_3O^+ added = (5.00 mL)(0.200 M) = 1.00 mmol

No. mmol $C_6H_5NH_3^+$ formed = No. mmol H_3O^+ added = 1.00 mmol

No. mmol $C_6H_5NH_2$ untitrated = 8.00 - 1.00 = 7.00 mmol

$$\frac{[C_6H_5NH_3^+]}{[C_6H_5NH_2]} = \frac{\text{No. mmol } C_6H_5NH_3^+ \text{ formed}}{\text{No. mmol } C_6H_5NH_2 \text{ untitrated}} = \frac{1.00}{7.00}$$

$$K_a(C_6H_5NH_3^+) = \frac{[H_3O^+][C_6H_5NH_2]}{[C_6H_5NH_3^+]} = 2.4\times10^{-5}$$

Therefore

$$[H_3O^+] = K_a\frac{[C_6H_5NH_3^+]}{[C_6H_5NH_2]} = (2.4\times10^{-5})\left(\frac{1.00}{7.00}\right)$$

$$3.43\times10^{-6} = 3.4\times10^{-6} \text{ M}$$

$$pH = -\log(3.43\times10^{-6}) = 5.46$$

$$[OH^-] = 1.00\times10^{-14}/(3.43\times10^{-6}) = 2.9\times10^{-9} \text{ M}$$

Note that the solution is already distinctly acidic after the addition of only 5.00 mL of strong acid. Aniline is a very weak base ($K_b = 4.2x10^{-10}$) and its conjugate weak acid, anilinium ion, is about as strong as acetic acid.

<u>When 10.00 mL acid have been added</u>

No. mmol H_3O^+ added = No. mmol $C_6H_5NH_3^+$ formed = 2.00 mmol

No. mmol $C_6H_5NH_2$ untitrated = 8.00 - 2.00 = 6.00 mmol

$$\frac{[C_6H_5NH_3^+]}{[C_6H_5NH_2]} = \frac{2.00}{6.00} = \frac{1.00}{3.00}$$

$$[H_3O^+] = (2.4x10^{-5})(1/3) = 0.80x10^{-5} = 8.0x10^{-6}$$

$$pH = -\log(8.0x10^{-6}) = 5.10$$

$$[OH^-] = 1.00x10^{-14}/(8.0x10^{-6}) = 1.2x10^{-9}\ M$$

<u>Note</u>: The entries in the table for all values before the equivalence point, that is, before 40.00 mL of 0.200F HCl have been added, are calculated in the same way as in the two previous examples.

<u>At the equivalence point</u> the solution is identical with 0.100 F $C_6H_5NH_3Cl$ (anilinium chloride). It contains 8.00 mmol of $C_6H_5NH_3^+$ in a volume of 80.00 mL. A detailed description of the procedure used to determine the pH at the equivalence point will be found in the solution to Exercise 23 of this chapter.

Let $x = [C_6H_5NH_2] = [H_3O^+]$ at the equivalence point

Then $[C_6H_5NH_3^+] = 0.100 - x$

$$K_a = 2.4x10^{-5} = \frac{x^2}{0.100 - x}$$

Assume x < 10% of 0.100. Then $0.100 - x \sim 0.100$,

$$x^2 = 2.4\times10^{-6} \quad \text{and} \quad x = 1.5\times10^{-3}$$

Check: Is $1.5\times10^{-3} < 10\%$ of 0.10? Yes, $1.5\times10^{-3} < 1.0\times10^{-2}$

Hence $$[H_3O^+] = 1.5\times10^{-3}\ M$$

$$pH = -\log(1.5\times10^{-3}) = 2.81$$

$$[OH^-] = 1.00\times10^{-14}/(1.5\times10^{-3}) = 6.5\times10^{-12}\ M$$

<u>When 42.00 mL acid have been added</u>

$$\text{No. mmol } H_3O^+ \text{ added} = 8.40 \text{ mmol}$$

$$\text{No. mmol } C_6H_5NH_3{}^+ \text{ present} = 8.00 \text{ mmol}$$

$$\text{No. mmol } H_3O^+ \text{ in excess} = 8.40 - 8.00 = 0.40 \text{ mol}$$

$$\text{Volume of solution} = 82.00 \text{ mL}$$

This is a mixture of a strong acid and a weak acid, but as there is considerably more weak acid present than strong acid we must consider both acids in determining the pH.

$$C_6H_5NH_3{}^+ + H_2O \rightleftharpoons C_6H_5NH_2 + H_3O^+$$

$$\text{Let } x = [C_6H_5NH_2] \text{ at equilibrium}$$

Then $$[H_3O^+] = \frac{0.400 \text{ mmol}}{82.00 \text{ mL}} + x = 4.88\times10^{-3} + x$$

$$[C_6H_5NH_3{}^+] = \frac{8.00 \text{ mmol}}{82.00 \text{ mL}} - x = 9.76\times10^{-2} - x$$

$$2.4\times10^{-5} = \frac{(x)(4.88\times10^{-3} + x)}{(9.76\times10^{-2} - x)}$$

Assume $x < 10\%$ of 4.9×10^{-3}. Then $4.88\times10^{-3} + x \sim 4.88\times10^{-3}$ and $9.76\times10^{-2} - x \sim 9.76\times10^{-2}$, so that

$$x = \frac{(2.4\times10^{-5})(9.76\times10^{-2})}{4.88\times10^{-3}} = 4.8\times10^{-4}$$

Check: Is $4.8\times10^{-4} < 10\%$ of 4.9×10^{-3}? Not really. It is very close to $4.9x10^{-4}$, so we should make a better approximation, using the result of the first approximation.

<u>Second approximation</u>:

$$\text{Assume } 4.88x10^{-3} + x = 4.88x10^{-3} + 4.8x10^{-4} = 5.36x10^{-3}$$

$$\text{and } 9.76x10^{-2} - x = 9.76x10^{-2} - 4.8x10^{-4} = 9.71x10^{-2}$$

$$\text{Then } x = \frac{(2.4x10^{-5})(9.71x10^{-2})}{(5.36x10^{-3})} = 4.3x10^{-4}$$

<u>Third approximation</u>:

$$\text{Assume } 4.88x10^{-3} + x = 4.88x10^{-3} + 4.3x10^{-4} = 5.31x10^{-3}$$

$$\text{and } 9.76x10^{-2} - x = 9.76x10^{-2} - 4.3x10^{-4} = 9.72x10^{-2}$$

$$\text{Then } x = \frac{(2.4x10^{-5})(9.72x10^{-2})}{(5.31x10^{-3})} = 4.4x10^{-4}$$

<u>Fourth approximation</u>:

$$\text{Assume } 4.88x10^{-3} + x = 4.88x10^{-3} + 4.4x10^{-4} = 5.32x10^{-3}$$

$$\text{and } 9.76x10^{-2} - x = 9.76x10^{-2} - 4.4x10^{-4} = 9.72x10^{-2}$$

$$\text{Then } x = \frac{(2.4x10^{-5})(9.72x10^{-2})}{(5.32x10^{-3})} = 4.4x10^{-4}$$

Since the third and fourth approximations give the same result, this is the correct answer.

$$[H_3O^+] = 4.88x10^{-3} + x = 4.88x10^{-3} + 4.4x10^{-4} = 5.32x10^{-3}$$

$$pH = -\log(5.32x10^{-3}) = 2.27$$

$$[OH^-] = 1.0x10^{-14}/(5.32x10^{-3}) = 1.9x10^{-12} \text{ M}$$

<u>When 50.00 mL acid have been added</u>

No. mmol H_3O^+ added = 10.00 mmol

No. mmol H_3O^+ in excess = 2.00 mmol

$$\text{Volume of solution} = 90.00\ \text{mL}$$

$$[H_3O^+] = \frac{2.00\ \text{mmol}}{90.00\ \text{mL}} + x = 2.22\text{x}10^{-2} + x$$

$$[C_6H_5NH_3{}^+] = \frac{8.00\ \text{mmol}}{90.00\ \text{mL}} - x = 8.89\text{x}10^{-2} - x$$

$$2.4\text{x}10^{-5} = \frac{(2.22\text{x}10^{-2} + x)(x)}{(8.89\text{x}10^{-2} - x)}$$

Assume $x < 10\%$ of $2.22\text{x}10^{-2}$. Then

$$2.4\text{x}10^{-5} = x/4 \quad \text{and} \quad x = 9.6\text{x}10^{-5}$$

Check: Is $9.6\text{x}10^{-5} < 10\%$ of $2.22\text{x}10^{-2}$? Yes, $9.6\text{x}10^{-5} < 2.22\text{x}10^{-3}$. Hence

$$[H_3O^+] = 2.22\text{x}10^{-2} + 9.6\text{x}10^{-5} = 2.23\text{x}10^{-2} = 2.2\text{x}10^{-2}\text{M}$$

We see that enough excess HCl has been added so that we can neglect the contribution to the $[H_3O^+]$ from the weak acid, that is, from the proton-transfer reaction between $C_6H_5NH_3{}^+$ and H_2O. We can calculate the $[H_3O^+]$ just from the excess HCl added.

$$\text{pH} = -\log(2.23\text{x}10^{-2}) = 1.65$$

$$[OH^-] = 1.0\text{x}10^{-14}/(2.23\text{x}10^{-2}) = 4.5\text{x}10^{-13}$$

<u>When 60.00 mL acid have been added</u>

$$\text{No. mmol } H_3O^+ \text{ added} = 12.00$$

$$\text{No. mmol } H_3O^+ \text{ in excess} = 12.00 - 8.00 = 4.00$$

$$\text{Volume of solution} = 100.00\ \text{mL}$$

$$[H_3O^+] = \frac{4.00\ \text{mmol}}{100.00\ \text{mL}} = 4.0\text{x}10^{-2}\ \text{M}$$

$$\text{pH} = -\log(4.0\text{x}10^{-2}) = 1.40$$

$$[OH^-] = 1.0\text{x}10^{-14}/(4.0\text{x}10^{-2}) = 2.5\text{x}10^{-13}\ \text{M}$$

mL HCl added	Total volume(mL)	$[H_3O^+]$	$[OH^-]$	pH
0.00	40.00	1.1×10^{-9}	9.2×10^{-6}	8.96
5.00	45.00	3.4×10^{-6}	2.9×10^{-9}	5.46
10.00	50.00	8.0×10^{-6}	1.2×10^{-9}	5.10
20.00	60.00	2.4×10^{-5}	4.2×10^{-10}	4.62
25.00	65.00	4.0×10^{-5}	2.5×10^{-10}	4.40
30.00	70.00	7.2×10^{-5}	1.4×10^{-10}	4.14
35.00	75.00	1.7×10^{-4}	6.0×10^{-11}	3.77
38.00	78.00	4.6×10^{-4}	2.2×10^{-11}	3.34
40.00	80.00	1.5×10^{-3}	6.5×10^{-12}	2.81
42.00	82.00	5.3×10^{-3}	1.9×10^{-12}	2.27
50.00	90.00	2.2×10^{-2}	4.5×10^{-13}	1.65
60.00	100.00	4.0×10^{-2}	2.5×10^{-13}	1.40

The titration curve for the titration of 40.00 mL of 0.200F aniline versus 0.200 F HCl is shown below.

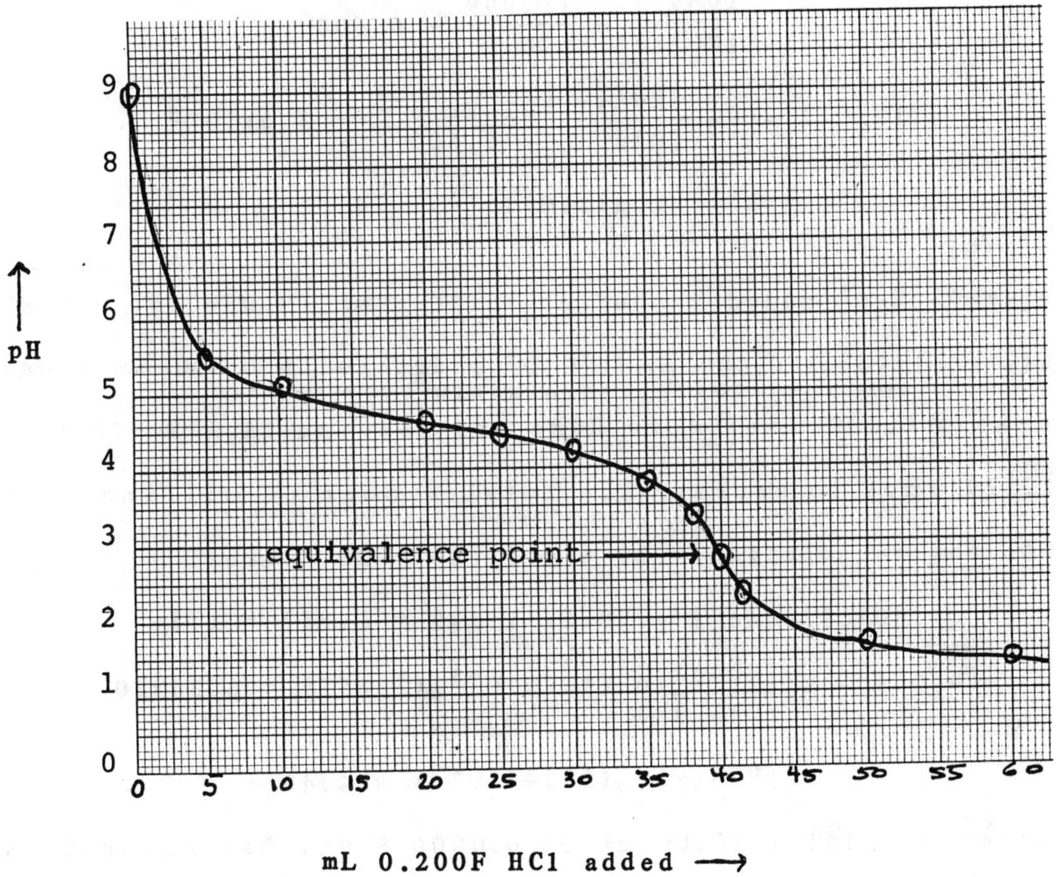

10.8. (a) The formula weight of sodium acetate is 82.034 g/mol. Thus

$$\text{No. mol } OAc^- \text{ added} = \frac{2.6250 \text{ g}}{82.034 \text{ g/mol}} = 3.1999\text{x}10^{-2} \text{ mol}$$

$$\text{No. mmol } H_3O^+ \text{ added} = (250.00 \text{ mL})(0.0800 \text{ M}) = 20.0 \text{ mmol}$$

$$H_3O^+ + OAc^- \rightleftharpoons HOAc + H_2O$$

This reaction goes virtually to completion to the right because acetic acid is a weak acid. Thus 20.0 mmol H_3O^+ react with 20.0 mmol OAc^- to produce 20.0 mmol HOAc. As $3.1999\text{x}10^{-2}$ mol = 31.999 mmol, there are 11.999 mmol OAc^- in excess.

$$\frac{[OAc^-]}{[HOAc]} = \frac{11.999}{20.0} = 0.600$$

$$[H_3O^+] = K_a \frac{[HOAc]}{[OAc^-]} = \frac{1.8\text{x}10^{-5}}{0.600} = 3.0\text{x}10^{-5}$$

$$pH = -\log(3.0\text{x}10^{-5}) = 4.52$$

(b)

No. mmol H_3O^+ added to buffer = (10.0 mL)(0.0800 M) = 0.800

This additional 0.800 mmol H_3O^+ reacts with 0.800 mmol OAc^- forming 0.800 mmol more HOAc and leaving 11.999 - 0.800 = 11.199 mmol in excess. The total number of millimoles of HOAc now in solution = 20.0 + 0.800 = 20.8 mmol.

$$[HOAc]/[OAc^-] = 20.8/11.199 = 1.857 = 1.86$$

$$[H_3O^+] = K_a \frac{[HOAc]}{[OAc^-]} = (1.8\text{x}10^{-5})(1.857) = 3.34\text{x}10^{-5}$$

$$pH = -\log(3.34\text{x}10^{-5}) = 4.48$$

Therefore adding 10.00 mL of 0.0800 F HCl has changed the

pH of this buffer solution from 4.52 to 4.48, a change of 0.04 pH units.

(c) We are adding 10.00 mL of 0.0800 F HCl, or 0.800 mmol of H_3O^+, to 250.00 mL of H_2O, making the total volume 260.00 mL.

$$[H_3O^+] = \frac{0.800 \text{ mmol}}{260.00 \text{ mL}} = 3.08\text{x}10^{-3} \text{ M}$$

$$\text{pH} = -\log(3.08\text{x}10^{-3}) = 2.51$$

Adding 10.00 mL of 0.0800 F HCl to 250.00 mL of water changes the pH from 7.00 to 2.51, a change of 5.49 units. This problem illustrates how effective the buffer is in maintaining the pH at an approximately constant value.

10.9. Acetic acid reacts with OH^- to produce acetate ions, so that this will be an $HOAc/OAc^-$ buffer.

$$HOAc + OH^- \rightleftharpoons OAc^- + H_2O$$

$$K_a(HOAc) = 1.8\text{x}10^{-5}; \quad pK_a = -\log(1.8\text{x}10^{-5}) = 4.74$$

$$\text{pH} = pK_a + \log\frac{[OAc^-]}{[HOAc]}$$

$$5.00 = 4.74 + \log\frac{[OAc^-]}{[HOAc]} \quad \text{so that} \quad 0.26 = \log\frac{[OAc^-]}{[HOAc]}$$

In order to make a buffer with pH = 5.00 we must ensure that the $[OAc^-]/[HOAc]$ ratio is antilog(0.26) = 1.82.

No. mmol HOAc at start = (50.00 mL)(1.00 F) = 50.00 mmol

Let V = volume, in mL, of 1.00 F KOH added

No. mmol OH^- added = (V mL)(1.00 F) = V mmol

No. mmol OAc^- formed = No. mmol HOAc used up = V mmol

No. mmol HOAc in excess = 50.00 - V

$$\frac{[OAc^-]}{[HOAc]} = \frac{V}{50.00 - V} = 1.82$$

Hence V = 91.0 - 1.82V, or 2.82V = 91.0 and V = 32.3 mL

Add 32.3 mL of 1.00 F KOH to 50.00 mL of 1.00 F HOAc and the resulting solution will be an $HOAc/OAc^-$ buffer with pH = 5.00.

10.10. (a) $H_3O^+ + HCOO^- \rightleftharpoons HCOOH + H_2O$

No. mmol H_3O^+ at start = (500.0 mL)(0.500 M) = 250 mmol

No. mmol $HCOO^-$ at start = 750 mmol

The reaction goes virtually to completion because HCOOH is a weak acid. Thus 250 mmol H_3O^+ react with 250 mmol $HCOO^-$ to produce 250 mmol HCOOH, leaving 750 - 250 = 500 mmol in excess, in a volume of 500.00 mL.

$$HCOOH + H_2O \rightleftharpoons HCOO^- + H_3O^+$$

Let $x = [H_3O^+]$ at equilibrium

$$\text{Then} \quad [HCOO^-] = \frac{500 \text{ mmol}}{500 \text{ mL}} + x = 1.00 + x$$

$$[HCOOH] = \frac{250 \text{ mmol}}{500 \text{ mL}} - x = 0.500 - x$$

$$K_a = 1.8 \times 10^{-4} = \frac{[H_3O^+][HCOO^-]}{[HCOOH]} = \frac{(x)(1.00 + x)}{(0.500 - x)}$$

Assume x<10% of 0.500. Then 0.500 - x ~ 0.500 and 1.00 + x ~ 1.00

$$1.8 \times 10^{-4} = x\frac{(1.00)}{(0.500)} \quad \text{and} \quad x = 9.0 \times 10^{-5}$$

Check: Is $9.0 \times 10^{-5} < 10\%$ of 0.500? Yes, $9.0 \times 10^{-5} < 5.0 \times 10^{-2}$

Hence, $[H_3O^+] = 9.0 \times 10^{-5}$ M

$$[HCOO^-] = 1.00 + 9.0 \times 10^{-5} = 1.00 \text{ M}$$

$$[HCOOH] = 0.500 + 9.0 \times 10^{-5} = 0.500 \text{ M}$$

$$[OH^-] = 1.0 \times 10^{-14}/(9.0 \times 10^{-5}) = 1.1 \times 10^{-10} \text{ M}$$

(b) Since the $[HCOO^-]/[HCOOH]$ ratio is $1.00/0.500 = 2$, which is larger than 1/10 but smaller than 10, this is an effective buffer.

10.11. (a) Both Cl^- and Na^+ are bystander (spectator) ions and take no part in any reaction.

No. mmol Cl^- added = (100.00 mL)(0.300 M) = 30.0 mmol

No. mmol Na^+ added = (50.00 mL)(0.240 M) = 12.0 mmol

Volume of solution = 150.00 mL

$$[Cl^-] = \frac{30.0 \text{ mmol}}{150.00 \text{ mL}} = 0.200 \text{ M}$$

$$[Na^+] = \frac{12.0 \text{ mmol}}{150.00 \text{ mL}} = 0.0800 \text{ M}$$

No. mmol $NH_4{}^+$ added = No. mmol Cl^- added = 30.0 mmol

No. mmol OH^- added = No. mmol Na^+ added = 12.0 mmol

$$NH_4{}^+ + OH^- \rightleftharpoons NH_3 + H_2O$$

This reaction goes virtually to completion as NH_3 is a weak base. Thus 12.0 mmol OH^- react with 12.0 mmol $NH_4{}^+$, producing 12.0 mmol NH_3 and leaving (30.0 - 12.0) = 18.0 mmol $NH_4{}^+$ in excess, in a volume of 150.00 mL.

$$NH_3 + H_2O \rightleftharpoons NH_4{}^+ + OH^-$$

Let $x = [OH^-]$ at equilibrium

Then $$[NH_4^+] = \frac{18.0\ \text{mmol}}{150.00\ \text{mL}} + x = 0.120 + x$$

$$[NH_3] = \frac{12.0\ \text{mmol}}{150.00\ \text{mL}} - x = 0.0800 - x$$

$$K_b(NH_3) = \frac{[NH_4^+][OH^-]}{[NH_3]} = 1.8\text{x}10^{-5} = \frac{(0.120 + x)(x)}{(0.0800 - x)}$$

Assume $x < 10\%$ of 0.0800. Then $0.0800 - x \sim 0.0800$ and $0.120 + x \sim 0.120$

$$1.8\text{x}10^{-5} = \frac{0.120x}{0.0800} \quad \text{and} \quad x = \tfrac{2}{3}(1.8\text{x}10^{-5}) = 1.2\text{x}10^{-5}\ M$$

Check: Is $1.2\text{x}10^{-5} < 10\%$ of 0.0800? Yes, $1.2\text{x}10^{-5} < 8.0\text{x}10^{-3}$

Hence $$[OH^-] = 1.2\text{x}10^{-5}\ M$$

$$[NH_4^+] = 0.120 + 1.2\text{x}10^{-5} = 0.120\ M$$

$$[NH_3] = 0.0800 - 1.2\text{x}10^{-5} = 0.0800\ M$$

$$[H_3O^+] = 1.0\text{x}10^{-14}/(1.2\text{x}10^{-5}) = 8.3\text{x}10^{-10}\ M$$

$$pH = -\log(8.3\text{x}10^{-10}) = 9.08$$

(b) Since the $[NH_3]/[NH_4^+]$ ratio is $0.0800/0.120 = 2/3$, which is larger than 1/10 but smaller than 10, this is an effective buffer.

10.12.

(a) $CH_3NH_2 + HCOOH \rightleftharpoons CH_3NH_3^+ + HCOO^-$

(b) $2NH_4^+ + SO_4^{2-} + Ba^{2+} + 2OH^- \rightleftharpoons 2NH_3 + 2H_2O + BaSO_4\downarrow$

(c) $Ag_2CO_3(s) + 2H_3O^+ \rightleftharpoons 2Ag^+ + 3H_2O + CO_2\uparrow$

(d) $NH_4^+ + OH^- \rightleftharpoons NH_3 + H_2O$

(e) $HCO_3^- + H_3O^+ \rightleftharpoons 2H_2O + CO_2\uparrow$

(f) $HCO_3^- + OH^- \rightleftharpoons H_2O + CO_3^{2-}$

10.13. Let the unknown acid be denoted HA. The titration reaction is $HA + OH^- \rightleftharpoons A^- + H_2O$.

No. mmol OH^- added = No. mmol A^- formed = 3.748 mmol

No. mmol H_3O^+ added = 1.874 mmol

$$H_3O^+ + A^- \rightleftharpoons HA + H_2O$$

Therefore 1.874 mmol H_3O^+ react with 1.874 mmol A^- to produce 1.874 mmol HA, leaving 3.748 - 1.874 = 1.874 mmol A^- in excess.

$$\frac{[A^-]}{[HA]} = \frac{1.874}{1.874} = \frac{1}{1}$$

$$pH = pK_a + \log\frac{[A^-]}{[HA]} = pK_a + \log(1) = pK_a$$

Hence $pK_a = 4.13$ and $K_a = 10^{-4.13} = 7.4x10^{-5}$

10.14.(a) $[OAc^-]/[HOAc] = 6.00/8.00 = 3/4$

$pH = pK_a(HOAc) + \log(3/4) = 4.74 - 0.12 = 4.62$

(b) No. mol OH^- added = (30.00 mL)(0.100 M) = 3.00

No. mmol HOAc added = (70.00 mL)(0.100 M) = 7.00

$$OH^- + HOAc \rightleftharpoons H_2O + OAc^-$$

Thus 3.00 mmol OH^- react with 3.00 mmol HOAc to produce 3.00 mmol OAc^-, leaving (7.00 - 3.00) = 4.00 mmol HOAc in excess. Therefore

$$[OAc^-]/[HOAc] = 3.00/4.00$$

and $$pH = pK_a + \log(3/4) = 4.62$$

as in part (a). Note that the buffers prepared by the two methods are identical.

10.15. Addie has not made a buffer at all. She has mixed a strong acid, H_3O^+, and a weak acid, NH_4^+.

Barney has made a 1:1 $HOAc/OAc^-$ buffer, since he mixed 5.00 mmol OAc^- with 5.00 mmol HOAc.

$$pH = pK_a(HOAc) + \log(1) = -\log(1.8\times10^{-5}) + 0 = 4.74$$

Thus Barney's procedure is correct.

Cecile mixed 2.50 mmol OH^- with 5.00 mmol HOAc. They react as follows: $OH^- + HOAc \rightleftharpoons H_2O + OAc^-$

Thus 2.50 mmol OH^- react with 2.50 mmol HOAc to produce 2.50 mmol OAc^-, leaving 5.00 - 2.50 = 2.50 mmol HOAc in excess. Cecile, like Barney, has prepared a 1:1 $HOAc/OAc^-$ buffer. Her procedure is correct.

Dawn has mixed 8.00 mmol HCOOH with 2.00 mmol $HCOO^-$. She has made a buffer with $[HCOO^-]/[HCOOH]$ = 2.00/8.00 = 1/4.

$$pH = pK_a(HCOOH) + \log(1/4) = 3.74 - 0.60 = 3.14$$

Since the pH of Dawn's buffer is not between 4.6 and 5.0, her procedure is not correct.

Errol has mixed 5.00 mmol NH_4^+ with 5.00 mmol NH_3. He has made a 1:1 NH_4^+/NH_3 buffer.

$$pH = pK_a(NH_4^+) + \log(1) = -\log(5.7\times10^{-10}) + 0 = 9.24$$

Since the pH of Errol's buffer is far outside the desired range, his procedure is not correct.

Faye has mixed 8.00 mmol OAc^- with 4.00 mmol HOAc. She has made an $HOAc/OAc^-$ buffer with an $[OAc^-]/[HOAc]$ ratio of

8.00/4.00 = 2. The pH of her buffer is

$$pH = pK_a(HOAc) + \log(2) = 4.74 + 0.30 = 5.04$$

The pH of Faye's buffer is not between 4.6 and 5.0, but just slightly larger than 5.0. (She would probably receive partial credit on a lab practical exam!)

10.16. (a)

$$K_b = \frac{\alpha^2 C}{1 - \alpha} = \frac{(0.0633)^2(0.150)}{1 - 0.0633} = \frac{6.01\text{x}10^{-4}}{0.9367} = 6.42\text{x}10^{-4}$$

(b) In this buffer the $[C_2H_5NH_2]/[C_2H_5NH_3^+]$ ratio is 0.090/0.120 = 3/4.

$$pH = pK_a(C_2H_5NH_3^+) + \log(3/4)$$

$$K_a(C_2H_5NH_3^+) = K_w/K_b(C_2H_5NH_2) = 1.0\text{x}10^{-14}/(6.42\text{x}10^{-4})$$

$$= 1.56\text{x}10^{-11}$$

$$pH = -\log(1.56\text{x}10^{-11}) + \log(3/4) = 10.81 - 0.12 = 10.69$$

10.17. (a) $HOAc + OH^- \rightleftharpoons H_2O + OAc^-$

$$K_{eq} = \frac{[OAc^-]}{[HOAc][OH^-]} = \frac{[OAc^-][H_3O^+]}{[HOAc][OH^-][H_3O^+]} = \frac{K_a(HOAc)}{K_w}$$

$$= 1.8\text{x}10^{-5}/(1.0\text{x}10^{-14}) = 1.8\text{x}10^{+9}$$

(b) $NH_3 + H_3O^+ \rightleftharpoons NH_4^+ + H_2O$

$$K_{eq} = \frac{[NH_4^+]}{[NH_3][H_3O^+]} = \frac{[NH_4^+][OH^-]}{[NH_3][H_3O^+][OH^-]} = \frac{K_b(NH_3)}{K_w}$$

$$= 1.8\text{x}10^{-5}/(1.0\text{x}10^{-14}) = 1.8\text{x}10^{+9}$$

Note that both of these titration reactions have very large equilibrium constants, i.e., $K_{eq} >> 1$. For the equivalence point of a titration to be easy to determine, K_{eq} for the titration reaction must be very much larger than 1.

10.18. Only Riva has proposed an appropriate procedure. The weak acid of her conjugate pair is NH_4^+, and $pK_a(NH_4^+)$ = 9.24. pH values between 8.8 and 9.0 are within 1 pH unit of 9.24.

Pansy's buffers will be too acidic, since $pK_a(HOAc)$ = 4.74 and effective $HOAc/OAc^-$ buffers have pH values between 3.74 and 5.74.

Quincy's buffers will be too basic, since $pK_a(HCO_3^-) = -\log(4.7\times10^{-11}) = 10.33$. Effective HCO_3^-/CO_3^{2-} buffers have pH values between 9.33 and 11.33, outside the desired range.

10.19. (a)

No. mmol N_2H_4 at start = (60.00 mL)(0.100 M) = 6.00 mmol

No. mmol H_3O^+ added = (20.00 mL)(0.150 M) = 3.00 mmol

Thus 3.00 mmol H_3O^+ react with 3.00 mmol N_2H_4 to produce 3.00 mmol $N_2H_5^+$ (hydrazinium ion), leaving (6.00 - 3.00) = 3.00 mmol N_2H_4 untitrated.

$$\frac{[N_2H_4]}{[N_2H_5^+]} = \frac{\text{No. mmol } N_2H_4 \text{ untitrated}}{\text{No. mmmol } N_2H_5^+ \text{ formed}} = \frac{3.00}{3.00} = 1$$

This is, therefore, the halfway point in the titration, and $pH = pK_a(N_2H_5^+)$.

$$K_a(N_2H_5^+) = K_w/K_b(N_2H_4) = 1.0\times10^{-14}/(3.0\times10^{-6}) = 3.3\times10^{-9}$$

$$pK_a(N_2H_5^+) = -\log(3.33\times10^{-9}) = 8.48$$

When 20.0 mL of 0.150 M H_3O^+ have been added, pH = 8.48.

(b) Let V = volume, in mL, of 0.150 F HCl needed to reach the equivalence point.

$$(V)(0.150\ M) = (60.00\ mL)(0.100\ M) = 6.00$$

$$V = 6.00/0.150 = 40.00\ mL$$

Alternatively, one could have reasoned from the work in part (a), that if adding 20.00 mL of the acid gets us to the halfway point in the titration, it requires 40.00 mL to reach the equivalence point. At the equivalence point there are 6.00 mmol $N_2H_5^+$ in 100.00 mL of solution.

$$N_2H_5^+ + H_2O \rightleftharpoons N_2H_4 + H_3O^+$$

$$K_a(N_2H_5^+) = 3.3x10^{-9} = \frac{[N_2H_4][H_3O^+]}{[N_2H_5^+]}$$

Let $x = [N_2H_4] = [H_3O^+]$ at the equivalence point

Then $$[N_2H_5^+] = \frac{6.00\ mmol}{100.00\ mL} - x = 0.0600 - x$$

and $$3.3x10^{-9} = \frac{x^2}{0.0600 - x}$$

Assume x < 10% of 0.0600. Then $0.0600 - x \sim 0.0600$, and

$$x^2 = (3.3x10^{-9})(6.00x10^{-2}) = 1.98x10^{-10}$$

$$x = 1.4x10^{-5}$$

Check: Is $1.4x10^{-5}$ < 10% of 0.060? Yes, $1.4x10^{-5} < 6.0x10^{-3}$

$$[H_3O^+] = 1.4x10^{-5}\ M \quad \text{and} \quad pH = -\log(1.4x10^{-5}) = 4.85$$

The pH at the equivalence point in this titration of hydrazine, a weak base, versus a strong acid is 4.85.

(c) Either bromcresol green or methyl red could be used for this titration.

Solutions to Exercises, Chapter 11

1. $K_{sp} = [Ag^+][BrO_3^-]$; $K_{sp} = [Zn^{2+}][OH^-]^2$;

$K_{sp} = [Cu^{2+}][IO_3^-]^2$; $K_{sp} = [Sr^{2+}][CrO_4^{2-}]$;

$K_{sp} = [Ag^+][SCN^-]$; $K_{sp} = [Ca^{2+}][C_2O_4^{2-}]$

2. $Hg_2SO_4(s) \rightleftharpoons Hg_2^{2+}(aq) + SO_4^{2-}(aq)$

$PbCO_3(s) \rightleftharpoons Pb^{2+}(aq) + CO_3^{2-}(aq)$

$AgIO_3(s) \rightleftharpoons Ag^+(aq) + IO_3^-(aq)$

$Cr(OH)_3(s) \rightleftharpoons Cr^{3+}(aq) + 3OH^-(aq)$

$La(IO_3)_3(s) \rightleftharpoons La^{3+}(aq) + 3IO_3^-(aq)$

3. (a) TRUE (b) TRUE (c) TRUE (d) False. The units of a solubility product depend on the type of electrolyte. Only 1:1 electrolytes, such as AgCl, CuS, or $PbSO_4$, have units M^2. Electrolytes such as Ag_2S or PbI_2 (2:1 or 1:2 electrolytes) have units M^3 and 1:3 electrolytes such as $Al(OH)_3$ have units M^4.

4. **(a)** $AgBr(s) \rightleftharpoons Ag^+(aq) + Br^-(aq)$

Let s = molar solubility of AgBr in H_2O

Then $[Ag^+] = [Br^-] = s$ and $K_{sp} = [Ag^+][Br^-] = s^2$

$s^2 = 5.0\times10^{-13}$ and $s = 7.1\times10^{-7}$ M

(b) $Ba(IO_3)_2(s) \rightleftharpoons Ba^{2+}(aq) + 2IO_3^-(aq)$

Let s = molar solubility of $Ba(IO_3)_2$ in H_2O

Then $[Ba^{2+}] = s$ and $[IO_3^-] = 2s$

$K_{sp} = [Ba^{2+}][IO_3^-]^2 = (s)(2s)^2 = 4s^3 = 6\times10^{-10}$

$s^3 = 1.5\times10^{-10} = 150\times10^{-12}$ and $s = 5.3\times10^{-4}$ M

(c) $SrSO_4(s) \rightleftharpoons Sr^{2+}(aq) + SO_4{}^{2-}(aq)$

Let x = molar solubility of $SrSO_4$ in H_2O

Then $[Sr^{2+}] = [SO_4{}^{2-}] = x$

$$K_{sp} = [Sr^{2+}][SO_4{}^{2-}] = x^2 = 2.8\text{x}10^{-7} = 28\text{x}10^{-8}$$

$$x = 5.3\text{x}10^{-4}\ M$$

(d) $PbI_2(s) \rightleftharpoons Pb^{2+}(aq) + 2I^-(aq)$

Let z = molar solubility of PbI_2 in H_2O

Then $[Pb^{2+}] = z$ and $[I^-] = 2z$

$$K_{sp} = [Pb^{2+}][I^-]^2 = (z)(2z)^2 = 4z^3 = 8.7\text{x}10^{-9}$$

$$z^3 = 2.2\text{x}10^{-9} \quad \text{and} \quad z = 1.3\text{x}10^{-3}\ M$$

5. (a) $AgIO_3(s) \rightleftharpoons Ag^+(aq) + IO_3^-(aq)$

Let s = molar solubility of $AgIO_3$ in H_2O

Then $[Ag^+] = s$ and $[IO_3^-] = s$

$$K_{sp} = [Ag^+][IO_3^-] = s^2 = 3\text{x}10^{-8} \quad \text{and} \quad s = 1.7\text{x}10^{-4}\ M$$

Formula weight of $AgIO_3$ = 282.771 g/mol

$$(1.7\text{x}10^{-4}\ \text{mol/L})(282.771\ \text{g/mol}) = 4.8\text{x}10^{-2}\ \text{g/L} = 5\text{x}10^{-2}\ \text{g/L}$$

The solubility of $AgIO_3$ in grams per 100 mL of solution is therefore $5\text{x}10^{-3}$, or 0.005 g per 100 mL.

(b) $PbBr_2(s) \rightleftharpoons Pb^{2+}(aq) + 2Br^-(aq)$

Let y = molar solubility of $PbBr_2$ in H_2O

Then $[Pb^{2+}] = y$ and $[Br^-] = 2y$

$$K_{sp} = [Pb^{2+}][Br^-]^2 = (y)(2y)^2 = 4y^3 = 6.3\text{x}10^{-6}$$

$$y^3 = 1.58\text{x}10^{-6} \quad \text{and} \quad y = 1.16\text{x}10^{-2} = 1.2\text{x}10^{-2}\ M$$

Formula weight of $PbBr_2$ = 367.0 g/mol

$$(1.16\times10^{-2}\ mol/L)(367.0\ g/mol) = 4.26\ g/L$$

The solubility of $PbBr_2$ is therefore 0.43 g per 100 mL.

6. (a) $PbSO_4(s) \rightleftharpoons Pb^{2+}(aq) + SO_4^{2-}(aq)$

Let s = molar solubility of $PbSO_4$ in H_2O

Then $[Pb^{2+}] = [SO_4^{2-}] = s$ and $K_{sp} = [Pb^{2+}][SO_4^{2-}] = s^2$

$$s = (K_{sp})^{1/2}$$

(b) $Ce(IO_3)_3(s) \rightleftharpoons Ce^{3+}(aq) + 3IO_3^-(aq)$

Let s = molar solubility of $Ce(IO_3)_3$ in H_2O

Then $[Ce^{3+}] = s$ and $[IO_3^-] = 3s$

$$K_{sp} = [Ce^{3+}][IO_3^-]^3 = (s)(3s)^3 = 27s^4$$

$$s = (K_{sp}/27)^{1/4}$$

(c) $Zn(OH)_2(s) \rightleftharpoons Zn^{2+}(aq) + 2OH^-(aq)$

Let s = molar solubility of $Zn(OH)_2$ in H_2O

Then $[Zn^{2+}] = s$ and $[OH^-] = 2s$

$$K_{sp} = [Zn^{2+}][OH^-]^2 = (s)(2s)^2 = 4s^3$$

$$s = (K_{sp}/4)^{1/3}$$

(d) $AgBrO_3(s) \rightleftharpoons Ag^+(aq) + BrO_3^-(aq)$

Let s = molar solubility of $AgBrO_3^-$ in H_2O

Then $[Ag^+] = [BrO_3^-] = s$ and $K_{sp} = [Ag^+][BrO_3^-] = s^2$

$$s = (K_{sp})^{1/2}$$

(e) $Hg_2I_2(s) \rightleftharpoons Hg_2^{2+}(aq) + 2I^-(aq)$

Let s = molar solubility of Hg_2I_2 in H_2O

Then $[Hg_2^{2+}] = s$ and $[I^-] = 2s$

$K_{sp} = [Hg_2^{2+}][I^-]^2 = (s)(2s)^2 = 4s^3$ and $s = (K_{sp}/4)^{1/3}$

7. (a) $AgI(s) \rightleftharpoons Ag^+(aq) + I^-(aq)$

Let y = molar solubility of AgI in 0.15 F NaI

Then $[Ag^+] = y$ and $[I^-] = 0.15 + y$

$$K_{sp} = [Ag^+][I^-] = y(0.15 + y)$$

If y < 10% of 0.15, then $y = K_{sp}/0.15$

(b) $PbI_2(s) \rightleftharpoons Pb^{2+}(aq) + 2I^-(aq)$

Let y = molar solubility of PbI_2 in 0.15 F NaI

Then $[Pb^{2+}] = y$ and $[I^-] = 0.15 + 2y$

$$K_{sp} = [Pb^{2+}][I^-]^2 = (y)(0.15 + 2y)^2$$

If 2y < 10% of 0.15 then $y = K_{sp}/(0.15)^2 = K_{sp}/0.0225$

(c) $Hg_2I_2(s) \rightleftharpoons Hg_2{}^{2+}(aq) + 2I^-(aq)$

Let y = molar solubility of Hg_2I_2 in 0.15 F NaI

Then $[Hg_2{}^{2+}] = y$ and $[I^-] = 0.15 + 2y$

$$K_{sp} = [Hg_2{}^{2+}][I^-]^2 = (y)(0.15 + 2y)^2$$

If 2y < 10% of 0.15 then $y = K_{sp}/(0.15)^2 = K_{sp}/0.0225$

8. (a) $PbCl_2(s) \rightleftharpoons Pb^{2+}(aq) + 2Cl^-(aq)$

Let z = molar solubility of $PbCl_2$ in 0.086 F $Pb(NO_3)_2$

Then $[Pb^{2+}] = z + 0.086$ and $[Cl^-] = 2z$

$$K_{sp} = [Pb^{2+}][Cl^-]^2 = (z + 0.086)(2z)^2$$

If z < 10% of 0.086, then $(0.086)(4z^2) = 0.344z^2 = K_{sp}$

$$z = (K_{sp}/0.344)^{1/2}$$

(b) $PbSO_4(s) \rightleftharpoons Pb^{2+}(aq) + SO_4{}^{2-}(aq)$

Let z = molar solubility of $PbSO_4$ in 0.086 F $Pb(NO_3)_2$

Then $[Pb^{2+}] = 0.086 + z$ and $[SO_4{}^{2-}] = z$

$$K_{sp} = [Pb^{2+}][SO_4^{2-}] = (0.086 + z)(z)$$

If $z < 10\%$ of 0.086, then $z = K_{sp}/0.086$

(c) $$PbC_2O_4(s) \rightleftharpoons Pb^{2+}(aq) + C_2O_4^{2-}(aq)$$

Let z = molar solubility of PbC_2O_4 in 0.086 F $Pb(NO_3)_2$

Then $[Pb^{2+}] = 0.086 + z$ and $[C_2O_4^{2-}] = z$

$$K_{sp} = [Pb^{2+}][C_2O_4^{2-}] = (0.086 + z)(z)$$

If $z < 10\%$ of 0.086, then $z = K_{sp}/0.086$

(d) $$Pb(OH)_2(s) \rightleftharpoons Pb^{2+}(aq) + 2OH^-(aq)$$

Let z = molar solubility of $Pb(OH)_2$ in 0.086 F $Pb(NO_3)_2$

Then $[Pb^{2+}] = 0.086 + z$ and $[OH^-] = 2z$

$$K_{sp} = [Pb^{2+}][OH^-]^2 = (0.086 + z)(2z)^2$$

If $z < 10\%$ of 0.086, then $(0.086)(4z^2) = 0.344z^2 = K_{sp}$

$$z = (K_{sp}/0.344)^{1/2}$$

9. $$AgI(s) \rightleftharpoons Ag^+(aq) + I^-(aq)$$

Let x = molar solubility of AgI in 0.20 F KI

Then $[Ag^+] = x$ and $[I^-] = 0.20 + x$

$$K_{sp} = [Ag^+][I^-] = 1.5\times10^{-16} = (x)(0.20 + x)$$

Assume $x < 10\%$ of 0.20. Then $0.20 + x \sim 0.20$,

$$(x)(0.20) = 1.5\times10^{-16} \quad \text{and} \quad x = 7.5\times10^{-16}$$

Check: Is $7.5\times10^{-16} < 10\%$ of 0.20? Yes, $7.5\times10^{-16} < 2.0\times10^{-2}$

Hence $[Ag^+] = 7.5\times10^{-16}$ M, $[I^-] = 0.20$ M, and the molar solubility of AgI in 0.20 F KI is 7.5×10^{-16} mol per liter.

10. Formula weight of Cd(OH)2 = 146.42 g/mol

If the solubility is 2.6×10^{-4} g per 100 mL, it is 2.6×10^{-3}

g per liter, or

$$\frac{2.6\times10^{-3}\ g/L}{146.42\ g/mol} = 1.78\times10^{-5}\ mol/L$$

$$Cd(OH)_2(s) \rightleftharpoons Cd^{2+}(aq) + 2OH^-(aq)$$

$$[Cd^{2+}] = 1.78\times10^{-5}\ M \quad \text{and} \quad [OH^-] = 3.55\times10^{-5}\ M$$

$$K_{sp} = [Cd^{2+}][OH^-]^2 = (1.78\times10^{-5})(3.55\times10^{-5})^2$$

$$= (1.78)(3.55)^2\times10^{-15} = 2.2\times10^{-14}$$

11. Formula weight of $SrSO_4$ = 183.68 g/mol

If the solubility is 0.0113 g per 100 mL, it is 0.113 g/L

or $$\frac{0.113\ g/L}{183.68\ g/mol} = 6.152\times10^{-4}\ mol/L$$

$$SrSO_4(s) \rightleftharpoons Sr^{2+}(aq) + SO_4{}^{2-}(aq)$$

$$K_{sp} = [Sr^{2+}][SO_4{}^{2-}] = (6.152\times10^{-4})^2 = 3.8\times10^{-7}$$

12. $$Ba(IO_3)_2(s) \rightleftharpoons Ba^{2+}(aq) + 2IO_3{}^-(aq)$$

Let x = molar solubility of $Ba(IO_3)_2$ in 0.125 F KIO_3

Then $[Ba^{2+}] = x$ and $[IO_3^-] = 0.125 + 2x$

$$K_{sp} = [Ba^{2+}][IO_3^-]^2 = (x)(0.125 + 2x)^2 = 6\times10^{-10}$$

Assume 2x < 10% of 0.125. Then $0.125 + 2x \sim 0.125$, and

$$6\times10^{-10} = x(0.125)^2 = (x)(1.56\times10^{-2})$$

$$x = 6\times10^{-10}/(1.56\times10^{-2}) = 3.8\times10^{-8} = 4\times10^{-8}\ M$$

Check: Is $2(4\times10^{-8})$ < 10% of 0.125? Yes, $8\times10^{-8} < 1.25\times10^{-2}$

Therefore the molar solubility of $Ba(IO_3)_2$ in 0.125 F KIO_3 is 4×10^{-8} mol per liter.

13. $$AgBr(s) \rightleftharpoons Ag^+(aq) + Br^-(aq)$$

Let s = molar solubility AgBr in H_2O

$$\text{Then } [Ag^+] = [Br^-] = s \quad \text{and} \quad K_{sp} = [Ag^+][Br^-] = s^2$$

$$s^2 = 5.0\times10^{-13} \quad \text{and} \quad s = 7.1\times10^{-7}\ M$$

Let x = molar solubility AgBr in 0.12 F KBr

$$\text{Then } [Ag^+] = x \quad \text{and} \quad [Br^-] = 0.12 + x$$

$$K_{sp} = [Ag^+][Br^-] = 5.0\times10^{-13} = (x)(0.12 + x)$$

Assume x < 10% of 0.12. Then $0.12 + x \sim 0.12$ and

$$x = 5.0\times10^{-13}/(0.12) = 4.2\times10^{-12}$$

Check: Is 4.2×10^{-12} < 10% of 0.12? Yes, $4.2\times10^{-12} < 1.2\times10^{-2}$

Therefore the molar solubility of AgBr in 0.12 F KBr is 4.2×10^{-12} M. Note that the molar solubility has decreased from 7.1×10^{-7} M in pure water to 4.2×10^{-12} in 0.12 F KBr, a factor of 170,000 times smaller! This is an example of the common ion effect: the solubility of a slightly soluble electrolyte is smaller in a solution containing an ion in common with the slightly soluble electrolyte than it is in pure water.

14. $$Mn(OH)_2(s) \rightleftharpoons Mn^{2+}(aq) + 2OH^-(aq)$$

Let s = molar solubility of $Mn(OH)_2$ in pure water

$$\text{Then } [Mn^{2+}] = s \quad \text{and} \quad [OH^-] = 2s$$

$$K_{sp} = [Mn^{2+}][OH^-]^2 = (s)(2s)^2 = 4s^3 = 4.5\times10^{-14}$$

$$s^3 = 1.1\times10^{-14} = 11\times10^{-15} \quad \text{and} \quad s = 2.2\times10^{-5}\ M$$

Let x = molar solubility of $Mn(OH)_2$ in 0.10 F $Mn(NO_3)_2$

$$\text{Then } [Mn^{2+}] = 0.10 + x \quad \text{and} \quad [OH^-] = 2x$$

$$K_{sp} = (0.10 + x)(2x)^2 = 4.5\times10^{-14}$$

Assume x < 10% of 0.10. Then $0.10 + x \sim 0.10$,

$$(0.10)(4x^2) = 4.5\text{x}10^{-14} \quad \text{and} \quad x^2 = 11.25\text{x}10^{-14}$$

$$x = 3.4\text{x}10^{-7} \text{ M}$$

Check: Is $3.4\text{x}10^{-7} < 10\%$ of 0.10? Yes, $3.4\text{x}10^{-7} < 1.0\text{x}10^{-2}$

Note that the molar solubility has decreased from $2.2\text{x}10^{-5}$ in water to $3.4\text{x}10^{-7}$ M in 0.10 F $Mn(NO_3)_2$. This decrease by a factor of 65 is another example of the common ion effect.

15. **(a)** $Pb^{2+}(aq) + CrO_4{}^{2-}(aq) \rightleftharpoons PbCrO_4\downarrow$

(b) $S^{2-}(aq) + 2Ag^+(aq) \rightleftharpoons Ag_2S\downarrow$

(c) $Ba^{2+}(aq) + C_2O_4{}^{2-}(aq) \rightleftharpoons BaC_2O_4\downarrow$

(d) $Zn^{2+}(aq) + S^{2-}(aq) \rightleftharpoons ZnS\downarrow$

(e) $2PO_4{}^{3-}(aq) + 3Ca^{2+}(aq) \rightleftharpoons Ca_3(PO_4)_2\downarrow$

(f) $Cu^{2+}(aq) + 2IO_3^-(aq) \rightleftharpoons Cu(IO_3)_2\downarrow$

16. The volume of solution after mixing is 100.00 mL. Thus $[Ag^+] = (0.10\text{ M})(50.00\text{ mL})/(100.00\text{ mL}) = 5.0\text{x}10^{-2}$ M and $[SCN^-] = (0.10\text{ M})(50.00\text{ mL})/(100.00\text{ mL}) = 5.0\text{x}10^{-2}$ M

At the instant of mixing, $Q = [Ag^+][SCN^-] = (5.0\text{x}10^{-2})^2$

$$= 2.5\text{x}10^{-3} \gg K_{sp} = 1.0\text{x}10^{-12}$$

Since $Q > K_{sp}$, the reaction $AgSCN(s) \rightleftharpoons Ag^+(aq) + SCN^-(aq)$ must go to the left to achieve equilibrium, and AgSCN precipitates.

17. The volume of solution after mixing is 50.00 mL. Thus $[Ag^+] = (30.00\text{ mL})(0.075\text{ M})/(50.00\text{ mL}) = 4.5\text{x}10^{-2}$ M and $[OAc^-] = (20.00\text{ mL})(0.050\text{ M})/(50.00\text{ ml}) = 2.0\text{x}10^{-2}$ M

At the instant of mixing, $Q = [Ag^+][OAc^-] = 9.0x10^{-4}$. Since $Q < K_{sp} = 2.3x10^{-3}$, no silver acetate will precipitate.

18. The volume of solution after mixing is 60.00 mL. Thus $[IO_3^-] = (20.00 \text{ ml})(0.18 \text{ M})/(60.00 \text{ mL}) = 0.060 \text{ M}$

and $[Ba^{2+}] = (40.00 \text{ mL})(0.12 \text{ M})/(60.00 \text{ mL}) = 0.080 \text{ M}$

At the instant of mixing,

$$Q = [Ba^{2+}][IO_3^-]^2 = (0.080)(0.060)^2 = 2.9x10^{-4} > 6x10^{-10}$$

Since $Q >> K_{sp}$, the reaction $Ba(IO_3)_2(s) \rightleftharpoons Ba^{2+} + 2IO_3^-$ must proceed to the left to reach equilibrium, and $Ba(IO_3)_2$ precipitates.

19. The volume of solution after mixing is 100.00 mL. Thus $[Pb^{2+}] = (80.00 \text{ mL})(0.052 \text{ M})/(100.00 \text{ mL}) = 4.16x10^{-2} \text{ M}$

and $[Cl^-] = (20.00 \text{ mL})(0.035 \text{ M})/(100.00 \text{ mL}) = 7.0x10^{-3} \text{ M}$

At the instant of mixing,

$Q = [Pb^{2+}][Cl^-]^2 = (4.16x10^{-2})(7.0x10^{-3})^2 = (4.16)(49)x10^{-8}$

$$Q = 2.0x10^{-6} < 1.6x10^{-5} = K_{sp}(PbCl_2)$$

Since $Q < K_{sp}$, no $PbCl_2$ precipitates.

20. No. mmol Ca^{2+} added = (40.00 mL)(0.100 M) = 4.00

No. mmol $CO_3{}^{2-}$ added = (10.00 mL)(0.200 M) = 2.00

Volume of solution after mixing = 50.00 mL

At the instant of mixing, $[Ca^{2+}]$ = 4.00 mmol/(50.00 mL) = 0.080 M and $[CO_3{}^{2-}]$ = 2.00 mmol/(50.00 mL) = 0.040 M. Thus $Q = [Ca^{2+}][CO_3{}^{2-}] = 3.2x10^{-3} >> K_{sp} = 4.8x10^{-9}$, so $CaCO_3$ precipitates. Since Ca^{2+} and $CO_3{}^{2-}$ react in a 1:1 molar ratio, 2.00 mmol of CO_3^{2-} combine with 2.00 mmol Ca^{2+} leaving 2.00 mmol Ca^{2+} in excess.

Let $x = [CO_3^{2-}]$ after the system has come to equilibrium

$$\text{Then } [Ca^{2+}] = \frac{2.00 \text{ mmol}}{50.00 \text{ mL}} + x = 0.0400 + x$$

$$K_{sp} = 4.8x10^{-9} = [Ca^{2+}][CO_3^{2-}] = (0.0400 + x)(x)$$

Assume $x < 10\%$ of 0.0400. Then $0.0400 + x \sim 0.0400$,

$$0.0400x = 4.8x10^{-9} \quad \text{and} \quad x = 1.2x10^{-7}$$

Check: Is $1.2x10^{-7} < 10\%$ of 0.0400? Yes, $1.2x10^{-7} < 4.0x10^{-3}$

$[Ca^{2+}] = 0.0400$ M and $[CO_3^{2-}] = 1.2x10^{-7}$ M at equilibrium

21. **(a)** $AgOAc(s) + H^+(aq) \rightleftharpoons HOAc + Ag^+(aq)$

(b) $Mg(OH)_2(s) + 2H^+(aq) \rightleftharpoons Mg^{2+}(aq) + 2H_2O$

(c) $CaC_2O_4(s) + 2H^+(aq) \rightleftharpoons Ca^{2+}(aq) + H_2C_2O_4$

or $CaC_2O_4(s) + H^+(aq) \rightleftharpoons Ca^{2+}(aq) + HC_2O_4^-$

(d) $FeS(s) + 2H^+(aq) \rightleftharpoons Fe^{2+}(aq) + H_2S$

Note: Ferrous ion, Fe^{2+}, is not stable in nitric acid but is oxidized to ferric ion, Fe^{3+}. Oxidation is discussed in Chapter 15.

(e) $PbCO_3(s) + 2H^+(aq) \rightleftharpoons Pb^{2+}(aq) + H_2O + CO_2\uparrow$

(f) $Hg_2(CN)_2(s) + 2H^+(aq) \rightleftharpoons 2HCN(g) + Hg_2^{2+}(aq)$

Note: Mercurous ion, Hg_2^{2+}, is not stable in nitric acid, but is oxidized to mercuric ion, Hg^{2+}. Oxidation is discussed in Chapter 15.

22. The dissolution reaction is

$$SrSO_4(s) + H_3O^+ \rightleftharpoons Sr^{2+}(aq) + HSO_4^-(aq) + H_2O$$

Let x = molar solubility of $SrSO_4$ in 1.20 F HNO_3

Then $[Sr^{2+}] = [HSO_4^-] = x$ and $[H_3O^+] = 1.20 - x$

$$K_{eq} = \frac{[Sr^{2+}][HSO_4^-]}{[H_3O^+]} = \frac{[Sr^{2+}][SO_4^{2-}][HSO_4^-]}{[H_3O^+][SO_4^{2-}]} = \frac{K_{sp}(SrSO_4)}{K_a(HSO_4^-)}$$

$$= \frac{2.8x10^{-7}}{1.2x10^{-2}} = 2.3x10^{-5}$$

Therefore $\frac{(x)(x)}{1.20 - x} = 2.3x10^{-5}$

Assume $x < 10\%$ of 1.20. Then $1.20 - x \sim 1.20$, and

$$x^2 = (2.3x10^{-5})(1.20) = 2.8x10^{-5} = 28x10^{-6}$$

$$x = 5.3x10^{-3} \text{ mol per liter}$$

Check: Is $5.3x10^{-3} < 10\%$ of 1.20? Yes, $5.3x10^{-3} < 1.20x10^{-1}$

Then $5.3x10^{-3}$ mol will dissolve in 1 L and $5.3x10^{-4}$ mol will dissolve in 100 mL. The formula weight of $SrSO_4$ is 183.68 g/mol. Thus the number of grams of $SrSO_4$ that will dissolve in 100.00 mL of 1.20F HNO_3 is

$$(5.3x10^{-4} \text{ mol})(183.68 \text{ g/mol}) = 0.097 \text{ g}$$

23. (a) $K_{eq} = \frac{[H_2S][Zn^{2+}]}{[H^+]^2} = \frac{[H_2S][Zn^{2+}][S^{2-}]}{[H^+]^2[S^{2-}]}$

$$K_{eq} = \frac{K_{sp}(ZnS)}{K_a(H_2S)\cdot K_a(HS^-)} = \frac{1.1x10^{-21}}{(1.0x10^{-7})(1.3x10^{-13})} = 8.5x10^{-2}$$

(b) $K_{eq} = \frac{[Ag^+][HCN]}{[H^+]} = \frac{[Ag^+][CN^-][HCN]}{[H^+][CN^-]} = \frac{K_{sp}(AgCN)}{K_a(HCN)}$

$$= \frac{1.2x10^{-16}}{4x10^{-10}} = 3x10^{-7}$$

(c) $$K_{eq} = \frac{[Ba^{2+}][HCO_3^-]}{[H^+]} = \frac{[Ba^{2+}][CO_3^{2-}][HCO_3^-]}{[H^+][CO_3{}^{2-}]}$$

$$= \frac{K_{sp}(BaCO_3)}{K_a(HCO_3^-)} = \frac{8.1\text{x}10^{-9}}{4.7\text{x}10^{-11}} = 1.7\text{x}10^2$$

(d) $$K_{eq} = \frac{[H_2S][Tl^+]^2}{[H^+]^2} = \frac{[H_2S][Tl^+]^2[S^{2-}]}{[H^+]^2[S^{2-}]}$$

$$K_{eq} = \frac{K_{sp}(Tl_2S)}{K_a(H_2S)\cdot K_a(HS^-)} = \frac{1\text{x}10^{-22}}{(1.0\text{x}10^{-7})(1.3\text{x}10^{-13})} = 8\text{x}10^{-3}$$

(e) $$K_{eq} = \frac{[Pb^{2+}][HSO_4^-]}{[H^+]} = \frac{[Pb^{2+}][SO_4^{2-}][HSO_4^-]}{[H^+][SO_4{}^{2-}]}$$

$$= \frac{K_{sp}(PbSO_4)}{K_a(HSO_4^-)} = \frac{1.8\text{x}10^{-8}}{1.2\text{x}10^{-2}} = 1.5\text{x}10^{-6}$$

24. (a) $$K_{eq} = \frac{[H^+]^2}{[H_2S][Cd^{2+}]} = \frac{[H^+]^2[S^{2-}]}{[H_2S][Cd^{2+}][S^{2-}]}$$

$$K_{eq} = \frac{K_a(H_2S)K_a(HS^-)}{K_{sp}(CdS)} = \frac{(1.0\text{x}10^{-7})(1.3\text{x}10^{-13})}{4\text{x}10^{-29}} = 3.2\text{x}10^8$$

(b) $$K_{eq} = \frac{[H^+]}{[Ag^+][HOAc]} = \frac{[H^+][OAc^-]}{[Ag^+][HOAc][OAc^-]} = \frac{K_a(HOAc)}{K_{sp}(AgOAc)}$$

$$= \frac{1.8\text{x}10^{-5}}{2.3\text{x}10^{-3}} = 7.8\text{x}10^{-3}$$

(c) $$K_{eq} = \frac{[SO_4^{2-}]}{[S^{2-}]} = \frac{[Pb^{2+}][SO_4^{2-}]}{[Pb^{2+}][S^{2-}]} = \frac{K_{sp}(PbSO_4)}{K_{sp}(PbS)}$$

$$= \frac{1.8\text{x}10^{-18}}{8\text{x}10^{-28}} = 2.2\text{x}10^9$$

25. $$K_a(H_2S)K_a(HS^-) = \frac{[H^+]^2[S^{2-}]}{[H_2S]} = (1.0\text{x}10^{-7})(1.3\text{x}10^{-13})$$

Thus $\frac{(1)^2[S^{2-}]}{(0.10)} = 1.3\text{x}10^{-20}$ and $[S^{2-}] = 1.3\text{x}10^{-21}$ M

$$Q = [Cd^{2+}][S^{2-}] = (0.10)(1.3\text{x}10^{-21}) = 1.3\text{x}10^{-22}$$

$K_{sp}(CdS) = 4\times10^{-29}$ Since $Q > K_{sp}$, CdS does precipitate.

26. (a) $$[SO_4^{2-}] = \frac{K_{sp}(BaSO_4)}{[Ba^{2+}]} = \frac{1.1\times10^{-10}}{(0.10)} = 1.1\times10^{-9}$$

(b) If 99.9% of all the Ba^{2+} originally present is in the precipitate, then 0.1% is still in solution.

$$[Ba^{2+}] = 0.1\% \text{ of } 0.10\ M = (0.001)(0.10\ M) = 1.0\times10^{-4}\ M$$

$$[SO_4^{2-}] = \frac{K_{sp}(BaSO_4)}{[Ba^{2+}]} = \frac{1.1\times10^{-10}}{1.0\times10^{-4}} = 1.1\times10^{-6}\ M$$

(c) $Q = [Ca^{2+}][SO_4^{2-}] = (0.10)(1.1\times10^{-6}) = 1.1\times10^{-7}$

$K_{sp}(CaSO_4) = 2.4\times10^{-5}$ Since $Q < K_{sp}$, no $CaSO_4$ will precipitate.

27. (a) If 99.9% of the Pb^{2+} is precipitated, then 0.1% is in solution, and $[Pb^{2+}] = (0.001)(0.10) = 1.0\times10^{-4}$ M.

$$K_{sp}(PbS) = [Pb^{2+}][S^{2-}] = 8\times10^{-28} = (1.0\times10^{-4})[S^{2-}]$$

$[S^{2-}] = 8\times10^{-24}$ M required to precipitate 99.9% of the Pb^{2+}

$Q = [Zn^{2+}][S^{2-}] = (0.12)(8\times10^{-24}) = 9.6\times10^{-25} < K_{sp}(ZnS)$, since $K_{sp}(ZnS) = 1.1\times10^{-21}$. Hence it is possible to precipitate 99.9% of the Pb^{2+} without precipitating any ZnS.

(b) The first trace of ZnS precipitate will appear when $[S^{2-}] = K_{sp}(ZnS)/[Zn^{2+}] = 1.1\times10^{-21}/(0.12) = 9.2\times10^{-22}$ M. As long as the $[S^{2-}]$ is less than 9.2×10^{-22} M, no ZnS will precipitate, but more than 99.9% of the Pb^{2+} will be precipitated. Thus we can effect an analytical separation of Pb^{2+} and Zn^{2+} by controlling the $[S^{2-}]$.

Solutions to Multiple Choice Questions, Chapter 11

1. **(b)** The mercurous ion is diatomic, Hg_2^{2+}.

2. **(a)** $$K_{eq} = \frac{[HX][M^+]}{[H^+]} = \frac{[HX][M^+][X^-]}{[H^+][X^-]} = \frac{K_{sp}(MX)}{K_a(HX)}$$

3. **(c)** $Mn(OH)_2(s) \rightleftharpoons Mn^{2+}(aq) + 2OH^-(aq)$

Let s = molar solubility of $Mn(OH)_2$ in water

Then $[Mn^{2+}] = s$ and $[OH^-] = 2s$

$$K_{sp} = [Mn^{2+}][OH^-]^2 = (s)(2s)^2 = 4s^3$$

4. **(d)** Option (a) is incorrect because KCl is a soluble salt. At the instant of mixing,

$$[Ba^{2+}] = \frac{(50.00\ mL)(0.050\ M)}{(100.00\ mL)} = 0.025\ M$$

However, the reaction $Ba^{2+}(aq) + SO_4^{2-}(aq) \rightleftharpoons BaSO_4\downarrow$ goes virtually to completion so that the $[Ba^{2+}]$ in the final solution is much less than 0.025 M. The $[K^+]$ in the mixture is $\frac{(50.00\ mL)(0.10\ M)(2)}{(100.00\ mL)} = 0.10$ M.

5. **(c)** All of the choices are 1:1 electrolytes, that is, electrolytes in which the molar ratio of cation:anion is 1:1. For this type of electrolyte, $s = (K_{sp})^{1/2}$, and the one with largest K_{sp} has the largest molar solubility in water.

$K_{sp}(SrCO_3) = 9.4x10^{-10}$ $\qquad$ $K_{sp}(MnS) = 5x10^{-15}$

$K_{sp}(PbSO_4) = 1.8x10^{-8}$ $\qquad$ $K_{sp}(FeS) = 5x10^{-18}$

$K_{sp}(AgCl) = 1.8x10^{-10}$

6. **(a)** $[Ba^{2+}] = K_{sp}(BaSO_4)/[SO_4^{2-}]$

$= 1.1x10^{-10}/(5.5x10^{-4}) = 2.0x10^{-7}$ M

7. **(b)** $AgBr(s) \rightleftharpoons Ag^+(aq) + Br^-(aq)$

Let z = molar solubility of AgBr in 0.20 F KBr

Then $[Ag^+] = z$ and $[Br^-] = 0.20 + z$

$K_{sp} = [Ag^+][Br^-] = (z)(0.20 + z) = 5.0x10^{-13}$

Assume z < 10% of 0.20. Then $0.20 + z \sim 0.20$, and

$z = (5.0x10^{-13})/(0.20) = 2.5x10^{-12}$

Since $2.5x10^{-12} \ll 10\%$ of 0.20, $z = K_{sp}/0.20$

8. **(b)** The relationship between molar solubility and K_{sp} is different for different types of electrolytes. For 1:1 electrolytes, $K_{sp} = s^2$. There are three 1:1 electrolytes among the options. The K_{sp} values of these 3 are:

AgI $1.5x10^{-16}$, $SrSO_4$ $2.8x10^{-7}$, MnS $5.0x10^{-15}$

Of these three, $SrSO_4$ has by far the largest K_{sp} and therefore the largest molar solubility.

There are two 1:2 electrolytes, for which $K_{sp} = 4s^3$.

$K_{sp}(PbI_2) = 8.7x10^{-9}$ and $K_{sp}\{Zn(OH)_2\} = 4.5x10^{-17}$

so that PbI_2 has the larger molar solubility of these two. The question therefore really comes down to: Which has the larger molar solubility in water, $SrSO_4$ or PbI_2?

For $SrSO_4$, $s = (K_{sp})^{1/2} = (28x10^{-8})^{1/2} = 5.3x10^{-4}$ M

For PbI_2, $s = (K_{sp}/4)^{1/3} = (2.2)^{1/3}x10^{-3} = 1.3x10^{-3}$ M

Hence PbI_2 has the largest molar solubility of the 5 salts.

9. (b) $[K^+] = \dfrac{(20.00\ mL)(0.100\ M)(2)}{100.00\ mL} = 0.040\ M$

$[NO_3^-] = \dfrac{(80.00\ mL)(0.120\ M)(2)}{100.00\ mL} = 0.192\ M$

Since $CaCO_3$ is an insoluble electrolyte, it precipitates from this solution, and the $[Ca^{2+}]$ and $[CO_3{}^{2-}]$ are both considerably smaller than at the instant of mixing.

No. mmol Ca^{2+} added = (80.00 mL)(0.120 M) = 9.60

No. mmol $CO_3{}^{2-}$ added = (20.00 mL)(0.100 M) = 2.00

As there is excess Ca^{2+}, virtually all the $CO_3{}^{2-}$ is precipitated, and there are 9.60 - 2.00 = 7.60 mmol of Ca^{2+} left in 100.00 mL of solution, so that $[Ca^{2+}] = 0.076\ M$

10. (a) $[Pb^{2+}] = K_{sp}(PbSO_4)/[SO_4{}^{2-}] = 1.7\text{x}10^{-8}/(0.10)$
$= 1.7\text{x}10^{-7}\ M$

11. (c) For any 1:1 electrolyte in pure water, $K_{sp} = s^2$

Therefore $s = (K_{sp})^{1/2} = (1.7\text{x}10^{-8})^{1/2} = 1.3\text{x}10^{-4}\ M$.

12. (c) Calcium carbonate reacts with any strong acid:

$$CaCO_3(s) + 2H^+(aq) \rightleftharpoons H_2O + CO_2\uparrow + Ca^{2+}(aq)$$

As the CO_2 escapes into the air, a sample of $CaCO_3$ can be dissolved completely by adding sufficient acid.

13. (c) At the instant of mixing,

$[Ca^{2+}] = \dfrac{(60.00\ mL)(0.010\ M)}{100.00\ mL} = 6.0\text{x}10^{-3}\ M$

$[CrO_4{}^{2-}] = \dfrac{(40.00\ mL)(0.025\ M)}{100.00\ mL} = 1.0\text{x}10^{-2}\ M$

$Q = [Ca^{2+}][CrO_4{}^{2-}] = 6.0\text{x}10^{-5} < K_{sp} = 7.1\text{x}10^{-4}$

Since $Q < K_{sp}$, no $CaCrO_4$ will precipitate.

$$[NO_3^-] = \frac{(2)(0.010\ M)(60.00\ mL)}{100.00\ mL} = 0.012\ M$$

No KNO_3 will precipitate becaue KNO_3 is a soluble salt.

14. __(c)__ For a 1:2 electrolyte, $K_{sp} = 4s^3$, where s is the molar solubility in water. Therefore

$$s^3 = (7.9x10^{-10})/4 = 2.0x10^{-10} = 200x10^{-12}$$

$$s = 5.8x10^{-4}\ M$$

15. __(b)__ $SrF_2(s) \rightleftharpoons Sr^{2+}(aq) + 2F^-(aq)$

Let x = molar solubility of SrF_2 in 0.10 F NaF

Then $[Sr^{2+}] = x$ and $[F^-] = 0.10 + 2x$

$$[Sr^{2+}][F^-]^2 = (x)(0.10 + 2x)^2 = 7.9x10^{-10}$$

Assume $2x < 10\%$ of 0.10. Then $0.10 + 2x \sim 0.10$,

$$x(0.10)^2 = 7.9x10^{-10} \quad \text{and} \quad x = 7.9x10^{-8}\ M$$

Check: Is $2(7.9x10^{-8}) < 10\%$ of 0.10? Yes, $1.8x10^{-7} < 1.0x10^{-2}$

Thus the molar solubility of SrF_2 in 0.10 F NaF is $7.9x10^{-8}$

Compare the answers to Exercises 14 and 15 and note how much smaller the solubility of SrF_2 is in a solution containing a common ion (F^-) than it is in pure water.

16. __(e)__ Let y = molar solubility of SrF_2 in 0.10 F $Sr(NO_3)_2$. Then $[Sr^{2+}] = 0.10 + y$ and $[F^-] = 2y$.

$$K_{sp} = [Sr^{2+}][F^-]^2 = 7.9x10^{-10} = (0.10 + y)(2y)^2$$

Assume $y < 10\%$ of 0.10. Then $0.10 + y \sim 0.10$,

$$(0.10)(4y^2) = 7.9x10^{-10} \quad \text{and} \quad y^2 = 7.9x10^{-10}/(0.40)$$

$$y^2 = 19.8x10^{-10} \quad \text{and} \quad y = 4.4x10^{-5}\ M$$

17. **(a)** $K_{eq} = \frac{[Pb^{2+}][HSO_4^-]}{[H^+]} = \frac{[Pb^{2+}][SO_4^{2-}][HSO_4^-]}{[H^+][SO_4{}^{2-}]}$

$= K_{sp}(PbSO_4)/K_a(HSO_4^-) = 1.8x10^{-6}$

18. **(e)** The anion I^- has virtually no tendency to accept a proton in dilute aqueous solution because HI is a strong acid, 100% dissociated into ions. The anions of all the other salts are bases, and react with H_3O^+ to form their conjugate weak acids.

19. **(e)** $[Pb^{2+}] = 2.3x10^{-2}$ M and $[Br^-] = 4.6x10^{-2}$ M

$K_{sp} = [Pb^{2+}][Br^-]^2 = (2.3x10^{-2})(4.6x10^{-2})^2$

$= (2.3)(4.6)^2x10^{-6} = 4.9x10^{-5}$

20. **(e)** $[Ca^{2+}] = K_{sp}/[F^-]^2 = K_{sp}(0.080)^2$

21. **(b)** If pH = 8.30 then pOH = 14.00 - 8.30 = 5.70

$[OH^-] = antilog(-5.70) = 2.0x10^{-6}$ M

$Zn(OH)_2(s) \rightleftharpoons Zn^{2+}(aq) + 2OH^-(aq)$

If $[OH^-] = 2.0x10^{-6}$ M then $[Zn^{2+}] = 1.0x10^{-6}$ M

$K_{sp} = [Zn^{2+}][OH^-]^2 = (1.0x10^{-6})(2.0x10^{-6})^2 = 4x10^{-18}$

22. **(d)** If 99.9% is precipitated, then 0.1% is still in solution. Therefore

$[Pb^{2+}] = (0.001)(0.120\ M) = 1.2x10^{-4}$ M

$[CrO_4{}^{2-}] = K_{sp}(PbCrO_4)/[Pb^{2+}] = \frac{1.8x10^{-14}}{1.2x10^{-4}} = 1.5x10^{-10}$ M

23. **(b)** $MgF_2(s) \rightleftharpoons Mg^{2+}(aq) + 2F^-(aq)$

Let z = molar solubility of MgF_2 in 0.10 F $Mg(NO_3)_2$

Then $[Mg^{2+}] = 0.10 + z$ and $[F^-] = 2z$

$$K_{sp} = [Mg^{2+}][F^-]^2 = (0.10 + z)(2z)^2$$

Assume $z < 10\%$ of 0.10. Then

$$(0.10)(4z^2) = K_{sp} \quad \text{and} \quad z = (K_{sp}/0.40)^{1/2}$$

24. (b)

No. mmol Pb^{2+} added = (20.00 mL)(0.100 M) = 2.00

No. mmol $C_2O_4^{2-}$ added = (30.00 mL)(0.150 M) = 4.50

There are 2.50 mmol $C_2O_4^{2-}$ in excess in 50.00 mL solution.

$$\text{Hence} \quad [C_2O_4^{2-}] = \frac{2.50 \text{ mmol}}{50.00 \text{ mL}} = 5.00\text{x}10^{-2} \text{ M}$$

25. (c)

No. mmol Ca^{2+} added = (60.00 mL)(0.100 M) = 6.00

No. mmol CO_3^{2-} added = (40.00 mL)(0.125 M) = 5.00

$$Ca^{2+}(aq) + CO_3^{2-}(aq) \rightleftharpoons CaCO_3\downarrow$$

Since Ca^{2+} and CO_3^{2-} react in a 1:1 molar ratio, there is 1.00 mmol Ca^{2+} in excess. Let $x = [CO_3^{2-}]$ at equilibrium.

$$\text{Then} \quad [Ca^{2+}] = \frac{1.00 \text{ mmol}}{100.00 \text{ mL}} + x = 0.0100 + x$$

$$K_{sp} = [Ca^{2+}][CO_3^{2-}] = 5\text{x}10^{-9} = (x)(0.0100 + x)$$

Assume $x < 10\%$ of 0.0100. Then $0.0100 + x \sim 0.0100$, and

$$x = 5\text{x}10^{-7} \text{ M}$$

Since $5\text{x}10^{-7} < 1.0\text{x}10^{-3}$, $[CO_3^{2-}] = 5\text{x}10^{-7}$ M.

26. (b) $$K_{eq} = \frac{[OH^-]^2}{[S^{2-}]} = \frac{[Cu^{2+}][OH^-]^2}{[Cu^{2+}][S^{2-}]} = \frac{K_{sp}\{Cu(OH)_2\}}{K_{sp}(CuS)}$$

$$= \frac{2\text{x}10^{-19}}{8.7\text{x}10^{-36}} = 2\text{x}10^{+16}$$

27. (e) $ZnCO_3(s) + 2H^+(aq) \rightleftharpoons Zn^{2+} + H_2O + CO_2\uparrow$

Solutions to Problems, Chapter 11

11.1. The formula weight of $Ce(IO_3)_4$ is 839.73 g/mol. If the solubility is 0.015 g per 100 mL, or 0.15 g/L, the molar solubility is

$$\frac{0.15\ g/L}{839.73\ g/mol} = 1.79x10^{-4}\ M$$

$$Ce(IO_3)_4(s) \rightleftharpoons Ce^{4+}(aq) + 4IO_3^-(aq)$$

Therefore in a saturated solution of $Ce(IO_3)_4$ in water

$$[Ce^{4+}] = 1.79x10^{-4}\ M \quad \text{and} \quad [IO_3^-] = 7.16x10^{-4}\ M$$

$$K_{sp} = [Ce^{4+}][IO_3^-]^4 = (1.79x10^{-4})(7.16x10^{-4})^4$$

$$= (1.79)(7.16)^4x10^{-20} = 4.7x10^{-17}$$

11.2. (a) $$PbI_2(s) \rightleftharpoons Pb^{2+}(aq) + 2I^-(aq)$$

Let s = molar solubility of PbI_2 in water

Then $[Pb^{2+}] = s$ and $[I^-] = 2s$

$$K_{sp} = [Pb^{2+}][I^-]^2 = (s)(2s)^2 = 4s^3 = 8.7x10^{-9}$$

$$s^3 = 2.2x10^{-9} \quad \text{and} \quad s = (2.2)^{1/3}x10^{-3} = 1.3x10^{-3}\ M$$

(b) Let x = molar solubility of PbI_2 in 0.10 F $Pb(NO_3)_2$

Then $[Pb^{2+}] = 0.10 + x$ and $[I^-] = 2x$

$$K_{sp} = (0.10 + x)(2x)^2 = 8.7x10^{-9}$$

Assume $x < 10\%$ of 0.10. Then $0.10 + x \sim 0.10$, and

$$(0.10)(4x^2) = 0.40x^2 = 8.7x10^{-9}$$

$$x^2 = 2.2x10^{-8} \quad \text{and} \quad x = 1.5x10^{-4}\ M$$

Check: Is $1.5x10^{-4} < 10\%$ of 0.10? Yes, $1.5x10^{-4} < 1.0x10^{-2}$

(c) Let z = molar solubility of PbI_2 in 0.10 F KI

Then $[Pb^{2+}] = z$ and $[I^-] = 0.10 + 2z$

$$K_{sp} = (z)(0.10 + 2z)^2 = 8.7x10^{-9}$$

Assume 2z < 10% of 0.10. Then 0.10 + 2z ~ 0.10, and

$$(z)(0.10)^2 = (z)(0.010) = 8.7x10^{-9} \quad \text{and} \quad z = 8.7x10^{-7}\ M$$

Check: Is 2z < 10% of 0.10? Yes, $1.7x10^{-6} < 1.0x10^{-2}$

Hence the molar solubility of PbI_2 in 0.10 F KI is $8.7x10^{-7}$ mol per liter.

This problem illustrates the common ion effect. The solubility of PbI_2 in a solution containing a common ion, either Pb^{2+} or I^-, is less than it is in pure water. Note that the <u>decrease</u> in solubility is considerably greater in 0.10 F KI than in 0.10 F $Pb(NO_3)_2$, because the $[I^-]$ is <u>squared</u> in the solubility product expression.

11.3. (a) $Mg(OH)_2(s) \rightleftharpoons Mg^{2+}(aq) + 2OH^-(aq)$

Let s = molar solubility of $Mg(OH)_2$ in water

Then $[Mg^{2+}] = s$ and $[OH^-] = 2s$

$$K_{sp} = [Mg^{2+}][OH^-]^2 = (s)(2s)^2 = 4s^3 = 1.5x10^{-11}$$

$$s^3 = (15/4)x10^{-12} \quad \text{and} \quad s = 1.55x10^{-4} = 1.6x10^{-4}\ M$$

(b) $[OH^-] = 2s = 3.1x10^{-4}$ M

(c) $pOH = -\log(3.1x10^{-4}) = 3.51$

$pH = 14.00 - pOH = 10.49$ and $[H_3O^+] = 3.2x10^{-11}$ M

11.4. (a) CaF_2 is a 1:2 salt. For this type of electrolyte, $K_{sp} = 4s^3$, where s is the molar solubility in water.

$$K_{sp}(CaF_2) = 3.9x10^{-11} = 4s^3 = 39x10^{-12}$$

$$s^3 = 9.75x10^{-12} \quad \text{and} \quad s = (9.75)^{1/3}x10^{-4} = 2.1x10^{-4}\ M$$

For a 1:1 electrolyte, like CaC_2O_4, $K_{sp} = s^2$. Thus

$$s = (K_{sp})^{1/2} = (2.3x10^{-9})^{1/2} = (23x10^{-10})^{1/2} = 4.8x10^{-5}\ M$$

Therefore CaF_2 has a larger molar solubility in water than does CaC_2O_4.

(b) $Cu(OH)_2$ is a 1:2 electrolyte, so $K_{sp} = 4s^3$.

$$4s^3 = 2x10^{-19} = 200x10^{-21} \quad \text{and} \quad s^3 = 50x10^{-21}$$

$$s = (50)^{1/3}x10^{-7} = 3.7x10^{-7}\ M = 4x10^{-7}\ M$$

$La(OH)_3$ is a 1:3 electrolyte. The K_{sp} of $La(OH)_3$ is given in Example 11.4, and the molar solubility is calculated in that Example. For a 1:3 electrolyte, $K_{sp} = 27s^4$.

$$27s^4 = 1x10^{-19} = 100x10^{-21} \quad \text{and} \quad s^4 = 3.7x10^{-21}$$

$$s = 7.8x10^{-6}\ M$$

The important thing to note from these calculations is that when comparing the solubilities of different types of electrolytes you cannot just look at the K_{sp} values and see which is larger. Thus although K_{sp} for CaC_2O_4 is larger than K_{sp} for CaF_2, the molar solubiulity of CaF_2 is larger than the molar solubility of CaC_2O_4. Similarly, although the K_{sp} for $Cu(OH)_2$ is larger than the K_{sp} for $La(OH)_3$, the molar solubility of $La(OH)_3$ is larger than that of $Cu(OH)_2$.

11.5. (a)

$$K_{eq} = \frac{[H^+]^2}{[HCN]^2[Hg_2{}^{2+}]} = \frac{[H^+]^2[CN^-]^2}{[HCN]^2[Hg_2{}^{2+}][CN^-]^2}$$

$$K_{eq} = \frac{K_a^2(HCN)}{K_{sp}\{Hg_2(CN)_2\}} = \frac{(4x10^{-10})^2}{5x10^{-40}} = \frac{16x10^{-20}}{5x10^{-40}} = 3.2x10^{+20}$$

(b)

$$K_{eq} = \frac{[F^-]^2}{[IO_3^-]^2} = \frac{[Pb^{2+}][F^-]^2}{[Pb^{2+}][IO_3^-]^2} = \frac{K_{sp}(PbF_2)}{K_{sp}\{Pb(IO_3)_2\}}$$

$$= \frac{3.7\text{x}10^{-8}}{6\text{x}10^{-13}} = 6\text{x}10^4$$

(c) $$K_{eq} = \frac{[Ba^{2+}][H_2C_2O_4]}{[H^+]^2} = \frac{[H_2C_2O_4][Ba^{2+}][C_2O_4{}^{2-}]}{[H^+]^2[C_2O_4{}^{2-}]}$$

$$K_{eq} = \frac{K_{sp}(BaC_2O_4)}{K_a(H_2C_2O_4)K_a(HC_2O_4^-)} = \frac{1.1\text{x}10^{-7}}{(5.9\text{x}10^{-2})(6.4\text{x}10^{-5})} = 2.9\text{x}10^{-2}$$

(d) $$K_{eq} = \frac{[H^+]^2}{[Ag^+]^2[H_2S]} = \frac{[H^+]^2[S^{2-}]}{[H_2S][Ag^+]^2[S^{2-}]}$$

$$K_{eq} = \frac{K_a(H_2S)K_a(HS^-)}{K_{sp}(Ag_2S)} = \frac{(1.0\text{x}10^{-7})(1.3\text{x}10^{-13})}{7\text{x}10^{-50}} = 1.9\text{x}10^{+29}$$

Note that this is a very large K_{eq}. Silver sulfide is so insoluble (has such a small K_{sp}) that it can be precipitated even in the presence of concentrated strong acid.

(e) $$K_{eq} = \frac{[Ni^{2+}]}{[H^+]^2} = \frac{[Ni^{2+}][OH^-]^2}{[H^+]^2[OH^-]^2} = \frac{K_{sp}\{Ni(OH)_2\}}{K_w^2}$$

$$= \frac{2\text{x}10^{-15}}{1\text{x}10^{-28}} = 2\text{x}10^{+13}$$

(f) $$K_{eq} = \frac{[H^+]^2[Cl^-]^2}{[H_2S]} = \frac{[H^+]^2[Cl^-]^2[Pb^{2+}][S^{2-}]}{[H_2S][Pb^{2+}][S^{2-}]}$$

$$K_{eq} = \frac{K_{sp}(PbCl_2)K_a(H_2S)K_a(HS^-)}{K_{sp}(PbS)}$$

$$K_{eq} = \frac{(1.6\text{x}10^{-5})(1.0\text{x}10^{-7})(1.3\text{x}10^{-13})}{8\text{x}10^{-28}} = 2.6\text{x}10^2$$

11.6. If pH = 7.8, pOH = 14.0 - pH = 6.2

$[OH^-]$ = antilog(-6.2) = $10^{-6.2}$ = $6.3\text{x}10^{-7}$ M

For $Mn(OH)_2$, $Q = [Mn^{2+}][OH^-]^2 = (5.0\text{x}10^{-2})(6.3\text{x}10^{-7})^2$

$$Q = (5.0)(6.3)^2 x10^{-16} = 2.0x10^{-14}$$

K_{sp} for $Mn(OH)_2$ = $4.5x10^{-14}$ Since $Q < K_{sp}$ no $Mn(OH)_2$ will precipitate.

For $Fe(OH)_3$, $Q = [Fe^{3+}][OH^-]^3 = (5.0x10^{-2})(6.3x10^{-7})^3$

$Q = 1.3x10^{-20}$ and K_{sp} for $Fe(OH)_3$ = $6.3x10^{-38}$. Since $Q > K_{sp}$, $Fe(OH)_3$ will precipitate.

For $La(OH)_3$, $Q = [La^{3+}][OH^-]^3 = 1.3x10^{-20}$, and K_{sp} = $1x10^{-19}$ (given in Example 11.4). Since $Q < K_{sp}$, no $La(OH)_3$ will precipitate. Although all 3 hydroxides are insoluble, if the pH is kept at 7.8 only $Fe(OH)_3$ will precipitate.

11.7. (a) 1. $2Bi^{3+}(aq) + 3H_2S \rightleftharpoons Bi_2S_3\downarrow + 6H^+(aq)$

(b) 1. $$K_{eq} = \frac{[H^+]^6}{[H_2S]^3[Bi^{3+}]^2} = \frac{[H^+]^6[S^{2-}]^3}{[H_2S]^3[Bi^{3+}]^2[S^{2-}]^3}$$

$$= \frac{K_a^3(H_2S)K_a^3(HS^-)}{K_{sp}(Bi_2S_3)} = \frac{(1.3x10^{-20})^3}{2x10^{-72}} = 1x10^{+12}$$

(c) 1. Because $1x10^{12} >> 1$ (and Q = 1 if all substances in solution are at 1 M concentration), this reaction proceeds to the right, virtually to completion.

(a) 2. $PbI_2(s) + S^{2-} \rightleftharpoons PbS\downarrow + 2I^-$

(b) 2. $$K_{eq} = \frac{[I^-]^2}{[S^{2-}]} = \frac{[Pb^{2+}][I^-]^2}{[Pb^{2+}][S^{2-}]} = \frac{K_{sp}(PbI_2)}{K_{sp}(PbS)}$$

$$= \frac{8.7x10^{-9}}{8x10^{-28}} = 1x10^{+19} >> 1$$

(c) 2. Because $K_{eq} >> 1$, this reaction proceeds to the right, virtually to completion.

(a) 3. $Cd(OH)_2(s) + 2H^+(aq) \rightleftharpoons Cd^{2+}(aq) + 2H_2O$

(b) 3. $$K_{eq} = \frac{[Cd^{2+}]}{[H^+]^2} = \frac{[Cd^{2+}][OH^-]^2}{[H^+]^2[OH^-]^2} = \frac{K_{sp}\{Cd(OH)_2\}}{K_w^2}$$

$$= \frac{1.2x10^{-14}}{1.0x10^{-28}} = 1.2x10^{14} >> 1$$

(c) 3. Since $K_{eq}>>1$, this reaction proceeds to the right, virtually to completion.

(a) 4. $Ni^{2+}(aq) + 2OH^-(aq) \rightleftharpoons Ni(OH)_2\downarrow$

(b) 4. $$K_{eq} = \frac{1}{[Ni^{2+}][OH^-]^2} = \frac{1}{K_{sp}\{Ni(OH)_2\}} = \frac{1}{2x10^{-15}}$$

$$= 5x10^{+14} >> 1$$

(c) 4. Since $K_{eq}>>1$, this reaction proceeds to the right, virtually to completion.

(a) 5. $HSO_4^-(aq) + OAc^-(aq) \rightleftharpoons HOAc + SO_4{}^{2-}(aq)$

(b) 5. $$K_{eq} = \frac{[HOAc][SO_4{}^{2-}]}{[OAc^-][HSO_4^-]} = \frac{[HOAc][SO_4{}^{2-}][H^+]}{[OAc^-][H^+][HSO_4^-]}$$

$$= \frac{K_a(HSO_4^-)}{K_a(HOAc)} = \frac{1.2x10^{-2}}{1.8x10^{-5}} = 6.7x10^2 > 1$$

(c) 5. Since $K_{eq} > 1$, this reaction proceeds to the right to an appreciable extent.

11.8. $BaC_2O_4(s) \rightleftharpoons Ba^{2+}(aq) + C_2O_4{}^{2-}(aq)$

Let s = molar solubility of BaC_2O_4 in water.

Then $K_{sp} = [Ba^{2+}][C_2O_4{}^{2-}] = s^2 = 1.1x10^{-7}$

$$s = 3.3x10^{-4} \text{ M}$$

The formula weight of BaC_2O_4 is 225.35 g/mol. Thus the solubility in g/L is

$$(3.3\text{x}10^{-4}\ \text{mol/L})(225.35\ \text{g/mol}) = 7.4\text{x}10^{-2}\ \text{g/L}$$

or $7.4\text{x}10^{-3}$ g per 100 mL. The actual solubility is somewhat larger than that just calculated ($9.4\text{x}10^{-3}$ g per 100 mL) because $C_2O_4^{2-}$ ions react with H_2O as follows:

$$C_2O_4^{2-} + H_2O \rightleftharpoons HC_2O_4^- + OH^-$$

This reaction removes $C_2O_4^{2-}$ ions from solution and drives the dissolution reaction of BaC_2O_4 to the right (remember Le Chatelier's Principle!)

11.9. (a) $$CaSO_4(s) \rightleftharpoons Ca^{2+}(aq) + SO_4^{2-}(aq)$$

Let s = molar solubility of $CaSO_4$ in pure water

Then $[Ca^{2+}] = [SO_4^{2-}] = s$ and $K_{sp} = s^2 = 2.4\text{x}10^{-5}$

$$s^2 = 24\text{x}10^{-6} \quad \text{and} \quad s = 4.9\text{x}10^{-3}\ M$$

(b) $$CaSO_4(s) + H^+(aq) \rightleftharpoons Ca^{2+}(aq) + HSO_4^-(aq)$$

$$K_{eq} = \frac{[Ca^{2+}][HSO_4^-]}{[H^+]} = \frac{[Ca^{2+}][SO_4^{2-}][HSO_4^-]}{[H^+][SO_4^{2-}]} = \frac{K_{sp}(CaSO_4)}{K_a(HSO_4^-)}$$

$$= \frac{2.4\text{x}10^{-5}}{1.2\text{x}10^{-2}} = 2.0\text{x}10^{-3}$$

Let x = molar solubility of $CaSO_4$ in 2.500 F HCl

Then $[Ca^{2+}] = [HSO_4^-] = x$ and $[H^+] = 2.500 - x$

$$K_{eq} = \frac{x^2}{2.500 - x} = 2.0\text{x}10^{-3}$$

Assume x < 10% of 2.500. Then $2.500 - x \sim 2.500$, and

$$x^2 = 5.0\text{x}10^{-3} = 50\text{x}10^{-4}$$

$$x = 7.1\text{x}10^{-2}\ M$$

Check: Is x < 10% of 2.500? Yes, $7.1\text{x}10^{-2} < 2.500\text{x}10^{-1}$

Thus the molar solubility of $CaSO_4$ in 2.500 F HCl is 7.1×10^{-2} moles per liter. Note that the molar solubility has increased from 4.9×10^{-3} in water to 7.1×10^{-2} in 2.500 F HCl, but that it is only moderately soluble in both.

11.10. $PbCl_2(s) + SO_4^{2-} \rightleftharpoons PbSO_4(s) + 2Cl^-$

$$K_{eq} = \frac{[Cl^-]^2}{[SO_4^{2-}]} = \frac{[Pb^{2+}][Cl^-]^2}{[Pb^{2+}][SO_4^{2-}]} = \frac{K_{sp}(PbCl_2)}{K_{sp}(PbSO_4)}$$

$$= \frac{1.6\times10^{-5}}{1.8\times10^{-8}} = 8.9\times10^2$$

$$Q = \frac{[Cl^-]^2}{[SO_4^{2-}]} = \frac{(1.0\times10^{-3})^2}{0.20} = 5\times10^{-6}$$

Since $Q \ll K_{eq}$, the reaction must proceed to the right to reach equilibrium. As $PbSO_4$ is on the right-hand side of this equation, $PbSO_4$ will be formed.

11.11. The formula weight of MgF_2 is 62.302 g/mol. A solubility of 7.6×10^{-3} g per 100 mL is 7.6×10^{-2} g/L. The molar solubility is therefore

$$\frac{7.6\times10^{-2}\ g/L}{62.302\ g/mol} = 1.22\times10^{-3}\ mol/L$$

$$MgF_2(s) \rightleftharpoons Mg^{2+}(aq) + 2F^-(aq)$$

In a saturated solution of MgF_2 in H_2O,

$$[Mg^{2+}] = 1.22\times10^{-3}\ M \quad \text{and} \quad [F^-] = 2.44\times10^{-3}\ M$$

$$K_{sp} = [Mg^{2+}][F^-]^2 = (1.22\times10^{-3})(2.44\times10^{-3})^2 = 7.3\times10^{-9}$$

The value listed in Table E2 is slightly smaller, 6.4×10^{-9}. The actual solubility is slightly larger than the solubility calculated from the K_{sp} because F^- is a weak base (the anion of a weak acid) and reacts with H_2O as follows:

$$F^-(aq) + H_2O \rightleftharpoons HF + OH^-$$

This hydrolysis reaction decreases the $[F^-]$ slightly from that calculated just using the K_{sp} of MgF_2, and more MgF_2 dissolves to counter this decrease.

11.12. $2AgCl(s) + CO_3{}^{2-} \rightleftharpoons Ag_2CO_3(s) + 2Cl^-(aq)$

$$K_{eq} = \frac{[Cl^-]^2}{[CO_3{}^{2-}]} = \frac{[Ag^+]^2[Cl^-]^2}{[Ag^+]^2[CO_3{}^{2-}]} = \frac{K_{sp}^2(AgCl)}{K_{sp}(Ag_2CO_3)}$$

$$= \frac{(1.8\text{x}10^{-10})^2}{(8.2\text{x}10^{-12})} = 4.0\text{x}10^{-9}$$

$$Q = \frac{(3.0\text{x}10^{-3})^2}{0.45} = 2.0\text{x}10^{-5}$$

Since $Q > K_{eq}$, the reaction would have to proceed to the left to reach equilibrium. No Ag_2CO_3 will form. If there were any Ag_2CO_3 present, it would react with Cl^- to form AgCl. Since there is no Ag_2CO_3, no reaction will occur.

11.13. The NO_3^- and K^+ ions are bystander (spectator) ions, and take no part in reaction. Their concentrations are therefore

$$[NO_3^-] = \frac{(40.00\text{ mL})(0.162\text{ M})}{60.00\text{ mL}} = 0.108\text{ M}$$

$$[K^+] = \frac{(20.00\text{ mL})(2)(0.144\text{ M})}{60.00\text{ mL}} = 0.0960\text{ M}$$

The reaction between Ag^+ and $CrO_4{}^{2-}$ is

$$2Ag^+(aq) + CrO_4{}^{2-}(aq) \rightleftharpoons Ag_2CrO_4\downarrow$$

$$K_{sp}(Ag_2CrO_4) = [Ag^+]^2[CrO_4{}^{2-}] = 9\text{x}10^{-12}$$

At the instant of mixing,

$[Ag^+] = [NO_3^-] = 0.108$ M and $[CrO_4^{2-}] = (1/2)[K^+] = 0.0480$ M

$$Q = (0.108)^2(0.0480) = 5.6x10^{-4}$$

Since $Q >> K_{sp}$, Ag_2CrO_4 will precipitate.

No. mmol Ag^+ added = (40.00 mL)(0.162 M) = 6.48

No. mmol CrO_4^{2-} added = (20.00 mL)(0.144 M) = 2.88

Thus 2.88 mmol of CrO_4^{2-} ions react with 2(2.88) = 5.76 mmol of Ag^+ ions to precipitate 2.88 mmol of Ag_2CrO_4, leaving 6.48 - 5.76 = 0.72 mmol of Ag^+ in excess, in a total volume of 60.00 mL.

Let $x = [CrO_4^{2-}]$ at equilibrium

Then $[Ag^+] = \dfrac{0.72 \text{ mmol}}{60.00 \text{ mL}} + 2x = 0.0120 + 2x$

$$K_{sp} = 9x10^{-12} = (0.0120 + 2x)^2(x)$$

Assume 2x < 10% of 0.0120. Then $0.0120 + 2x \sim 0.0120$ and

$$9x10^{-12} = (0.0120)^2(x) = (1.44x10^{-4})x$$

$$x = 6x10^{-8}$$

Check: Is 2x < 10% of 0.0120? Yes, $1.2x10^{-7} < 1.2x10^{-3}$.

$$[CrO_4^{2-}] = 6x10^{-8} \text{ M}$$

$$[Ag^+] = 0.0120 + 2(6x10^{-8}) = 0.0120 \text{ M}$$

We can check our work by making sure the solution is electrically neutral. The electroneutrality equation is

$$[Ag^+] + [K^+] = 2[CrO_4^{2-}] + [NO_3^-]$$

$$0.0120 + 2(6x10^{-8}) + 0.096 = 2(6x10^{-8}) + 0.108$$

11.14. No. mmol K^+ added = No. mmol IO_3^- added

= (50.00 mL)(0.096 M) = 4.80

No. mmol Pb^{2+} added = (30.00 mL)(0.112 M) = 3.36

No. mmol NO_3^- added = 2(No. mmol Pb^{2+} added) = 6.72

$$Pb^{2+}(aq) + 2IO_3^-(aq) \rightleftharpoons Pb(IO_3)_2\downarrow$$

To precipitate all the IO_3^- only 2.40 mmol of Pb^{2+} are needed, so there are 3.36 - 2.40 = 0.96 mmol of Pb^{2+} in excess in a volume of 80.00 mL of solution.

Let $x = [IO_3^-]$ at equilibrium

$$\text{Then } [Pb^{2+}] = \frac{0.96 \text{ mmol}}{80.00 \text{ mL}} + (1/2)x = 0.012 + (1/2)x$$

$$K_{sp} = [Pb^{2+}][IO_3^-]^2 = (0.012 + x/2)(x^2) = 2.6\text{x}10^{-13}$$

Assume $x/2 < 10\%$ of 0.012. Then $0.012 + x/2 \sim 0.012$, and

$$x^2 = \frac{2.6\text{x}10^{-13}}{0.012} = 21.7\text{x}10^{-12}$$

$$x = 4.7\text{x}10^{-6}$$

Check: Is $x/2 < 10\%$ of 0.012? Yes, $2.35\text{x}10^{-6} < 1.2\text{x}10^{-3}$

Then $$[IO_3^-] = 4.7\text{x}10^{-6} \text{ M}$$

$$[Pb^{2+}] = 0.012 + 2.35\text{x}10^{-6} = 0.012 \text{ M}$$

The K^+ and NO_3^- ions are bystander (spectator) ions and take no part in any reaction.

$$[K^+] = \frac{4.80 \text{ mmol}}{80.00 \text{ mL}} = 0.0600 \text{ M}$$

$$[NO_3^-] = \frac{6.72 \text{ mmol}}{80.00 \text{ mL}} = 0.0840 \text{ M}$$

11.15. (a) The unknown cannot be Na_2CO_3, NH_4NO_3, or KI, because each of these is readily soluble in water.

(b) The unknown is $SrCO_3$. All carbonates dissolve in strong acid to form CO_2, a colorless, odorless gas. The three white insoluble solids $BaSO_4$, Hg_2Cl_2, and $PbSO_4$ dissolve only slightly in strong acid because their anions are the anions of strong acids. Although ZnS does dissolve in acid, a foul-smelling gas, H_2S, is formed.

(c) $SrCO_3(s) + 2H^+(aq) \rightleftharpoons Sr^{2+}(aq) + H_2O + CO_2\uparrow$

11.16. (a) The formula weight of Ag_2SO_4 is 311.79 g/mol A solubility of 0.568 g per 100 mL or 5.68 g/L corresponds to a molar solubility of

$$\frac{5.68 \text{ g/L}}{311.79 \text{ g/mol}} = 1.82\text{x}10^{-2} \text{ mol/L}$$

$$Ag_2SO_4(s) \rightleftharpoons 2Ag^+(aq) + SO_4{}^{2-}(aq)$$

$$K_{sp} = [Ag^+]^2[SO_4{}^{2-}] = (3.64\text{x}10^{-2} \text{ M})^2(1.82\text{x}10^{-2} \text{ M})$$
$$= (3.64)^2(1.82)\text{x}10^{-6} = 2.41\text{x}10^{-5} \text{ M}^3$$

(b) Let x = molar solubility of Ag_2SO_4 in 0.300 F K_2SO_4

$$\text{Then } [SO_4{}^{2-}] = 0.300 + x \quad \text{and} \quad [Ag^+] = 2x$$

$$K_{sp} = (4x^2)(0.300 + x) = 2.41\text{x}10^{-5}$$

Assume $x < 10\%$ of 0.300 Then $0.300 + x \sim 0.300$, and

$$(4x^2)(0.300) = 1.20x^2 = 2.41\text{x}10^{-5}$$

$$x^2 = 2.009\text{x}10^{-5} = 20.09\text{x}10^{-6}$$

$$x = 4.48\text{x}10^{-3} \text{ M}$$

Check: Is $x < 10\%$ of 0.300? Yes, $4.48\text{x}10^{-3} < 3.00\text{x}10^{-2}$

For 3 significant figures it is best to have the smaller term in a sum significantly less than 10% of the larger, which is not the case here. We can make a better approximation as follows:

$$\text{Assume } 0.300 + x = 0.300 + 0.00448 = 0.304$$

$$\text{Then} \quad (4x^2)(0.304) = 2.41\text{x}10^{-5}$$

$$x^2 = 19.83\text{x}10^{-6} \quad \text{and} \quad x = 4.45\text{x}10^{-3}\ M$$

(c) The molar solubility of Ag_2SO_4 in water at $0^\circ C$ is $1.82\text{x}10^{-2}$ mol/L, whereas in 0.300 F K_2SO_4 it is $4.45\text{x}10^{-3}$ M The molar solubility is less in a solution with a common ion ($SO_4{}^{2-}$) than it is in pure water. If the equilibrium between solid Ag_2SO_4 and its ions is established in pure water, and a salt with a common ion is added, the equilibrium shifts to the left to precipitate more Ag_2SO_4 and counter the effect of the added common ion, in accordance with Le Chatelier's Principle. In other words, if $[SO_4{}^{2-}]$ is increased, the $[Ag^+]$ must decrease to keep K_{sp} constant. The only way to decrease the $[Ag^+]$ is to have the equilibrium shift to the left, using up Ag^+ ions and some of the added $SO_4{}^{2-}$ ions, and precipitating more solid.

11.17. (a) If 99.99% of the Fe^{3+} is precipitated, 0.01% is still in solution.

$$[Fe^{3+}] = (0.0001)(0.100\ M) = 1.00\text{x}10^{-5}\ M$$

$$K_{sp} = [Fe^{3+}][OH^-]^3 = 6.3\text{x}10^{-38}$$

$$[OH^-]^3 = \frac{6.3x10^{-38}}{1.0x10^{-5}} = 6.3x10^{-33}$$

$$[OH^-] = 1.85x10^{-11} = 1.8x10^{-11} \text{ M}$$

$$[H_3O^+] = K_w/[OH^-] = \frac{1.0x10^{-14}}{1.85x10^{-11}} = 5.4x10^{-4} \text{ M}$$

$$pH = -\log(5.4x10^{-4}) = 3.27$$

(b) For $Ni(OH)_2$, $Q = [Ni^{2+}][OH^-]^2$

If $[OH^-] = 1.85x10^{-11}$ M, $Q = (0.100)(1.85x10^{-11})^2$

$$= 3.4x10^{-23}$$

As K_{sp} for $Ni(OH)_2$ is $2x10^{-15}$, $Q \ll K_{sp}$, and no $Ni(OH)_2$ will precipitate.

(c) The first precipitate of $Ni(OH)_2$ will appear when $[Ni^{2+}][OH^-]^2 = 2x10^{-15}$, that is, when

$$[OH^-]^2 = \frac{2x10^{-15}}{0.100} = 2x10^{-14}$$

$$[OH^-] = 1.4x10^{-7} \text{ M}$$

$$[H_3O^+] = 1.0x10^{-14}/(1.4x10^{-7}) = 7.1x10^{-8} \text{ M}$$

$$pH = -\log(7.1x10^{-8}) = 7.15$$

As long as the pH does not exceed 7.15, no $Ni(OH)_2$ will precipitate. The two ions, Ni^{2+} and Fe^{3+}, can be analytically separated by keeping the pH at any value between 3.27 and 7.15. An $HOAc/OAc^-$ buffer can be used for this purpose. As long as the pH is above 3.27 but below 7.15, more than 99.99% of the Fe^{3+} is precipitated as $Fe(OH)_3$ and none of the Ni^{2+} is precipitated.

11.18. (a) $K_{sp}(FeS) = [Fe^{2+}][S^{2-}] = 5x10^{-18}$

$$[S^{2-}] = \frac{5x10^{-18}}{3.00x10^{-4}} = 1.67x10^{-14} = 2x10^{-14}$$

(b) If $[S^{2-}] = 1.67x10^{-14}$ M,

$$[Co^{2+}] = \frac{K_{sp}(CoS)}{1.67x10^{-14}} = \frac{8x10^{-23}}{1.67x10^{-14}} = 5x10^{-9}\text{ M}$$

$$\%\ Co^{2+}\ \underline{\text{not}}\text{ precipitated} = \frac{5x10^{-9}\text{ M}}{0.100\text{ M}} \times 100 = 5x10^{-6}\ \%$$

(c) $$\frac{[H^+]^2[S^{2-}]}{[H_2S]} = K_a(H_2S)\cdot K_a(HS^-) = 1.3x10^{-20}$$

$$[H^+]^2 = \frac{1.3x10^{-20}(0.10)}{1.67x10^{-14}} = 7.8x10^{-8}\text{ M}$$

$[H^+] = 2.8x10^{-4}$ M and $pH = -\log(2.8x10^{-4}) = 3.6$

11.19. (a) If 99.9% of the Cl^- is precipitated, 0.1% is still in solution.

$$[Cl^-] = (0.001)(0.036\text{ M}) = 3.6x10^{-5}\text{ M}$$

$$[Ag^+] = K_{sp}(AgCl)/[Cl^-] = \frac{1.8x10^{-10}}{3.6x10^{-5}} = 5.0x10^{-6}\text{ M}$$

(b) $$Q = [Ag^+]^2[CrO_4^{2-}] = (5.0x10^{-6})^2(1.2x10^{-2})$$

$$= 30x10^{-14} = 3.0x10^{-13}$$

Since K_{sp} for Ag_2CrO_4 is $9x10^{-12}$, $Q < K_{sp}$ and no Ag_2CrO_4 will precipitate.

(c) The minimum $[Ag^+]$ necessary for precipitation of Ag_2CrO_4 is obtained as follows:

$$[Ag^+]^2 = \frac{9x10^{-12}}{[CrO_4^{2-}]} = \frac{9x10^{-12}}{1.2x10^{-2}} = 7.5x10^{-10}$$

$$[Ag^+] = 2.7x10^{-5}\text{ M}$$

As long as the $[Ag^+]$ is kept less than $2.7x10^{-5}$ M, no

Ag_2CrO_4 will precipitate. If the $[Ag^+]$ is above 5.0×10^{-6} M, more than 99.9% of the Cl^- will be precipitated as AgCl. Thus an analytical separation of Cl^- and CrO_4^{2-} is possible by carefully controlling the $[Ag^+]$.

11.20. $$CH_3NH_2 + H_2O \rightleftharpoons CH_3NH_3^+(aq) + OH^-(aq)$$

Let $x = [OH^-]$ at equilibrium

$$\text{Then} \quad [CH_3NH_3^+] = \frac{0.075 \text{ mol}}{0.1000 \text{ L}} + x = 0.75 + x$$

$$[CH_3NH_2] = \frac{0.050 \text{ mol}}{0.1000 \text{ L}} - x = 0.50 - x$$

$$K = 3.7 \times 10^{-4} = \frac{[CH_3NH_3^+][OH^-]}{[CH_3NH_2]} = \frac{(0.75 + x)(x)}{(0.50 - x)}$$

Assume $x < 10\%$ of 0.50. Then $0.50 - x \sim 0.50$ and $0.75 + x \sim 0.75$, so that

$$3.7 \times 10^{-4} = \frac{0.75x}{0.50} = 3x/2$$

$$x = (2/3)(3.7 \times 10^{-4}) = 2.5 \times 10^{-4}$$

Check: Is $x < 10\%$ of 0.50? Yes, $2.5 \times 10^{-4} < 5.0 \times 10^{-2}$. Hence

$$[OH^-] = 2.5 \times 10^{-4} \text{ M}$$

The formula weight of $Mn(NO_3)_2 \cdot 4H_2O$ is 251.009 g/mol. In aqueous solution this salt is 100% Mn^{2+} and NO_3^- ions.

$$\text{No. mol } Mn(NO_3)_2 \cdot 4H_2O = \text{No. mol } Mn^{2+} = \frac{2.1085 \text{ g}}{251.009 \text{ g/mol}}$$

$$= 8.4001 \times 10^{-3} \text{ mol}$$

$$[Mn^{2+}] = \frac{8.4001 \times 10^{-3} \text{ mol}}{0.1000 \text{ L}} = 8.400 \times 10^{-2} \text{ M}$$

Since $[Mn^{2+}] = 8.400 \times 10^{-2}$ M and $[OH^-] = 2.5 \times 10^{-4}$ M at the instant of mixing,

$$Q = [Mn^{2+}][OH^-]^2 = (8.400x10^{-2})(2.5x10^{-4})^2 = 5.2x10^{-9}$$

For $Mn(OH)_2$, $K_{sp} = 4.5x10^{-14}$. As $Q > 4.5x10^{-14}$, $Mn(OH)_2$ will precipitate.

11.21. (a) The equilibrium in aqueous NH_3 is

$$NH_3 + H_2O \rightleftharpoons NH_4^+ + OH^-$$

If ammonium nitrate is added, the $[NH_4^+]$ increases. To counter or oppose this disturbance the equilibrium shifts to the left, forming more NH_3 and decreasing the $[OH^-]$. The net effect is that the solution becomes less basic (i.e. more acidic as we are adding a weak acid, NH_4^+) and the pH decreases somewhat.

(b) Let $x = [OH^-]$ at equilibrium

$$K_b(NH_3) = 1.8x10^{-5} = \frac{[NH_4^+][OH^-]}{[NH_3]} = \frac{(1.20)[OH^-]}{0.150}$$

$$[OH^-] = \frac{(1.8x10^{-5})(0.150)}{1.20} = 2.25x10^{-6} = 2.2x10^{-6}$$

$$K_{sp}\{Al(OH)_3\} = [Al^{3+}][OH^-]^3 = 1.9x10^{-33}$$

If $[OH^-] = 2.25x10^{-6}$ M, then the maximum concentration of Al^{3+} in solution is given by $K_{sp}/[OH^-]^3$, or

$$[Al^{3+}] = \frac{1.9x10^{-33}}{(2.25)^3x10^{-18}} = \frac{19x10^{-16}}{(2.25)^3} = 1.7x10^{-16}$$

$$K_{sp}\{Mg(OH)_2\} = [Mg^{2+}][OH^-]^2 = 1.5x10^{-11}$$

The maximum $[Mg^{2+}]$ that can exist in a solution in which the $[OH^-]$ is $2.25x10^{-6}$ M is given by

$$[Mg^{2+}] = 1.5x10^{-11}/(2.25x10^{-6})^2 = 2.96 \text{ M} = 3.0 \text{ M}$$

(c) The calculations in (b) show that if a solution is buffered so that the $[OH^-]$ is maintained at 2.2×10^{-6} M, no $Mg(OH)_2$ will precipitate unless the $[Mg^{2+}]$ is greater than 3.0 M, whereas any Al^{3+} will be precipitated as $Al(OH)_3$ until the $[Al^{3+}]$ is decreased to the exceedingly small value of 1.7×10^{-16} M. Thus an analytical separation of Al^{3+} and Mg^{2+} is easy to achieve.

11.22. At the instant of mixing, since the volume is doubled, each concentration is halved.

$$[NH_4^+] = 0.100\ M \quad \text{and} \quad [NH_3] = 0.200\ M$$

$$K_b(NH_3) = \frac{[NH_4^+][OH^-]}{[NH_3]} = 1.8\times10^{-5}$$

$$[OH^-] = 1.8\times10^{-5}\frac{[NH_3]}{[NH_4^+]} = \frac{(1.8\times10^{-5})(0.200)}{(0.100)} = 3.6\times10^{-5}$$

The $[La^{3+}]$ in equilibrium with this $[OH^-]$ is

$$[La^{3+}] = \frac{K_{sp}\{La(OH)_3\}}{[OH^-]^3} = \frac{1\times10^{-19}}{(3.6\times10^{-5})^3} = 2.1\times10^{-6} = 2\times10^{-6}\ M$$

$$\%\ La^{3+}\ \underline{\text{not}}\ \text{precipitated} = \frac{2.1\times10^{-6}}{0.0500} \times 100 = 4\times10^{-3} = 0.004\%$$

Hence, % La^{3+} precipitated = 100.000 − 0.004% = 99.996%.

11.23. The added OH^- reacts with HOAc to form acetate ions:

$$HOAc + OH^-(aq) \rightleftharpoons OAc^-(aq) + H_2O$$

No. mmol OH^- added = (10.00 mL)(6.00 M) = 60.0 mmol

No. mmol HOAc added = (90.00 mL)(2.00 M) = 180 mmol

Since HOAc and OH^- react in a 1:1 molar ratio, 60.0 mmol

OH^- combine with 60.0 mmol HOAc to form 60.0 mmol OAc^-, leaving 120 mmol HOAc in excess, in a volume of 100.00 mL.

$$K_a(HOAc) = \frac{[H_3O^+][OAc^-]}{[HOAc]} = 1.8x10^{-5}$$

Since the $[OAc^-]/[HOAc]$ ratio is 60/120 = 1/2,

$$[H_3O^+] = 2(1.8x10^{-5}) = 3.6x10^{-5} \text{ M}$$

$$[OH^-] = K_w/[H_3O^+] = 1.0x10^{-14}/(3.6x10^{-10}) = 2.8x10^{-10}$$

For $Ni(OH)_2$, $K_{sp} = 2x10^{-15}$. At the instant of mixing, $[Ni^{2+}] = \frac{(90.00 \text{ mL})(0.120 \text{ M})}{(100.00 \text{ mL})} = 0.108$ M. The reaction quotient, Q, is given by

$$Q = [Ni^{2+}][OH^-]^2 = (0.108)(2.8x10^{-10})^2 = 8.3x10^{-21}$$

Since $Q < K_{sp}$, no $Ni(OH)_2$ will precipitate.

For $Cr(OH)_3$, $K_{sp} = 7x10^{-31}$. At the instant of mixing, $[Cr^{3+}] = (0.9000)(0.092 \text{ M}) = 8.3x10^{-2}$ M. The reaction quotient for $Cr(OH)_3$ is given by

$$Q = [Cr^{3+}][OH^-]^3 = (8.28x10^{-2})(2.78x10^{-10})^3 = 1.8x10^{-30}$$

Since $Q > K_{sp}$, some $Cr(OH)_3$ will precipitate. However, for $Cr(OH)_3$, Q is not very much greater than K_{sp}. As a practical matter, in order to obtain a sizeable precipitate that is readily observable, Q should be several orders of magnitude greater than K_{sp}.

11.24. This solution contains an $HOAc/OAc^-$ buffer.

$$\frac{[OAc^-]}{[HOAc]} = \frac{\text{No. mol } OAc^-}{\text{No. mol HOAc}} = \frac{0.10}{1.00}$$

$$[H_3O^+]\{[OAc^-]/[HOAc]\} = 0.10[H_3O^+] = K_a = 1.8x10^{-5}$$

Hence $[H_3O^+] = 1.8x10^{-4}$ M

We can determine the $[S^{2-}]$ in this buffered solution by using the overall K_{eq} for the two stages of ionization of H_2S:

$$K_a(H_2S)\cdot K_a(HS^-) = 1.3x10^{-20} = \frac{[H_3O^+]^2[S^{2-}]}{[H_2S]}$$

$$= \frac{(1.8x10^{-4})^2[S^{2-}]}{(0.10)}$$

Thus,

$$[S^{2-}] = \frac{(1.3x10^{-20})(0.10)}{(1.8x10^{-4})^2} = 4.0x10^{-14} \text{ M}$$

For MnS, $K_{sp} = 5x10^{-15}$. The reaction quotient, Q, at the instant of mixing is

$$Q = [Mn^{2+}][S^{2-}] = (0.100)(4.0x10^{-14}) = 4.0x10^{-15}$$

Since $Q < K_{sp}$, no MnS will precipitate.

For CuS, $K_{sp} = 8.7x10^{-36}$. The reaction quotient, Q, at the instant of mixing is

$$Q = [Cu^{2+}][S^{2-}] = (0.100)(4.0x10^{-14}) = 4.0x10^{-15}$$

Since $Q >> K_{sp}$, CuS will precipitate.

11.25. **(a)** $$K_{eq} = \frac{[Mg^{2+}][NH_3]^2}{[NH_4^+]^2} = \frac{[Mg^{2+}][OH^-][NH_3]^2}{[NH_4^+]^2[OH^-]^2}$$

$$= K_{sp}\{Mg(OH)_2\}/K_b^2(NH_3)$$

(b) If pH = 9.07, pOH = 14.00 - 9.07 = 4.93, and

$$[OH^-] = \text{antilog}(-4.93) = 1.17x10^{-5} \text{ M}$$

$$K_{eq} = \frac{[NH_4^+][OH^-]}{[NH_3]} = \frac{(0.200)(1.17x10^{-5})}{[NH_3]} = 1.8x10^{-5}$$

$$[NH_3] = (0.200)(1.17)/(1.8) = 1.3x10^{-1}$$

$$[Mg^{2+}] = \frac{1}{2}[NH_3] = 6.5_3\text{x}10^{-2}\ M$$

$$K_{eq} = \frac{(6.53\text{x}10^{-2})(1.31\text{x}10^{-1})^2}{(0.200)^2} = 2.78\text{x}10^{-2}$$

$$K_{sp}\{Mg(OH)_2\} = K_{eq} \cdot K_b^2(NH_3) = (2.78\text{x}10^{-2})(1.8\text{x}10^{-5})^2$$
$$= 9.0\text{x}10^{-12}$$

An alternative, and easier, way of calculating K_{sp} for $Mg(OH)_2$ is just to use the $[Mg^{2+}]$ and $[OH^-]$ we calculated for this solution:

$$K_{sp} = [Mg^{2+}][OH^-]^2 = (6.53\text{x}10^{-2})(1.175\text{x}10^{-5})^2 = 9.0\text{x}10^{-12}$$

If we round all values to 2 significant figures as we proceed with this calculation, the values of K_{sp} calculated by the two methods will not agree in the second significant figure, but the disagreement is not real, and is only due to rounding errors.

Solutions to Exercises, Chapter 12

1. The charge to mass ratio, e/m, is larger for the electron because the mass is so much smaller. The mass of the proton is 1836 times larger than the mass of the electron. Thus,

$$\text{mass proton} = (1836)(9.1096\text{x}10^{-31}\ \text{kg}) = 1.673\text{x}10^{-27}\ \text{kg}$$

2. In Thomson's cathode-ray experiments, he measured the charge to mass ratio (e/m) of the particles comprising cathode rays. He found that the e/m ratio was the same regardless of the metal used for the cathode or anode, and that when various gases at very low pressure are in the tube the e/m ratio is still the same. Even more striking, the e/m ratio observed for cathode-ray particles was almost two thousand times larger than for any other particle observed prior to Thomson's experiments. These observations led Thomson to conclude that the particles comprising cathode rays are a universal fragment of all matter.

3. Rutherford initially assumed, like other scientists of his time, that the positive charge of an atom, as well as the mass, was uniformly distributed throughout the entire atom. He therefore expected the alpha particles to pass straight through the metal foil target, with either no deflections at all or deflections of very small angles. The observation of deflections between 90° and 180° proved conclusively that the mass and positive charge of an atom must be contained in a very small fraction of the volume of the atom.

4. Since 1 Å = 1×10^{-10} m = 0.1 nm,

$$\lambda = 20{,}000 \text{ Å} = 2{,}000 \text{ nm} = 2.000\times10^{-6} \text{ m} = 2.000\times10^{-4} \text{ cm}$$

The wavenumber $\tilde{\nu} = 1/\lambda = 1/(2.000\times10^{-6}\text{ m}) = 5.000\times10^{5}\text{ m}^{-1}$

The frequency, ν, is c/λ or $c\tilde{\nu}$. Thus

$$\nu = (2.997925\times10^{8}\text{ m}\cdot\text{s}^{-1})(5.000\times10^{5}\text{ m}^{-1}) = 1.499\times10^{14}\text{ s}^{-1}$$

This radiation is in the near IR region (see Table 12.3).

5. If $\nu = 1.8\times10^{15}\text{ s}^{-1}$,

$$\lambda = c/\nu = \frac{2.998\times10^{8}\text{ m}\cdot\text{s}^{-1}}{1.8\times10^{15}\text{ s}^{-1}} = 1.67\times10^{-7}\text{ m} = 170\text{ nm}$$

$$\tilde{\nu} = 1/\lambda = 1/(1.67\times10^{-7}\text{ m}) = 6.0\times10^{6}\text{ m}^{-1} = 6.0\times10^{4}\text{ cm}^{-1}$$

This radiation occurs in the far ultraviolet region.

6. The prism in a spectrometer serves to disperse the light, that is, to separate a beam of light into its constituent wavelengths or frequencies.

7. The Brackett series in the spectrum of atomic hydrogen consists of all the lines for which $n_L = 4$. For the third line in the Brackett series, $n_H = 7$, $n_L = 4$.

8. $$\tilde{\nu} = 109{,}678\left(\frac{1}{3^2} - \frac{1}{4^2}\right)\text{ cm}^{-1} = 5331.57\text{ cm}^{-1}$$

$$\lambda = 1/\tilde{\nu} = 1/(5331.57\text{ cm}^{-1}) = 1.87562\times10^{-4}\text{ cm} = 1875.62\text{ nm}$$

$$\nu = c\tilde{\nu} = (2.997925\times10^{8}\text{ m}\cdot\text{s}^{-1})(5.33157\times10^{5}\text{ m}^{-1})$$

$$\nu = 1.59836\times10^{14}\text{ s}^{-1}$$

9. The limiting line in each series is the line for which $n_H = \infty$, so that $1/n_H^2 = 0$. For the Balmer series

$$\tilde{\nu} = 109{,}678\left(\frac{1}{2^2}\right) = 109{,}678/4 = 2.74470\times10^4\ \text{cm}^{-1}$$

$$\nu = c\tilde{\nu} = (2.997925\times10^8\ \text{m}\cdot\text{s}^{-1})(2.74470\times10^6\ \text{m}^{-1})$$

$$\nu = 8.22840\times10^{14}\ \text{s}^{-1}$$

This line is in the near ultraviolet region.

10. Frequencies from 4.2×10^{14} to $6.5\times10^{14}\ \text{s}^{-1}$ are all in the visible region. Only 4 lines in the spectrum of atomic hydrogen are in the visible region, those with frequencies 4.5681×10^{14}, 6.1669×10^{14}, 6.9069×10^{14}, and $7.3089\times10^{14}\ \text{s}^{-1}$ (see Table 12.2).

11. For the ground state $n_L = 1$, and for the third excited state $n_H = 4$. Using Eq. (12-14) we obtain

$$E_4 - E_1 = -(1312\ \text{kJ/mol})\left(\frac{1}{4^2} - \frac{1}{1^2}\right) = (15/16)(1312\ \text{kJ/mol})$$

$$= 1230\ \text{kJ/mol}$$

The Bohr frequency condition, $\nu = \Delta E/h$, is used to calculate the frequency. Use ΔE in joules, as h is in J·s

$$\Delta E = E_4 - E_1 = (15/16)(13.60\ \text{eV}) = 12.75\ \text{eV}$$

The conversion factor to joules is given as Eq. (12-13a):

$$\Delta E = (12.75\ \text{eV})(1.6022\times10^{-19}\ \text{J/eV}) = 2.0428\times10^{-18}\ \text{J}$$

$$\nu = \Delta E/h = \frac{2.0428\times10^{-18}\ \text{J}}{6.62618\times10^{-34}\ \text{J}\cdot\text{s}} = 3.083\times10^{15}\ \text{s}^{-1}$$

This transition occurs in the far ultraviolet.

12.

$$\nu = \frac{\Delta E}{h} = \frac{(2.856\ \text{eV})(1.6022\text{x}10^{-19}\ \text{J/eV})}{6.6262\text{x}10^{-34}\ \text{J}\cdot\text{s}} = 6.906\text{x}10^{14}\ \text{s}^{-1}$$

$$\lambda = c/\nu = \frac{2.997925\text{x}10^{8}\ \text{m}\cdot\text{s}^{-1}}{6.906\text{x}10^{14}\ \text{s}^{-1}} = 4.341\text{x}10^{-7}\ \text{m} = 434.1\ \text{nm}$$

This is visible radiation, blue-violet in color.

13. The energy required to remove the electron from the $n = 3$ level to $n = \infty$ (infinite separation) is $-E_3$, since E_∞ is 0.

$$-E_3 = 13.60/3^2\ \text{eV} = 1.51\ \text{eV} \quad \text{or} \quad 1312/9 = 145.8\ \text{kJ/mol}$$

14. Since energy is directly proportional to frequency, and frequency is inversely proportional to wavelength, a wave of shorter wavelength has higher energy. Thus the violet ray has higher energy than the orange ray.

15. The wavelength associated with a particle of mass m, traveling with speed v, is given by the de Broglie relation, Eq. (12-26): $\lambda = h/mv$.

If $\lambda = 0.100\ \text{nm} = 1.00\text{x}10^{-10}\ \text{m}$,

$$v = \frac{6.6262\text{x}10^{-34}\ \text{J}\cdot\text{s}^{-1}}{(9.1096\text{x}10^{-31}\ \text{kg})(1.00\text{x}10^{-10}\ \text{m})} = 7.27\text{x}10^{6}\ \text{m}\cdot\text{s}^{-1}$$

16. $$\text{KE} = \tfrac{1}{2}mv^2 = \tfrac{1}{2}(9.1096\text{x}10^{-31}\ \text{kg})(4.0\text{x}10^{6}\ \text{m/s})^2$$
$$= 7.3\text{x}10^{-18}\ \text{J}$$

17. An electron accelerated through a potential difference of 1000.0 volts has 1000.0 eV of energy. To convert to joules, use Eq. (12-13a):

$$E = (1000.0\ \text{eV})(1.6022\text{x}10^{-19}\ \text{J/eV}) = 1.6022\text{x}10^{-16}\ \text{J}$$

Since $E = (1/2)mv^2$, $v^2 = 2E/m$, so

$$v^2 = \frac{2(1.6022\text{x}10^{-16}\ \text{J})}{9.1096\text{x}10^{-31}\ \text{kg}} = 3.5176\text{x}10^{14}\ \text{m}^2/\text{s}^2$$

$$v = 1.8755\text{x}10^{7}\ \text{m/s}$$

$$\lambda = h/mv = \frac{6.62618\text{x}10^{-34}\ \text{J}\cdot\text{s}}{(9.1096\text{x}10^{-31}\ \text{kg})(1.8755\text{x}10^{7}\ \text{m}\cdot\text{s}^{-1})}$$

$$= 3.8783\text{x}10^{-11}\ \text{m} = 0.038783\ \text{nm}$$

This radiation is in the X-ray region.

18. $$\lambda = c/\nu = \frac{2.998\text{x}10^{8}\ \text{m}\cdot\text{s}^{-1}}{6.6\text{x}10^{14}\ \text{s}^{-1}} = 4.5\text{x}10^{-7}\ \text{m}$$

$$E = h\nu = (6.6262\text{x}10^{-34}\ \text{J}\cdot\text{s})(6.6\text{x}10^{14}\ \text{s}^{-1}) = 4.4\text{x}10^{-19}\ \text{J}$$

19. For an H-like ion, $E_n = -Z^2K/n^2$

(a) E_1 for $He^+ = -(2)^2(13.60\ \text{eV}) = -54.40\ \text{eV}$

(b) E_2 for $Li^{2+} = -(3)^2(13.60\ \text{eV}) = -122.4\ \text{eV}$

20. $$E_n = \frac{-hc\mathcal{R}Z^2}{n^2} = \frac{-13.60(2)^2}{9} = -6.044\ \text{eV for He}^+$$

$$= \frac{-13.60(1)^2}{9} = -1.51\ \text{eV for H},\quad \text{for } n = 3.$$

An electron is lower in energy in the $n = 3$ state of the He^+ ion than in the $n = 3$ state of the H atom. Since the nucleus of the He^+ ion has twice as much positive charge, the electron is more strongly attracted to the He nucleus than to the H nucleus, and is 4 times (2^2) lower in energy.

21. $$\lambda = 400\ \text{nm} = 4.00\text{x}10^{-7}\ \text{m}$$

$$E = h\nu = hc/\lambda = \frac{(6.6262\text{x}10^{-34}\ \text{J}\cdot\text{s})(2.9979\text{x}10^{8}\ \text{m}\cdot\text{s}^{-1})}{4.00\text{x}10^{-7}\ \text{m}}$$

Thus the energy of the photon is $E = 4.97\times10^{-19}$ J.

For the electron $E = \frac{1}{2}mv^2 = \frac{1}{2}(9.1096\times10^{-31}\ \text{kg})\left(1.0\times10^{12}\ \frac{\text{m}^2}{\text{s}^2}\right)$

$$= 4.55\times10^{-19}\ \text{J}$$

The energy of the photon of light is greater than the energy of the electron. When the photon strikes the electron, the electron will move from its initial location and will change its velocity. The act of determining the position will change the position and the momentum of the electron, as described by the Uncertainty Principle.

22. $\Delta E = 13.60(3)^2\left(\frac{1}{1^2} - \frac{1}{2^2}\right) = 91.80\ \text{eV}$

To calculate the wavelength we need ΔE in joules.

$$\Delta E = (91.80\ \text{eV})(1.6022\times10^{-19}\ \text{J/eV}) = 1.471\times10^{-17}\ \text{J}$$

$$\lambda = hc/\Delta E = \frac{(6.6262\times10^{-34}\ \text{J}\cdot\text{s})(2.997925\times10^{8}\ \text{m/s})}{1.471\times10^{-17}\ \text{J}}$$

$$= 1.350\times10^{-9}\ \text{m} = 13.50\ \text{nm}$$

This radiation occurs in the far ultraviolet region.

Solutions to Multiple Choice Questions

1. **(b)** $E = h\nu$ and $\nu = c\tilde{\nu}$, so that $E = hc\tilde{\nu}$. The energy is directly proportional to the wavenumber. For electromagnetic radiation, energy does not depend on the speed or the amplitude of the wave, and is inversely proportional to λ and to the time for one cycle to pass a given point in space, which is the inverse of frequency.

2. __(d)__ Only (d) correctly describes the spectrum. All the others are wrong.

3. __(c)__ Atomic emission spectra consist of frequencies or wavelengths of radiation corresponding to the difference in energy between pairs of allowed states of the atom. From these frequencies we can construct an energy level diagram for the atom, and determine the ionization energy of the atom, but the spectra themselves are not a direct measurement of the ionization energy.

4. __(c)__ $$E = \left(495.80\ \frac{kJ}{mol}\right)\left(10^3\ \frac{J}{kJ}\right)\left(\frac{1\ mol}{6.022x10^{23}\ atom}\right)$$

$$= 82.33x10^{-20}\ J/atom$$

$$\nu = E/h = \frac{82.33x10^{-20}\ J}{6.6262x10^{-34}\ J \cdot s} = 1.243x10^{15}\ s^{-1}$$

5. __(e)__ Thomson's experiment measured e/m for electrons. The charge to mass ratio for a hydrogen ion was already known.

6. __(d)__ The lower level quantum number is 4 for the Brackett series of lines in the spectrum of H atoms.

7. __(a)__ $\lambda = 1/\tilde{\nu} = 1/(1.028x10^{-2}\ nm^{-1}) = 97.3\ nm$. A wavelength of 97.3 nm is in the far ultraviolet.

8. __(e)__ Some drops are positively charged and some are negatively charged. Some have as much as 5 to 9 times the magnitude of charge on an electron. In the absence of a field the speed with which the drops fall is determined by

the viscosity of the air as well as by the acceleration of gravity. Oil drops are used because water evaporates so much more readily.

9. <u>**(e)**</u> Option (a) is a true statement, but was known before Rutherford's experiment. Option (b) is false. Option (c) is true but was determined by combining Thomson's value of the e/m ratio with Millikan's measurement of the charge on an electron. Option (d) is true, but was determined from the results of Thomson's cathode-ray experiments.

10. <u>**(d)**</u> Convert from eV/atom to kJ/mol as follows:

$$\left(12.084\ \frac{\text{eV}}{\text{atom}}\right)\left(1.6022\text{x}10^{-19}\ \frac{\text{J}}{\text{eV}}\right)\left(6.022\text{x}10^{23}\ \frac{\text{atom}}{\text{mol}}\right)$$

$$=\ 116.6\text{x}10^{4}\ \text{J/mol}\ =\ 1166\ \text{kJ/mol}$$

11. <u>**(d)**</u> If the speed of light is in m/s, the wavenumber must be in m^{-1}, as $\nu = c\tilde{\nu}$. To convert from cm^{-1} to m^{-1}, multiply by 100: (5331.6 1/cm)(100 cm/m) = $5.3316\text{x}10^{5}$ m^{-1}.

$$\nu = (2.997925\text{x}10^{8}\ \text{m/s})(5.3316\text{x}10^{5}\ \text{m}^{-1}) = 1.598\text{x}10^{14}\ \text{s}^{-1}$$

12. <u>**(e)**</u> For an H-like ion,

$$\Delta E = hc\mathcal{R}Z^{2}\left(\frac{1}{n_L^2} - \frac{1}{n_H^2}\right)$$

The ionization energy is the energy required to move the electron from $n_L = 1$ to $n_H = \infty$, or $hc\mathcal{R}Z^2$. Since Z = 1 for H and 3 for Li^{2+}, it requires $3^2 = 9$ times as much energy to ionize the electron in Li^{2+} as it does in H.

13. (c) The de Broglie wavelength is $\lambda = h/mv$, where m must be in kg in SI units.

$$\lambda = \frac{6.6262\text{x}10^{-34}\ \text{J}\cdot\text{s}}{(4.00\text{x}10^{-2}\ \text{kg})(20.0\ \text{m/s})} = 8.28\text{x}10^{-34}\ \text{m} = 8.28\text{x}10^{-25}\ \text{nm}$$

14. (a) $E = h\nu = hc/\lambda$

$$E = \frac{(6.6262\text{x}10^{-34}\ \text{J}\cdot\text{s})(2.997925\text{x}10^{8}\ \text{m/s})}{(4.0\text{x}10^{-6}\ \text{m})} = 5.0\text{x}10^{-20}\ \text{J}$$

15. (e) For the Brackett series, $n_L = 4$. The most intense line is the one with the smallest possible value for n_H, i.e., $n_H = 5$. When the atoms are excited, the state with n = 5 has a greater population than any state with n greater than 5.

Solutions to Problems, Chapter 12

12.1. For $n_H = 4$ to $n_L = 3$,

$$\Delta E = hc\mathcal{R}\left(\frac{1}{9} - \frac{1}{16}\right) = \frac{7}{144}\,hc\mathcal{R}$$

For $n_H = 9$ to $n_L = 8$,

$$\Delta E = hc\mathcal{R}\left(\frac{1}{64} - \frac{1}{81}\right) = \frac{17hc\mathcal{R}}{(64)(81)}$$

The ratio of these two values is $\frac{(64)(81)(7)}{(17)(144)} = 14.82$

Note that the $hc\mathcal{R}$ factor cancels out and that no substitution of these values is necessary for this problem.

12.2. A line with $\tilde{\nu} = 97{,}491\ \text{cm}^{-1}$ is in the far ultraviolet region. The only series of the H atom spectrum that is in the far UV is the Lyman series, for which $n_L = 1$.

$$\tilde{\nu} = \mathcal{R}(1 - 1/n_H^2) = 97{,}491\ \text{cm}^{-1}$$

$$(1 - 1/n_H^2) = 97{,}491/109{,}678 = 0.8889$$

$$1/n_H^2 = 0.1111 \quad \text{so that } n_H^2 = 9 \quad \text{and} \quad n_H = 3$$

This transition is the one from $n_H = 3$ to $n_L = 1$.

12.3. According to the Uncertainty Principle it is impossible to know both the radius of the orbit (the distance from the nucleus) and the speed of the electron simultaneously.

12.4. The de Broglie wavelength is $\lambda = h/mv$.

(a) $$\lambda = \frac{6.6262\text{x}10^{-34}\ \text{J}\cdot\text{s}}{(9.1096\text{x}10^{-31}\ \text{kg})(5.9\text{x}10^{7}\ \text{m/s})} = 1.233\text{x}10^{-11}\ \text{m}$$

$$= 0.012\ \text{nm} = 0.12\ \text{Å}$$

(b) $$\lambda = \frac{6.6262\text{x}10^{-34}\ \text{J}\cdot\text{s}}{(6.0\text{x}10^{-3}\ \text{kg})(2.0\ \text{m/s})} = 5.5\text{x}10^{-32}\ \text{m} = 5.5\text{x}10^{-23}\ \text{nm}$$

(c) The wavelength of the electron is in the X-ray region and is therefore observable. The wavelength of the marble is much too small to be observed. Wave properties of atomic and subatomic particles are observable, but wave properties of macroscopic objects, of the size we can see and handle, are not observable.

12.5. A photon with a wavelength $\lambda = 0.20$ nm or $2.0\text{x}10^{-10}$ m has a frequency c/λ:

$$\nu = \frac{2.9979\text{x}10^{8}\ \text{m/s}}{2.0\text{x}10^{-10}\ \text{m}} = 1.50\text{x}10^{18}\ \text{s}^{-1}$$

$$E = h\nu = (6.6262\text{x}10^{-34}\ \text{J}\cdot\text{s})(1.50\text{x}10^{18}\ \text{s}^{-1}) = 9.94\text{x}10^{-16}\ \text{J}$$

The mass of an H atom is

$$m = \frac{1.00794 \text{ g/mol}}{6.022\text{x}10^{23} \text{ atoms/mol}} = 1.67\text{x}10^{-24} \text{ g} = 1.67\text{x}10^{-27} \text{ kg}$$

When it is moving with a speed $1.5\text{x}10^3$ m/s, its kinetic energy is $(1/2)mv^2$ or

$$\frac{1}{2}(1.67\text{x}10^{-27} \text{ kg})(1.5\text{x}10^3 \text{ m/s})^2 = 1.88\text{x}10^{-21} \text{ J}$$

The photon therefore has

$$\frac{9.94\text{x}10^{-16}}{1.88\text{x}10^{-21}} = 5.29\text{x}10^5$$

times as much kinetic energy as the H atom. This means that if the photon strikes the H atom so that we can 'see' it and determine the atom's location, the photon will impart a momentum to the atom, which will then move from its original location with an uncertain momentum.

12.6. (a) $E_n = -54.38/n^2$. For the state with n = 5, $E_5 = -54.38/25 = -2.175$ eV. Similarly, $E_2 = -54.38/4 = -13.60$ eV.

(b) $\Delta E = E_5 - E_2 = -2.175 + 13.60 = 11.42$ eV

$\Delta E = (11.42 \text{ eV})(1.6022\text{x}10^{-19} \text{ J/eV}) = 1.830\text{x}10^{-18}$ J

(c) $\nu = \Delta E/h = \dfrac{1.830\text{x}10^{-18} \text{ J}}{6.6262\text{x}10^{-34} \text{ J·s}} = 2.762\text{x}10^{15} \text{ s}^{-1}$

$$\lambda = c/\nu = \frac{2.997925\text{x}10^8 \text{ m·s}^{-1}}{2.762\text{x}10^{15} \text{ s}^{-1}} = 1.086\text{x}10^{-7} \text{ m} = 108.6 \text{ nm}$$

A line with a wavelength of 108.6 nm is in the far UV.

12.7. The photoelectric effect. If light of frequency ν is shined on a metal surface

$$h\nu = h\nu_{th} + KE$$

where ν_{th} is the threshold frequency and KE is the kinetic energy ($\frac{1}{2}mv^2$) of the emitted electrons.

(a) If λ = 589.0 nm = 5.890×10^{-7} m, the frequency is

$$\nu = c/\lambda = \frac{2.997925 \times 10^{8} \text{ m/s}}{5.890 \times 10^{-7} \text{ m}} = 5.090 \times 10^{14} \text{ s}^{-1}$$

$$E = h\nu = (6.6262 \times 10^{-34} \text{ J·s})(5.090 \times 10^{14} \text{ s}^{-1}) = 33.72 \times 10^{-20} \text{ J}$$

Hence $$33.72 \times 10^{-20} \text{ J} = h\nu_{th} + 5.77 \times 10^{-20} \text{ J}$$

and $$h\nu_{th} = 27.95 \times 10^{-20} \text{ J}$$

The work function of the metal is $h\nu_{th}$ or 2.795×10^{-19} J.

The threshold frequency is

$$\nu_{th} = \frac{27.95 \times 10^{-20} \text{ J}}{6.6262 \times 10^{-34} \text{ J·s}} = 4.218 \times 10^{14} \text{ s}^{-1}$$

(b) If λ = 253.7 nm = 2.537×10^{-7} m, the frequency is

$$\nu = c/\lambda = \frac{2.997925 \times 10^{8} \text{ m/s}}{2.537 \times 10^{-7} \text{ m}} = 1.1817 \times 10^{15} \text{ s}^{-1}$$

$$h\nu = (6.6262 \times 10^{-34} \text{ J·s})(1.1817 \times 10^{15} \text{ s}^{-1}) = 7.830 \times 10^{-19} \text{ J}$$

Using the work function calculated in part (a) we obtain

$$7.830 \times 10^{-19} \text{ J} = 2.795 \times 10^{-19} \text{ J} + KE$$

Hence $$KE = 5.035 \times 10^{-19} \text{ J} = \frac{1}{2}mv^2$$

The mass of an electron is 9.1096×10^{-31} kg. Thus

$$v^2 = \frac{(2)(5.035 \times 10^{-19} \text{ J})}{9.1096 \times 10^{-31} \text{ kg}} = 1.105 \times 10^{12} \text{ m}^2/\text{s}^2$$

$$v = 1.051 \times 10^{6} \text{ m/s}$$

The speed of the emitted electrons is 1.051×10^{6} m/s.

12.8. Looking at the frequencies we observe that

$$\nu_6 = \nu_4 + \nu_3 \quad \text{and} \quad \nu_5 = \nu_4 + \nu_2$$

Since ν_6 is larger than ν_5, ν_6 must arise from the transition $E_4 \rightarrow E_1$ and ν_5 must arise from the transition $E_3 \rightarrow E_1$. Therefore ν_2 is the frequency of the transition from E_3 to E_2 and ν_3 is the frequency of the transition from E_4 to E_2. The diagram above shows the transitions and we see that $\nu_3 = \nu_1 + \nu_2$, which is consistent with the data. The transition $E_4 \rightarrow E_3$ gives rise to the frquency ν_1.

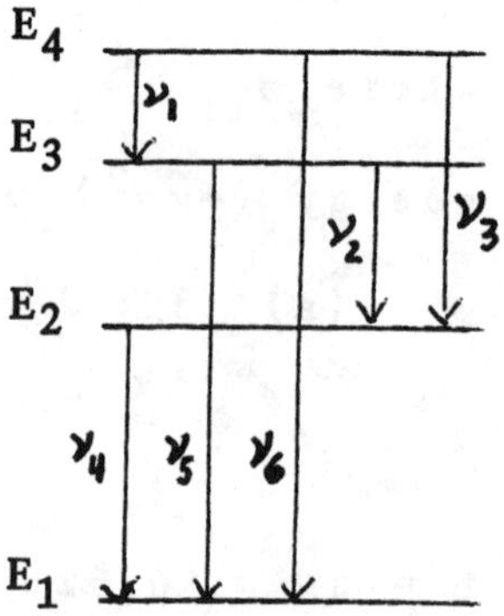

12.9. **(a)** The ground state energy of the H atom is -13.60 eV, and of any H-like ion is $-13.60Z^2$ eV. For this ion the ground state energy is -122.36 eV, so that $Z^2 = 9$ and Z = 3. This is therefore the Li^{2+} ion.

(b) The diagram is on the following page.

(c) The second most intense line of the Lyman series is the transition from n = 3 to n = 1. For this transition ΔE is $E_3 - E_1 = -13.60 + 122.36 = 108.76$ eV.

$$\Delta E = (108.76 \text{ eV})(1.6022\text{x}10^{-19} \text{ J/eV}) = 1.7426\text{x}10^{-17} \text{ J}$$

The frequency and wavenumber are

$$\nu = \Delta E/h = \frac{1.7426\text{x}10^{-17} \text{ J}}{6.62618\text{x}10^{-34} \text{ J}\cdot\text{s}} = 2.6298\text{x}10^{16} \text{ s}^{-1}$$

$$\tilde{\nu} = \nu/c = \frac{2.6298\times10^{16}\ s^{-1}}{2.997925\times10^{8}\ m\cdot s^{-1}} = 8.7721\times10^{7}\ m^{-1}$$

This line is in the far UV, very close to the border with X-rays.

(d) The ionization energy is the energy required for the transition from the ground state to infinite separation from the nucleus, where the energy is zero, by definition. Thus we must supply +122.36 eV of energy to ionize the electron in the Li^{2+} ion. The reaction that occurs is

$$Li^{2+} \rightarrow Li^{3+} + e^-$$

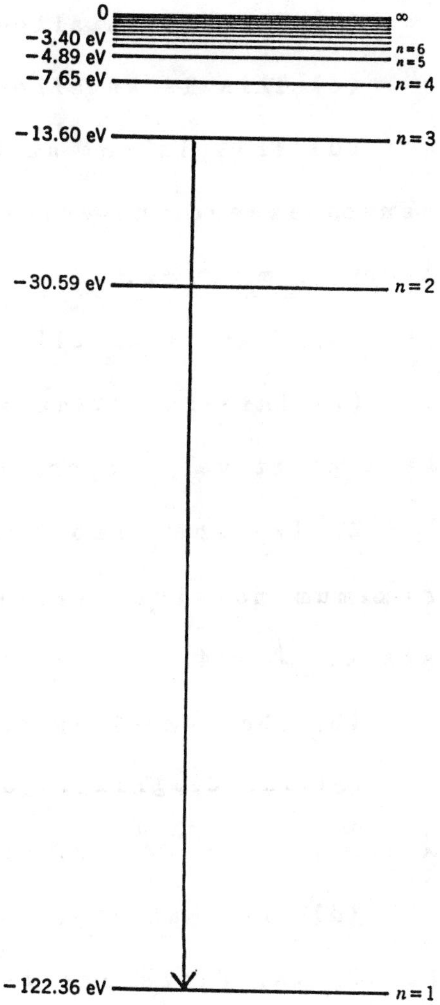

Solutions to Exercises, Chapter 13

1. (a) This is not an allowed state. The value of ℓ must not exceed n−1. For n = 4, the largest possible value of ℓ is 3.

(b) This is an allowed state.

(c) This is an allowed state.

(d) This is not an allowed state. The magnitude of m_ℓ cannot exceed the value of ℓ. The minimum value of m_ℓ for ℓ = 1 is m_ℓ = −1.

(e) This is an allowed state.

(f) This is not an allowed state. The value of ℓ must be a positive integer, or zero.

2. (a) The symbol 4g is unaccpetable. For n = 4, the maximum possible value of ℓ is 3, an f state. For a g state, ℓ = 4.

(b) The symbol 5g is acceptable.

(c) The symbol 3f is unacceptable. The maximum value of ℓ for n = 3 is ℓ = 2. For an f state, ℓ = 3.

(d) The symbol 6d is acceptable.

3. (a) There are three degenerate 6p orbitals. Their quantum numbers are:

n	ℓ	m_ℓ
6	1	1
6	1	0
6	1	−1

(b) There are five degenerate 5d orbitals. Their quantum numbers are:

n	ℓ	m_ℓ
5	2	2
5	2	1
5	2	0
5	2	-1
5	2	-2

(c) There are seven degenerate 6f orbitals. Their quantum numbers are:

n	ℓ	m_ℓ
6	3	3
6	3	2
6	3	1
6	3	0
6	3	-1
6	3	-2
6	3	-3

4.

Shell	n	Orbitals	Total No. of Orbitals
K	1	1s	1
L	2	2s, 2p	4
M	3	3s, 3p, 3d	9
N	4	4s, 4p, 4d, 4f	16
O	5	5s, 5p, 5d, 5f, 5g	25

For a given value of n, the total number of orbitals in each shell is n^2.

5. The number of nodal spheres for an ns orbital is n-1 (see Fig. 13.5). Thus a 5s electron charge cloud has 4 nodal spheres.

6. Zero. All five d orbitals have zero electron density right at the nucleus.

7. (a) For a g state, $\ell = 4$. The degeneracy is 2(4) + 1 = 9. Each of the nine g orbitals can hold 2 electrons, so the maximum number of electrons in the 5g orbitals is 18.

(b) For an f state, $\ell = 3$. The degeneracy is $2(3) + 1 = 7$. Each of the seven f orbitals can hold 2 electrons, so the maximum number of electrons in the 6f orbitals is 14.

(c) There is only a single 7s orbital, which can accommodate 2 electrons. For an s orbital, $\ell = 0$.

8. The orbitals with n = 4 are 4s, 4p, 4d, and 4f. This is a total of 16 orbitals: one 4s, three 4p, five 4d, and seven 4f. With 2 electrons per orbital, a total of 32 electrons completely fills the N shell.

9.

N $(1s)^2\underline{(2s)^2(2p_x)(2p_y)(2p_z)}$

P $(1s)^2(2s)^2(2p)^6\underline{(3s)^2(3p_x)(3p_y)(3p_z)}$

As $(1s)^2(2s)^2(2p)^6(3s)^2(3p)^6(3d)^{10}\underline{(4s)^2(4p_x)(4p_y)(4p_z)}$

10. (a) An excited state of an O atom.

(b) The ground state of an O atom.

(c) An impossible configuration. Both electrons in one of the 2p orbitals have the same spin.

(d) An excited state of an O atom.

(e) An excited state of an O atom.

(f) The ground state of an O atom.

11. (a)

↑ ↑↓ ↑
2p

↑↓
2s

↑↓
1s

Ground state of O

(b)

↑ ↑↓ ↑↓
2p

↑↓
2s

↑↓
1s

Ground state of F

(c)

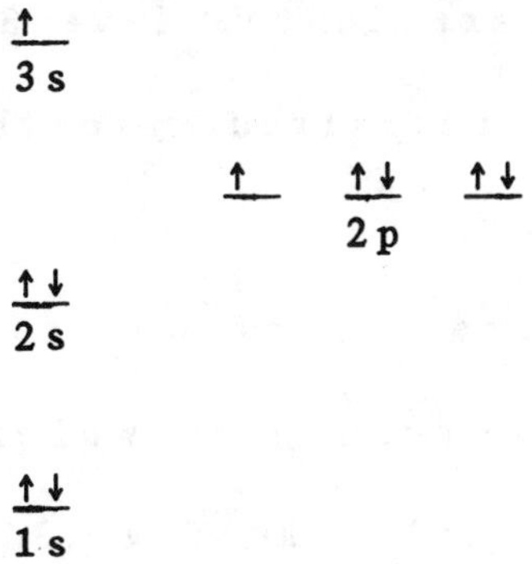

Lowest excited state of Ne: $(1s)^2(2s)^2(2p)^5(3s)$

12. (a) Sc^{3+} $(Ar)^{18}$ $Z = 21$

(b) Ti^{3+} $(Ar)^{18}(3d)$ $Z = 22$

(c) V^{3+} $(Ar)^{18}(3d)^2$ $Z = 23$

(d) Cr^{3+} $(Ar)^{18}(3d)^3$ $Z = 24$

13. **(a)** There are no unpaired electrons in Ca^{2+}. For Ca, $Z = 20$, and Ca^{2+} has 18 electrons in the argon electronic configuration.

(b) There are 2 unpaired electrons in Ti^{2+}. For titanium, $Z = 22$, so Ti^{2+} has 20 electrons, of which 18 are in the argon configuration and 2 are unpaired in two of the five 3d atomic orbitals.

(c) There are 5 unpaired electrons in Mn^{2+}. For manganese, $Z = 25$, so Mn^{2+} has 23 electrons, of which 18 are in the argon configuration and 5 are unpaired in each of the five 3d atomic orbitals.

(d) There is 1 unpaired electron in Cu^{2+}. For copper, $Z = 29$, so Cu^{2+} has 27 electrons, of which 18 are in the argon configuration and 9 are in the five 3d atomic orbitals. Eight of these 9 must be paired, and there is a single unpaired electron.

(e) There are no unpaired electrons in Zn^{2+}. For zinc, Z = 30, so Zn^{2+} has 28 electrons, of which 18 are in the argon configuration and 10 fill the five 3d AO's.

14. (a) There are no unpaired electrons in the ground state of Ca(g). The ground state electronic configuration of Ca (Z = 20) is $(Ar)^{18}(4s)^2$.

(b) There are 3 unpaired electrons in the ground state of Co(g). The ground state electronic configuration of Co (Z = 27) is $(Ar)^{18}(3d)^7(4s)^2$. As there are five 3d AO's, when they are occupied by 7 electrons, 4 must pair up and 3 are unpaired.

(c) There are no unpaired electrons in the ground state of Zn(g). The ground state electronic configuration of Zn (Z = 30) is $(Ar)^{18}(3d)^{10}(4s)^2$.

(d) There is 1 unpaired electron in the ground state of Ga(g). The ground state electronic configuration of gallium (Z = 31) is $(Ar)^{18}(3d)^{10}(4s)^2(4p)$. Gallium is a member of Group IIIA: B, Al, Ga, In, and Tl.

15. Iron is atomic number 26. The Fe^{2+} ion has 24 electrons and the Fe^{3+} has 23 electrons. The electronic configurations are: Fe^{2+} $(Ar)^{18}(3d)^6$, Fe^{3+} $(Ar)^{18}(3d)^5$.

The Fe^{2+} ion is more chemically reactive than Fe^{3+}. Of the 23 electrons in Fe^{3+} 18 are in closed shells and 5 just half-fill the 3d AO's, with parallel spin. This configuration minimizes electron-electron repulsion and is quite stable. In Fe^{2+} ion, the 6th 3d electron must pair up with another electron, and there is more electron-electron repulsion between the pair in the same AO than between those in different AO's with parallel spin, so it is easier to lose that 6th electron. In fact, most Fe^{2+} salts are not stable in air, but react with oxygen to form the corresponding Fe^{3+} salt. The Fe^{2+} ion engages in many reactions in which Fe^{3+} is formed.

16. Element 117 must be a halogen, in Group VIIA. The first 6 rows of the periodic table comprise 86 elements. The 7th row would be completed with 32 more elements, so the next rare gas would be atomic number 118 = 86 + 32. The halogen family members have Z one less than the succeeding rare gas.

17. **(a)** Potassium nitride is K_3N. The K^+ ion has argon configuration and the nitride ion, N^{3-}, has neon configuration.

(b) Aluminum sulfide is Al_2S_3. The sulfide (S^{2-}) ion has argon configuration, and the Al^{3+} ion has neon configuration.

(c) Strontium iodide is SrI_2. The Sr^{2+} ion has krypton configuration and the iodide ion (I^-) has xenon configuration.

(d) There are three different titanium oxides, TiO_2, TiO, and Ti_2O_3. The oxide ion (O^{2-}) has neon configuration. Titanium is element number 22. To attain the argon configuration it must lose 4 electrons. As this requires a very large amount of energy, the bonding in TiO_2 is polar covalent. In TiO the Ti^{2+} ion is used, and in Ti_2O_3 the Ti^{3+} ion is used. Neither of these ions has the electronic configuration of one of the rare gases.

(e) Zinc bromide is $ZnBr_2$. The Zn^{2+} has completely filled electron shells, configuration $(Ar)^{18}(3d)^{10}$, but does not have the configuration of any rare gas. The bromide ion (Br^-) has krypton configuration.

18. The plot for part (a) is on the next page.

(b) As a general trend, the ionization energy increases as Z increases from Na to Ar, because the nuclear charge is increasing and the electron being ionized is an n = 3 electron in all of these atoms. The outer n = 3 electrons are held more tightly as the positive charge in the nucleus increases, and it requires more energy to remove an electron. However, the effective nuclear charge experienced by a valence electron depends upon how much shielding of the nuclear charge is provided by the inner electrons, and on how much the valence electron penetrates to the nucleus.

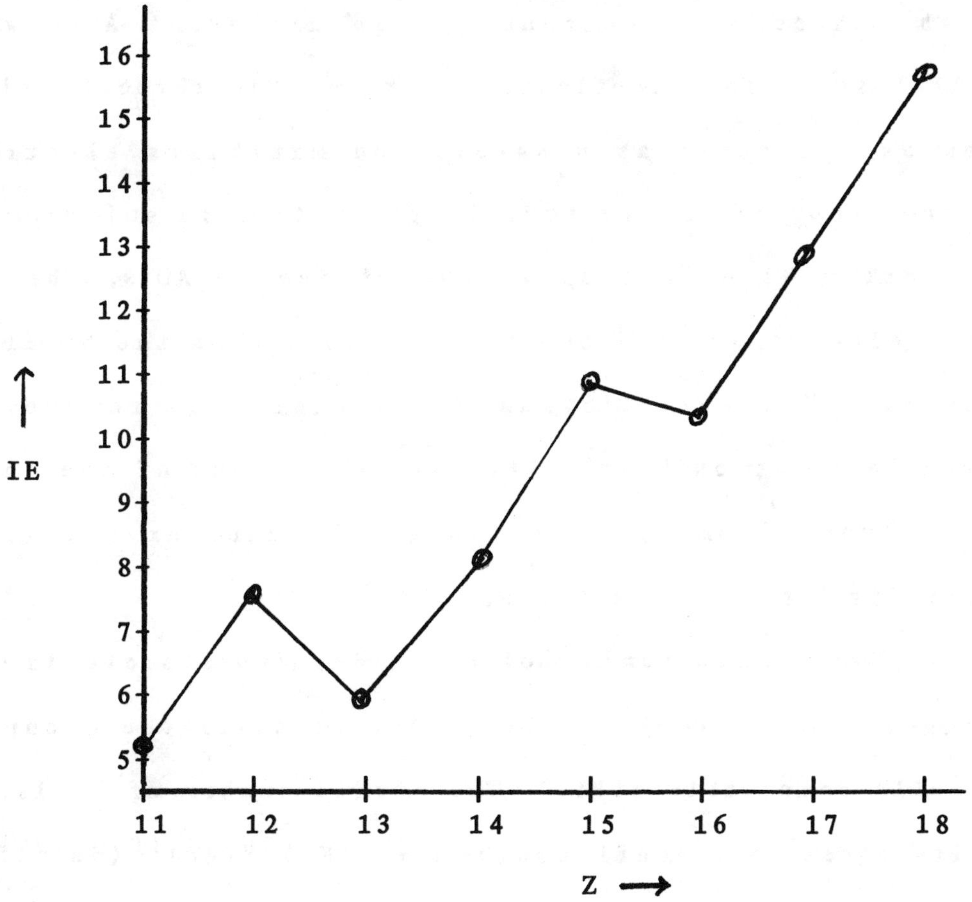

There are two irregularities in this general trend. The ionization energy of Al is lower than the ionization energy of the preceding element, Mg. In Al a 3p electron is being removed, in Mg it is a 3s electron. A 3p electron does not penetrate to the nucleus as much as a 3s electron, and is more effectively shielded by the inner electrons than a 3s electron. Consequently it is easier to ionize the 3p electron of Al (Z = 13), than a 3s electron of Mg (Z = 12).

There is a second irregularity at elements 15 and 16, P and S. The electron configuration of P is $(Ne)^{10}(3s)^2(3p)^3$, and the three 3p electrons are in different AO's with parallel spin. This configuration keeps the three 3p electrons as far apart as possible and minimizes electron-electron repulsion. The fourth 3p electron in sulfur must necessarily be paired up in one of the 3p AO's. The two paired electrons repel one another more than the 3p electrons in different AO's and it is easier to remove the fourth 3p electron from S than to remove one of the three 3p electrons from P, even though the nuclear charge is larger for S than it is for P.

19. The atomic number of Cd is 48, and its electronic configuration is $(Kr)^{36}(4d)^{10}(5s)^2$, with all the occupied subshells completely filled. The atomic number of In is 49, and its electronic configuration is $(Kr)^{36}(4d)^{10}(5s)^2(5p)$. Thus for the first ionization energy, a 5p electron is being removed from In whereas a 5s electron is being removed from Cd. A 5p electron penetrates to the nucleus less than a 5s electron, and is more shielded from the nuclear charge. Although the actual nuclear charge is greater for In than for Cd, the effective nuclear charge experienced by the valence 5p electron in In is lower than the effective nuclear charge experienced by the 5s electron in Cd.

20. The electron affinity generally increases across one period from metallic to nonmetallic elements. Adding an electron to the outer or valence shell releases more energy if the nuclear charge is greater. Since it is the 3p subshell to which an electron is being added in the 4 atoms Si through Cl, the distance to and penetration to the nucleus is roughly the same, and the greater nuclear charge accounts for the greater electron affinity as Z increases. The low value of the electron affinity for P is due to the fact that the 3p orbitals are half-full at P, with a single electron in each 3p AO, with parallel spin. This configuration minimizes electron-electron repulsion. Adding a fourth electron necessarily causes two electrons to pair up, and the increased electron-electron repulsion when that 4th electron is added accounts for the low value of the electron affinity of P.

21.

F	S	As	Zn	Y
4.0	2.5	2.0	1.6	1.2

In general, electronegativity increases across a period in the periodic table, and as we go up to the lighter elements within a family. Fluorine is in Group VIIA, Z = 9, and is the most electronegative element in the periodic table. Sulfur is in group VIA, Z = 16. Arsenic is in Group VA, Z = 33. Both Zn and Y are transition metals, but Zn is in the

4th period (Z = 30) and Y is in the 5th period (Z = 39).

22. (a) HI, HBr, HCl, HF

increasing dipole moment ⟶

The dipole moment increases with increasing electronegativity of the halogen. The ability of the halogen to pull electron density towards itseslf and away from hydrogen is greatest for F and least for I of the four halogens. The more electron density around the halogen, and the less around hydrogen, the greater the dipole moment of the molecule.

(b) In general, the greater the difference in electronegativity between the two atoms, the greater the dipole moment of the diatomic molecule.

smallest dipole moment	BrCl	$x_{Cl} - x_{Br} = 3.0 - 2.8 = 0.2$
↓	NO	$x_{O} - x_{N} = 3.5 - 3.0 = 0.5$
↓	HCl	$x_{Cl} - x_{H} = 3.0 - 2.1 = 0.9$
↓	ClF	$x_{F} - x_{Cl} = 4.0 - 3.0 = 1.0$
largest dipole moment	LiI	$x_{I} - x_{Li} = 2.5 - 1.0 = 1.5$

23. For a bond to be classified as mainly ionic, the difference in electronegativity between the bonded atoms should be greater than or equal to 1.8. For a bond to be classified as mainly covalent, the difference in electronegativity should be less than 1.0.

(a) NCl_3 covalent $x_{Cl} - x_{N} = 3.0 - 3.0 = 0$

(b) YCl_3 ionic $x_{Cl} - x_{Y} = 3.0 - 1.2 = 1.8$

(c) CI_4 covalent $x_I - x_C = 2.5 - 2.5 = 0$

(d) BaO ionic $x_O - x_{Ba} = 3.5 - 0.9 = 2.6$

(e) $BeBr_2$ polar covalent $x_{Br} - x_{Be} = 2.8 - 1.5 = 1.3$

(f) FeS covalent $x_S - x_{Fe} = 2.5 - 1.8 = 0.7$

24. The amount of ionic character in the bond increases as the electronegativity difference between the two bonded atoms increases.

least ionic character ↓	BrCl	$x_{Cl} - x_{Br}$	$= 3.0 - 2.8 = 0.2$
	$AsCl_3$	$x_{Cl} - x_{As}$	$= 3.0 - 2.0 = 1.0$
	$GeCl_4$	$x_{Cl} - x_{Ge}$	$= 3.0 - 1.8 = 1.2$
	$GaCl_3$	$x_{Cl} - x_{Ga}$	$= 3.0 - 1.6 = 1.4$
	$CaCl_2$	$x_{Cl} - x_{Ca}$	$= 3.0 - 1.0 = 2.0$
most ionic character	KCl	$x_{Cl} - x_K$	$= 3.0 - 0.8 = 2.2$

25. (a) H:F̤̈:

(b) As has 5 valence electrons and each I atom has 7 valence electrons, for a total of 7x3 + 5 = 26 electrons to use for octets.

```
    ..
   :I:
 .. ..  ..
:I:As:I:
 ..  ..  ..
```

(c) Each Cl has 7 valence electrons and O has 6 valence electrons, for a total of 7x2 + 6 = 20 electrons to use for octets.

```
 ..  ..  ..
:Cl:O:Cl:
 ..  ..  ..
```

26. Beryllium is the smallest atom in the alkaline earth family, and its 2s valence electrons are close to the nucleus and experience a greater effective nuclear charge than the valence ns electrons of the other alkaline earth metals. Because of its very small size, the first and second ionization energies of Be are relatively high compared to those of other alkaline earths, and the compounds of beryllium are partly covalent and partly ionic, rather than the mainly ionic compounds formed by other members of this family.

27.

	Ca^{2+}	K^+	Ar	Cl^-	S^{2-}
Z =	20	19	18	17	16

smallest radius ⟶ largest radius

All have 18 electrons. The larger the nuclear charge, the more tightly the 18 electrons are held, and the smaller the radius. The anions, which have more electrons than protons, are significantly larger than the cations.

28. Group IVA atoms all have outer electronic configuration $(ns)^2(np)^2$. This is the family of atoms beginning with carbon: C, Si, Ge, Sn, and Pb.

29. Iodine is atomic number 53. By accepting one electron from a metal to form the iodide ion, it attains the same electronic configuration as the rare gas xenon, atomic number 54.

30. **(a)** Si (Z = 14) $(Ne)^{10}(3s)^2(3p)^2$ 2 unpaired

(b) Cl (Z = 17) $(Ne)^{10}(3s)^2(3p)^5$ 1 unpaired

(c) Sr (Z = 38) $(Kr)^{36}(5s)^2$ 0 unpaired

(d) Cs (Z = 55) $(Xe)^{54}(6s)$ 1 unpaired

31. (a) $2K(s) + 2H_2O \rightarrow H_2(g) + 2OH^-(aq) + 2K^+(aq)$

(b) The electronic configurations are:

$$K \quad (Ar)^{18}(4s) \quad \text{and} \quad Li \quad (He)^2(2s)$$

It takes less energy to ionize the 4s electron of K than the 2s electron of Li. Both valence electrons experience about the same effective nuclear charge due to the screening of the nucleus by inner electrons, but the distance between the nucleus and the valence electron is significantly larger for K than for Li. Since the first ionization energy of Li is greater than that of K, more energy will be released when K reacts with H_2O than when Li reacts with H_2O. The reaction between K and H_2O is more exothermic.

32. (a) $2K(s) + Cl_2(g) \rightarrow 2KCl(s)$

(b) $Sr(s) + Cl_2(g) \rightarrow SrCl_2(s)$

In order to compare the exothermicities of these two reactions, the same number of moles of $Cl_2(g)$ must be used in both, as in the equations above. In the reaction with 2 moles of potassium, twice the first ionization energy per mole of K must be expended, to make 2 moles of K^+ ions. In the reaction with 1 mole of strontium, both the first and the second ionization energies of Sr must be expended, to make 1 mole of Sr^{2+} ions. Strontium is an alkaline earth and its first ionization energy is larger than the first ionization energy of K, an alkali metal (see Fig. 13.18).

The second ionization energy of Sr is very much larger than the first ionization energy, because it always takes significantly more energy to remove a second electron from a singly charged positive ion. As a result, the reaction of 1 mole of $Cl_2(g)$ with 2 moles of K releases more energy than the reaction of 1 mole of $Cl_2(g)$ with 1 mole of Sr.

33. $$3Mg(s) + N_2(g) \rightarrow Mg_3N_2(s)$$

The ions in magnesium nitride are Mg^{2+} and N^{3-}. The atomic number of Mg is 12. When Mg loses loses two electrons, the Mg^{2+} has the same electronic configuration as the rare gas neon, $(1s)^2(2s)^2(2p)^6$. The atomic number of N is 7. When a nitrogen atom gains 3 electrons, it achieves the rare gas configuration of neon. Thus the electronic configurations of both ions, Mg^{2+} and N^{3-}, are the same.

Solutions to Multiple Choice Questions, Chapter 13

1. **(d)** Both Ca and Zn have completely filled subshells. The electronic configuration of Ca (Z = 20) is $(Ar)^{18}(4s)^2$ and that of Zn (Z = 30) is $(Ar)^{18}(3d)^{10}(4s)^2$. Vanadium, cobalt, and arsenic each have 3 unpaired electrons in the ground state. Their electronic configurations are

V (Z = 23) $(Ar)^{18}(3d)^3(4s)^2$

Co (Z = 27) $(Ar)^{18}(3d)^7(4s)^2$

As (Z = 33) $(Ar)^{18}(3d)^{10}(4s)^2(4p)^3$

2. (e) Because it is inner 3d electrons that are being added as we progress along the transition elements, the atomic radius does not vary much as we go from Cr (Z = 24) to Co (Z = 27). The outer 4s electrons of these 4 atoms experience roughly the same effective nuclear charge at approximately the same distance from the nucleus.

As we go down a family in the periodic table the atomic radius increases significantly as the outermost electrons are further and further from the nucleus, and the effective nuclear charge is roughly constant. Thus in series (a) and (b) the atomic radius is getting larger as Z increases.

As we go across a period, if the outer electrons are in the same atomic orbital and Z is increasing, the size decreases. For the series B, C, N, O the outer electrons are 2p electrons, and the increase in nuclear charge causes the atomic radius to decrease. For the series Ga, Ge, As, Se the outer electrons are 3p electrons and the atomic radius decreases as we go from Z = 31 to Z = 34.

3. (e) The element is phosphorus, Z = 15, as can be seen by counting electrons. In reacting with an active metal like Ca, which only reacts to give away 2 electrons, P accepts 3 electrons to achieve the argon electronic configuration. The ion formed is phosphide ion, P^{3-}. The only possible neutral compound between Ca^{2+} ions and P^{3-}

ions is Ca_3P_2, calcium phosphide.

4. <u>(d)</u> There are 6 unpaired electrons in the ground state of Mo (Z = 42): $(Kr)^{36}(4d)^5(5s)$. There is 1 unpaired electron in the ground state of Ag, none in Cd, 2 in Sn, and 3 in Co.

5. <u>(c)</u> The effective nuclear charge experienced by the outermost electrons of both Ne and Ar is very similar, because the increase in Z from Ne to Ar is counterbalanced by an increase in shielding by a larger inner core of electrons. Since the atomic radius of Ar is larger than that of Ne, and the force of attraction is inversely proportional to the square of the distance between charges (Coulomb's Law), the outer electrons of Ar are less tightly held than the outer electrons of Ne, and it is easier to ionize Ar than Ne.

6. <u>(c)</u> The atomic number of iron is 26. When 3 electrons are removed to form the Fe^{3+} ion, there are 23 electrons remaining. Therefore options (b) and (e) are immediately ruled out as they involve more than 23 electrons. Option (b) is the ground state of the Fe atom, and (e) is the ground state of the Fe^{2+} ion. For the first series of transition metals, the 4s electrons are lost first on forming the ions. Options (a) and (d) are therefore excited states of Fe^{3+}. The ground state has no 4s electrons.

7. <u>(b)</u> The outermost electrons of Sr are 5s electrons, for which n = 5 and $\ell = 0$. Therefore m_ℓ must be 0, and m_s can be either 1/2 or -1/2.

8. <u>(d)</u> The atoms of the various options are: (a) Si, (b) P, (c) S, (d) N, and (e) As. Three of these are Group VA elements: N, P, As. All have their outermost electrons in half-filled p orbitals, but the smaller size of the N atom gives it the largest ionization energy of the three. Silicon and sulfur, atomic numbers 14 and 16, both have lower ionization energies than phosphorus, Z = 15.

9. <u>(c)</u> Cesium is the most electropositive element in the periodic table, fluorine the most electronegative.

10. <u>(e)</u> Option (a) is the Heisenberg Uncertainty Principle. Option (b) is part of Hund's Rule. Option (c) is the de Broglie relation. Option (d) is an experimental fact.

11. <u>(c)</u> Options (a), (b), and (e) are transition metals. Selenium is a nonmetal.

12. <u>(d)</u> The largest halogen is I; the atomic radius decreases in order of decreasing atomic number. All three halogens are larger than either H or He. Helium is smaller than H as the outer electrons are in the 1s orbital for both, but He has twice the nuclear charge and pulls the 1s orbital in more closely to the nucleus. Thus the order of decreasing atomic radius is I>Br>Cl>H>He.

13. <u>(b)</u> Yttrium has 3 more electrons than Kr, and forms a Y^{3+} ion with krypton electron configuration. Indium can form a 3+ ion, but In^{3+} does not have rare gas electronic configuration.

14. <u>(a)</u> Both Be^{2+} and Li^{+} have configuration $(1s)^2$. With 4 protons in the nucleus the 1s electrons of Be^{2+} are pulled in closer to the nucleus than the 1s electrons of Li^{+}, which has only 3 protons in the nucleus. The Be^{2+} ion is very tiny; its ionic radius is only 0.31 Å. The anions are significantly larger than the cations.

15. <u>(c)</u> The three anions all have 10 electrons, and the electronic configuration of neon. The N^{3-} ion is the largest as there are only 7 protons in the nucleus to hold onto the 10 electrons.

16. <u>(b)</u> All the other sets have at least 1 compound in which two nonmetals have combined, and the difference in electronegativity between the bonded nonmetals is small.

17. <u>(b)</u> The Zn^{2+}, Cd^{2+}, and Ag^{+} ions do not have rare gas configuration. The Sc^{3+} ion has argon configuration.

18. <u>(e)</u> Set III is improper because if $\ell = 0$, m_ℓ can only be zero. Set V is improper because ℓ cannot exceed n-1 so that if n = 3, the largest value of ℓ allowed is 2.

19. <u>(c)</u> Alkali metal salts are soluble. The carbonates of the alkaline earths are not soluble.

20. <u>(e)</u> Element 110 will be directly below Pt, in the Ni, Pd, Pt column, if it is ever made.

21. <u>(a)</u> Copper has configuration $(Ar)^{18}(3d)^{10}(4s)$. It is atomic number 29. Argon has no 3d electrons, Cr has 5. Both Zn and Kr have a filled 3d subshell, but their atomic numbers are higher than that of Cu.

22. <u>(b)</u> The electronic configuration of Fe^{3+}, with 23 electrons, is $(Ar)^{18}(3d)^5$, and each of the five 3d electrons is in a different AO with parallel spin, in accord with Hund's Rule. The Cr^{2+} ion has 3 unpaired electrons, Mn^{3+} has 4, Ni^{2+} has 2, and Cu^{2+} has 1 unpaired electron.

23. <u>(c)</u> For a d electron, $\ell = 2$. The lowest value of n for which $\ell = 2$ is 3, so the atom with lowest electronic configuration $(n-1)d^6ns^2$ is iron, with outer configuration $3d^64s^2$, in the fourth period.

24. <u>(b)</u> Atomic weights just increase regularly with Z, they do not have any periodicity.

25. <u>(a)</u> Nitrogen has a higher ionization energy than P because it is smaller, and they are in the same family. Neon has a higher ionization energy than N because it is in the same period (the second) and terminates that period. An alakli metal has the lowest ionization energy of any element in its period, and has a lower ionization energy than any element in the preceding period. Values of the first

ionization energy of these elements in eV/atom are:

Na (5.14), P (11.0), N (14.5) and Ne (21.6).

26. <u>**(b)**</u> The first ionization energy is the energy required to remove a single electron from a <u>gaseous</u> atom to form a singly charged gaseous ion.

<u>Solutions to Problems, Chapter 13</u>

13.1.

Shell	n	Orbitals	Total No. of Electrons
K	1	1s	2
L	2	2s, 2p	8
M	3	3s, 3p, 3d	18
N	4	4s, 4p, 4d, 4f	32
O	5	5s, 5p, 5d, 5f, 5g	50

The maximum number of electrons in a shell with principal quantum number n is $2n^2$.

13.2. (a) Ca^{2+}, S^{2-}, Sc^{3+} all have argon configuration.

(b) Ag^+, Cd^{2+}, Fe^{3+}, Ti^{2+}, Zn^{2+}, do not have the configuration of any rare gas.

13.3. (a) The d_{xz} AO has two nodal planes. One of these is the xy plane, the other the yz plane.

(b) The $d_{x^2-y^2}$ AO has two nodal planes. These are the planes perpendicular to the xy plane, passing through the origin, making $\pm 45^\circ$ angles to both the x and y axes.

13.4. $Ca^{2+}(aq) + CO_2(g) + 2OH^-(aq) \longrightarrow CaCO_3\downarrow + H_2O$

13.5. The electronic configurations are

Rb $(Kr)^{36}(5s)$ and Sr $(Kr)^{36}(5s)^2$

Removal of the 5s electron in Rb produces the Rb^+ ion, with configuration $(Kr)^{36}$. To ionize a second electron is energetically very difficult because it requires removing a 4p electron from a filled subshell and producing an ion that does not have the configuration of any rare gas. Thus the reaction

$$Rb^+(g) \rightarrow Rb^{2+}(g) + e^-$$

requires the expenditure of more than 6.5 times as much energy as removal of the first (5s) electron.

On the other hand, both the electrons being removed from Sr, for the first and second ionization energies, are 5s electrons. While it always requires more energy to remove a second electron from a singly charged positive ion than to remove the first electron from a neutral atom, the removal of the second 5s electron in Sr

$$Sr^+(g) \rightarrow Sr^{2+}(g) + e^-$$

which produces the Sr^{2+} ion with krypton electronic configuration, requires less than twice as much energy as removing the first 5s electron.

13.6. (a) The electron configuration of arsenic is $(Ar)^{18}(3d)^{10}(4s)^2(4p)^3$. The three 4p electrons are in different AO's with parallel spin. This configuration keeps the electrons as far apart as possible and minimizes electron-electron repulsion. The electron configuration of Se is $(Ar)^{18}(3d)^{10}(4s)^2(4p)^4$. The fourth 4p electron must necessarily pair up with another 4p electron. The two electrons in the same AO repel one another more than the three 4p electrons of As, and it requires less energy to remove the fourth 4p electron of Se than to remove one of the three 4p electrons of As from the half-filled orbitals.

(b) In He and in H the electron being ionized is a 1s electron. However, the 1s orbital is pulled in considerably closer to the nucleus in He than in H, because of the +2 nuclear charge in He, as compared to the +1 nuclear charge in H. Thus the 1s electrons of He are held much more tightly than the 1s electron of H, and it requires almost twice as much energy to remove one electron from He than from H.

13.7. Europium, the element before gadolinium, has electronic configuration $(Xe)^{54}(4f)^7(6s)^2$. In the lanthanide elements it is the 4f orbitals that are being filled. If the configuration of Gd placed 8 electrons into the 4f orbitals, there would necessarily be one pair of electrons in the same AO. Having electrons in different AO's with parallel spin minimizes electron-electron repulsion, and therefore minimizes the energy of the many electron system. Even though the 5d orbital is somewhat higher in energy than the 4f orbital, the total energy of all the electrons is less when the configuration is $(Xe)^{54}(4f)^7(5d)(6s)^2$.

There are then eight unpaired electrons, with parallel spin, and the total configuration is lower in energy than having a pair of electrons in one of the seven 4f orbitals.

13.8. The ions listed all have 36 electrons and are isoelectronic with the rare gas krypton. The nuclear charge is increasing regularly from arsenic (Z = 33) to yttrium (Z = 39). The greater the nuclear charge, the more tightly the 36 electrons with the same configuration are held. Thus the ionic radius decreases regularly as Z increases. Note that the cations have significantly smaller radii than the anions.

13.9. **(a)** The ions that have rare gas configuration are Ba^{2+}, I^-, S^{2-}, and Y^{3+}. **(b)** The ions that do not have rare gas configuration but have completely filled subshells are Ag^+, Cd^{2+}, Pb^{2+}, and Zn^{2+}. **(c)** The ions that are colored are Cr^{3+}, Cu^{2+}, Fe^{3+}, Mn^{2+}, Ni^{2+}, and Ti^{3+}. Note that the ions that are able to absorb light in the visible region are those with electrons in subshells that are not completely filled.

13.10. The electron configuration of Li is $(1s)^2(2s)$. If we add an electron it can go into the 2s atomic orbital. The electron configuration of Be is $(1s)^2(2s)^2$. If we add an electron it must go into the 2p AO, considerably higher in energy than the 2s. Thus the electron affinity of Be is negative, indicating that we must expend energy to add one electron to Be, whereas the electron affinity of Li is positive (although very small), indicating that energy is released when one electron is added to a gaseous Li atom.

13.11. All the configurations shown represent various excited states of Cr. The ground state electronic configuration of Cr is $(Ar)^{18}(3d)^5(4s)$, with all six unpaired electrons having parallel spin. Configurations (a) and (c) have five 3d electrons and one 4s, but all six electrons do not have parallel spin. None of the configurations violates the Pauli Principle, so none is impossible. But only when all six valence electrons have parallel spin does the many electron system have lowest energy.

13.12. (a) Of these ions, Cl^- has the largest ionic radius, and Sc^{3+} the smallest. These ions all have 18 electrons, and are isoelectronic with Ar. The larger the nuclear charge, the more closely the 18 electrons are pulled in toward the nucleus. The nuclear charge of Cl^- is 17, while that of Sc^{3+} is 21.

(b) Of these atoms, Ar has the largest first IE and Al the smallest. These three atoms are all in the third period of the periodic table, and the electron being ionized for all is one with $n = 3$. However, the electron being ionized in Mg ($Z = 12$) is a 3s electron, while the electron being ionized for Al (Z = 13) and Ar (Z = 18) is a 3p electron. Generally, as Z increases across a period the IE increases, as a larger nuclear charge holds valence electrons in the same AO more tightly. But the 3p electron of Al is easier to ionize than the 3s electron of Mg, because a 3p electron penetrates to the nucleus less than a 3s electron. The effective nuclear charge experienced by the valence 3p electron of Al is less than the effective nuclear charge experienced by the 3s electron of Mg, even though the actual nuclear charge is larger by 1.

(c) The second IE is largest for Na and smallest for Mg. The electron configuration of Na is $(Ne)^{10}(3s)$, of Mg is $(Ne)^{10}(3s)^2$, and of Al is $(Ne)^{10}(3s)^2(3p)$. For Na, the second electron ionized is an inner 2p electron in the neon core. Ionizing an inner 2p electron requires a great deal of energy. Removing the second 3s electron of Mg is much easier, and produces the Mg^{2+} ion with neon configuration. The second electron ionized from Al is one of the 3s electrons. This ionization requires slightly more energy than removing a 3s electron from Mg, because the Al nucleus has a higher nuclear charge (13, compared to 12 for Mg). The values of the second ionization energies (in kJ/mol) are 4565 for Na, 1816 for Al, and 1450 for Mg. Note how much larger the second IE is for Na than for the others.

13.13. Indium (Z = 49) has electronic configuration $(Kr)^{36}(4d)^{10}(5s)^2(5p)$. There is no way In can form a cation with the electronic configuration of one of the rare gases, but if it loses a single electron (the 5p) to form a +1 cation, the ion formed does have completely filled subshells. We do find that a +1 ion is formed, and that accounts for InCl and In_2S. By losing all three of the n = 5 electrons, a +3 ion with completely filled subshells is attained, and indeed $InCl_3$ and In_2S_3 are formed. However, the amount of energy required to completely remove three electrons is extremely large, and these bonds have a lot of covalent character. The compound with simplest formula $InCl_2$ does not contain a +2 ion. It is rather $In^+InCl_4^-$. The $InCl_4^-$ ion has In–Cl bonds that are polar covalent, and an octet of electrons around the In, with structure

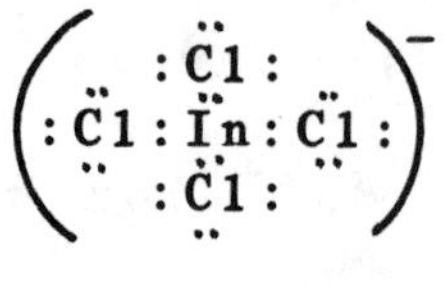

Indium is in Group IIIA, and it most frequently forms compounds that involve the loss or sharing of the three valence electrons. None of these are purely ionic compounds. The trihalide dimerizes to In_2Cl_6. The melting points increase with the formation of structures having an octet of electrons around indium, which is not possible with the +1 ion.

13.14.

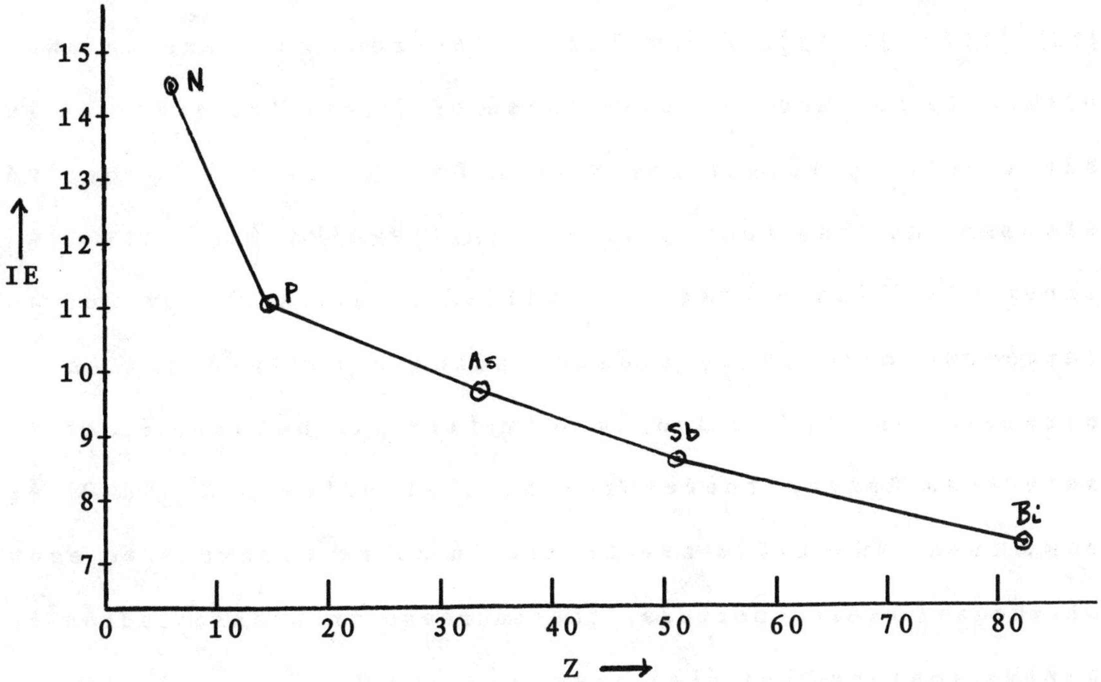

The valence electrons of these Group VA elements have configuration $(ns)^2(np)^3$. As Z increases, the valence electrons are further from the nucleus, but experience about the same effective nuclear charge. The actual nuclear charge has of course increased, but the core of inner electrons screening the valence electrons from the nuclear charge has also increased. Since the effective nuclear charge is about the same, but the distance from the nucleus is increasing, it is easier to ionize one electron as Z increases. Note that nitrogen is a nonmetal, but metallic character increases as Z increases, and bismuth is a metal with $(IE)_1$ just about half that of nitrogen.

The electronic configuration of N is $1s^2 2s^2 2p^3$, and of P is $(Ne)^{10} 3s^2 3p^3$. The valence electrons of N are so much closer to the nucleus than those of P that the first IE is significantly larger for N than for P. The next group VA element, As, has configuration $(Ar)^{18} 3d^{10} 4s^2 4p^3$. Thus the inner 3d orbitals have been filled in and there is not as large an increase in atomic radius between P and As as between N and P. The decrease in first IE between P and As is not as large, therefore, as that between N and P. As some inner subshells are filled in as we progress to each of the succeeding periods, the increase in atomic radius is always smaller than that between N and P.

13.15. Compounds with cations that do not have rare gas electronic configuration are those that would be expected to be colored. Of those listed, $Cu(NO_3)_2$ is blue-green, Tl_2S is blue-black, HgS is vermillion (brilliant deep red), RhF_3 is red, and $PdBr_2$ is red-brown. All the other compounds are white, and have cations with the electronic configuration of one of the rare gases, except for $CdCl_2$. The Cd^{2+} ion has completely filled subshells (although it does not have rare gas configuration) and the Cl^- ion is small and not very polarizable. The electrons of the Cd^{2+} and Cl^- ions are therefore not loosely held, and the compound is not colored.

13.16. (a) 1. For the elements of the second period, the outer or valence electrons have n = 2. Lithium only has a single valence 2s electron. For the <u>second</u> ionization energy, two electrons are being ionized, and for Li this means removing one of the inner 1s electrons. For all of the other elements, only outer electrons are being removed for the second IE, and therefore the second IE is very much larger for Li than for any other element in this period.

2. From Be to Ne the nuclear charge is increasing, but the electron being removed is in the same shell, the n = 2 shell. The amount of shielding or screening of the nuclear charge by inner electrons is not increasing as rapidly as the increase in nuclear charge, and the IE (both first and second) increases with increasing Z.

3. The electronic configuration of B is $1s^22s^22p$; that of C is $1s^22s^22p^2$. For the second IE, a 2s electron is being removed from B, a 2p electron from C. As 2p electrons do not penetrate to the nucleus as much as 2s electrons do, $(IE)_2$ is a little less for C than for B, even though the nuclear charge is larger by 1.

4. The electronic configuration of O is $1s^22s^22p^4$; that of F is $1s^22s^22p^5$. Removing two electrons from F leaves an ion with half-filled 2p AO's, one in each AO with parallel spin. Both the electrons ionized for $(IE)_1$ and $(IE)_2$ are electrons that are paired in the same AO. Repulsion between electrons in the same AO is greater than repulsion between electrons in different AO's with parallel spin. For oxygen, the electron ionized for $(IE)_2$ is not a paired electron. It is easier to remove an electron in the same AO with another than to remove an electron in a different AO. The half-filled 2p subshell with all spins parallel is the configuration that minimizes electron-electron repulsion.

(b) The second ionization energy of Na is between 41.1 and 75.6 eV. It is less than $(IE)_2$ for Li because the electron being ionized in Na is a 2p electron, while that in Li is a 1s electron. Although the nuclear charge of Na is larger, the 2p electron penetrates less to the nucleus, and is further away, and $(IE)_2$ is smaller for Na than for Li. The value of $(IE)_2$ for Na is, however, larger than the value for Ne. For both of these atoms a 2p electron is being ionized, but the nuclear charge is larger for Na (11 as compared to 10 for Ne) and it requires more energy to remove a 2p electron from Na than from Ne.

Solutions to Exercises, Chapter 14

1. (a) At infinite separation the Coulombic energy is zero. At a distance of 2.24 Å = $2.24\text{x}10^{-10}$ m, the Coulombic energy of a Li^+Br^- ion pair is

$$\frac{-(8.988\text{x}10^{9}\ \text{J}\cdot\text{m/C}^{2})(1.602\text{x}10^{-19}\ \text{C})^{2}}{(2.24\text{x}10^{-10}\ \text{m})} = -10.30\text{x}10^{-19}\ \frac{\text{J}}{\text{ion-pair}}$$

Therefore $1.030\text{x}10^{-18}$ J of energy are released when one ion-pair Li^+Br^- monomer is formed from the separate ions.

(b) For a mole of such ion-pairs, the energy released is $(1.030\text{x}10^{-18})(6.022\text{x}10^{23}) = 6.201\text{x}10^{5}$ J/mol = 620 kJ/mol

2.

$$\begin{array}{ll} Li(g) \rightarrow Li^+(g) + e^- & IE(Li) = 520\ \text{kJ/mol} \\ Br(g) + e^- \rightarrow Br^-(g) & -EA(Br) = -324\ \text{kJ/mol} \\ \hline Li(g) + Br(g) \rightarrow Li^+(g) + Br^-(g) & \end{array}$$

$$\Delta H = 520 - 324 = +196\ \text{kJ/mol}$$

A mole of $Li^+(g)$ ions plus a mole of $Br^-(g)$ ions is higher in energy than a mole of Li(g) atoms plus a mole of Br(g) atoms by 196 kJ.

3. (a) The BH_4^- ion has 8 valence electrons, 3 from B, 1 from each H atom, and 1 from the negative charge on the ion. The Lewis structure is

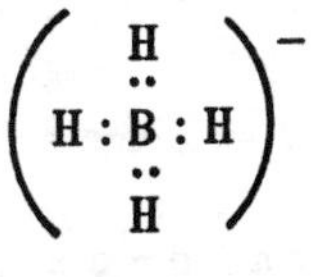

(b) The CN^- ion has 10 valence electrons, 4 from C, 5 from N, and 1 from the negative charge on the ion. The Lewis structure is $(:C\equiv N:)^-$

(c) Formic acid has 18 valence electrons, 4 from C, 6 from each of the two O atoms and 1 from each of the two H atoms. The Lewis structure is

$$H-\overset{\overset{\displaystyle :\!O\!:}{\|}}{C}-\ddot{O}-H$$

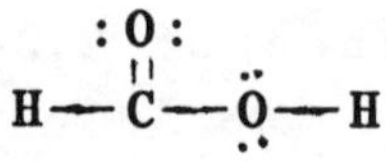

(d) There are 8 valence electrons, 6 from S, 1 from each of two H atoms. The Lewis structure is $H-\ddot{\underset{..}{S}}-H$

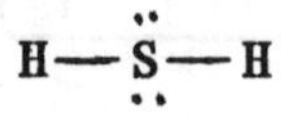

(e) The hypochlorite ion has 14 valence electrons, 7 from Cl, 6 from O, and 1 from the negative charge on the ion. The Lewis structure is $(:\!\ddot{\underset{..}{O}}\!-\!\ddot{\underset{..}{C}l\!:})^-$

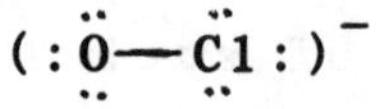

4. (a) Nitrite ion has 18 valence electrons, 5 from N, 6 from each of two O atoms, and 1 from the negative charge. The resonance structures are

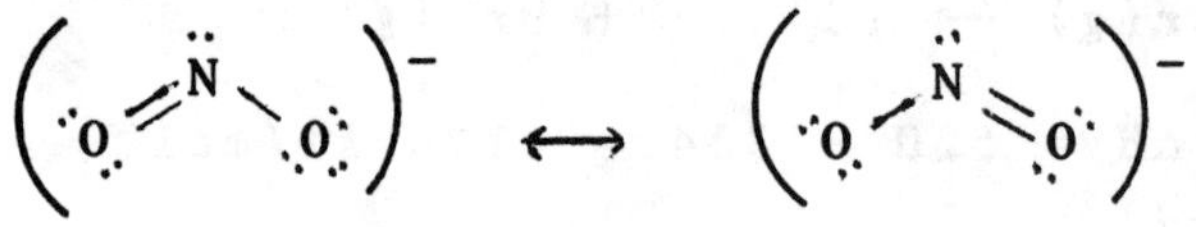

(b) The resonance structures for acetate ion, CH_3COO^-, are

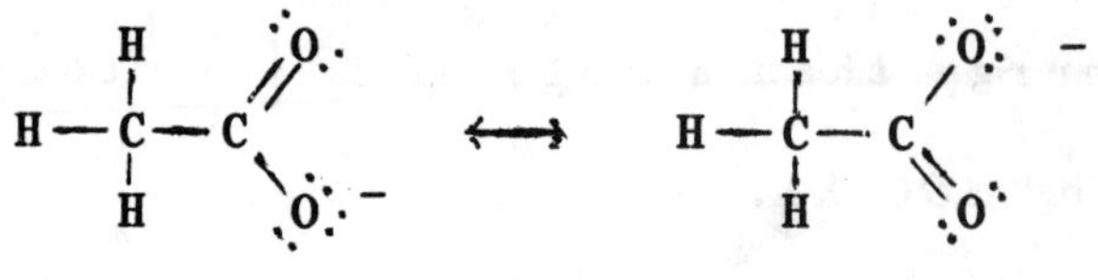

(c) Thiocyanate ion has 16 valence electrons, 6 from S, 4 from C, 5 from N, and 1 from the charge on the ion. The resonance structures are

$$(:\!\ddot{S}\!=\!C\!=\!\ddot{N}\!:)^- \quad\longleftrightarrow\quad (:\!\ddot{\underset{..}{S}}\!-\!C\!\equiv\!N\!:)^-$$

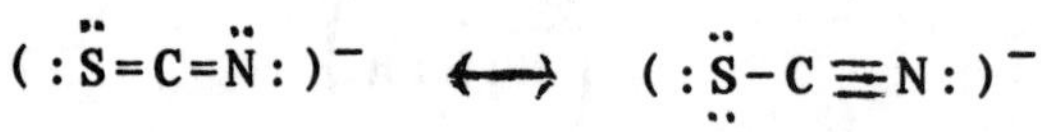

(d) Ozone has 18 valence electrons, 6 from each of three O atoms. The resonance structures are

$$:\!\ddot{\underset{..}{O}}\overset{\overset{\displaystyle \ddot{O}}{\diagup}}{}\!\diagdown\!\ddot{\underset{..}{O}}\!: \quad\longleftrightarrow\quad :\!\ddot{\underset{..}{O}}\!\diagup\overset{\displaystyle \ddot{O}}{}\!\diagdown\!\ddot{\underset{..}{O}}\!:$$

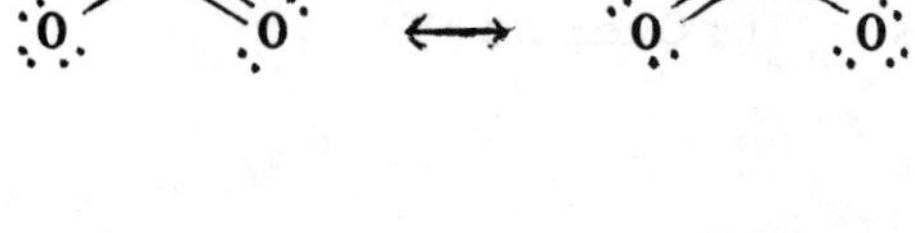

5. (a) The SO_4^{2-} ion has 32 valence electrons, as S and O atoms contribute 6 each, and there are 2 negative charges on the ion. The Lewis structure with an octet of electrons around each atom is

$$\left(\begin{array}{c} :\ddot{O}: \\ | \\ :\ddot{O}-S-\ddot{O}: \\ | \\ :\ddot{O}: \end{array}\right)^{2-}$$

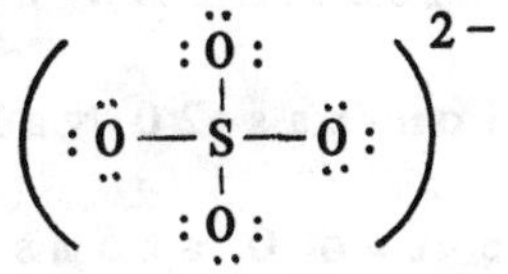

For this structure the formal charge on the S atom is +2 and on each O atom is -1. If there are 4 single bonds from S to each O atom, then 1 electron from each of those bonds is assigned to S. As the isolated S atom has 6 valence electrons, the formal charge on S is 6 - 4 = 2. Each O has 7 electrons assigned to it in this structure, 3 lone pairs plus 1 from the S—O bond. As there are 6 electrons around O in an isolated O atom, the formal charge is -1.

Although S is less electronegative than O, a charge of +2 on an S atom is unlikely. There are four resonance structures with one double bond between S and O, but these place 10 electrons around S rather than the Lewis octet. An expanded valence shell around S is possible because the 3d orbitals may be used. The four resonance structures, each of which has a formal charge of +1 on S and -3/4 on each O, are

$$\left(\begin{array}{c} :\ddot{O}: \\ \| \\ :\ddot{O}-S-\ddot{O}: \\ | \\ :\ddot{O}: \end{array}\right)^{2-} \longleftrightarrow \left(\begin{array}{c} :\ddot{O}: \\ | \\ :\ddot{O}-S=\ddot{O} \\ | \\ :\ddot{O}: \end{array}\right)^{2-} \longleftrightarrow \left(\begin{array}{c} :O: \\ | \\ :\ddot{O}-S-\ddot{O}: \\ \| \\ :\ddot{O}: \end{array}\right)^{2-} \longleftrightarrow \left(\begin{array}{c} :\ddot{O}: \\ | \\ \ddot{O}=S-\ddot{O}: \\ | \\ :\ddot{O}: \end{array}\right)^{2-}$$

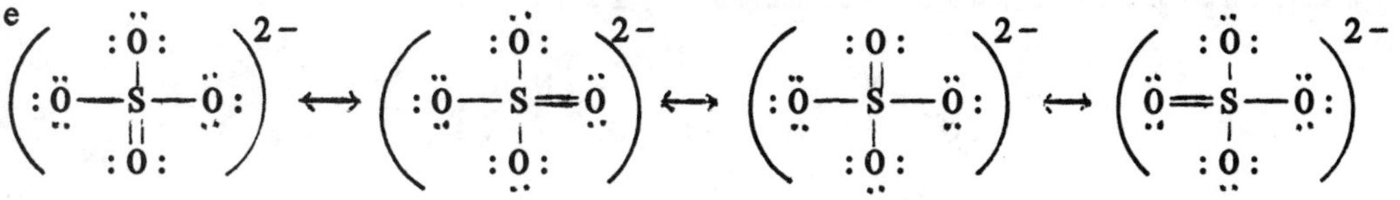

(b) There is zero formal charge on each atom in BeH_2, which has Lewis structure H:Be:H. For formal charge calculations, 2 electrons are assigned to Be, which has 2 valence electrons, and 1 electron is assigned to each H atom.

(c) The chlorite ion has 20 valence electrons, 7 from Cl, 6 from each of the two O atoms, and 1 from the charge on the ion. The Lewis structure is

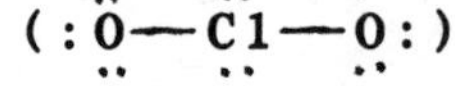

For the formal charge calculation 6 electrons are assigned to Cl, which gives it a formal charge of +1, and 7 electrons are assigned to each O atom, so that each has a formal charge of −1.

(d) The BF_3 molecule has 24 valence electrons, 3 from B and 7 from each of the three F atoms. The best Lewis structure leaves boron with only 6 electrons around it, but the formal charge on each atom is zero.

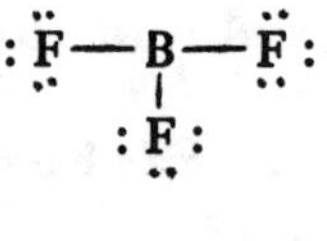

6. (a) Nitrogen dioxide has 17 valence electrons, 5 from N and 6 from each O atom. With an odd number of electrons it is impossible for each atom to have a complete octet. The best Lewis structure is

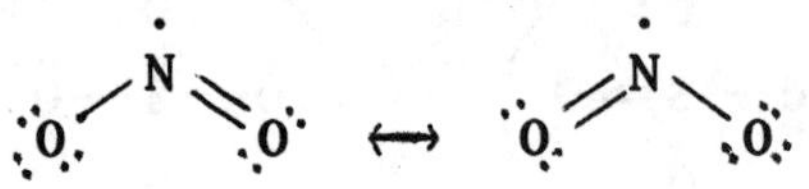

which places less than a complete octet on the less electronegative N atom, rather than on an O atom.

(b) There are 40 valence electrons in AsF_5, 5 from As, and 7 from each of the five F atoms. The only possible structure puts 10 electrons around As, but this is allowed since the 4d AO's may be used.

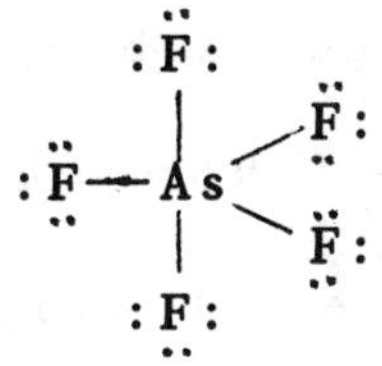

(c) There are 48 valence electrons in SF_6, 6 from S, and 7 from each of the six F atoms. The only possible structure puts 12 electrons around S in an expanded valence shell. This is possible because the 3d AO's can be used.

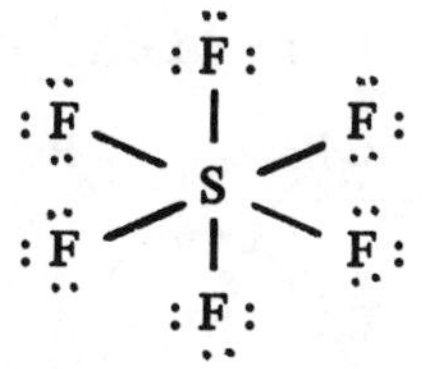

7. Each Br has 7 valence electrons, each O has 6. Any molecule with an odd number of valence electrons is paramagnetic. Thus Br_3O_8 with 69 valence electrons, and BrO_2 with 19 valence electrons, are both paramagnetic.

8. (a) The phosphate ion has 32 valence electrons, 5 from P, 6 from each of four O atoms, plus 3 from the −3 charge. This gives the central atom, P, 4 bonded pairs and the structure is tetrahedral, an AX_4 structure.

(b) Oxygen difluoride is bent (V-shaped). It has 2

bonded pairs and 2 lone pairs, an AX_2E_2 structure, :F-O-F:

(c) The NCl_3 molecule is trigonal pyramidal. There are 3 bonded pairs and 1 lone pair on the N atom (just as in NH_3), so it is an AX_3E molecule.

(d) There are 5 bonded pairs around Sb in $SbCl_5$. It is an AX_5 molecule with trigonal bipyramidal structure.

(e) There are three bonded pairs around N in the nitrate ion (24 valence electrons), so it has an AX_3 structure and is trigonal planar.

9. The BF_3 molecule has trigonal planar geometry and is completely symmetric. Although each bond is polar, the vector sum of the bond-dipoles is zero.

10. The structure of 1,1-dichloroethylene is

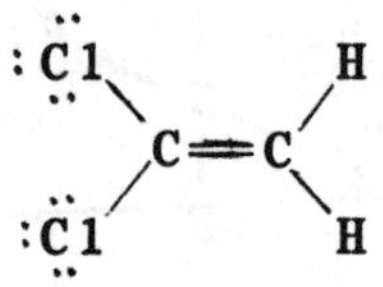

All bond angles are approximately 120°. Because there is more repulsion from a double bond than from a single bond, the H-C-H and Cl-C-Cl bond angles are a little less than 120° and tha H-C-C and Cl-C-C bond angles are a little more than 120°.

11. (a) Hypochlorous acid, HOCl, is an AX_2E_2 molecule, with structure H—O—Cl: The two lone pairs on the O atom exert more repulsion than bonded pairs, and to minimize repulsion the H-O-Cl bond angle is decreased from the tetrahedral bond angle to somewhat less than 109°28′.

(b) There are 2 bonded pairs and 1 lone pair on the central N atom, so :C̈l—N̈=Ö is an AX_2E system. The extra repulsion of the lone pair (compared to a bonded pair) pushes the bonded pairs together and decreases the bond angle from the 120° expected for a trigonal planar structure to something less than 120°, in this case 116°.

(c) Nitrogen trifluoride, like NH_3, is an AX_3E molecule with trigonal pyramidal structure. The greater repulsion of the lone pair on nitrogen pushes the bonded pairs closer together and decreases the bond angles from the tetrahedral angle of 109°28′ to 102°.

12.

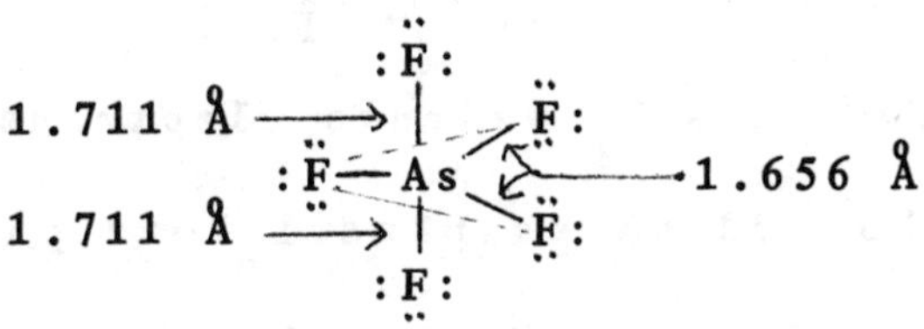

Each axial bond is 90° from 3 bonded pairs, while each equatorial bond is 90° from only 2 bonded pairs. The axial bonds therefore experience greater repulsion than the equatorial bonds, and the two axial bonds are longer than the three equatorial bonds.

13. There are 3 bonded pairs around the central C atom in $Cl_2C{=}O$. The double bond between C and O exerts a greater repulsion than a single bond, and therefore the single bonds are pushed closer together, increasing the O-C-Cl bond angles above 120°, and decreasing the Cl-C-Cl bond angles to something less than 120°. The structure is

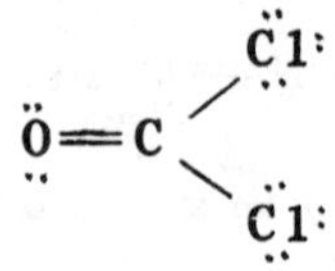

14. There are 36 valence electrons in IF_4^-, which gives the central I atom 4 bonded pairs and 2 lone pairs, an AX_4E_2 structure. For 6 pairs of electrons, we start with an octahedral structure. To minimize repulsion, the lone pairs occupy the axial positions, and the four F atoms occupy the 4 equatorial positions, giving the IF_4^- ion square planar geometry.

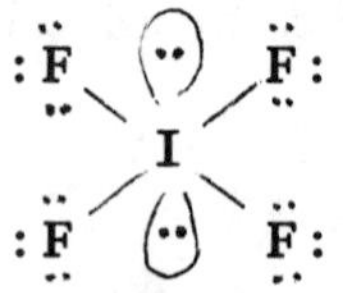

15. (a) Ozone has 18 valence electrons, and the central O atom has 2 bonded pairs plus 1 lone pair. It is an AX_2E molecule, and is bent or V-shaped.

Carbon disulfide has 16 valence electrons, and the structure is :S̈=C=S̈: With two bonded pairs and no lone pairs on the central C atom, the molecule is linear.

Nitrogen dioxide is bent or V-shaped. The central N atom has 2 bonded pairs and one unpaired electron, or one lone pair (in the resonance structures that place the unpaired electron on an O atom).

The HCN molecule is linear, H—C≡N: There are just two bonded pairs around the central C atom.

The H_2S molecule is bent or angular, just like H_2O. There are two bonded pairs and two lone pairs on the central S atom, H—$\ddot{\underset{..}{S}}$—H, so it is an AX_2E_2 molecule.

(b) Ozone is polar. The two bonds are identical. The lone pair of electrons on the central atom makes the electron charge cloud about the central atom different from that about the other two oxygens, and the molecule as a whole is polar.

Carbon disulfide is nonpolar, because it is linear and symmetric, like CO_2. The vector sum of the two bond dipoles is zero.

Nitrogen dioxide is polar. Oxygen is more electronegative than nitrogen, so each bond is polar. Since the molecule is bent, the vector sum of the bond dipoles is not zero.

The HCN molecule is polar. It is an asymmetric linear molecule, and as N is more electronegative than H, the N end has a slight negative charge and the H end a slight positive charge.

Like H_2O, H_2S is polar. Each bond is polar, and the molecule is bent, so the vector sum of the bond dipoles is not zero.

16. The MO diagram is on the following page. The bond length in F_2 is longer than the bond lengths in C_2, N_2, and

O_2 because there is only a net single σ bond in F_2, so that the bond order is 1. The bond order in O_2 and C_2 is 2, and the bond order in N_2 is 3. Of these 4 molecules, N_2 has the shortest and strongest bond, a triple bond, F_2 the longest and weakest bond.

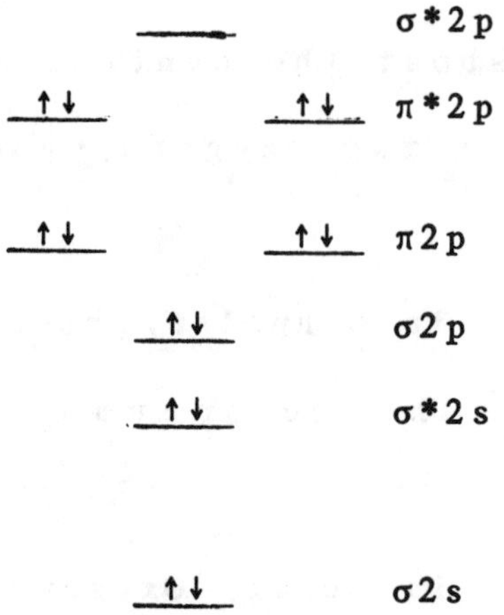

17. If Ne_2 existed there would be 16 valence electrons to occupy MO's. Sixteen electrons completely fill both the bonding and antibonding MO's formed by linear combination of 2s and 2p AO's. As there is no excess of electrons in bonding MO's over those in antibonding MO's, the bond order is zero, and the molecule cannot be stable.

18. There are 12 valence electrons to occupy MO's in O_2, 11 in $O_2{}^+$, and 13 in O_2^-. The three MO energy level diagrams are shown on the next page. Because the electron removed from O_2 to produce $O_2{}^+$ is an antibonding electron, the bond strength in $O_2{}^+$ is greater than that in O_2. Because the electron added to O_2 to produce O_2^- is an antibonding electron, the bond strength in O_2^- is less than that in O_2. Thus the order of bond energies is

$$O_2^+ > O_2 > O_2^-$$

Each of these species is paragmagnetic, because there is at least one unpaired electron in each, as can be seen by looking at the energy level diagrams below.

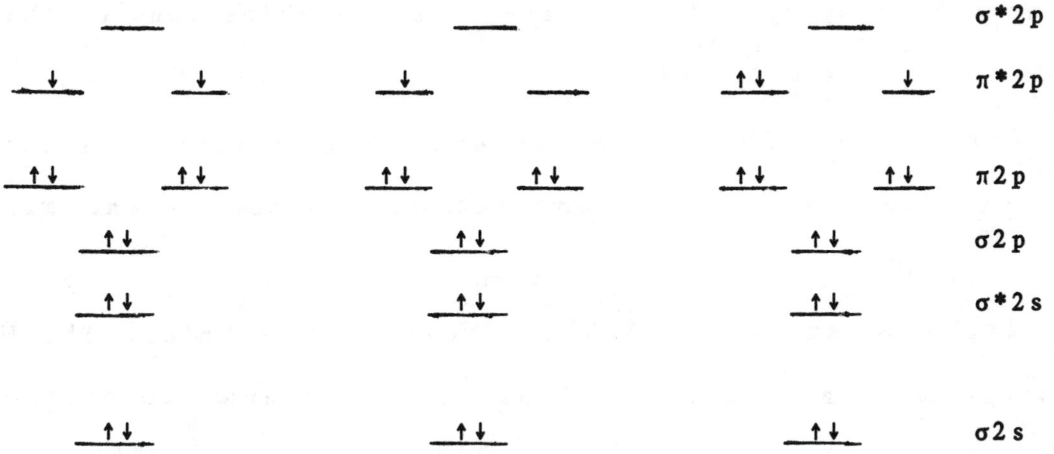

O_2	O_2^+	O_2^-
Bond order 2.0	Bond order 2.5	Bond order 1.5

19. There are 14 valence electrons to occupy MO's in F_2, but only 13 in F_2^+. The MO energy level diagram for F_2 is shown in the solution to Exercise 16. When F_2^+ is formed from F_2, the electron ionized is in an antibonding π*2p MO. Hence the net number of bonding electrons is 2 for F_2 and 3 for F_2^+. The bond order is 1 for F_2 and 1.5 for F_2^+. The bond in F_2^+ is therefore shorter than the bond in F_2.

20. (a) The ammonium ion, NH_4^+, has tetrahedral geometry. The N atom uses sp^3 hybrid AO's to bond to each H.

(b) Boron trichloride, BCl_3, is trigonal planar. The B atom uses sp^2 hybrid atomic orbitals to bond to each Cl.

(c) Sulfur hexafluoride, SF_6, is octahedral. The S atom uses sp^3d^2 hybrid AO's which are linear combinations of the 3s, three 3p, $4d_{x^2-y^2}$, and $4d_{z^2}$ AO's.

(d) Beryllium hydride, BeH_2, is a linear molecule. The Be atom uses sp hybrids that are linear combinations of the 2s and one of the 2p AO's.

(e) Silane, SiH_4, is tetrahedral. The Si atom uses sp^3 hybrids that are linear combinations of the 3s and all three 3p AO's.

21. Bond angles of 120° indicate sp^2 hybrids. The N atom forms linear combinations of the 2s and two of the three 2p AO's to make sp^2 hybrid AO's to use in bonding to the three O atoms in NO_3^-.

22. Formaldehyde, $H_2C{=}O$, has two C–H single σ bonds, and a carbon-oxygen double bond consisting of a σ bond plus a π bond. The central carbon atom uses trigonal sp^2 hybrid AO's to form the three σ bonds. The bonds between C and H are formed by the overlap of a carbon sp^2 hybrid AO with the 1s AO of hydrogen. The σ bond between C and O is formed by the overlap between a carbon sp^2 and an oxygen sp^2 AO. The trigonal hybrids on both C and O are linear combinations of the 2s and two of the three 2p AO's. The π bond between C and O is formed by the overlap of the 2p AO on each of the atoms that is not used in hybrid formation.

23. The electron configuration of I is $Kr^{36}4d^{10}5s^{2}5p^{5}$. In IF_4^- iodine uses sp^3d^2 octahedral hybrid AO's that are linear combinations of the 5s, $5p_x$, $5p_y$, $5p_z$, $5d_{z^2}$, and $5d_{x^2-y^2}$ AO's. There are 36 valence electrons, with 4 bonded pairs and 2 lone pairs around I. The lone pairs occupy the hybrids perpendicular to the plane of the 5 atoms.

24. Iodoform has tetrahedral geometry. The carbon atom uses sp^3 hybrids formed by linear combination of the 2s and all three 2p AO's. The C–H bond is formed by the overlap of an sp^3 hybrid on C and the 1s AO of H. The C–I bonds are formed by the overlap of an sp^3 hybrid on carbon and a 5p AO of iodine. The I–C–H bond angle is very close to the tetrahedral angle of 109°28′, but is slightly larger, due to the large size of the iodine atom.

25. The three resonance structures for naphthalene are:

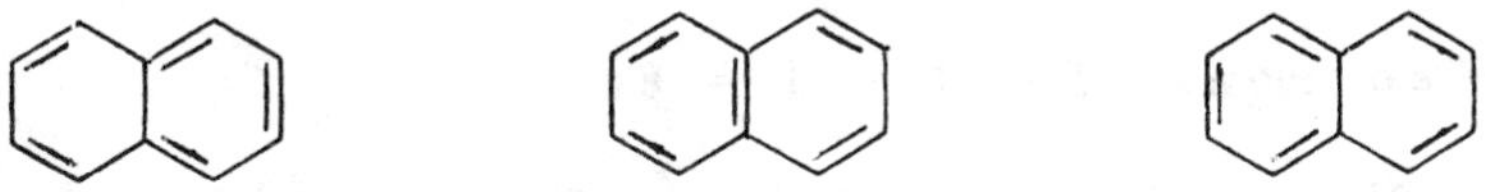

Each carbon is sp^2 hybridized. The C–H σ bonds are formed by the overlap of an sp^2 on C and the 1s AO of H. The C–C σ bonds are formed by the overlap of an sp^2 hybrid on each C. The 2p AO's, one on each C, that are not used in hybrid formation, form a delocalized π orbital, occupied by the 10 2p electrons, so there are 5 π bonds shared by 10 C atoms.

Solutions to Multiple Choice Questions, Chapter 14

1. (b) Any molecule with an odd number of valence electrons is paramagmetic. Chlorine dioxide, ClO_2, has 19 valence electrons. All the others have an even number of valence electrons, as they have an even number of Cl atoms.

2. (e) Methane has 4 single C–H σ bonds, formed by the overlap of an sp^3 hybrid on C and the 1s AO of each H.

3. (a) Benzene, C_6H_6, has planar hexagonal geometry and the vector sum of the six C–H bond dipoles is zero.

4. (d) The Zr, Mo, and Sb atoms all have unpaired electrons in the ground state. Electronic configurations can be found in Table 13.8.

5. (d) Phosphorus trifluoride has the same geometry as ammonia, NH_3, that is, trigonal pyramidal.

6. (a) Phosphorus, in group VA, has 5 valence electrons and each of the four H atoms has 1. One electron is lost on forming the PH_4^+ cation, so there are a total of 8 valence electrons, 5 + 4 − 1 = 8.

7. (a) There are 28 valence electrons for ICl_3, 7 from each of the four halogens. The structure is

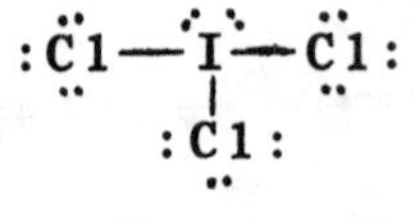

The formal charge on I is zero, as all four of the lone pair electrons, plus one from each of the bonded pairs are assigned to I. The molecule is T-shaped, an AX_3E_2 system.

8. __(e)__ In sulfur dioxide, SO_2, the S atom has two bonded pairs and one lone pair of electrons around it. Sulfur dioxide is an AX_2E molecule, with a bond angle just slightly less than 120°. Thus S uses sp^2 hybrids in bonding to oxygen and the lone pair is also in an sp^2 hybrid AO.

9. __(a)__ There are 26 valence electrons for the $SO_3{}^{2-}$ ion, 6 from each O and from S, and 2 from the -2 charge on the ion. In the Lewis structure there are 3 bonded pairs around S, and one lone pair. Thus $SO_3{}^{2-}$ is an AX_3E system, like NH_3, and is trigonal pyramidal.

10. __(e)__ In the best Lewis structure, with only octets of electrons, there are four single bonds from Cl to each O, and since 1 electron from each bond is assigned to Cl, it has a formal charge of +3 (as there are 7 valence electrons around a gaseous Cl atom). In order to reduce the formal charge on Cl, one must include double-bonded structures, which have 10 (one double bond) or 12 (two double bonds) electrons around Cl.

11. __(c)__ Carbon tetrafluoride has tetrahedral geometry.

12. __(b)__ In a square planar AX_4 system, with 4 bonded pairs and no lone pairs on the central atom, the central atom uses dsp^2 hybrids. Count the number of atomic orbitals combined to obtain the number of hybrid orbitals. In an AX_4E_2 system, with two lone pairs on the central atom,

octahedral d^2sp^3 hybrids are used, and the two lone pairs occupy the axial positions, so the molecule or ion has square planar geometry. In that sense, (d) is also a correct answer, although d^2sp^3 hybrids are octahedral.

13. <u>(d)</u> Ozone has two bonded pairs and one lone pair around the central O atom, so the bond angle in this AX_2E structure should be slightly less than 120°. Both CS_2 and N_2O are linear, and H_2O and OF_2 are AX_2E_2 systems, with bond angles slightly less than the tetrahedral bond angle of 109°28′.

14. <u>(e)</u> The P atom has 5 valence electrons, each of the four O atoms has 6, and there are 3 more due to the −3 charge on the ion, for a total of 5 + 4(6) + 3 = 32.

15. <u>(c)</u> There are 32 valence electrons in SiF_4, silicon tetrafluoride (also called tetrafluoro silane), with 4 bonded pairs forming an octet around Si, and one bonded pair and 3 lone pairs around each F. Hydrogen atoms never have 8 electrons in the valence shell, but only 2 (helium configuration) in bonded structures such as C_2H_4 and KH, potassium hydride, K^+H^-. There are an odd number of valence electrons, 17, in NO_2, and there are 12 electrons around I in IF_5, which is an AX_5E structure (42 valence electrons).

16. <u>(c)</u> The electronegativity difference between H and F is larger than the electronegativity difference between any of the other pairs of atoms, so the HF bond has the greatest amount of ionic character of those listed.

17. **(b)** The ions in strontium nitride, Sr_3N_2, are the Sr^{2+} and N^{3-} ions. The bonding is ionic as there is an electronegativity difference of 2.0 between N and Sr. However, the bonding is best described as ionic with some coivalent character.

18. **(c)** There are 26 valence electrons in $SO_3{}^{2-}$, with three bonded pairs and one lone pair around S. It is an AX_3E system, using tetrahedral sp^3 hybrid AO's.

19. **(d)** Boron forms many electron deficient compounds. There are only 12 valence electrons for B_2H_6. The three center bonds used in diborane are shown in Fig. 14.43.

20. **(b)** The bond order is 3 in CO and NO^+, 2.5 in $O_2{}^+$ and $N_2{}^+$, but only 1.5 in O_2^-, with 13 electrons to occupy MO's.

21. **(b)** Three resonance structures are needed to describe the bonding in NO_3^-. For ClO_3^-, there is only one structure with an octet about each atom, but that does give the Cl atom a formal charge of +3. If one includes double-bonded structures with 10 or 12 electrons around Cl, then resonance structures are necessary.

22. **(d)** There are 24 valence electrons for $CO_3{}^{2-}$. There are 3 bonded pairs around C, so it is trigonal planar.

23. <u>(e)</u> Tetrachloroethylene, C_2Cl_4, has one π bond between the two C atoms. There are no π bonds in $RaCl_2$ or F_2, and 2 in CS_2 and HCN.

24. <u>(a)</u> Carbon disulfide, like CO_2, has 2 double bonds, and is a linear molecule, $:\ddot{S}{=}C{=}\ddot{S}:$

25. <u>(c)</u> The structure of hydrocyanic acid is $H{-}C{\equiv}N$.

26. <u>(b)</u> Radium is an alkaline earth. The ions in $RaCl_2$ are Ra^{2+} and Cl^-.

27. <u>(c)</u> At room temperature HCN is a gas, and as the molecule is asymmetric, it is polar. The CS_2, F_2, and C_2Cl_4 molecules are all nonpolar due to their symmetry. Radium chloride is an ionic crystalline solid and does not consist of discrete molecules, but an essentially infinite array in three dimensions of Ra^{2+} and Cl^- ions.

28. <u>(d)</u> There is one σ bond in F_2, and it is nonpolar.

29. <u>(b)</u> Of the substances listed, only $RaCl_2$ is a solid. Both HCN and F_2 are gases, while CS_2 and $Cl_2C{=}CCl_2$ are liquids.

30. <u>(c)</u> Sulfur trioxide, SO_3, has polar bonds because S and O differ in electronegativity, but the molecule as a whole is trigonal planar, and nonpolar because the sum of the bond-dipole vectors is zero. The NO_2, H_2O, and SO_2 molecules are bent and are therefore polar. The HCl molecule is asymetric and therefore polar.

Solutions to Problems, Chapter 14

14.1. Nitrogen dioxide has an odd number of valence electrons and therefore cannot obey the octet rule. On dimerization, the N_2O_4 molecule is formed, which has an even number of electrons and a structure that satisfies the octet rule.

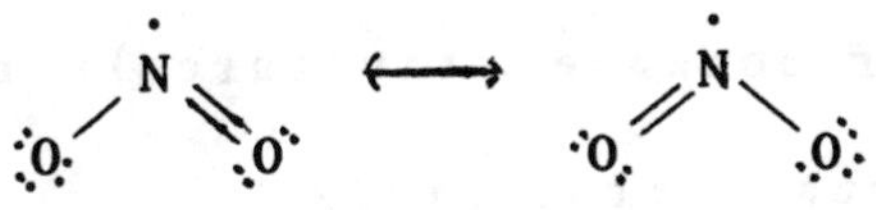

NO_2 17 valence electrons

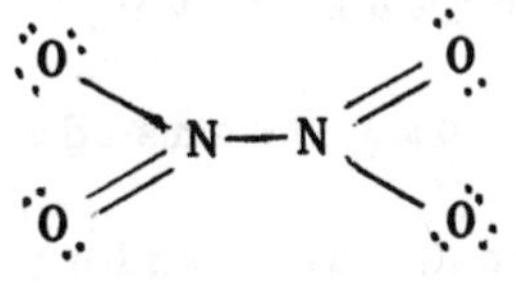

N_2O_4 34 valence electrons

14.2. There are 8 + 28 = 36 valence electrons for XeF_4. With four complete octets (4 single Xe–F bonds) there must also be two lone pairs on Xe, making XeF_4 an AX_4E_2 system. The two lone pairs occupy the axial octahedral hybrids, 180° apart, a structure that minimizes repulsion by keeping the lone pairs as far apart as possible. Thus the four F atoms lie in the equatorial plane, with square planar geometry.

14.3. (a) There are 32 valence electrons in MnO_4^-, 7 from Mn, 6 from each O atom, plus 1 from the negative charge on the anion. The best Lewis structure is

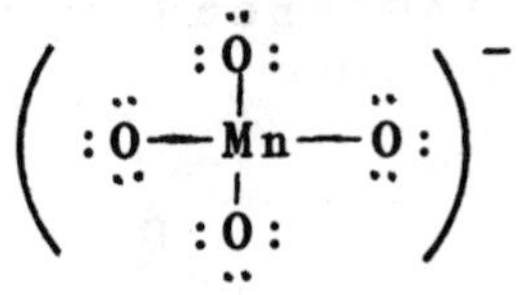

which gives Mn a formal charge of 7 − 4 = +3, and each O atom a formal charge of −1. With four bonded pairs, the geometry is tetrahedral, and the bond angles are $109^\circ 28'$.

Although Mn is more electropositive than O, a charge of +3 on Mn is highly unlikely. Double-bonded structures in which Mn uses an expanded valence shell, such as

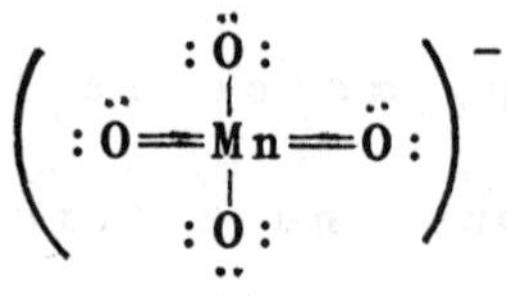

put a formal charge of +1 on Mn and -1/2 on each of the four O atoms (considering all 4 resonance structures), and undoubtedly contribute to the actual structure.

(b) There are 14 valence electrons in H_2O_2, 6 from each O atom and 1 from each H. The Lewis structure is

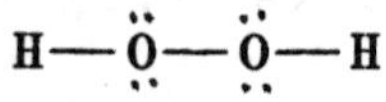

with no formal charge on any atom. Each O atom has an AX_2E_2 structure, so the bond angles should be less than $109°28'$. In fact, the H-O-O bond angles are $97°$. The H_2O_2 molecule is not planar.

(c) There are 24 valence electrons in boric acid, 3 from B, 6 from each of three O atoms, and 1 from each of three H atoms. This leaves boron electron deficient, with only 6 electrons in its valence shell. The structure is trigonal planar, with $120°$ bond angles. There is no formal charge on any atom.

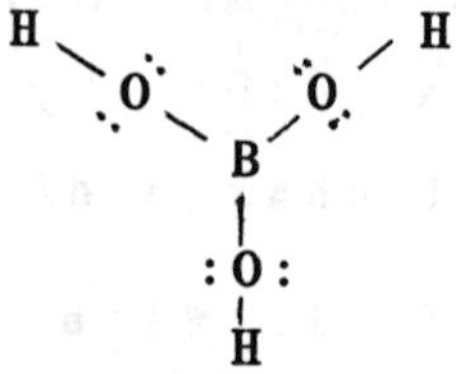

(d) There are 34 valence electrons in SF_4, 6 from S and 7 from each of four F atoms. This places a lone pair on S, and makes SF_4 an AX_4E system.

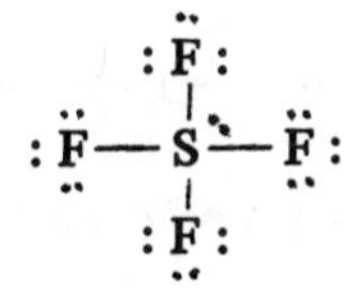

There is no formal charge on any atom, but there are 10 electrons around S rather than an octet. The lone pair of electrons lies in the equatorial plane of a distorted trigonal bipyramidal or sawhorse structure. The F-S-F bond angles involving one axial and one equatorial F should be slightly less than 90° and the F-S-F bond angles involving both equatorial F atoms should be somewhat less than 120°.

(e) There are 28 valence electrons for ICl_3, 7 from each halogen. This gives the iodine 3 bonded pairs plus two lone pairs

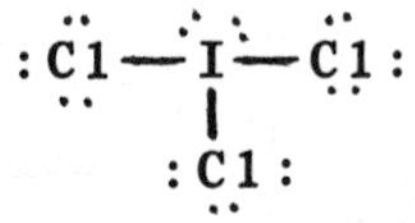

which makes the molecule T-shaped, as it is an AX_3E_2 system. The bond angles are slightly less than 90° to minimize repulsion with the lone pairs, which occupy two of the three equatorial positions.

(f) There are 44 valence electrons in I_2O_5, 7 from each I atom, plus 6 from each O atom. The Lewis structure is

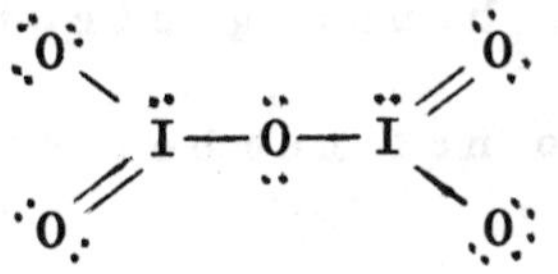

plus its resonance forms. This puts a formal charge of +1 (7 - 6) on each I atom. There is no formal charge on the central bridging O atom, but (considering resonance forms) there is a formal charge of -1/2 on each of the terminal O atoms. Each I atom is at the center of an AX_3E system, so the O-I-O bond angles should be less than $109^\circ 28'$. The bridging O atom is at the center of an AX_2E_2 system, so the I-O-I bond angle should also be less than $109^\circ 28'$.

14.4. Of the 5 species listed, the one with largest N-O bond distance is the nitrate ion, NO_3^-, with structure

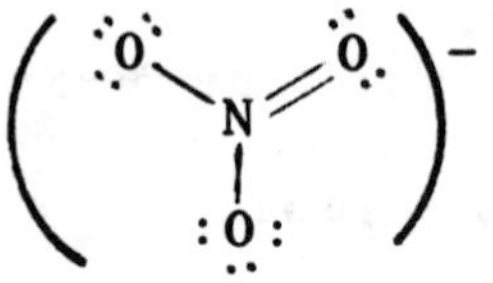

and two additional resonance forms, for a bond order of 1⅓. The nitrite ion, NO_2^-, is next, with a bond order of 1.5, as the structure is

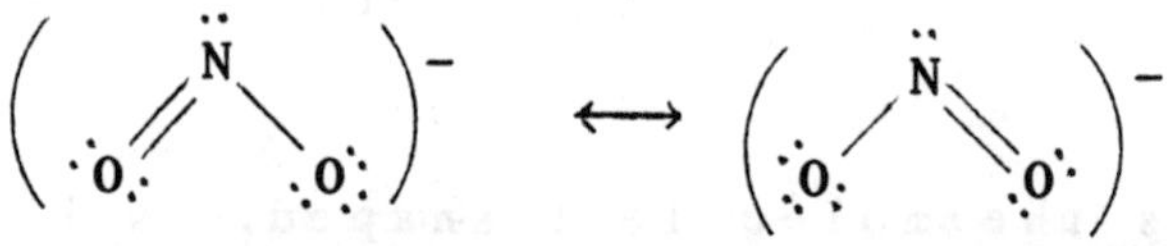

There are 16 valence electrons for NO_2^+. The structure is $:\ddot{O}{=}\overset{+}{N}{=}\ddot{O}:$, and the bond order is 2.0, so the N-O bonds are shorter than those in NO_2^- ion.

There are 10 valence electrons for NO^+ and 11 for NO. As the odd electron in NO has to occupy a π^* antibonding MO, the net number of bonding electrons is 5, for a bond order of 2.5 in NO. The net number of bonding electrons in

NO^+ is 6, making the bond order 3 (as in N_2), so that NO^+ has the shortest bond length of the 5 species.

In order of decreasing bond length, therefore, we have

$$NO_3^- > NO_2^- > NO_2{}^+ > NO > NO^+$$

bond order 1.33 1.5 2.0 2.5 3.0

14.5. There are 32 valence electrons for $SO_4{}^{2-}$. The structure with only octets

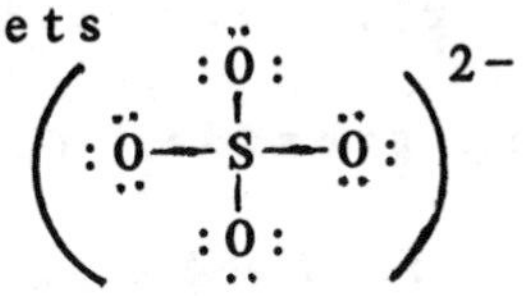

puts a formal charge of +2 on S, −1 on each O atom. The geometry is tetrahedral, with 109°28′ bond angles.

There are also four resonance structures with one double bond between S and O, and 10 electrons around S (see the answer to Exercise 5), such as

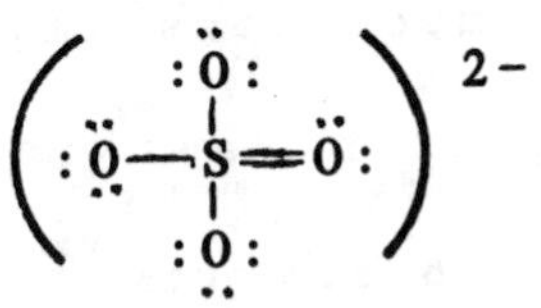

which gives the S a formal charge of +1 and each oxygen a formal charge (considering all four resonance forms) of −3/4. One could also include four resonance structures with two double bonds between S and O, and 12 electrons around S, such as

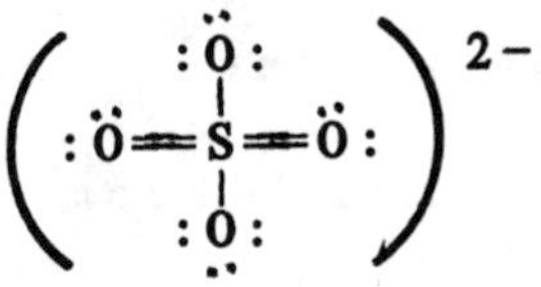

which puts a zero formal charge on S, and a −1/2 formal charge on each O atom (considering all four resonance structures). Since the ion is tetrahedral, the orbitals used by S for the σ bond to oxygen are sp^3 hybrids.

14.6. In the reaction

$$Ag^+ + 2\ :\ddot{\underset{..}{Cl}}:^- \longrightarrow (:\ddot{\underset{..}{Cl}}—Ag—\ddot{\underset{..}{Cl}}:)^-$$

the Ag^+ ion, with vacant 5s and 5p orbitals, is a Lewis acid (an electron pair acceptor) and Cl^- is a Lewis base (an electron pair donor). As the complex is linear, Ag^+ must use two digonal sp hybrids, formed by linear combination of the 5s and one of the 5p AO's.

14.7. In white phosphorus, the four P atoms are at the four apices of a regular tetrahedron, and each P-P-P bond angle is 60°. For an AX_3E system, VSEPR theory predicts a bond angle somewhat less than 109°28′ as in PH_3 (or NH_3). The 60° angle is very much less than the tetrahedral angle, and therefore we expect strain in the structure. This is consistent with the high reactivity of P_4, as the bonds are easily ruptured to form structures with bond angles closer to the 109°28′ tetrahedral angle. The structure is

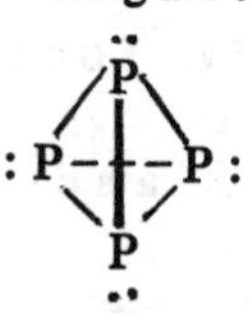

14.8. There are 24 valence electrons in O_2NCl, 6 from each O atom, 5 from N, and 7 from Cl. The Lewis structure is

which places a zero formal charge on Cl, +1 on N, and −1/2 on each O atom. As there are three bonded pairs around N, the bond angle should be approximately 120°. The double bonds exert more repulsion than the single bond, so we expect an O-N-O bond angle a little greater than 120° and a Cl-N-O bond angle a little less than 120°. The bond order of the N-O bond is 1.5, 1 σ bond and 1/2 a π bond.

14.9. There are 22 valence electrons for XeF_2, which puts 2 bonded pairs and 3 lone pairs around Xe. The three lone pairs occupy the three equatorial positions of a trigonal bipyramid, in an AX_2E_3 system, and the two F atoms occupy axial positions, 180° apart.

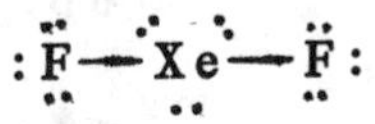

14.10. There are 24 valence electrons for BCl_3 and 26 valence electrons for PCl_3. Thus there are just 3 octets in BCl_3, an AX_3 system, with trigonal planar geometry and an electron deficient valence shell for B with only 6 electrons. In PCl_3 there is a lone pair of electrons on P, and it is an AX_3E system, a distorted tetrahedron (like NH_3), with a bond angle somewhat less than the tetrahedral angle of 109°28′.

14.11. There are 28 valence electrons for Sb_2O_3, 5 from each Sb and 6 from each O atom. The best Lewis structure is

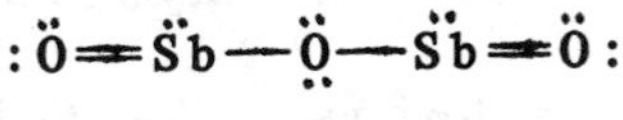

which makes the terminal Sb=O bonds shorter than the central Sb-O bonds, and cannot be correct because experimental evidence tells us that all Sb—O bond distances are equal. An all double-bonded structure :Ö=S̈b=O=S̈b=Ö: is unacceptable because it puts a formal charge of +2 on the central O atom, and -1 on each Sb, but O is considerably more electronegative than Sb. The structure of Sb_4O_6 is shown in Figure 15.3.

14.12.

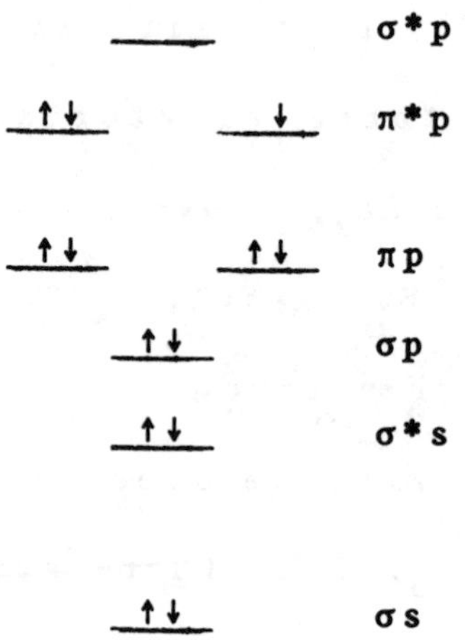

ClO Bond order 1.5

There are 13 valence electrons to occupy MO's in ClO, so that it has an unpaired electron and its three highest energy electrons are in antibonding π* orbitals, which makes it highly reactive. The Cl atom uses 3s and 3p AO's to form MO's, and the O atom uses 2s and 2p AO's. As there is a net of 3 bonding electrons, the bond order is 1.5.

14.13. Both C and N use sp^2 hybrid AO's formed from the 2s and two 2p AO's for σ bonds. The C-H bonds are formed by the overlap of sp^2 AO's on C and the 1s AO on each H. The structure is

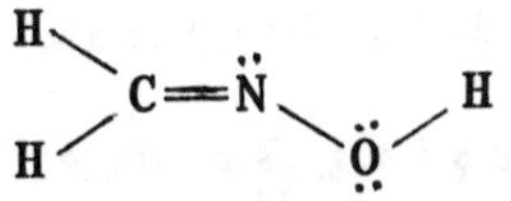

The N–C σ bond is formed by the overlap of an sp^2 AO on C and an sp^2 AO on N. The 2p AO's on N and C not used in hybrid formation overlap to form a π MO.

The O atom uses tetrahedral sp^3 orbitals, and the N-O-H bond angle is 108°, slightly less than the tetrahedral angle of 109°28′ because of the extra repulsion of the lone pairs. Thus the N–O bond is formed by the overlap of an sp^2 hybrid on N and an sp^3 hybrid on O. The O–H bond is formed by the overlap of an sp^3 hybrid on O and the 1s AO of H.

14.14.

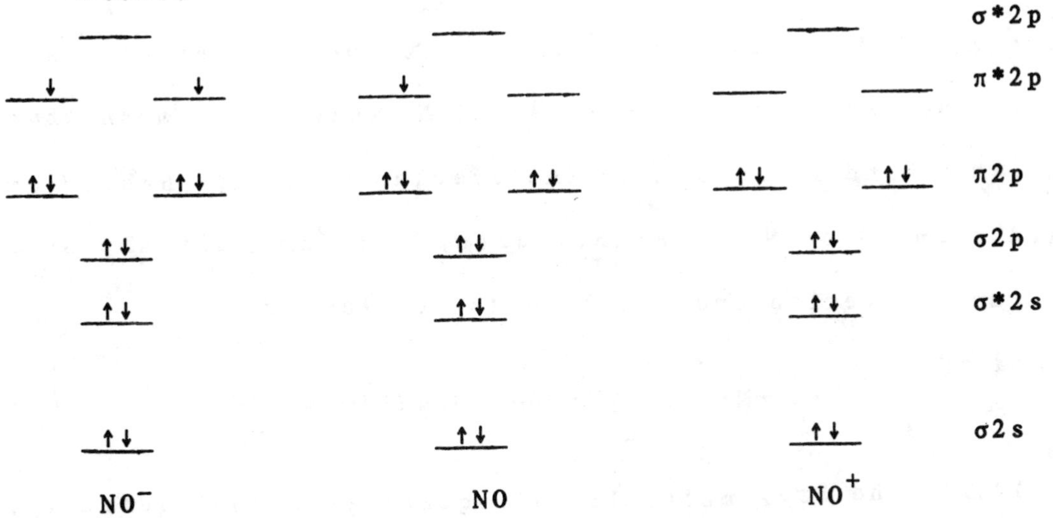

Bond order 2.0 Bond order 2.5 Bond order 3.0

The bond in NO^+ is the shortest and has the largest bond energy, as it has the largest bond order.

14.15. There are 10 valence electrons in HCN, with a triple bond between C and N, H—C≡N: As the molecule is linear, carbon must be using sp digonal hybrids that are combinations of the 2s and one of the 2p AO's. Thus the MO used for the C–H bond is formed by the overlap of an sp hybrid on C and the 1s AO of H.

There have been two schools of thought on the AO's used by N for its lone pair electrons in structures like HCN. One is that in order to strengthen the bond between C and N, N uses sp hybrids for the bond to C and also for its lone pair of electrons. That makes the σ bond between C and N an overlap of an sp hybrid on C and an sp hybrid on N.

The other is that the lone pair of electrons, since it forms no bond, should have the lowest energy possible, and should therefore be in the 2s AO of N. That would mean that the C–N σ bond is formed by the overlap of an sp^2 hybrid on C and a 2p AO on N. In either case, the remaining 2p AO's on C and N overlap and two π bonds are formed.

14.16.

$$:\overset{-}{N}=\overset{+}{N}=\overset{..}{N}\diagdown_H \quad\longleftrightarrow\quad :N\equiv\overset{+}{N}-\overset{-}{\underset{..}{N}}:\diagdown_{H}$$

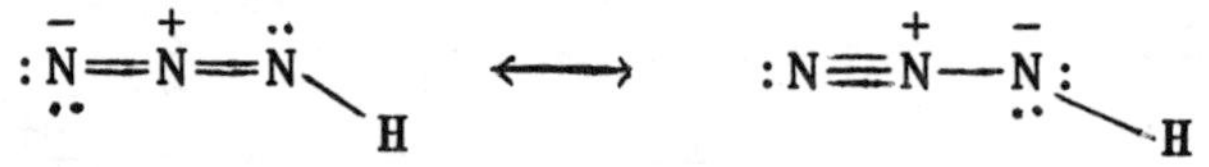

14.17. The BrF_5 molecule has square pyramidal geometry, as it is an AX_5E system. There are 42 valence electrons, 7 from each of the six halogens. Thus there are 5 bonded pairs and one lone pair on Br. To minimize repulsion, the lone pair occupies an axial octahedral hybrid orbital. The F atom in the other axial position is 180° from the lone pair, whereas the four F atoms in the equatorial positions are 90° away from the lone pair, and experience greater repulsion. The short Br-F bond is therefore along the perpendicular to the other four.

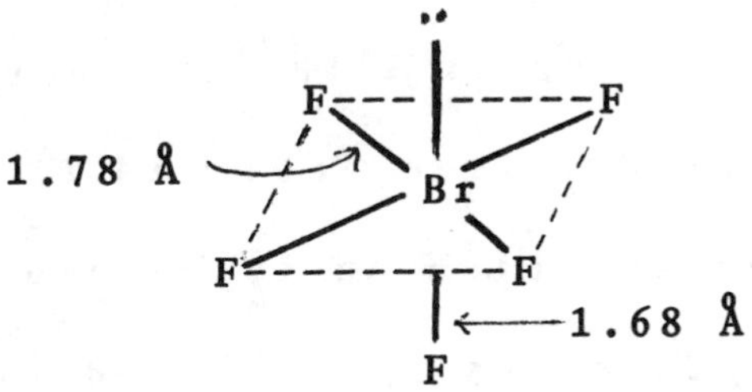

Because of the extra repulsion of the lone pair electrons, the four F atoms in the equatorial plane move slightly closer to the axial F atom, thus decreasing the F-Br-F' angle from 90° to 85° (where F' stands for the axial F).

14.18. The cyanate ion has 16 valence electrons, 5 from N, 4 from C, 6 from O, and 1 from the charge on the anion. The two resonance structures that obey the octet rule are

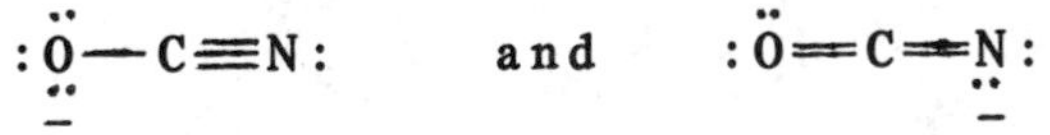

$$:\ddot{O}—C\equiv N: \qquad \text{and} \qquad :\ddot{O}=C=N:$$
$$(I) \qquad\qquad\qquad (II)$$

In structure (I) the negative charge is on the oxygen and in (II) it is on the nitrogen. We might think that resonance form (I) contributes more importantly to the structure because oxygen is more electronegative than nitrogen, but measurement of the C-O bond distance will tell us whether the real structure is closer to (I) or (II).

There is a known acid of this ion, and in it hydrogen is bonded to nitrogen and not to oxygen. Isocyanic acid, HNCO, has the following structure

$$\underset{H}{N}\overset{1.20\ \overset{\circ}{A}}{\rule{2cm}{0.4pt}}C\overset{1.18\ \overset{\circ}{A}}{\rule{2cm}{0.4pt}}O$$

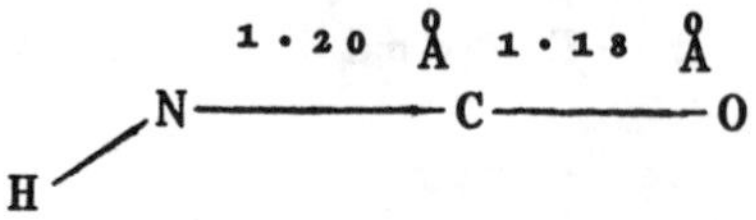

The C-O bond distance of 1.18 Å is very close to the C=O bond distance in CO_2 (see Table 14.2). There is also a silver compound in which Ag is bonded to N and not to O, and the C-O distance is 1.18 Å, indicating a C=O double bond. There is one bond distance measurement in an ionic cyanate, Na^+ NCO^-, and the C-O bond distance reported for that compound is 1.13 Å, with a large experimental uncertainty. Thus the experimental evidence seems to indicate that the structure is closer to (II) than to (I).

14.19. (a) There are 17 valence electrons in nitrogen dioxide, NO_2, for which the Lewis structure is

There are 16 valence electrons in the nitrosyl ion, NO_2^+, for which the Lewis structure is $:\ddot{O}\!=\!\overset{+}{N}\!=\!\ddot{O}:$

There are 18 valence electrons in the nitrite ion, NO_2^-, for which the Lewis structure is

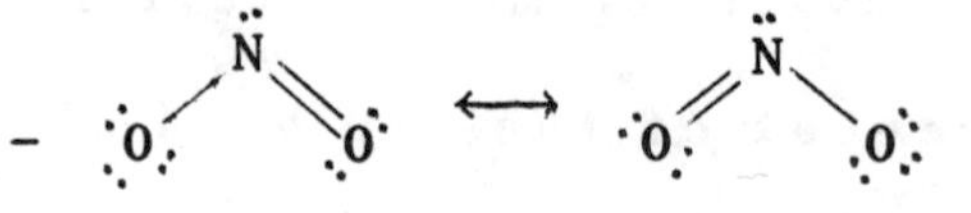

(b) With one unpaired electron, NO_2 is paramagnetic.

(c) Nitrosyl ion, NO_2^+, is a linear molecule-ion. There are two bonded pairs and no lone pairs on N. To minimize repulsion, the bonded pairs stay as far apart as possible, that is, 180° apart.

The bond angle in NO_2^- should be approximately 120°. There are two bonded pairs and one lone pair on the N atom, so it is an AX_2E system. As the lone pair exerts greater repulsion than a bonded pair, we expect a bond angle slightly less than 120°.

In NO_2 there are two bonded pairs and a single unpaired electron around N. The single unpaired electron does not exert as much repulsion on the bonded pairs as a lone pair, and the bonded pairs move further apart. Thus the bond angle in NO_2 is between the 120° bond angle in NO_2^- with a lone pair on N, and the 180° bond angle in NO_2^+ with only two bonded pairs about N.

(d) Of these three species, the one with the shortest and strongest bonds is the NO_2^+ ion, which has a bond order of 2.0, two double bonds and no lone pairs on N. The species with the longest and weakest bonds of these three is the nitrite ion, NO_2^-, with a bond order of 1.5, 1 σ bond and 1/2 a π bond between N and O, and the repulsion of a lone pair. In NO_2 there is also 1 σ and 1/2 a π bond, but the bonded pairs do not experience as much repulsion from the single unpaired electron as from the lone pair on NO_2^-.

14.20.

$$\%\ \text{ionic character} = \frac{\text{actual dipole moment}}{\text{theoretical pure ionic dipole moment}}$$

Since by definition a single positive and negative charge separated by 1.00 Å has a dipole moment of 4.80 D, and the dipole moment is the product of charge and the distance separating the charges, the theoretical pure ionic dipole moment is the charge x bond distance x 4.80 D.

For HF, the pure ionic moment is (1)(0.917)(4.80) = 4.40_2 D, and the % ionic character is (1.82/4.402)x100 = 41.3%. Results for all three molecules are tabulated below.

Molecule	Dipole Moment (D)	Bond Length (Å)	Pure Ionic Dipole Moment (D)	% Ionic Character
HF	1.82	0.917	4.40	41.3
HCl	1.08	1.274	6.175	17.7
BrF	1.29	1.756	8.429	15.3

14.21. The dipole moment of a molecule is the vector sum of bond dipoles plus any lone pair moments, if a lone pair is in an orbital that extends in space along a particular direction. In NH_3 and NF_3 there is a lone pair of electrons on N in an sp^3 hybrid, as shown below.

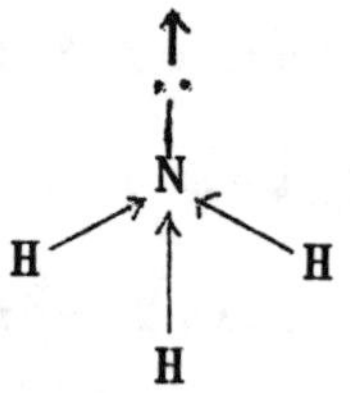

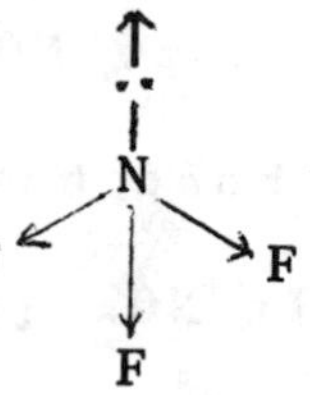

In the diagram on the preceding page, arrows point from the positive to the negative end of each bond dipole and the orbital dipole of the lone pair.

In NH_3, the orbital moment of the lone pair electrons is in the same direction as the resultant of the three N-H bond dipole vectors, and increases the molecular moment to a value greater than the resultant of the three N-H bond dipoles. On the other hand, in NF_3, the orbital moment of the lone pair electrons is in the opposite direction to the resultant of the three N-F bond-dipole vectors, and decreases the molecular moment substantially below the resultant of the three N-F bond dipoles. The net dipole moment of NH_3 is therefore larger than the net dipole moment of NF_3, even though each N-F bond dipole is larger than each N-H bond dipole, due to the greater electronegativity difference between N and F than between N and H.

Solutions to Exercises, Chapter 15

1. (a) $Li^+(aq) + e^- \rightarrow Li(s)$

   (b) $Br_2(liq) + 2e^- \rightarrow 2Br^-(aq)$

   (c) $Al^{3+}(aq) + 3e^- \rightarrow Al(s)$

   (d) $O_2(g) + 2H^+(aq) + 2e^- \rightarrow H_2O_2$

   (e) $O_2(g) + 4H^+(aq) + 4e^- \rightarrow 2H_2O$

   (f) $S_8(s) + 16e^- \rightarrow 8S^{2-}(aq)$

   (g) $8H^+(aq) + N_2(g) + 6e^- \rightarrow 2NH_4{}^+(aq)$

   (h) $Ca^{2+}(aq) + 2e^- \rightarrow Ca(s)$

2. (a) Let x = oxidation state of Mo in $MoO_4{}^{2-}$. Then

   $$x + 4(-2) = -2 \quad \text{and} \quad x = +6$$

   (b) Let x = oxidation state of S in SO_3. Then

   $$x + 3(-2) = 0 \quad \text{and} \quad x = +6$$

   (c) Let x = oxidation state of S in $SO_3{}^{2-}$. Then

   $$x + 3(-2) = -2 \quad \text{and} \quad x = +4$$

   (d) Let x = oxidation state of S in $S_2O_3{}^{2-}$. Then

   $$2x + 3(-2) = -2 \quad \text{and} \quad x = +2$$

   (e) Let x = oxidation state of C in CNO^-. Then

   $$x + (-3) + (-2) = -1 \quad \text{and} \quad x = +4$$

Note that the oxidation state of an atom in a covalently bonded molecule or ion is merely a formalism. There is certainly not anything like a +4 charge on C in CNO^-. The assignment of an oxidation state is fairly arbitrary in cases like this. The −3 state is the lowest and most common negative oxidation state for N, but N exhibits every oxidation state from −3 to +5. Of the three elements in CNO^-, carbon is the least electronegative and should have the most positive oxidation state, but it is possible to assign N the −1 oxidation state, for instance, which would put carbon in the +2 oxidation state. In balancing a redox equation involving CNO^- either keep the oxidation state of C constant and attribute the change in oxidation state to N, or keep the oxidation state of N constant and attribute the change in oxidation state to C. As long as you are consistent, the equation can be balanced correctly.

(f) Since $In(OH)_3$ contains 3 OH^- ions and is a neutral compound, the oxidation state of In must be +3.

(g) Let x = oxidation state of In in In_2S_3, indium sulfide. Then $2x + 3(-2) = 0$ and $x = +3$. Note that in any sulfide the oxidation state of S is −2.

(h) Think of this as K^+ and IO_3^-. Then the oxidation state of I is +5, as $+5 + 3(-2) = -1$. (By now you should be able to do these in your head.)

(i) The oxidation state of As is +5, as $5 + 4(-2) = -3$.

(j) Think of this as Fe^{3+} and AsO_4^{3-}. Thus the oxidation state of iron is +3.

(k) This is an ionic crystalline solid composed of Pd^{2+} and SO_4^{2-} ions. Thus the oxidation state of Pd is +2.

(l) This is a sulfide, so the oxidation state of S is −2, which makes the oxidation state of Pd = +4.

(m) Let x = oxidation state of B in $B_{10}H_{14}$. Then

$$10x + 14(+1) = 0 \quad \text{and} \quad x = -1.4$$

Note that the oxidation state of B in this covalently bonded molecule is only a formalism, with very little relation to actual charges on atoms. For electron deficient compounds like $B_{10}H_{14}$, fractional oxidation states are common. As long as the rules for determining oxidation states are consistently followed, you will be able to balance redox equations involving such molecules.

3. (a) The oxidation state of S in SO_4^{2-} is +6. The formal charge in the best Lewis structure with only octets is +2, but can be reduced to +1 or 0 by including structures with double bonds between S and O and using an expanded valence shell for S. See the answer to Problem 14.5.

The oxidation state of S in SO_3^{2-} is +4. The formal charge on S in the best Lewis structure with an octet around S is +1. If resonance forms with one double bond to O are included (and 10 electrons around S) there is a zero formal charge on sulfur.

(b) The oxidation state of Br in BrO_3^- is +5. The formal charge on Br in the best Lewis structure with an octet around Br is +2. This can be reduced to +1 or 0 by including structures with double bonds to O, using an expanded valence shell for Br.

The oxidation state of Br in BrO_2^- is +3. The formal charge on Br in BrO_2^- is +1, with an octet around Br.

The oxidation state of Br in BrO^- is +1. The formal charge on Br in BrO^- is 0.

(c) The oxidation state of N in NO_3^- is +5. The formal charge on N is +1. See the Lewis dot structure in the answer to Problem 14.4.

The oxidation state of N in NO_2^- is +3. There is a zero formal charge on N in NO_2^-. See the resonance forms in the answer to Problem 14.4.

4. (a) Chromium can be reduced from the +3 state to either the +2 state (Cr^{2+}) or the 0 state (Cr), or it can be oxidized to the +6 state, CrO_4^{2-} in basic solution or $Cr_2O_7^{2-}$ in acid solution.

(b) In H_2O_2, oxygen is in an intermediate oxidation state, the −1 state. It can be reduced to the −2 state in H_2O, or oxidized to the 0 state, $O_2(g)$.

(c) In NO, nitrogen is in an intermediate oxidation state, the +2 state. It can be oxidized either to the +3 state (NO_2^-), the +4 state (NO_2), or the +5 state (NO_3^-). It can be reduced to the 0 state (N_2) or the −3 state (NH_4^+ in acid, NH_3 in base), among others.

(d) Chromium is in its highest oxidation state, +6, in CrO_4^{2-}. A substance in its highest oxidation state can act only as an oxidizing agent, as it can only be reduced.

(e) In the Ba^{2+} ion, barium is in its highest oxidation state, the only possible state except for 0. It can only be reduced, and therefore cannot serve as a reducing agent. It is a very weak oxidizing agent, and, for the most part, does not participate in redox reactions.

(f) In Br^-, bromine is in its lowest oxidation state, the −1 state. It can only be oxidized, and therefore can serve as a reducing agent, but not as an oxidizing agent.

(g) Bromine is in the +1 state in BrO^-. It can serve as an oxidizing agent and be reduced to the −1 state (Br^-), or it can serve as a reducing agent and be oxidized to the +5 state (BrO_3^-).

(h) Titanium is in an intermediate oxidation state in Ti^{3+}. It can be oxidized to the +4 state, or reduced to the +2 or 0 state.

(i) Manganese is in an intermediate oxidation state (+4) in MnO_2. It can be oxidized to the +7 state, MnO_4^-, or reduced to the +2 state (Mn^{2+}) or the 0 state (Mn).

(j) Fluorine gas, F_2, is the most powerful oxidizing agent known. It is readily reduced to the −1 state (F^-) but there is nothing that can oxidize it.

(k) Nitrogen is in the +3 state in nitrous acid, HONO. It is therefore in an intermediate oxidation state and can act as both an oxidizing and a reducing agent. See the answer to part (c).

(l) In SO_2, sulfur is in the +4 state and can be oxidized to the +6 state (SO_3 or SO_4^{2-}) or reduced to the zero state or to the −2 state (S^{2-}).

In summary, whenever an element is in an intermediate oxidation state and can either be reduced or oxidized, it is capable of acting both as an oxidizing agent or as a reducing agent. The species in (a), (b), (c), (g), (h), (i), (k), and (l) can serve either as oxidizing or reducing agents.

5. To answer this question, look at a periodic table and find the Group to which the element belongs. The group number is the maximum oxidation state for the element.

The maximum oxidation state of (a) C is +4, (b) Ba is +2, (c) Br is +7, (d) Se is +6, (e) Sc is +3, (f) Mn is +7, and (g) P is +5.

6. For nonmetals, the minimum oxidation state is 8 less than the Group number, and for metals it is zero. Thus the minimum oxidation state for (a) C is −4, (b) Ba is 0, (c) Br is −1, (d) Se is −2, (e) Sc is 0 (f) Mn is 0, and (g) P is −3.

7. (a) The reducing agent is Zn (it is oxidized to Zn^{2+}). The oxidizing agent is $H^+(aq)$, which is reduced to $H_2(g)$.

(b) The oxidizing agent is ClO_3^- (Cl is reduced from the +5 state to the +4 state in ClO_2) and the reducing agent is Cr^{3+}, which is oxidized to the +6 state in $Cr_2O_7^{2-}$.

(c) The oxidizing agent is $Cl_2(g)$ and the reducing agent is Na(s).

(d) The oxidizing agent is MnO_4^- (Mn is in its highest oxidation state, +7) and the reducing agent is Fe^{2+}.

8. (a) oxidation: $H_2S \longrightarrow S + 2e^- + 2H^+(aq)$

reduction: $2Fe^{3+} + 2e^- \longrightarrow 2Fe^{2+}$

$$H_2S + 2Fe^{3+} \longrightarrow S + 2Fe^{2+} + 2H^+(aq)$$

(b) oxidation: $Bi(s) \longrightarrow Bi^{3+}(aq) + 3e^-$

reduction: $2H^+(aq) + NO_3^- + e^- \longrightarrow NO_2\uparrow + H_2O$

$$6H^+(aq) + 3NO_3^- + Bi \longrightarrow 3NO_2\uparrow + Bi^{3+} + 3H_2O$$

(c) oxidation: $Fe(OH)_2(s) + OH^- \longrightarrow Fe(OH)_3(s) + e^-$

reduction: $H_2O_2 + 2e^- \longrightarrow 2OH^-(aq)$

$$2Fe(OH)_2(s) + H_2O_2 \longrightarrow 2Fe(OH)_3(s)$$

If there are OH^- ions in a species involved in a redox reaction, balance OH^- ions in the half reaction first. Note that the -2 state of oxygen in basic solution is OH^-.

(d) oxidation: $$2I^- \rightarrow I_2 + 2e^-$$

reduction: $$12H^+(aq) + 2IO_3^- + 10e^- \rightarrow I_2 + 6H_2O$$

$$12H^+(aq) + 2IO_3^- + 10I^- \rightarrow 6I_2 + 6H_2O$$

As each coefficient in the equation can be divided by 2, the correct equation is

$$6H^+(aq) + IO_3^-(aq) + 5I^-(aq) \rightarrow 3I_2 + 3H_2O$$

(e) oxidation: $$2I^- \rightarrow I_2 + 2e^-$$

reduction: $$2H_2O + O_2(g) + 4e^- \rightarrow 4OH^-$$

$$4I^- + 2H_2O + O_2(g) \rightarrow 2I_2 + 4OH^-$$

(f) oxidation: $$Al(s) + 4OH^- \rightarrow Al(OH)_4^- + 3e^-$$

reduction: $$6H_2O + NO_3^- + 8e^- \rightarrow NH_3 + 9OH^-$$

$$8Al + 5OH^- + 18H_2O + 3NO_3^- \rightarrow 8Al(OH)_4^- + 3NH_3$$

The simplest way to balance this reduction half-reaction is to balance it first as if it were in acid solution and then add enough OH^- to both sides of the equation so that, making use of the reaction $H^+(aq) + OH^-(aq) \rightarrow H_2O$, only H_2O and OH^- appear in the overall reaction. Thus start with the reduction of NO_3^- (the +5 state of nitrogen) to NH_3 (the −3 state of nitrogen), which is an $8e^-$ transfer:

$$NO_3^- + 8e^- \rightarrow NH_3$$

Add $3H_2O$ on the right to balance the O atoms and $9H^+(aq)$ on the left to balance the H atoms:

$$9H^+(aq) + NO_3^- + 8e^- \rightarrow NH_3 + 3H_2O$$

Now add $9OH^-$ to both sides of the equation, and on the left combine $9H^+ + 9OH^-$ to form $9H_2O$:

$$9H_2O + NO_3^- + 8e^- \rightarrow NH_3 + 3H_2O + 9OH^-$$

Combine the $9H_2O$ on the left and the $3H_2O$ on the right, to form $6H_2O$ on the left:

$$6H_2O + NO_3^- + 8e^- \rightarrow NH_3 + 9OH^-$$

Whenever you are having difficulty with balancing a half-reaction in basic solution, balance it as if the solution were acid and then add OH^- so that no H^+ ions appear in the final equation.

(g) oxidation: $Bi_2S_3(s) \rightarrow 3S\downarrow + 2Bi^{3+}(aq) + 6e^-$

reduction: $4H^+(aq) + NO_3^- + 3e^- \rightarrow NO(g) + 2H_2O$

$$Bi_2S_3(s) + 8H^+(aq) + 2NO_3^- \rightarrow 2NO(g) + 3S\downarrow + 2Bi^{3+} + 4H_2O$$

(h) oxidation: $H_2C_2O_4 \rightarrow 2CO_2\uparrow + 2H^+(aq) + 2e^-$

reduction: $8H^+(aq) + MnO_4^- + 5e^- \rightarrow Mn^{2+} + 4H_2O$

$$5H_2C_2O_4 + 6H^+(aq) + 2MnO_4^- \rightarrow 2Mn^{2+} + 8H_2O + 10CO_2\uparrow$$

(i) oxidation: $2OH^- + Mn(OH)_2 \rightarrow MnO_2(s) + 2H_2O + 2e^-$

reduction: $2e^- + ClO^- + H_2O \rightarrow Cl^- + 2OH^-$

$$Mn(OH)_2(s) + ClO^- \rightarrow MnO_2(s) + H_2O + Cl^-$$

(j) oxidation: $4OH^- + N_2H_4 \rightarrow N_2 + 4e^- + 4H_2O$

reduction: $2e^- + Cu(OH)_2(s) \rightarrow Cu(s) + 2OH^-$

$$N_2H_4 + 2Cu(OH)_2(s) \rightarrow 2Cu(s) + N_2 + 4H_2O$$

Note that in hydrazine, N_2H_4, N is in the −2 oxidation state. Each N is oxidized from the −2 to the 0 state, requiring a loss of $2(2e^-) = 4e^-$.

(k) oxidation: $H_2C{=}O + H_2O \rightarrow HCOOH + 2e^- + 2H^+(aq)$

reduction: $14H^+(aq) + Cr_2O_7^{2-} + 6e^- \rightarrow 2Cr^{3+} + 7H_2O$

$8H^+(aq) + Cr_2O_7^{2-} + 3H_2C{=}O \rightarrow 4H_2O + 2Cr^{3+} + 3HCOOH$

This reaction is the oxidation of formaldehyde, $H_2C{=}O$, to formic acid using dichromate ion as the oxidizing agent.

(l) oxidation: $2OH^- + SO_3^{2-} \rightarrow SO_4^{2-} + 2e^- + H_2O$

reduction: $2H_2O + O_2(g) + 4e^- \rightarrow 4OH^-$

$2SO_3^{2-} + O_2(g) \rightarrow 2SO_4^{2-}$

9. (a)

oxidation: $Bi_2S_3(s) \rightarrow 2Bi^{3+}(aq) + 3S\downarrow + 6e^-$

reduction: $2H^+(aq) + NO_3^- + e^- \rightarrow NO_2\uparrow + H_2O$

$12H^+(aq) + 6NO_3^- + Bi_2S_3 \rightarrow 2Bi^{3+} + 3S\downarrow + 6NO_2\uparrow + 6H_2O$

(b) oxidation: $PbS(s) \rightarrow Pb^{2+} + S\downarrow + 2e^-$

reduction: $4H^+(aq) + NO_3^- + 3e^- \rightarrow NO\uparrow + 2H_2O$

$3PbS + 8H^+(aq) + 2NO_3^- \rightarrow 3Pb^{2+} + 3S\downarrow + 2NO\uparrow + 4H_2O$

10. (a)

oxidation: $2MnO_4^{2-} \rightarrow 2MnO_4^- + 2e^-$

reduction: $4H^+(aq) + MnO_4^{2-} + 2e^- \rightarrow MnO_2\downarrow + 2H_2O$

$4H^+(aq) + 3MnO_4^{2-} \rightarrow 2MnO_4^- + MnO_2\downarrow + 2H_2O$

(b) oxidation: $4OH^- + ClO^- \rightarrow ClO_3^- + 4e^- + 2H_2O$

reduction: $H_2O + 2e^- + ClO^- \rightarrow Cl^- + 2OH^-$

$3ClO^- \rightarrow 2Cl^- + ClO_3^-$

11.

(a) oxidation: $HONO + H_2O \rightarrow NO_3^- + 2e^- + 3H^+(aq)$

reduction: $8H^+ + MnO_4^- + 5e^- \rightarrow Mn^{2+} + 4H_2O$

$5HONO + 2MnO_4^- + H^+(aq) \rightarrow 3H_2O + 2Mn^{2+} + 5NO_3^-$

(b) oxidation: $2I^- \rightarrow I_2 + 2e^-$

reduction: $H^+(aq) + HONO + e^- \rightarrow NO(g) + H_2O$

$$2H^+(aq) + 2HONO + 2I^- \rightarrow 2NO\uparrow + 2H_2O + I_2$$

(c) oxidation: $2NH_4{}^+ \rightarrow N_2 + 8H^+(aq) + 6e^-$

reduction: $2HONO + 6e^- + 6H^+(aq) \rightarrow N_2\uparrow + 4H_2O$

$$2HONO + 2NH_4{}^+ \rightarrow 2N_2\uparrow + 2H^+(aq) + 4H_2O$$

Since each coefficient is divisible by 2, the simplest equation is $HONO + NH_4{}^+ \rightarrow N_2\uparrow + H^+(aq) + 2H_2O$

(d) oxidation: $Zn(s) + 4OH^- \rightarrow Zn(OH)_4{}^{2-} + 2e^-$

reduction: $5H_2O + NO_2^- + 6e^- \rightarrow NH_3 + 7OH^-$

$$3Zn(s) + 5OH^- + 5H_2O + NO_2^- \rightarrow 3Zn(OH)_4{}^{2-} + NH_3$$

(e) oxidation: $2Cl^- \rightarrow Cl_2 + 2e^-$

reduction: $4H^+(aq) + 2e^- + MnO_2(s) \rightarrow Mn^{2+} + 2H_2O$

$$4H^+(aq) + 2Cl^- + MnO_2(s) \rightarrow Cl_2 + Mn^{2+} + 2H_2O$$

(f) oxidation: $2Br^- \rightarrow Br_2 + 2e^-$

reduction: $MnO_4^- + 5e^- + 8H^+(aq) \rightarrow Mn^{2+} + 4H_2O$

$$10Br^- + 2MnO_4^- + 16H^+(aq) \rightarrow 2Mn^{2+} + 5Br_2 + 8H_2O$$

(g) oxidation: $2I^- \rightarrow I_2 + 2e^-$

reduction: $14H^+(aq) + Cr_2O_7{}^{2-} + 6e^- \rightarrow 2Cr^{3+} + 7H_2O$

$$6I^- + 14H^+(aq) + Cr_2O_7{}^{2-} \rightarrow 3I_2 + 2Cr^{3+} + 7H_2O$$

(h) oxidation: $Mn^{2+} + 2H_2O \rightarrow MnO_2\downarrow + 2e^- + 4H^+(aq)$

reduction: $2H^+(aq) + ClO_3^- + e^- \rightarrow ClO_2\uparrow + H_2O$

$$Mn^{2+} + 2ClO_3^- \rightarrow MnO_2\downarrow + 2ClO_2\uparrow$$

(i) oxidation: $Cr(OH)_4^- + 4OH^- \rightarrow CrO_4^{2-} + 4H_2O + 3e^-$

reduction: $H_2O_2 + 2e^- \rightarrow 2OH^-$

$$2Cr(OH)_4^- + 2OH^- + 3H_2O_2 \rightarrow 2CrO_4^{2-} + 8H_2O$$

Make use of Fig. 15.4 to do this problem. The green chromite ion is the form of the +3 oxidation state of chromium in strongly basic solution. It can be oxidized only to the +6 state, in which chromium exists as the bright yellow chromate ion, CrO_4^{2-}, in basic solution.

(j) oxidation: $2OH^- + Mn(OH)_2 \rightarrow MnO_2 + 2e^- + 2H_2O$

reduction: $2H_2O + O_2 + 4e^- \rightarrow 4OH^-$

$$2Mn(OH)_2 + O_2(g) \rightarrow 2H_2O + 2MnO_2(s)$$

<u>Solutions to Multiple Choice Questions, Chapter 15</u>

1. <u>(c)</u> In order to be a reducing agent a substance must be able to be oxidized. The highest oxidation state of sulfur is +6, as S is in Group VIA. Since sulfur is in the +6 oxidation state in H_2SO_4, it cannot be oxidized further. Thus sulfuric acid can serve only as an oxidizing agent and not as a reducing agent.

2. <u>(d)</u> The lowest possible oxidation state for S is −2, since 6 − 8 = −2, and sulfur is in group VIA. The −2 oxidation state is the sulfide ion, S^{2-}, and as this ion cannot be reduced, it cannot serve as an oxidizing agent.

3. __(b)__ Reduction is a decrease in oxidation state. In the change from $BrO_3^- \rightarrow BrO^-$, the oxidation state of bromine decreases from +5 to +1. Option (a) is a change that is neither an oxidation nor a reduction. In both CrO_4^{2-} and $Cr_2O_7^{2-}$ chromium is in the +6 oxidation state. Which form exists depends on the pH of the solution; chromate ion exists in base and dichromate ion in acid:

$$2CrO_4^{2-} + 2H^+(aq) \rightarrow Cr_2O_7^{2-} + H_2O$$

Option (c) is the oxidation of oxygen from the −1 state (in H_2O_2) to the zero state, $O_2(g)$. Option (d) is the oxidation of arsenic from the +3 state to the +5 state. Option (e) is a change that is neither an oxidation nor a reduction, as in both $Al(OH)_3$ and $Al(OH)_4^-$ aluminum is in the +3 oxidation state.

4. __(d)__ If we assign to nitrogen its most common negative oxidation state, −3, in both of these ions, then carbon is in the +2 state in CN^-, and the +4 state in CNO^-. To effect a change in oxidation state from +2 to +4 requires the loss of $2e^-$. This change must take place in basic solution because CN^- is a base, and in acid solution accepts a proton to become HCN. The half-reaction is

$$CN^- + 2OH^- \rightarrow CNO^- + 2e^- + H_2O$$

5. __(a)__ The reducing agent is the species that is oxidized. Metallic tin reduces the NO_3^- ion to $NO_2(g)$ (a

decrease from the +5 to the +4 state of nitrogen). The Sn is oxidized from the zero state to the +4 state in $SnCl_6^{2-}$.

6. <u>(c)</u> The NO_3^- ion is the oxidizing agent, as it is reduced from the +5 state to the +4 state of nitrogen, NO_2. It oxidizes tin from the 0 to the +4 state, in $SnCl_6^{2-}$.

7. <u>(e)</u> Carbon is in the −2 oxidation state in CH_3OH, and the +2 state in formic acid, HCOOH. The change from the −2 to the +2 state requires the loss of four electrons.

8. <u>(d)</u> In this reaction sulfur is reduced from the +6 state in H_2SO_4 to the −2 state, in H_2S. Thus H_2SO_4 is the oxidizing agent. It oxidizes I^- from the −1 state to the zero state in I_2.

9. <u>(d)</u> In the thiosulfate ion, $S_2O_3^{2-}$, sulfur is in the +2 oxidation state. It is reduced to elemental sulfur, the 0 state. Each sulfur must gain 2 electrons, and as there are 2 S atoms in the $S_2O_3^{2-}$ ion, the reduction requires the gain of 4 electrons:

$$6H^+(aq) + S_2O_3^{2-} + 4e^- \rightarrow 2S(s) + 3H_2O$$

10. <u>(c)</u> The change from CrO_4^{2-} in base to $Cr_2O_7^{2-}$ in acid is neither an oxidation nor a reduction, as in both forms chromium is in the +6 oxidation state. The addition of strong acid to a solution containing CrO_4^{2-} ions produces the dimeric, red-orange dichromate ion.

11. <u>(e)</u> To answer this, balance the equation.

oxidation: 3 x $(4OH^- + C_2O_4^{2-} \rightarrow 2CO_3^{2-} + 2e^- + 2H_2O)$

reduction: 2 x $(MnO_4^- + 3e^- + 2H_2O \rightarrow MnO_2\downarrow + 4OH^-)$

After multiplying the oxidation half-reaction by 3 and the reduction half-reaction by 2 to make the electrons lost and gained the same, there are $12OH^-$ on the left and $8OH^-$ on the right, for a net of $4OH^-$ on the left.

12. <u>(a)</u> The change from N_2H_4 to N_2 is the oxidation of nitrogen from the -2 to the 0 state. Option (b) is the reduction of manganese from the +7 to the +4 state. Option (c) is neither an oxidation nor a reduction, just a loss of H_2O by sulfurous acid. The change in option (d) is the reduction of antimony from the +5 to the +3 state. In option (e), the Cu^{2+} ion has combined with 4 NH_3 molecules to form a complex ion, but there has not been any change in the oxidation state of copper, it is +2 in both ions.

13. <u>(e)</u> The chlorate ion in acid solution is a powerful oxidizing agent (see Table 15.4) and simultaneously oxidizes both the arsenic and the sulfur in As_2S_3.

14. <u>(a)</u> The equation for the reaction is

oxidation: $2S_2O_3^{2-} \rightarrow S_4O_6^{2-} + 2e^-$

reduction: $I_2 + 2e^- \rightarrow 2I^-$

$$2S_2O_3^{2-} + I_2 \rightarrow S_4O_6^{2-} + 2I^-$$

No. moles of I_2 used = (1/2)(No. moles of $S_2O_3^{2-}$ used)

No. millimoles of $S_2O_3^{2-}$ used = (32.78 mL)(0.1000M) = 3.278

Hence, No. mmol I_2 in solution = (1/2)(3.278) = 1.639

15. **(b)** Options (d) and (e) are eliminated because in basic solution Mn^{2+} combines with OH^- to precipitate as $Mn(OH)_2$. Option (c) is eliminated because there is no way to obtain O_2 as a product. When MnO_4^- acts as an oxidizing agent in basic solution it is reduced either to the green manganate ion, MnO_4^{2-}, (as in this reaction) or to MnO_2. It is not reduced all the way to metallic Mn. See Fig. 15.5.

16. **(b)** In disproportionation, a single element is simultaneously oxidized and reduced. There must therefore be two products of the same element, one in a higher and one in a lower oxidation state than the initial species. Options (a), (c), and (d) are not redox reactions, as there is no element that changes its oxidation state. Option (d) is an ordinary redox reaction, not a disproportionation.

17. **(b)** Dilute nitric acid is an oxidizing agent that oxidizes sulfide ion (the −2 oxidation state of sulfur) to elemental sulfur. The NO_3^- is reduced principally to NO(g).

18. **(a)** Nitrogen is in its lowest oxidation state, −3, in NH_4^+. Thus NH_4^+ can serve as a reducing agent, and is usually oxidized to N_2, as in this reaction.

Solutions to Problems, Chapter 15

15.1.

(a) oxidation: $(4OH^- + C_2O_4{}^{2-} \rightarrow 2CO_3{}^{2-} + 2e^- + 2H_2O) \times 3$

reduction: $(2H_2O + MnO_4^- + 3e^- \rightarrow MnO_2\downarrow + 4OH^-) \times 2$

$$4OH^- + 3C_2O_4{}^{2-} + 2MnO_4^- \rightarrow 2MnO_2\downarrow + 6CO_3{}^{2-} + 2H_2O$$

(b) oxidation: $\{H_2O + CH_3CHO \rightarrow CH_3COOH + 2e^- + 2H^+(aq)\} \times 3$

reduction: $14H^+(aq) + Cr_2O_7{}^{2-} + 6e^- \rightarrow 2Cr^{3+} + 7H_2O$

$$8H^+(aq) + Cr_2O_7{}^{2-} + 3CH_3CHO \rightarrow 4H_2O + 2Cr^{3+} + 3CH_3COOH$$

(c) oxidation: $\{Ag_2S(s) + 4CN^- \rightarrow S\downarrow + 2Ag(CN)_2^- + 2e^-\} \times 2$

reduction: $4e^- + O_2(g) + 2H_2O \rightarrow 4OH^-$

$$2Ag_2S + 8CN^- + O_2(g) + 2H_2O \rightarrow 2S\downarrow + 4Ag(CN)_2^- + 4OH^-$$

(d) oxidation: $Pb(s) + SO_4{}^{2-} \rightarrow PbSO_4 + 2e^-$

reduction: $PbO_2 + 4H^+(aq) + SO_4{}^{2-} + 2e^- \rightarrow PbSO_4 + 2H_2O$

$$4H^+(aq) + Pb + PbO_2 + 2SO_4{}^{2-} \rightarrow 2PbSO_4 + 2H_2O$$

This is the reaction that occurs in the storage battery, the battery used in automobiles.

(e) oxidation: $8H_2O + As_2S_3 \rightarrow 2H_3AsO_4 + 3S\downarrow + 10e^- + 10H^+$

reduction: $\{2H^+(aq) + NO_3^- + e^- \rightarrow NO_2\uparrow + H_2O\} \times 10$

$$As_2S_3 + 10NO_3^- + 10H^+(aq) \rightarrow 2H_3AsO_4 + 3S\downarrow + 10NO_2\uparrow$$

In this oxidation half-reaction, two As atoms are oxidized from the +3 to the +5 state, requiring a loss of $4e^-$, and simultaneously three S atoms are oxidized from the −2 to the 0 state, requiring the loss of $6e^-$, so that a total of 10 electrons is lost.

(f) oxidation: $8OH^- + Cr^{2+} \rightarrow CrO_4^{2-} + 4e^- + 4H_2O$

$$8OH^- + I^- \rightarrow IO_4^- + 8e^- + 4H_2O$$

reduction: $\{Cl_2(g) + 2e^- \rightarrow 2Cl^-\} \times 6$

$$16OH^- + Cr^{2+} + I^- + 6Cl_2(g) \rightarrow 12Cl^- + IO_4^- + 8H_2O + CrO_4^{2-}$$

In this reaction two different species are oxidized, the I^- ion and the Cr^{2+} ion. The oxidizing agent is $Cl_2(g)$, and the reduction half-reaction must show the gain of $12e^-$, the total of those lost in the two oxidations.

(g) oxidation: $(3H_2O + ClO_3^- + 6e^- \rightarrow Cl^- + 6OH^-) \times 5$

reduction: $(2V + 13OH^- \rightarrow HV_2O_7^{3-} + 10e^- + 6H_2O) \times 3$

$$6V + 9OH^- + 5ClO_3^- \rightarrow 3HV_2O_7^{3-} + 3H_2O + 5Cl^-$$

(h) oxidation: $Hg + 4Cl^- \rightarrow HgCl_4^{2-} + 2e^-$

reduction: $\{2H^+(aq) + NO_3^- + e^- \rightarrow NO_2\uparrow + H_2O\} \times 2$

$$4H^+(aq) + 2NO_3^- + Hg + 4Cl^- \rightarrow HgCl_4^{2-} + 2NO_2\uparrow + 2H_2O$$

15.2. (a) $CdS(s) + 2H^+(aq) \rightleftharpoons Cd^{2+} + H_2S$

$$K_{eq} = \frac{[Cd^{2+}][H_2S]}{[H^+]^2} = \frac{[Cd^{2+}][S^{2-}][H_2S]}{[H^+]^2[S^{2-}]} = \frac{K_{sp}(CdS)}{K_a(H_2S)\cdot K_a(HS^-)}$$

$$= \frac{4\times10^{-29}}{(1.0\times10^{-7})(1.3\times10^{-13})} = 3\times10^{-9} << 1$$

Because the equilibrium constant is very much less than 1, the position of equilibrium is far to the left, and the solubility of CdS in dilute HCl is small.

(b) oxidation: $\{CdS(s) \rightarrow Cd^{2+} + S\downarrow + 2e^-\} \times 3$

reduction: $\{4H^+(aq) + NO_3^- + 3e^- \rightarrow NO\uparrow + 2H_2O\} \times 2$

$$3CdS(s) + 8H^+(aq) + 2NO_3^- \rightarrow 3Cd^{2+} + 3S\downarrow + 2NO\uparrow + 4H_2O$$

Nitric acid is an oxidizing agent; HCl is not. To drive the dissolution of CdS to the right, the $[S^{2-}]$ must be decreased. This is more effectively done by oxidizing S^{2-} to elemental S, which precipitates out of solution, than by combining S^{2-} with $H^+(aq)$ to form H_2S. Many insoluble sulfides with very small solubility products cannot be dissolved in HCl but do dissolve in warm nitric acid.

(c) oxidation: $CdS(s) \rightarrow Cd^{2+} + S\downarrow + 2e^-$

reduction: $\{2H^+(aq) + NO_3^- + e^- \rightarrow NO_2\uparrow + H_2O\} \times 2$

$$CdS(s) + 4H^+(aq) + 2NO_3^- \rightarrow Cd^{2+} + S\downarrow + 2NO_2\uparrow + 2H_2O$$

15.3.

The electronic configuration of Pb is $Xe^{54}4f^{14}5d^{10}6s^26p^2$ Lead can form a divalent ion by losing its two 6p valence electrons, and the Pb^{2+} ion can be part of ionic crystalline solids such as $PbCl_2$. The loss of four electrons requires too much energy to be feasible, but lead can form covalently bonded molecules in which it shares its four valence 6s and 6p electrons with other atoms. Lead tetrachloride, $PbCl_4$, is such a compound. The bond in $PbCl_2$ is best described as ionic with partial covalent character, and the bond in $PbCl_4$ is polar covalent.

15.4. (a)

oxidation: $(Fe^{2+} \rightarrow Fe^{3+} + e^-) \times 5$

reduction: $8H^+(aq) + MnO_4^- + 5e^- \rightarrow Mn^{2+} + 4H_2O$

$$8H^+(aq) + MnO_4^- + 5Fe^{2+} \rightarrow Mn^{2+} + 5Fe^{3+} + 4H_2O$$

(b) No. mmol MnO_4^- used = (31.95 mL)(0.0400 M) = 1.278

(1) No. mmol Fe^{2+} used = 5(1.278) = 6.390 mmol

(2) As the atomic weight of Fe is 55.85 g/mol, the mass of Fe in the sample was

$$(55.85\ g/mol)(6.390 x 10^{-3}\ mol) = 0.3569\ g\ Fe$$

$$\%\ Fe\ in\ ore = \left(\frac{0.3569\ g}{0.7545\ g}\right) x 100 = 47.30\%\ Fe$$

15.5. **(a)** $FeS(s) + 2H^+(aq) \longrightarrow H_2S + Fe^{2+}(aq)$

(b) oxidation: $\{NiS(s) \longrightarrow Ni^{2+} + S\downarrow + 2e^-\} \times 3$

reduction: $\{4H^+(aq) + NO_3^- + 3e^- \longrightarrow NO\uparrow + 2H_2O\} \times 2$

$3NiS(s) + 8H^+(aq) + 2NO_3^- \longrightarrow 3Ni^{2+} + 3S\downarrow + 2NO\uparrow + 4H_2O$

(c) $Pb(OH)_2(s) + 2H^+(aq) + SO_4^{2-} \longrightarrow PbSO_4\downarrow + 2H_2O$

(d) oxidation: $\{H_2SO_3 + H_2O \longrightarrow SO_4^{2-} + 2e^- + 4H^+(aq)\} \times 5$

reduction: $12H^+(aq) + 2IO_3^- + 10e^- \longrightarrow I_2 + 6H_2O$

$5H_2SO_3 + 2IO_3^- \longrightarrow 5SO_4^{2-} + I_2 + H_2O + 8H^+(aq)$

(e) oxidation: $(2OH^- + CN^- \longrightarrow CNO^- + 2e^- + H_2O) \times 3$

reduction: $(4H_2O + CrO_4^{2-} + 3e^- \longrightarrow Cr(OH)_3\downarrow + 5OH^-) \times 2$

$5H_2O + 2CrO_4^{2-} + 3CN^- \longrightarrow 2Cr(OH)_3\downarrow + 4OH^- + 3CNO^-$

15.6.

(a) oxidation: $N_2H_4 + 4OH^- \longrightarrow N_2\uparrow + 4H_2O + 4e^-$

reduction: $(I_2 + 2e^- \longrightarrow 2I^-) \times 2$

$N_2H_4 + 4OH^- + 2I_2 \longrightarrow N_2\uparrow + 4H_2O + 4I^-$

(b) oxidation: $\{2H_2O + SO_2(g) \longrightarrow SO_4^{2-} + 2e^- + 4H^+(aq)\} \times 3$

reduction: $14H^+(aq) + Cr_2O_7^{2-} + 6e^- \longrightarrow 2Cr^{3+} + 7H_2O$

$2H^+(aq) + Cr_2O_7^{2-} + 3SO_2(g) \longrightarrow 3SO_4^{2-} + 2Cr^{3+} + H_2O$

(c) oxidation: $2Cl^- \rightarrow Cl_2\uparrow + 2e^-$

reduction: $\{2H^+(aq) + ClO_3^- + e^- \rightarrow ClO_2\uparrow + H_2O\} \times 2$

$$2Cl^- + 4H^+(aq) + 2ClO_3^- \rightarrow Cl_2 + 2ClO_2\uparrow + 2H_2O$$

(d) oxidation: $6OH^- + 2NH_3 \rightarrow N_2\uparrow + 6e^- + 6H_2O$

reduction: $(H_2O + BrO^- + 2e^- \rightarrow Br^- + 2OH^-) \times 3$

$$3BrO^- + 2NH_3 \rightarrow N_2\uparrow + 3Br^- + 3H_2O$$

Hypobromite ion, like hypochlorite ion, serves as an oxidizing agent, and is reduced to Br^-. Ammonia is usually oxidized to N_2.

(e) oxidation: $(H_3AsO_3 + H_2O \rightarrow H_3AsO_4 + 2e^-) \times 2$

reduction: $6H^+(aq) + BrO_3^- + 6e^- \rightarrow Br^- + 3H_2O$

$$BrO_3^- + 3H_3AsO_3 \rightarrow Br^- + 3H_3AsO_4$$

(f) oxidation: $\{Fe(CN)_6{}^{4-} \rightarrow Fe(CN)_6{}^{3-} + e^-\} \times 5$

reduction: $8H^+(aq) + MnO_4^- + 5e^- \rightarrow Mn^{2+} + 4H_2O$

$$5Fe(CN)_6{}^{4-} + 8H^+(aq) + MnO_4^- \rightarrow 5Fe(CN)_6{}^{3-} + Mn^{2+} + 4H_2O$$

15.7. The Lewis structures of N_2O_5 and N_2O_3 are

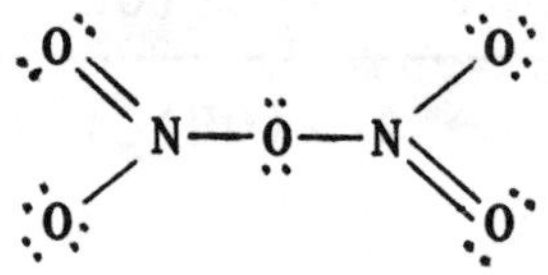

and

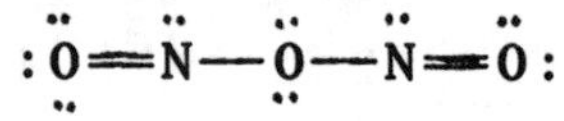

	N_2O_5	N_2O_3
oxidation state of N	+5	+3
formal charge on N	+1	0

As the oxidation state of N increases, the formal charge increases, and the actual charge on N and its electronegativity also increases. Electron density is pulled toward the N and away from the O. In the acids, H atoms are bonded to O atoms, and the strength of the O-H bond is weakened as the oxidation state of N increases. Thus HNO_3, formed by the reaction

$$N_2O_5 + H_2O \rightleftharpoons 2HNO_3$$

in which N is in its +5 oxidation state, is a strong acid, while nitrous acid, formed by the reaction

$$N_2O_3 + H_2O \rightleftharpoons 2HONO$$

is a weak acid.

15.8. (a) The knowledge that the solid dissolves readily in water immediately eliminates $CaCO_3$, $PbSO_4$, and Hg_2Cl_2 as possibilities because they are all insoluble in water. Of the remaining three, solutions of K_2S are strongly basic because S^{2-} is a base; it accepts a proton from water to form HS^-.

$$S^{2-} + H_2O \rightleftharpoons OH^- + HS^-$$

Hence with just the information given in part (a) we have narrowed the unknown down to being either NH_4NO_3 or NH_4I, both of which dissolve in water to give an acidic solution.

(b) Nitrogen is in its +3 oxidation state in nitrous acid. The reaction produces NO(g), in which nitrogen is in the +2 oxidation state. Thus the unknown must contain a reducing agent. The iodide ion, I^-, is a good reducing agent and is readily oxidized to I_2, which is brownish in color. The NO_3^- ion is not a reducing agent, since nitrogen is in the +5 oxidation state. Thus the unknown is NH_4I.

Further evidence of the fact that the unknown is NH_4I is provided by the color of the CCl_4 layer. Iodine, I_2, dissolves readily in CCl_4, and a solution of I_2 in CCl_4 is violet. The color is intense, so that even a very small concentration of I_2 in CCl_4 produces a distinct violet color. This property is used as a test to confirm the presence of I_2 in a reaction mixture.

The acidity of the solution is due to the proton-transfer reaction between NH_4^+ and water:

$$NH_4^+ + H_2O \rightleftharpoons H_3O^+ + NH_3$$

The reaction of I^- with HONO is a redox reaction.

oxidation: $2I^- \rightarrow I_2 + 2e^-$

reduction: $\dfrac{H^+(aq) + HNO_2 + e^- \rightarrow NO\uparrow + H_2O}{}$

$$2H^+(aq) + 2I^- + 2HNO_2 \rightarrow I_2 + 2NO\uparrow + 2H_2O$$

15.9. The Lewis structures of these acids, using only octets around each atom, are

$$
\begin{array}{cccc}
H & H & & \\
| & | & & \\
:\!\ddot{O}\!: & :\!\ddot{O}\!: & :\!\ddot{O}\!: & :\!\ddot{O}\!: \\
| & | & | & | \\
H\!-\!\ddot{O}\!-\!Si\!-\!\ddot{O}\!-\!H & H\!-\!\ddot{O}\!-\!P\!-\!\ddot{O}\!-\!H & H\!-\!\ddot{O}\!-\!S\!-\!\ddot{O}\!-\!H & :\!\ddot{O}\!-\!Cl\!-\!\ddot{O}\!-\!H \\
| & | & | & | \\
:\!\ddot{O}\!: & :\!\ddot{O}\!: & :\!\ddot{O}\!: & :\!\ddot{O}\!: \\
| & & & \\
H & & &
\end{array}
$$

| formal charge | 0 | +1 | +2 | +3 |
| oxidation state | +4 | +5 | +6 | +7 |

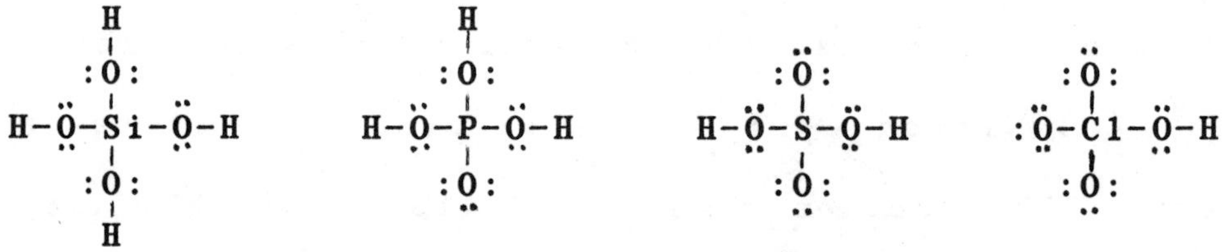

Silicic acid is an extremely weak acid, with $K_a = 1\times10^{-12}$, phosphoric acid is moderately weak, with $K_a = 7.5\times10^{-3}$, and both sulfuric acid and perchloric acid are strong acids.

Because of the leveling effect of water on strong acids (see Section 9.6) we cannot distinguish between the strengths of H_2SO_4 and $HClO_4$ in water, but from experiments in nonaqueous solvents such as alcohols, it has been found that perchloric acid is a stronger acid than sulfuric (see Fig. 9.2).

As the oxidation state and formal charge on the central atom increases, the actual charge and the electronegativity also increases. As electron density is pulled in toward the central atom it strengthens the bonds between the central atom and oxygen, and weakens the O–H bonds, making it easier for the proton to be lost, and thereby increasing the strength of the acid. For an element that can exhibit many oxidation states, the electronegativity of the atom increases as the oxidation state increases.

15.10. (a) The oxidizing agent is ClO_3^- and the reducing agent is As_2S_3.

oxidation: $8H_2O + As_2S_3 \rightarrow 2H_2AsO_4^- + 10e^- + 3S\downarrow + 12H^+(aq)$

reduction: $6H^+(aq) + ClO_3^- + 6e^- \rightarrow Cl^- + 3H_2O$

(b) The oxidizing agent is $Cu(NH_3)_4{}^{2+}$ and the reducing agent is cyanide ion, CN^-.

oxidation: $CN^- + 2OH^- \rightarrow CNO^- + 2e^- + H_2O$

reduction: $3CN^- + Cu(NH_3)_4{}^{2+} + e^- \rightarrow Cu(CN)_3{}^{2-} + 4NH_3$

Solutions to Exercises, Chapter 16

1. (a) The anode is the electrode at which oxidation occurs, and the cathode is the electrode at which reduction occurs.

$$\text{anode:} \quad Cd(s) \rightarrow Cd^{2+} + 2e^-$$

$$\text{cathode:} \quad I_2 + 2e^- \rightarrow 2I^-$$

A piece of Cd metal is used as the anode, and some inert metal, usually Pt in the lab, is used as the cathode.

(b)

$$\text{anode:} \quad Ni(s) \rightarrow Ni^{2+} + 2e^-$$

$$\text{cathode:} \quad Fe^{3+} + e^- \rightarrow Fe^{2+}$$

A piece of Ni is used as the anode, and some inert metal, usually Pt, is used as the cathode.

(c)

$$\text{anode:} \quad Cr(s) \rightarrow Cr^{3+} + 3e^-$$

$$\text{cathode:} \quad Cu^{2+} + 2e^- \rightarrow Cu(s)$$

A piece of Cr is used as the anode, and a piece of Cu as the cathode.

2. The charge in coulombs is the product of the current in amps and the time in seconds, $Q = It$.

$$\text{No. coulombs} = (1.25\ \text{A})(8.00\ \text{min})(60\ \text{s/min}) = 600\ \text{C}$$

$$\text{No. faradays} = \frac{600\ \text{C}}{96{,}485\ \text{C}/\mathcal{F}} = 6.22\text{x}10^{-3}$$

One mole of Zn is oxidized when $2\mathcal{F}$ have passed. Thus

$$\text{No. mol Zn oxidized} = (1/2)(6.22\text{x}10^{-3}) = 3.11\text{x}10^{-3}$$

and the mass of Zn that has been oxidized to Zn^{2+} ions is

$$(3.11\text{x}10^{-3}\ \text{mol})(65.38\ \text{g/mol}) = 0.203\ \text{g}$$

3. The value of the faraday is N_Ae, that is, the charge on one electron multiplied by the number of electrons in one mole, or Avogadro's number.

$$N_Ae = (6.022045\text{x}10^{23}\ \text{mol}^{-1})(1.60219\text{x}10^{-19}\ \text{C}) = 96,485\ \text{C/mol}$$

4. The formula weight of $PbSO_4$ is 303.3 g/mol. The number of moles of $PbSO_4$ formed is therefore

$$(21.08\ \text{g})/(303.3\ \text{g/mol}) = 0.06950\ \text{mol}$$

The oxidation reaction is

$$Pb(s) + SO_4^{2-} \rightarrow PbSO_4 + 2e^-$$

Thus $2\mathcal{F}$ of charge are passed per mole of $PbSO_4$ formed.

$$\text{No. coulombs passed} = (2\mathcal{F}/\text{mol})(0.6950\ \text{mol})(96,485\ \text{C}/\mathcal{F})$$
$$= 1.341\text{x}10^4\ \text{C}$$

5. anode reaction: $Cd(s) \rightarrow Cd^{2+} + 2e^-$

cathode reaction: $Fe^{3+} + e^- \rightarrow Fe^{2+}$

The anode is the negative terminal. Electrons leave the half-cell containing Cd(s) and enter the half-cell containing Fe^{3+}. Potassium ions from the salt bridge enter the Fe^{2+}/Fe^{2+} half-cell to keep it electrically neutral. Thus the positive charge lost when a ferric (Fe^{3+}) ion is reduced to ferrous is replaced by a K^+ ion.

6. (a) anode: $Co(s) \rightarrow Co^{2+} + 2e^-$

cathode: $Ag^+ + e^- \rightarrow Ag(s)$

net cell reaction: $Co(s) + 2Ag^+ \rightarrow 2Ag(s) + Co^{2+}$

The cobalt anode is the negative terminal.

(b) anode: $Zn(s) \rightarrow Zn^{2+} + 2e^-$

cathode: $Br_2(aq) + 2e^- \rightarrow 2Br^-$

net cell reaction: $Zn(s) + Br_2 \rightarrow Zn^{2+} + 2Br^-$

The zinc anode is the negative terminal.

(c) anode: $Pb(s) \rightarrow Pb^{2+} + 2e^-$

cathode: $2H^+(aq) + 2e^- \rightarrow H_2(g)$

net cell reaction: $Pb(s) + 2H^+(aq) \rightarrow Pb^{2+} + H_2(g)$

The lead anode is the negative terminal.

(d) anode: $H_2(g) \rightarrow 2H^+(aq) + 2e^-$

cathode: $Cu^{2+} + 2e^- \rightarrow Cu(s)$

net cell reaction: $H_2(g) + Cu^{2+} \rightarrow Cu(s) + 2H^+(aq)$

The platinum electrode with $H_2(g)$ passing over it is the negative terminal.

7. $\Delta\mathcal{E}^\circ_{cell} = \mathcal{E}^\circ_{H^+|H_2} - \mathcal{E}^\circ_{Zn^{2+}|Zn} = 0.000 - \mathcal{E}^\circ_{Zn^{2+}|Zn}$

Thus $\mathcal{E}^\circ_{Zn^{2+}|Zn} = -0.763\ V$

$$\Delta\mathcal{E}^\circ_{cell} = 0.427\ V = \mathcal{E}^\circ_{Tl^+|Tl} - \mathcal{E}^\circ_{Zn^{2+}|Zn} = \mathcal{E}^\circ_{Tl^+|Tl} + 0.763$$

$$\mathcal{E}^\circ_{Tl^+|Tl} = 0.427 - 0.763 = -0.336\ V$$

$$\Delta\mathcal{E}^\circ_{cell} = 1.32\ V = \mathcal{E}^\circ_{Zn^{2+}|Zn} - \mathcal{E}^\circ_{Sc^{3+}|Sc} = -0.763 - \mathcal{E}^\circ_{Sc^{3+}|Sc}$$

$$\mathcal{E}^\circ_{Sc^{3+}|Sc} = -0.763 - 1.32 = -2.08\ V$$

8. (a) The negative terminal is the one at which oxidation occurs, because oxidation is a loss of electrons. If, in the cell with a nickel electrode and a standard hydrogen electrode, the nickel electrode is the negative terminal, then the Ni electrode is the anode.

$$\Delta\mathcal{E}^\circ_{cell} = +0.25\ V = \mathcal{E}^\circ_{cathode} - \mathcal{E}^\circ_{anode} = 0.000 - \mathcal{E}^\circ_{Ni^{2+}|Ni}$$

so that $$\mathcal{E}^\circ_{Ni^{2+}|Ni} = -\ 0.25\ V$$

We know, from Exercise 7, that $\mathcal{E}^\circ_{Zn^{2+}|Zn} = -0.763$ V. This means that Zn is a stronger reducing agent than Ni, because the standard reduction potential is more negative for the $Zn^{2+}|Zn$ electrode. The direction of spontaneous reaction will be

$$Zn(s) + Ni^{2+} \rightarrow Ni(s) + Zn^{2+}$$

Since zinc will be oxidized, the zinc electrode will be the negative terminal in a cell using both a $Zn^{2+}|Zn$ and a $Ni^{2+}|Ni$ electrode.

(b) $$Zn(s)|Zn^{2+}||Ni^{2+}|Ni(s)$$

$$\Delta\mathcal{E}^\circ_{cell} = \mathcal{E}^\circ_{Ni^{2+}|Ni} - \mathcal{E}^\circ_{Zn^{2+}|Zn} = -0.25 - (-0.763) = +0.51\ V$$

(c) Since Zn is a stronger reducing agent than Ni, it necessarily follows that Ni^{2+} is a stronger oxidizing agent than Zn^{2+}. The stronger the reducing agent, the weaker its oxidizing agent couple.

9. (a) anode: $Sn^{2+} \rightarrow Sn^{4+} + 2e^-$

cathode: $Fe^{3+} + e^- \rightarrow Fe^{2+}$

net cell reaction: $2Fe^{3+} + Sn^{2+} \rightarrow 2Fe^{2+} + Sn^{4+}$

$$\Delta\mathcal{E}^\circ_{cell} = \mathcal{E}^\circ_{Fe^{3+}|Fe^{2+}} - \mathcal{E}^\circ_{Sn^{4+}|Sn^{2+}} = 0.771 - 0.15 = 0.62\ V$$

Since the standard cell potential is a positive number, the net cell reaction is spontaneous as written, from left to right.

(b) anode: $2Cl^- \rightarrow Cl_2(g) + 2e^-$

cathode: $2H^+(aq) + 2e^- \rightarrow H_2(g)$

net cell reaction: $2Cl^- + 2H^+(aq) \rightarrow Cl_2(g) + H_2(g)$

$$\Delta\mathcal{E}^\circ_{cell} = \mathcal{E}^\circ_{H^+|H_2(g)} - \mathcal{E}^\circ_{Cl_2(g)|Cl^-} = 0.000 - 1.36 \text{ V}$$
$$= -1.36 \text{ V}$$

Since this is negative, the net cell reaction written is not spontaneous. The spontaneous reaction is

$$H_2(g) + Cl_2(g) \rightarrow 2Cl^-(aq) + 2H^+(aq)$$

(c) anode: $Pb(s) \rightarrow Pb^{2+} + 2e^-$

cathode: $Cd^{2+} + 2e^- \rightarrow Cd(s)$

net cell reaction: $Pb(s) + Cd^{2+} \rightarrow Cd(s) + Pb^{2+}$

$$\Delta\mathcal{E}^\circ_{cell} = \mathcal{E}^\circ_{Cd^{2+}|Cd} - \mathcal{E}^\circ_{Pb^{2+}|Pb} = -0.403 - (-0.126) = -0.277 \text{ V}$$

Since this is negative, the net cell reaction written is not spontaneous. The spontaneous reaction is

$$Cd(s) + Pb^{2+} \rightarrow Cd^{2+} + Pb(s)$$

(d) anode: $Ni(s) \rightarrow Ni^{2+} + 2e^-$

cathode: $MnO_4^- + 5e^- + 8H^+(aq) \rightarrow Mn^{2+} + 4H_2O$

overall: $5Ni(s) + 2MnO_4^- + 16H^+(aq) \rightarrow 5Ni^{2+} + 2Mn^{2+} + 8H_2O$

$$\Delta\mathcal{E}^\circ_{cell} = \mathcal{E}^\circ_{MnO_4^-|Mn^{2+}} - \mathcal{E}^\circ_{Ni^{2+}|Ni} = 1.49 - (-0.25) = 1.74 \text{ V}$$

As $\Delta\mathcal{E}^\circ_{cell}$ is positive, the reaction is spontaneous.

10. (a) anode: $2Br^- \rightarrow Br_2 + 2e^-$

cathode: $Cl_2(g) + 2e^- \rightarrow 2Cl^-$

$$\Delta\mathcal{E}^\circ_{cell} = \mathcal{E}^\circ_{Cl_2|Cl^-} - \mathcal{E}^\circ_{Br_2|Br^-} = 1.36 - 1.09 = 0.27 \text{ V}$$

$$Pt(s)|Br_2, Br^-||Cl^-|Cl_2(g)|Pt(s)$$

(b) anode: $Al(s) \rightarrow Al^{3+} + 3e^-$

cathode: $Ni^{2+} + 2e^- \rightarrow Ni(s)$

$$\Delta\mathcal{E}^\circ_{cell} = \mathcal{E}^\circ_{Ni^{2+}|Ni} - \mathcal{E}^\circ_{Al^{3+}|Al} = -0.25 - (-1.66) = +1.41\ V$$

$$Al(s)|Al^{3+}||Ni^{2+}|Ni(s)$$

(c) anode: $Sc(s) \rightarrow Sc^{3+} + 3e^-$

cathode: $H^+(aq) + e^- \rightarrow (1/2)H_2(g)$

$$\Delta\mathcal{E}^\circ_{cell} = \mathcal{E}^\circ_{H^+|H_2} - \mathcal{E}^\circ_{Sc^{3+}|Sc} = 0.00 - (-2.08) = +2.08\ V$$

$$Sc(s)|Sc^{3+}||H^+(aq)|H_2(g)|Pt$$

11. (a) Yes, dichromate ion is a stronger oxidizing agent than stannic ion.

$$\mathcal{E}^\circ_{Cr_2O_7{}^{2-}|Cr^{3+}} = 1.33\ V \quad \text{and} \quad \mathcal{E}^\circ_{Sn^{4+}|Sn^{2+}} = 0.15\ V$$

(b) No, Cr(s) will reduce Ni^{2+} as Cr is a stronger reducing agent than Ni.

$$\mathcal{E}^\circ_{Ni^{2+}|Ni} = -0.25\ V \quad \text{and} \quad \mathcal{E}^\circ_{Cr^{2+}|Cr} = -0.91\ V$$

The spontaneous reaction is $Cr(s) + Ni^{2+} \rightarrow Ni(s) + Cr^{2+}$

(c) Yes, Cd reduces mercurous ion as Cd is a stronger reducing agent than Hg.

$$\mathcal{E}^\circ_{Cd^{2+}|Cd} = -0.403\ V \quad \text{and} \quad \mathcal{E}^\circ_{Hg_2{}^{2+}|Hg} = +0.854\ V$$

$Cd(s) + Hg_2{}^{2+} \rightarrow Cd^{2+} + 2Hg$ is spontaneous.

(d) No, Au^{3+} is a stronger oxidizing agent than NO_3^- in dilute acid solution, so dilute HNO_3 cannot oxidize Au(s).

$$\mathcal{E}^\circ_{Au^{3+}|Au} = +1.50\ V \quad \text{and} \quad \mathcal{E}^\circ_{NO_3{}^-|NO(g)|Pt} = +0.96\ V$$

12. anode: $Pb(s) \rightarrow Pb^{2+} + 2e^-$

cathode: $2H^+(aq) + 2e^- \rightarrow H_2(g)$

net cell reaction: $Pb(s) + 2H^+(aq) \rightarrow Pb^{2+} + H_2(g)$

$$\Delta\mathcal{E}^\circ_{cell} = 0.000 - \mathcal{E}^\circ_{Pb^{2+}|Pb} = 0.000 - (-0.126) = +0.126\ V$$

$$\Delta\mathcal{E}_{cell} = +0.126 - \frac{0.05916}{2} \log \frac{[Pb^{2+}]P_{H_2}}{[H^+]^2}$$

(a) The reaction quotient, Q, for this cell is

$$Q = \frac{[Pb^{2+}]P_{H_2}}{[H^+]^2} \quad \text{and} \quad n = 2$$

If $[Pb^{2+}] = 0.100\ M$, $[H^+] = 0.300\ M$, and $P_{H_2} = 1.00$ atm

$$Q = \frac{0.100}{(0.300)^2} = 1.11 \quad \text{and} \quad \log Q = 0.0458$$

$$\Delta\mathcal{E}_{cell} = 0.126 - (0.02958)(0.0458) = 0.126 - 0.0014$$

$$= 0.125\ V$$

(b) If $[Pb^{2+}] = 0.040\ M$, $[H^+] = 2.00\ M$, $P_{H_2} = 0.50$ atm,

$$Q = \frac{(4.0\times10^{-2})(5.0\times10^{-1})}{4.00} = 5.0\times10^{-3} \quad \text{and} \quad \log Q = -2.30$$

$$\Delta\mathcal{E}_{cell} = 0.126 - (0.02958)(-2.30) = 0.126 + 0.068 = 0.194\ V$$

(c) If $[Pb^{2+}] = 1.00\ M$, $[H^+] = 0.050\ M$, $P_{H_2} = 2.00$ atm,

$$Q = \frac{(1.00)(2.00)}{(5.0\times10^{-2})^2} = 800 \quad \text{and} \quad \log Q = 2.90$$

$$\Delta\mathcal{E}_{cell} = 0.126 - (0.02958)(2.90) = 0.126 - 0.086 = 0.040\ V$$

13. For any concentration cell, $\Delta\mathcal{E}^\circ_{cell} = 0$. For this cell

anode reaction: $Cd(s) \rightarrow Cd^{2+}(0.0050\ M) + 2e^-$

cathode reaction: $Cd^{2+}(0.600\ M) + 2e^- \rightarrow Cd(s)$

net cell reaction: $Cd^{2+}(0.600\ M) \rightarrow Cd^{2+}(0.0050\ M)$

Therefore, $n = 2$ and $Q = \dfrac{0.0050}{0.600} = 8.33\text{x}10^{-3}$

$$\Delta\mathcal{E}_{cell} = \frac{-0.05916}{2}\log Q = -(0.02958)(-2.079) = +0.0615\ V$$

14. (a) anode reaction: $Ag(s) \rightarrow Ag^{+}(0.018\ M) + e^{-}$

cathode reaction: $Ag^{+}(1.20\ M) + e^{-} \rightarrow Ag(s)$

net cell reaction: $Ag^{+}(1.20\ M) \rightarrow Ag^{+}(0.018\ M)$

$$Q = \frac{0.018\ M}{1.20\ M} = 1.50\text{x}10^{-2} \quad \text{and} \quad n = 1$$

$$\Delta\mathcal{E}_{cell} = -0.05916\ \log(1.50\text{x}10^{-2}) = -(0.05916)(-1.82)$$

$$= +0.108\ V$$

(b) If a solution containing Cl^{-} ions is added to the more dilute solution, the $[Ag^{+}]$ in that half cell will decrease significantly, as AgCl will precipitate. That will make the disparity between the two $[Ag^{+}]$ concentrations considerably larger, and increase the cell voltage. The greater the disparity between the more concentrated and the more dilute solution in a concentration cell, the greater the voltage of the cell.

15. For a $Cu^{2+}|Cu$ concentration cell, $n = 2$. As $\Delta\mathcal{E}^{\circ}_{cell}$ is zero for any concentration cell,

$$\Delta\mathcal{E}_{cell} = 0.100 = -\frac{(0.05916)}{2}\log Q$$

$\log Q = -(0.200)/(0.05916) = -3.38$ and $Q = 4.16\text{x}10^{-4}$

The reaction quotient is the ratio of the $[Cu^{2+}]$ in the anode compartment to that in the cathode compartment. Since this is less than 1, the solution in the anode compartment is the more dilute.

16. (a) anode: $Sc \rightarrow Sc^{3+} + 3e^-$

cathode: $3H^+(aq) + 3e^- \longrightarrow \frac{3}{2}H_2(g)$

Written this way, n = 3 in the Nernst equation.

$$\Delta\mathcal{E}_{cell} = \Delta\mathcal{E}^\circ_{cell} - \frac{0.05916}{3}(\log Q_a) = 2.08 - 0.01972(\log Q_a)$$

where

$$Q_a = \frac{P_{H_2}^{3/2}[Sc^{3+}]}{[H^+]^3}$$

(b) anode: $2Sc \rightarrow 2Sc^{3+} + 6e^-$

cathode: $6H^+(aq) + 6e^- \longrightarrow 3H_2(g)$

Written this way, n = 6 in the Nernst equation.

$$\Delta\mathcal{E}_{cell} = \Delta\mathcal{E}^\circ_{cell} - \frac{0.05916}{6}(\log Q_b) = 2.08 - 0.00986(\log Q_b)$$

where

$$Q_b = \frac{P_{H_2}^{3}[Sc^{3+}]^2}{[H^+]^6}$$

so that $Q_b = Q_a{}^2$ and $\log Q_b = 2(\log Q_a)$

Substituting $2(\log Q_a)$ for $\log Q_b$ into the Nernst equation yields

$$\Delta\mathcal{E}_{cell} = 2.08 - (0.00986)(2)(\log Q_a) = 2.08 - 0.01972(\log Q_a)$$

exactly what we found in (a). Thus the cell voltage is the same whether we write the equation in form (a) or (b). Note that n and Q change if we change the form of the net cell reaction by multiplying by a constant, but the cell voltage and the standard cell voltage do not change at all.

17. (a) anode: $Ni(s) \rightarrow Ni^{2+} + 2e^-$

cathode: $I_2 + 2e^- \rightarrow 2I^-$

$$\Delta\mathcal{E}^\circ_{cell} = \mathcal{E}^\circ_{cathode} - \mathcal{E}^\circ_{anode} = 0.535 - (-0.25) = 0.785 \text{ V}$$

For this reaction, n = 2 so that

$$\log K_{eq} = \frac{2(0.785)}{0.05916} = 26.5 \quad \text{and } K_{eq} = 3\text{x}10^{26}$$

(b) anode: $Zn(s) \rightarrow Zn^{2+} + 2e^-$

cathode: $2H^+(aq) + 2e^- \rightarrow H_2(g)$

$$\Delta\mathcal{E}^\circ_{cell} = 0.000 - (-0.763) = +0.763 \text{ V}, \quad \text{and} \quad n = 2$$

$$\log K_{eq} = \frac{2(0.763)}{0.05916} = 25.8 \quad \text{and } K_{eq} = 6\text{x}10^{25}$$

(c) anode: $2Fe(s) \rightarrow 2Fe^{3+} + 6e^-$

cathode: $3Cd^{2+} + 6e^- \rightarrow 3Cd(s)$

$$\Delta\mathcal{E}^\circ_{cell} = -0.403 - 0.771 = -1.174 \text{ V}, \quad \text{and} \quad n = 6$$

$$\log K_{eq} = \frac{6(-1.174)}{0.05916} = -119.07 = -119.1$$

Most calculators will not be able to evaluate $10^{-119.1}$ with the 10^x button. (Refer to Appendix B2). Write the logarithm as $\log K_{eq} = -120 + 0.93$

$$K_{eq} = (\text{antilog } 0.93)\text{x}10^{-120} = 9\text{x}10^{-120}$$

(d) anode: $2Br^- \rightarrow Br_2(aq) + 2e^-$

cathode: $Cl_2(g) + 2e^- \rightarrow 2Cl^-$

$$\Delta\mathcal{E}^\circ_{cell} = 1.36 - 1.087 = +0.27 \text{ V}, \quad \text{and} \quad n = 2$$

$$\log K_{eq} = \frac{(2)(0.27)}{(0.05916)} = 9.1_3 \quad \text{and} \quad K_{eq} = 1.3\text{x}10^9$$

18. (a) anode: $Co(s) \rightarrow Co^{2+} + 2e^-$

cathode: $Br_2 + 2e^- \rightarrow 2Br^-$

net cell reaction: $Co(s) + Br_2 \rightarrow Co^{2+} + 2Br^-$

$$K_{eq} = \frac{[Co^{2+}][Br^-]^2}{[Br_2]}$$

$\Delta\mathcal{E}^\circ_{cell} = 1.087 - (-0.28) = +1.367$ V, and $n = 2$

$$\log K = \frac{2(1.367)}{0.05916} = 46.2 \quad \text{and} \quad K = 1.52\text{x}10^{46} = 2\text{x}10^{46}$$

(b) anode: $Sc(s) \rightarrow Sc^{3+} + 3e^-$

cathode: $3e^- + 3H^+(aq) \rightarrow (3/2)H_2(g)$

net cell reaction: $Sc(s) + 3H^+(aq) \rightarrow Sc^{3+} + (3/2)H_2(g)$

$$K_{eq} = \frac{[Sc^{3+}]P_{H_2}^{3/2}}{[H^+]^3}$$

$\Delta\mathcal{E}^\circ_{cell} = 0.000 - (-2.08) = +2.08$ V, and $n = 3$

$$\log K = \frac{3(2.08)}{0.05016} = 105 \quad \text{and} \quad K = 10^{105}$$

Note: If you multiplied the net cell reaction above by 2, then $n = 6$, and K_{eq} is the square of that given. The expression is squared and $K = 10^{210}$. See Exercise 16.

(c) anode: $Pb(s) + SO_4^{2-} \rightarrow PbSO_4(s) + 2e^-$

cathode: $Zn^{2+} + 2e^- \rightarrow Zn(s)$

net cell reaction: $Pb(s) + Zn^{2+} + SO_4^{2-} \rightarrow PbSO_4(s) + Zn(s)$

$$K_{eq} = \frac{1}{[Zn^{2+}][SO_4^{2-}]}$$

$\Delta\mathcal{E}^\circ_{cell} = -0.763 - (-0.356) = -0.407$ V, and $n = 2$

$$\log K = \frac{2(-0.407)}{0.05916} = -13.75 \quad \text{and} \quad K = 2\text{x}10^{-14}$$

19. anode: $Pb(s) \rightarrow Pb^{2+} + 2e^-$

cathode: $Ag^+ + e^- \rightarrow Ag(s)$

net cell reaction: $Pb(s) + 2Ag^+ \rightarrow Pb^{2+} + 2Ag(s)$

$$\Delta\mathcal{E}^o_{cell} = 0.799 - (-0.126) = +0.925\ V, \quad \text{and} \quad n = 2$$

$$Q = \frac{[Pb^{2+}]}{[Ag^+]^2} = \frac{0.0125\ M}{(0.600\ M)^2} = 3.47\text{x}10^{-2} \quad \text{and} \quad \log Q = -1.459$$

$$\Delta\mathcal{E}_{cell} = 0.925 - \frac{0.05916}{2}(\log Q) = 0.925 - (0.02958)(-1.459)$$

$$= 0.925 + 0.0432 = 0.968\ V$$

$$\log K_{eq} = \frac{(2)(0.925)}{0.05916} = 31.27 \quad \text{and} \quad K_{eq} = 1.9\text{x}10^{31} = 2\text{x}10^{31}$$

The cell potential is positive; it is 0.968 V. A positive cell potential indicates that the net cell reaction goes spontaneously to the right. The reaction quotient, Q, is very much smaller than K_{eq}. If $Q < K_{eq}$, the reaction proceeds spontaneously to the right. Both criteria provide the same information, and they are consistent, as they must be.

20. (a) No galvanic cell that involves a gas as one of the reactants is suitable for use as a flashlight battery. A gas occupies a very large volume relative to the volume of an equimolar amount of a solid or liquid, and gases are stored in large tanks, obviously unsuitable for carrying around.

(b) Silver is a very expensive metal. Flashlight batteries must be relatively inexpensive to have a market. No commercial dry cell uses one of the more expensive metals.

21. The $PbSO_4$ formed as the product of the reaction in a storage battery remains embedded in the depressions of the grids of the lead electrodes. Because they are still in physical contact, when electricity is put into the cell, the cell reaction is reversed and the battery is recharged.

In the dry cell, Zn^{2+} ions are formed at the anode. These ions move through the paste containing MnO_2 and NH_4Cl. One of the products of the cathode reaction is NH_3, and Zn^{2+} and NH_3 react to form the complex ion $Zn(NH_3)_4{}^{2+}$. Thus there are no longer Zn^{2+} ions near the anode that can be reduced to Zn if electricity is passed into the battery.

22. anode: $Zn(s) + 4OH^- \rightarrow Zn(OH)_4{}^{2-} + 2e^-$

cathode: $H_2O + MnO_2(s) + e^- \rightarrow MnO(OH)(s) + OH^-$

23. The atomic weight of Cu is 63.546 g/mol. Thus the number of moles of Cu deposited is

$$\frac{1.525\ \text{g}}{63.546\ \text{g/mol}} = 2.400\text{x}10^{-2}$$

Since two faradays are required to deposit one mole of Cu,

No. faradays passed = $2(2.400\text{x}10^{-2}) = 4.800\text{x}10^{-2}\ \mathcal{F}$

No. coulombs passed = $(96{,}485\ \text{C}/\mathcal{F})(4.800\text{x}10^{-2}\ \mathcal{F}) = 4631\ \text{C}$

24. The reduction of Hg^{2+} to Hg requires $2\mathcal{F}$ per mole.

$$(1.50\ \frac{\text{C}}{\text{s}})(45.0\ \text{min})(60\ \frac{\text{s}}{\text{min}})\left(\frac{1\ \mathcal{F}}{96{,}485\ \text{C}}\right) = 4.20\text{x}10^{-2}\ \mathcal{F}\ \text{passed.}$$

No. mol Hg formed = $\left(\frac{1\ \text{mol}}{2\ \mathcal{F}}\right)(4.20\text{x}10^{-2}\ \mathcal{F}) = 2.10\text{x}10^{-2}$ mol

mass Hg formed = $(2.10\text{x}10^{-2}\ \text{mol})(200.59\ \text{g/mol}) = 4.21$ g Hg

25. (a) The electrolysis of a solution of $NaClO_4$ is just the electrolysis of water. It is more difficult to reduce Na^+ ions than to reduce H_2O or H^+ ions, and more difficult to oxidize ClO_4^- ions than H_2O or OH^- ions.

$$\begin{array}{ll} \text{anode reaction:} & 2H_2O \rightarrow O_2(g) + 4e^- + 4H^+(aq) \\ \text{cathode reaction:} & \underline{2H_2O + 2e^- \rightarrow H_2(g) + 2OH^-(aq)} \\ \text{overall reaction:} & 2H_2O \rightarrow 2H_2(g) + O_2(g) \end{array}$$

(b) Since Au^{3+} ions are readily reduced, Au(s) will be produced at the cathode. Both Cl^- ions and OH^- ions or H_2O can be oxidized at the anode. The principal product depends on the concentration of the $AuCl_3$. For a concentrated solution of $AuCl_3$, $Cl_2(g)$ is formed. For low concentrations, both anode reactions will occur. For a concentrated solution the electrode reactions are

$$\begin{array}{ll} \text{anode reaction:} & 2Cl^- \rightarrow Cl_2(g) + 2e^- \\ \text{cathode reaction:} & \underline{Au^{3+} + 3e^- \rightarrow Au\downarrow} \\ \text{overall reaction:} & 6Cl^- + 2Au^{3+} \rightarrow 3Cl_2(g) + 2Au\downarrow \end{array}$$

(c) Silver is above H_2 in the Table of Standard Reduction Potentials, so Ag is formed at the cathode. It is easier to oxidize H_2O than NO_3^- ions, so O_2 is formed at the anode.

$$\begin{array}{ll} \text{anode reaction:} & 2H_2O \rightarrow O_2(g) + 4e^- + 4H^+(aq) \\ \text{cathode reaction:} & \underline{Ag^+ + e^- \rightarrow Ag\downarrow} \\ \text{overall reaction:} & 4Ag^+ + 2H_2O \rightarrow O_2(g) + 4Ag\downarrow + 4H^+(aq) \end{array}$$

(d) Since Ba is a stronger reducing agent than H_2, H_2 is formed at the cathode. At the anode, Br^- is oxidized to Br_2.

$$\begin{array}{ll} \text{anode reaction:} & 2Br^- \rightarrow Br_2 + 2e^- \\ \text{cathode reaction:} & 2H_2O + 2e^- \rightarrow H_2(g) + 2OH^- \\ \hline \text{overall reaction:} & 2H_2O + 2Br^- \rightarrow Br_2 + H_2(g) + 2OH^- \end{array}$$

26. (a) The atomic weight of Na is 22.99 g/mol, so that 2.00 kg is $(2000\ g)/(22.99\ g{\cdot}mol^{-1}) = 86.99 = 87.0$ mol of Na. One $\mathcal{F}$ is required to deposit 1 mol of Na, so 87.0 $\mathcal{F}$ or $(87.0\ \mathcal{F})(96{,}485\ C/\mathcal{F}) = 8.39 \times 10^6$ C are needed.

$$(50.0\ A)(t) = 8.39 \times 10^6\ C \quad \text{and} \quad t = 1.68 \times 10^5\ s$$

To convert to hours, divide by 3600 s/h. It takes 46.6 hours to produce 2.00 kg of Na with a current of 50.0 A.

(b) One kg of Na is 43.5 mol, and therefore 43.5 $\mathcal{F}$ or $(43.5\ \mathcal{F})(96{,}485\ C/\mathcal{F}) = 4.20 \times 10^6$ C are needed. There are 600 seconds in 10 minutes.

$$(4.20 \times 10^6\ C)/(600\ s) = 6.99 \times 10^3\ A$$

27. Calcium is a stronger reducing agent than H_2, Cu a weaker reducing agent than H_2. It is easier to reduce Cu^{2+} ions than H^+ ions, but harder to reduce Ca^{2+} ions.

28.

$$\text{No. faradays passed} = \frac{(1.80\ A)(1320\ s)}{96{,}485\ C/\mathcal{F}} = 2.46 \times 10^{-2}\ \mathcal{F}$$

As two faradays are required to produce one mol of H_2, there will be 1.23×10^{-2} mol H_2 formed.

$$V = \frac{nRT}{P} = \frac{(0.0123\ \text{mol})(0.08206\ \text{L·atm·mol}^{-1}\text{K}^{-1})(298.15\ \text{K})}{(752/760\ \text{atm})}$$

$$= 0.304\ \text{L}$$

Solutions to Multiple Choice Questions, Chapter 16

1. (b) Lead is below silver in the Table of Standard Reduction Potentials, but above Ni. Thus it is a stronger reducing agent than Ag, but weaker than Ni.

2. (b) $\Delta\mathcal{E}^\circ_{cell} = \mathcal{E}^\circ_{cathode} - \mathcal{E}^\circ_{anode} = -0.126 - (-0.763)$

$$= +0.763 - 0.126 = 0.637\ \text{V}$$

3. (e) anode: $Zn(s) \rightarrow Zn^{2+} + 2e^-$

cathode: $Ag^+ + e^- \rightarrow Ag\downarrow$

net cell: $Zn(s) + 2Ag^+ \rightarrow Zn^{2+} + 2Ag\downarrow$

$$Q = [Zn^{2+}]/[Ag^+]^2 = (0.0100)/(1.25)^2 = 6.40\text{x}10^{-3}$$

4. (e) Zinc is a stronger reducing agent than H_2, so H_2 will be evolved at the cathode. Nitrate ions cannot be oxidized at the anode; H_2O or OH^- will be oxidized and $O_2(g)$ will be evolved at the anode. This is just the electrolysis of water.

5. (e) The oxidation state of manganese is +7 in MnO_4^- and +2 in Mn^{2+}, so 5 electrons must be gained for this reduction, or 5 faradays per mole of MnO_4^-.

6. (d) Cobaltic ion, Co^{3+}, is a powerful oxidizing agent, and is easily reduced to the +2 state, Co^{2+}. The value of $\mathcal{E}^\circ$ for $Co^{3+} + e^- \rightarrow Co^{2+}$ is 1.82 V. The other cations, Zn^{2+}, Fe^{2+}, and Mn^{2+}, are all weak oxidizing

agents, below H^+ in the Table. Option (a) is clearly wrong because Br^- can only serve as a reducing agent, not an oxidizing agent. It is the lowest oxidation state of Br.

7. <u>(d)</u> anode: $Cd(s) \rightarrow Cd^{2+} + 2e^-$

cathode: $Cu^{2+} + 2e^- \rightarrow Cu\downarrow$

net cell: $Cd(s) + Cu^{2+} \rightarrow Cd^{2+} + Cu\downarrow$

$$Q = [Cd^{2+}]/[Cu^{2+}] = 1.00$$

The way to increase the cell voltage is to decrease the reaction quotient, Q. There are two ways to understand this. (1) A reaction proceeds to the right if $Q < K_{eq}$. The smaller the value of Q, the greater the tendency for the reaction to proceed spontaneously to the right, and the larger the cell voltage. (2) Examine the term involving Q in the Nernst equation. It is $-(0.05916/n)(\log Q)$. If $Q < 1$, log Q is negative and the term in the Nernst equation is positive, so that the cell voltage is larger than $\Delta\mathcal{E}^\circ_{cell}$. The smaller Q is relative to 1, the more negative log Q is, and the larger (more positive) is the value of the term $-(0.05916/n)(\log Q)$ in the Nernst equation for the cell voltage.

Options (a) and (c) leave Q unchanged at 1.0. Options (b) and (e) increase Q. Only option (d) decreases Q, from 1.00 to 0.100.

8. <u>(a)</u> Metals that are weaker reducing agents than H_2 will plate out at the cathode during electrolysis. Of the 5 listed, only Cd and Cr are stronger reducing agents than H_2, so Ag, Cu, and Hg will all be produced at the cathode during electrolysis.

9. <u>(d)</u> Electrolysis of an aqueous solution of Li_2SO_4 is just the electrolysis of water. Lithium is a stronger reducing agent than H_2, and OH^- or H_2O are more readily oxidized than SO_4^{2-}.

10. <u>(c)</u>

$$\begin{array}{ll} \text{anode:} & Zn(s) \rightarrow Zn^{2+} + 2e^- \\ \text{cathode:} & Cu^{2+} + 2e^- \rightarrow Cu\downarrow \\ \hline \text{net cell:} & Zn(s) + Cu^{2+} \rightarrow Zn^{2+} + Cu\downarrow \end{array}$$

$$Q = [Zn^{2+}]/[Cu^{2+}]$$

If $Q > 1$, log Q is positive (> 0) and the cell voltage is less than the standard cell voltage, because the term in Q in the Nernst equation, $-(0.05916/n)(\log Q)$, is negative. The only way for Q to be > 1, is for $[Zn^{2+}] > [Cu^{2+}]$. Cell potentials are independent of the actual amount of material present, or of the size of the electrode.

11. <u>(c)</u> As two faradays are required to deposit 1 mol of Cu, 0.500 $\mathcal{F}$ are required to deposit 0.250 mol of Cu.

No. coulombs = $(96{,}485\ C/\mathcal{F})(0.500\ \mathcal{F}) = (15.0\ A)(t)$

where t is time in seconds. Hence it takes 3216 s, or 53.6 min to deposit 0.250 mol Cu with a current of 15.0 A.

12. (b) $\Delta\mathcal{E}^\circ_{cell} = \mathcal{E}^\circ_{cathode} - \mathcal{E}^\circ_{anode} = 0.799 - (-0.403)$

$$= 1.202 \text{ V}$$

$$\log K_{eq} = \frac{2(1.202)}{0.0592} = 40.6$$

13. (d) There are 4212 s in 70.2 min. The charge in coulombs is (30.0 A)(4212 s) = $1.26\text{x}10^5$ C. The number of faradays is ($1.26\text{x}10^5$ C)/(96,485 C/$\mathcal{F}$) = 1.31

14. (b)

anode:	$Co(s) \rightarrow Co^{2+} + 2e^-$
cathode:	$2H^+(aq) + 2e^- \rightarrow H_2(g)$
net cell:	$Co(s) + 2H^+(aq) \rightarrow Co^{2+} + H_2(g)$

$$Q = \frac{[Co^{2+}]P_{H_2}}{[H^+]^2}$$

A change that decreases the reaction quotient, Q, increases the cell voltage. (See the solution to multiple choice question 7, above) Increasing the $[H^+]$ decreases Q. Options (c) and (e) increase Q and therefore decrease the cell voltage. Cell voltages are independent of the amount of material present and depend only on the concentrations. Thus changing the mass of the electrode or the volume of the solution (but keeping the concentration constant) does not affect the cell voltage.

15. (c) The reaction at the anode is

$$4OH^-(aq) \rightarrow O_2(g) + 4e^- + 2H_2O$$

No. coulombs passed = (1.50 h)(3600 s/h)(8.00 A) = $4.32\text{x}10^4$

No. faradays passed = ($4.32\text{x}10^4$ C)/(96,485 C/$\mathcal{F}$) = $4.48\text{x}10^{-1}$

Since it requires 4 faradays to produce 1 mol of O_2, $4.48\times10^{-1}\ \mathcal{F}$ produce 1.12×10^{-1} mol = 0.112 mol of O_2.

16. (d) anode reaction: $Ni(s) \rightarrow Ni^{2+} + 2e^-$

cathode reaction: $Cl_2(g) + 2e^- \rightarrow 2Cl^-$

net cell reaction: $Ni(s) + Cl_2(g) \rightarrow Ni^{2+} + 2Cl^-$

$$Q = \frac{[Ni^{2+}][Cl^-]^2}{P_{Cl_2}} = \frac{(0.10)(0.40)^2}{0.50} = 3.2\times10^{-2}$$

17. (e) The standard reduction potential for dilute nitric acid

$$NO_3^- + 4H^+(aq) + 3e^- \rightarrow NO\uparrow + 2H_2O$$

is 0.96 V. Thus dilute nitric acid will oxidize any metal with a more negative reduction potential, that is, below +0.96 V in the Table. Hence Ag, Cd, Sn, and Cu can all be oxidized by warm dilute nitric acid, but Au and Pt cannot be oxidized. The reason Pt is used as an electrode in the lab is because it is a relatively inert metal, and is oxidized only with great difficulty.

Solutions to Problems, Chapter 16

16.1. (a) $\mathcal{E}^\circ_{Cd^{2+}|Cd} = -0.403$ V; $\mathcal{E}^\circ_{Pt|Fe^{3+},Fe^{2+}} = 0.771$ V

The only way the cell potential will be positive is if the $Pt|Fe^{3+},Fe^{2+}$ electrode is the cathode, and the $Cd^{2+}|Cd$ electrode is the anode. For a galvanic cell, the positive terminal is the cathode, or the Pt electrode in this cell.

(b) The $Pt|Fe^{3+},Fe^{2+}$ electrode is the cathode.

(c) anode reaction: $Fe^{3+} + e^- \rightarrow Fe^{2+}$

cathode reaction: $Cd(s) \rightarrow Cd^{2+} + 2e^-$

net cell reaction: $2Fe^{3+} + Cd(s) \rightarrow Cd^{2+} + 2Fe^{2+}$

(d) $\Delta\mathcal{E}^\circ_{cell} = \mathcal{E}^\circ_{cathode} - \mathcal{E}^\circ_{anode} = \mathcal{E}^\circ_{right} - \mathcal{E}^\circ_{left}$

$= +0.771 - (-0.403) = 1.174$ V

For this reaction, n = 2, so that

$$\log K = \frac{(2)(1.174)}{0.05916} = 39.69 \quad \text{and} \quad K = 4.9\text{x}10^{39}$$

(e) $$Q = \frac{[Cd^{2+}][Fe^{2+}]^2}{[Fe^{3+}]^2} = \frac{(0.500)(0.010)^2}{(0.850)^2} = 6.92\text{x}10^{-5}$$

(f) $\log Q = -4.16$ and $\Delta\mathcal{E}^\circ_{cell} = 1.174$ V from parts (d) and (e).

$$\Delta\mathcal{E}_{cell} = \Delta\mathcal{E}^\circ_{cell} - (0.05916/n)(\log Q)$$

Substituting the values for this reaction, we obtain

$\Delta\mathcal{E}_{cell} = 1.174 - (0.02958)(-4.16) = 1.174 + 0.123 = 1.297$ V

Note that since $Q < 1$, the cell potential is larger (more positive) than the standard cell potential, $\Delta\mathcal{E}^\circ_{cell}$.

16.2. oxidation: $Hg \rightarrow (1/2)Hg_2{}^{2+} + e^-$

reduction: $Hg^{2+} + e^- \rightarrow (1/2)Hg_2{}^{2+}$

net reaction: $Hg + Hg^{2+} \rightarrow Hg_2{}^{2+}$

Note that as written above, n = 1 in the Nernst equation. If you multiply each of the half-reactions shown by 2, and use n = 2, then the net cell reaction is

$$2Hg^{2+} + 2Hg \rightarrow 2Hg_2{}^{2+}$$

and the value of the equilibrium constant is the square of the one asked for. The $\mathcal{E}^\circ$ values for the electrode reactions, however, are exactly the same no matter how you write the half-reactions.

$$\Delta\mathcal{E}^\circ_{cell} = \mathcal{E}^\circ_{cathode} - \mathcal{E}^\circ_{anode} = \mathcal{E}^\circ_{right} - \mathcal{E}^\circ_{left}$$

$$= +0.920 - 0.789 = 0.131 \text{ V}$$

For this reaction, n = 1, so that

$$\log K = \frac{(1)(0.131)}{0.05916} = 2.214 \quad \text{and} \quad K = 1.6\text{x}10^2$$

16.3. (a) anode: $Tl(s) \rightarrow Tl^+ + e^-$

cathode: $Cl_2(g) + 2e^- \rightarrow 2Cl^-$

net cell: $2Tl(s) + Cl_2(g) \rightarrow 2Tl^+ + 2Cl^-$

(b) The anode of a galvanic cell is the negative terminal, which in this case is the Tl(s) electrode.

(c) $$\Delta\mathcal{E}_{cell} = \Delta\mathcal{E}^\circ_{cell} - (0.05916/n)(\log Q)$$

$$Q = \frac{[Tl^+]^2[Cl^-]^2}{P_{Cl_2}} = \frac{(0.200)^2(0.500)^2}{1} = 1.00\text{x}10^{-2}$$

Thus, $\log Q = -2.00$ and $n = 2$ for this reaction.

$$\Delta\mathcal{E}_{cell} = 1.755 \text{ V} = \Delta\mathcal{E}^\circ_{cell} - (0.02958)(-2.00)$$

$$= \Delta\mathcal{E}^\circ_{cell} + 0.0592$$

Thus, $\Delta\mathcal{E}^\circ_{cell} = 1.755 - 0.0592 = 1.696 \text{ V} = \mathcal{E}^\circ_{right} - \mathcal{E}^\circ_{left}$

Since the right-hand electrode (the one at which reduction occurs) is the $Cl_2|Cl^-$ electrode in this cell,

$$1.696 = 1.36 - \mathcal{E}^\circ_{Tl^+|Tl} \quad \text{and} \quad \mathcal{E}^\circ_{Tl^+|Tl} = -0.34 \text{ V}$$

16.4. anode: $Cr^{2+} \rightarrow Cr^{3+} + e^-$

cathode: $4H^+(aq) + O_2(g) + 4e^- \rightarrow 2H_2O$

net cell: $4H^+(aq) + 4Cr^{2+} + O_2(g) \rightarrow 4Cr^{3+} + 2H_2O$

$$\Delta\mathcal{E}^\circ_{cell} = \mathcal{E}^\circ_{cathode} - \mathcal{E}^\circ_{anode} = \mathcal{E}^\circ_{right} - \mathcal{E}^\circ_{left}$$
$$= +1.229 - (-0.41) = 1.64 \text{ V}$$

Since $\Delta\mathcal{E}^\circ_{cell}$ is positive and relatively large, the net cell reaction is spontaneous as written. Acidic solutions of Cr^{2+} are not stable, but are oxidized by the O_2 in the air to Cr^{3+}.

16.5. (a)

anode: $Zn(s) \rightarrow Zn^{2+} + 2e^-$

cathode: $14H^+(aq) + Cr_2O_7^{2-} + 6e^- \rightarrow 2Cr^{3+} + 7H_2O$

net cell: $3Zn + 14H^+(aq) + Cr_2O_7^{2-} \rightarrow 2Cr^{3+} + 7H_2O + 3Zn^{2+}$

$$\Delta\mathcal{E}^\circ_{cell} = \mathcal{E}^\circ_{cathode} - \mathcal{E}^\circ_{anode} = \mathcal{E}^\circ_{right} - \mathcal{E}^\circ_{left}$$
$$= +1.33 - (-0.763) = 2.09 \text{ V}$$

Yes, the net cell reaction proceeds spontaneously to the right as $\Delta\mathcal{E}^\circ_{cell} > 0$.

(b) anode: $2I^- \rightarrow I_2 + 2e^-$

cathode: $4H^+(aq) + PbO_2(s) + 2e^- \rightarrow Pb^{2+} + 2H_2O$

net cell: $4H^+(aq) + 2I^- + PbO_2(s) \rightarrow Pb^{2+} + I_2 + 2H_2O$

$$\Delta\mathcal{E}^\circ_{cell} = \mathcal{E}^\circ_{cathode} - \mathcal{E}^\circ_{anode} = \mathcal{E}^\circ_{right} - \mathcal{E}^\circ_{left}$$
$$= +1.46 - 0.535 = 0.92 \text{ V}$$

Yes, the net cell reaction proceeds spontaneously to the right as $\Delta\mathcal{E}^\circ_{cell} > 0$.

Note: The $\mathcal{E}^\circ$ value for the $PbO_2|Pb^{2+}$ electrode was inadvertantly omitted from Appendix F for the first printing of the text. However it can be calculated from other entries in the Table.

(1) $PbO_2(s) + SO_4^{2-} + 4H^+(aq) + 2e^- \longrightarrow PbSO_4(s) + 2H_2O$

(2) $PbSO_4(s) + 2e^- \longrightarrow Pb(s) + SO_4^{2-}$

(3) $Pb^{2+} + 2e^- \longrightarrow Pb(s)$

The desired electrode reaction is (1) + (2) - (3). Therefore the $\mathcal{E}°$ value needed is obtained by calculating exactly the same sum of the $\mathcal{E}°$ values.

$$\mathcal{E}°_{PbO_2|Pb^{2+}} = 1.685 - 0.356 - (-0.126) = 1.455 \text{ V}$$

(c) anode: $Ag(s) + Cl^- \longrightarrow AgCl(s) + e^-$

cathode: $2H^+(aq) + 2e^- \longrightarrow H_2(g)$

net cell: $2Ag(s) + 2Cl^- + 2H^+(aq) \longrightarrow 2AgCl(s) + H_2(g)$

$$\Delta\mathcal{E}°_{cell} = \mathcal{E}°_{cathode} - \mathcal{E}°_{anode} = \mathcal{E}°_{right} - \mathcal{E}°_{left}$$

$$= 0.0000 - 0.2223 = -0.2223 \text{ V}$$

No, the net cell reaction does not proceed spontaneously to the right as $\Delta\mathcal{E}°_{cell} < 0$. The reverse reaction

$$2AgCl(s) + H_2(g) \longrightarrow 2Ag(s) + 2Cl^- + 2H^+(aq)$$

is spontaneous.

(d) anode: $Pb(s) \longrightarrow Pb^{2+} + 2e^-$

cathode: $PbSO_4(s) + 2e^- \longrightarrow Pb(s) + SO_4^{2-}$

net cell: $PbSO_4(s) \longrightarrow Pb^{2+} + SO_4^{2-}$

$$\Delta\mathcal{E}°_{cell} = \mathcal{E}°_{cathode} - \mathcal{E}°_{anode} = \mathcal{E}°_{right} - \mathcal{E}°_{left}$$

$$= -0.356 - (-0.126) = -0.230 \text{ V}$$

No, the net cell reaction does not proceed spontaneously to the right as $\Delta\mathcal{E}°_{cell} < 0$. Note that the net cell reaction is the equation for which the equilibrium constant is the K_{sp} of $PbSO_4$. Since $PbSO_4$ is only very slightly soluble, the reaction is not spontaneous to the right, and $K_{sp} \ll 1$.

16.6. (a) oxidation: $Cu(s) \rightarrow Cu^{2+} + 2e^-$

reduction: $(Cu^{2+} + e^- \rightarrow Cu^+) \times 2$

net cell: $Cu(s) + Cu^{2+} \rightarrow 2Cu^+$

$$\Delta\mathcal{E}^\circ_{cell} = \mathcal{E}^\circ_{cathode} - \mathcal{E}^\circ_{anode} = \mathcal{E}^\circ_{right} - \mathcal{E}^\circ_{left}$$

$$= 0.153 - 0.337 = -0.184 \text{ V}$$

For this reaction n = 2, and

$$\log K = \frac{2(-0.184)}{0.05916} = -6.22 \quad \text{and} \quad K = 6.0\times10^{-7}$$

No, this reaction does not proceed to the right to an appreciable extent, as $K \ll 1$ and $\Delta\mathcal{E}^\circ_{cell} < 0$.

(b) $K_{sp}(CuBr) = [Cu^+][Br^-] = 4\times10^{-8}$

$$K = [Cu^+]^2/[Cu^{2+}] = 6.0\times10^{-7}$$

For the reaction $Cu(s) + Cu^{2+} + 2Br^- \rightleftharpoons 2CuBr(s)$

$$K_{eq} = \frac{1}{[Cu^{2+}][Br^-]^2} = \frac{K}{(K_{sp})^2}$$

$$= \frac{6.0\times10^{-7}}{(4\times10^{-8})^2} = 4\times10^9 \gg 1$$

The addition of Br^-, which precipitates CuBr, decreases the $[Cu^+]$ significantly. The decrease in $[Cu^+]$ drives the reaction $Cu(s) + Cu^{2+} \rightarrow 2Cu^+$ to the right, by Le Chatelier's Principle. The +1 oxidation state of copper is not stable as a free ion in solution, but disproportionates to solid Cu and Cu^{2+}. However, with an anion present that forms an insoluble salt with Cu^+, the reaction to form the insoluble copper(I) salt can be spontaneous, and this is the case for the formation of CuBr.

16.7. anode reaction: $Ag(s) \rightarrow Ag^+ + e^-$

cathode reaction: $AgCl(s) + e^- \rightarrow Ag(s) + Cl^-$

net cell reaction: $AgCl(s) \rightarrow Ag^+ + Cl^-$

$$\Delta\mathcal{E}^\circ_{cell} = \mathcal{E}^\circ_{cathode} - \mathcal{E}^\circ_{anode} = \mathcal{E}^\circ_{right} - \mathcal{E}^\circ_{left}$$

$$= 0.2223 - 0.799 = -0.577 \text{ V}$$

For this reaction n = 1, and

$$\log K = \frac{1(-0.577)}{0.05916} = -9.75 \quad \text{and} \quad K = 1.8\text{x}10^{-10}$$

$$K = [Ag^+][Cl^-] = K_{sp}(AgCl) = 1.8\text{x}10^{-10}$$

16.8. (a)

(i) anode: $Ag(s) + Cl^- \rightarrow AgCl(s) + e^-$

cathode: $2H^+(aq) + 2e^- \rightarrow H_2(g)$

net cell: $2Ag(s) + 2H^+(aq) + 2Cl^- \rightarrow 2AgCl(s) + H_2(g)$

$$\Delta\mathcal{E}^\circ_{cell} = \mathcal{E}^\circ_{cathode} - \mathcal{E}^\circ_{anode} = \mathcal{E}^\circ_{right} - \mathcal{E}^\circ_{left}$$

$$= 0.000 - 0.2223 = -0.2223 \text{ V}$$

(ii) anode: $Ag(s) + I^- \rightarrow AgI(s) + e^-$

cathode: $2H^+(aq) + 2e^- \rightarrow H_2(g)$

net cell: $2Ag(s) + 2H^+(aq) + 2I^- \rightarrow 2AgI(s) + H_2(g)$

$$\Delta\mathcal{E}^\circ_{cell} = \mathcal{E}^\circ_{cathode} - \mathcal{E}^\circ_{anode} = \mathcal{E}^\circ_{right} - \mathcal{E}^\circ_{left}$$

$$= 0.000 - (-0.152) = +0.152 \text{ V}$$

Silver will not liberate $H_2(g)$ from 1 M HCl, as $\Delta\mathcal{E}^\circ_{cell}$ for reaction (i) is negative, but it will liberate $H_2(g)$ from 1 M HI because $\Delta\mathcal{E}^\circ_{cell}$ is positive for reaction (ii).

16.9. anode: $H_2(g) \rightarrow 2H^+(5.0\text{x}10^{-4}) + 2e^-$

cathode: $2H^+(M_1) + 2e^- \rightarrow H_2(g)$

net cell: $2H^+(M_1) \rightarrow 2H^+(5.0\text{x}10^{-4})$

$$\Delta\mathcal{E}_{cell} = 0.154 = 0.00 - (0.0592/2)(\log Q)$$

$$Q = \frac{(5.0\text{x}10^{-4})^2}{(M_1)^2} = \left(\frac{5.0\text{x}10^{-4}}{M_1}\right)^2$$

$$\log Q = 2\ \log\{(5.0\text{x}10^{-4})/M_1\}$$

Thus, $\Delta\mathcal{E}^\circ_{cell} = 0.154 = -(0.0592/2)(2)\log\{(5.0\text{x}10^{-4})/M_1\}$

$$(-0.154)/(0.0592) = -2.60 = \log\{(5.0\text{x}10^{-4})/M_1\}$$

$$\{(5.0\text{x}10^{-4})/M_1\} = 10^{-2.60} = 2.49\text{x}10^{-3}$$

$$M_1 = \frac{5.0\text{x}10^{-4}}{2.49\text{x}10^{-3}} = 2.0\text{x}10^{-1}$$

Note: The simplest way to handle the logarithm is not to separate the fraction $(5.0\text{x}10^{-4})/M_1$ until after calculating the antilog of -2.60.

16.10. anode: $Zn(s) \rightarrow Zn^{2+} + 2e^-$

cathode: $PbO_2(s) + 2e^- + 4H^+(aq) \rightarrow Pb^{2+} + 2H_2O$

net cell: $PbO_2 + Zn + 4H^+(aq) \rightarrow Zn^{2+} + Pb^{2+} + 2H_2O$

The cathode single electrode potential is

$$\mathcal{E}_{cathode} = \mathcal{E}^\circ_{PbO_2|Pb^{2+}} - (0.0592/2)\log\frac{[Pb^{2+}]}{[H^+]^4}$$

Writing the anode reaction as a reduction

$$Zn^{2+} + 2e^- \rightarrow Zn(s)$$

yields for the reduction potential at the anode

$$\mathcal{E}_{anode} = \mathcal{E}^\circ_{Zn^{2+}|Zn} - (0.0592/2)\log(1/[Zn^{2+}])$$
$$= \mathcal{E}^\circ_{Zn^{2+}|Zn} + (0.0592/2)\log[Zn^{2+}]$$

using the fundamental property of logarithms discussed in Appendix B2, page 914 of the text.

$$\Delta\mathcal{E}_{cell} = \mathcal{E}_{cathode} - \mathcal{E}_{anode}$$
$$= \mathcal{E}^\circ_{PbO_2|Pb^{2+}} - (0.0592/2)\log\left(\frac{[Pb^{2+}]}{[H^+]^4}\right) - \mathcal{E}^\circ_{Zn^{2+}|Zn}$$
$$- (0.0592/2)\log[Zn^{2+}]$$

Collecting the logarithmic terms together and using the property log(ab) = loga + logb, we obtain

$$\Delta\mathcal{E}_{cell} = \Delta\mathcal{E}^\circ_{cell} - (0.0592/2)\log\{[Pb^{2+}][Zn^{2+}]/[H^+]^4\}$$

where $\Delta\mathcal{E}^\circ_{cell} = \mathcal{E}^\circ_{PbO_2|Pb^{2+}} - \mathcal{E}^\circ_{Zn^{2+}|Zn}$

This is exactly the Nernst equation, Eq. (16-22), for the net cell reaction written above.

16.11. (a) anode: $Zn(s) \rightarrow Zn^{2+} + 2e^-$

cathode: $Cl_2(g) + 2e^- \rightarrow 2Cl^-$

net cell: $Zn(s) + Cl_2(g) \rightarrow Zn^{2+} + 2Cl^-$

(b) $Q = [Zn^{2+}][Cl^-]^2/P_{Cl_2} = (0.0400)(5.00\text{x}10^{-3})^2/1$

$= 1.00\text{x}10^{-6}$

For this reaction n = 2 and log Q = −6.00, so that

$$\Delta\mathcal{E}_{cell} = \Delta\mathcal{E}^\circ_{cell} - (0.0592/2)(-6.00) = \Delta\mathcal{E}^\circ_{cell} + 0.178$$

Since $\Delta\mathcal{E}^\circ_{cell} = 1.36 - (-0.763) = 2.12$ V,

$$\Delta\mathcal{E}_{cell} = 2.12 + 0.178 = 2.30 \text{ V}$$

(c) If the $[Cl^-]$ is increased from 5.00×10^{-3} to 0.500, Q is increased to 1.00×10^{-2}, log Q = −2.00 and

$$\Delta\mathcal{E}_{cell} = 2.12 + 0.059 = 2.18\ V$$

Thus the cell voltage decreases from 2.30 V to 2.18 V when $[Cl^-]$ is increased from 5.00×10^{-3} M to 0.500 M. It is not necessary to do these calculations in detail, however, to answer the question asked. Any change that increases the reaction quotient, Q, decreases the cell voltage. Conversely, any change that decreases Q increases the cell voltage. (See also the solution to multiple choice question 7).

(d) Adding NH_3 to the anode compartment greatly decreases the $[Zn^{2+}]$ by forming the complex ion $Zn(NH_3)_4{}^{2+}$. As the reaction quotient, Q, is directly proportional to the $[Zn^{2+}]$, adding NH_3 decreases Q. Any change that decreases Q increases the cell voltage, as discussed above. As Q decreases, log Q becomes more negative and the second term in the Nernst equation becomes more positive, increasing $\Delta\mathcal{E}_{cell}$.

(e) As calculated in part (b), $\Delta\mathcal{E}^{o}_{cell} = 2.12$ V for this reaction, and n = 2. Thus,

$$\log K_{eq} = \frac{(2)(2.12)}{0.0592} = 71.6 \quad \text{and} \quad K_{eq} = 4 \times 10^{71}$$

This is an extremely large equilibrium constant, indicating that the combination of Zn and Cl_2 to form aqueous zinc chloride proceeds essentially to completion to the right.

16.12. oxidation: $Zn(s) \rightarrow Zn^{2+} + 2e^-$

reduction: $Ag^+ + e^- \rightarrow Ag\downarrow$

overall: $Zn(s) + 2Ag^+ \rightarrow Zn^{2+} + 2Ag\downarrow$

$$\Delta\mathcal{E}^\circ_{cell} = \mathcal{E}^\circ_{cathode} - \mathcal{E}^\circ_{anode} = \mathcal{E}^\circ_{right} - \mathcal{E}^\circ_{left}$$

$$= 0.799 - (-0.763) = 1.562 \text{ V}$$

For this reaction n = 2, so that

$$\log K_{eq} = \frac{(2)(1.562)}{0.05916} = 52.806 \quad \text{and} \quad K_{eq} = 6.4\text{x}10^{52}$$

Thus, at equilibrium, $[Zn^{2+}]/[Ag^+]^2 = 6.4\text{x}10^{52}$.

No. mol Ag^+ added = (0.08000 L)(0.1000 M) = $8.000\text{x}10^{-3}$ mol

$$\text{No. mol Zn added} = \frac{3.000 \text{ g}}{65.38 \text{ g/mol}} = 4.5886\text{x}10^{-2} = 4.589\text{x}10^{-2}$$

$$\text{Since} \quad \frac{\text{No. moles Zn used}}{\text{No. moles Ag}^+ \text{ used}} = \frac{1}{2}$$

it only requires $4.000\text{x}10^{-3}$ mol of Zn to completely react with all the Ag^+ in solution. Thus the Ag^+ is the limiting reagent, and $8.000\text{x}10^{-3}$ mol Ag^+ react with $4.000\text{x}10^{-3}$ mol Zn to produce $4.00\text{x}10^{-3}$ mol Zn^{2+}, in a volume of 80.00 mL.

$$[Zn^{2+}] = \frac{4.000 \text{ mmol}}{80.00 \text{ mL}} = 5.000\text{x}10^{-2} \text{ M}$$

$$[Ag^+]^2 = [Zn^{2+}]/K_{eq} = (5.000\text{x}10^{-2})/(6.4\text{x}10^{52}) = 7.81\text{x}10^{-55}$$

$$[Ag^+] = 8.8\text{x}10^{-28} \text{ M}$$

$$\text{No. mol Zn unreacted} = 4.5886\text{x}10^{-2} \text{ mol} - 4.000\text{x}10^{-3} \text{ mol}$$

$$= 4.1886\text{x}10^{-2} \text{ mol} = 4.189\text{x}10^{-2} \text{ mol}$$

$$\text{mass Zn unreacted} = (65.38 \text{ g/mol})(4.1886\text{x}10^{-2} \text{ mol})$$

$$= 2.738 \text{ g}$$

16.13. (a)

No. coulombs passed = (1.17 A)(1515 s) = $1.77_3 \times 10^3$ C

$$\text{No. faradays passed} = \frac{1773\ \text{C}}{96{,}485\ \text{C}/\mathcal{F}} = 1.84\times10^{-2}\ \mathcal{F}$$

(b) The vapor pressure of H_2O at 26.0°C = 25.2 mmHg. This can be found in Table 3.3, p. 109 of the text.

$$P_{H_2} = 762.0\ \text{mmHg} - 25.2\ \text{mmHg} = 736.8\ \text{mmHg}$$

$$\text{No. mol } H_2 = \frac{PV}{RT} = \frac{(736.8\ \text{mmHg})(0.2320\ \text{L})}{(62.363\ \text{L}\cdot\text{mmHg}\cdot\text{mol}^{-1}\text{K}^{-1})(299.2\ \text{K})}$$

$$= 9.163\times10^{-3}\ \text{mol}$$

$$\text{No. mol Cu oxidized} = \frac{0.583\ \text{g}}{63.546\ \text{g/mol}} = 9.17\times10^{-3}\ \text{mol}$$

Note that within the experimental uncertainty of ±1 in the third significant figure in the mass of Cu lost, the molar ratio of H_2 formed to Cu oxidized is 1:1.

(c) $$\frac{\text{No. mol Cu oxidized}}{\text{No. faradays passed}} = \frac{9.17\times10^{-3}\ \text{mol}}{1.837\times10^{-2}\ \mathcal{F}} = 0.499 = \frac{1}{2}$$

Within experimental uncertainty, the oxidation of 1 mol of Cu requires the passage of 2$\mathcal{F}$. Therefore the oxidation state of Cu must be +2, that is, the anode reaction must be

$$Cu(s) \rightarrow Cu^{2+} + 2e^-$$

(d) No. mol electrons transferred = $2(9.17\times10^{-3})$ mol

Charge on one electron = 1.602×10^{-19} C

$$\left(N_A\ \frac{\text{electrons}}{\text{mol}}\right)\left(1.602\times10^{-19}\ \frac{\text{C}}{\text{electron}}\right)(18.34\times10^{-3}\ \text{mol}) = 1773\ \text{C}$$

$$N_A = \frac{1773}{(1.602\times10^{-19})(18.34\times10^{-3})} = 6.03\times10^{23}$$

16.14. anode: $Ag(s) \rightarrow Ag^+ + e^-$

cathode: $Ag_2SO_4(s) + 2e^- \rightarrow 2Ag(s) + SO_4^{2-}$

net cell: $Ag_2SO_4(s) \rightarrow 2Ag^+ + SO_4^{2-}$

$$\Delta\mathcal{E}^\circ_{cell} = \mathcal{E}^\circ_{cathode} - \mathcal{E}^\circ_{anode} = \mathcal{E}^\circ_{right} - \mathcal{E}^\circ_{left}$$

$$= 0.653 - 0.799 = -0.146 \text{ V}$$

For this reaction n = 2, so that

$$\log K_{eq} = \frac{(2)(-0.146)}{0.05916} = -4.94 \quad \text{and} \quad K_{eq} = 1.16\text{x}10^{-5}$$

Since the equilibrium constant for the net cell reaction is the solubility product of Ag_2SO_4, and there are only 2 figures in the mantissa of the logarithm, $K_{sp} = 1.2\text{x}10^{-5}$.

16.15. anode: $H_2(g) \rightarrow 2H^+(aq) + 2e^-$

cathode: $Ag^+ + e^- \rightarrow Ag\downarrow$

net cell: $H_2(g) + 2Ag^+ \rightarrow 2H^+(aq) + 2Ag\downarrow$

$$\Delta\mathcal{E}^\circ_{cell} = \mathcal{E}^\circ_{cathode} - \mathcal{E}^\circ_{anode} = 0.799 - 0.000 = 0.799 \text{ V}$$

$$\Delta\mathcal{E}_{cell} = 0.459 = 0.799 - (0.0592/2)(\log Q)$$

$$-0.340 = -0.0296(\log Q) \quad \text{and} \quad \log Q = 11.49$$

$$Q = 3.12\text{x}10^{11} = \frac{[H^+]^2}{[Ag^+]^2 \, P_{H_2}}$$

Thus,

$$3.12\text{x}10^{11} = \frac{(0.010)^2}{[Ag^+]^2}$$

$$[Ag^+]^2 = (1.0\text{x}10^{-4})/(3.12\text{x}10^{11}) = 3.2\text{x}10^{-16}$$

$$[Ag^+] = 1.8\text{x}10^{-8} \text{ M}$$

in equilibrium with $[Cl^-] = 1.0\text{x}10^{-2}$ M. Thus

$$K_{sp}(AgCl) = [Ag^+][Cl^-] = (1.8\text{x}10^{-8})(1.0\text{x}10^{-2}) = 1.8\text{x}10^{-10}$$

Solutions to Exercises, Chapter 17

1. First calculate the final volume of the gas. Since T is constant, Boyle's law applies and $P_1V_1 = P_2V_2$.

$$V_2 = P_1V_1/P_2 = (1.00\ \text{atm})(3.00\ \text{L})/(2.50\ \text{atm}) = 1.20\ \text{L}$$

$$\Delta V = V_2 - V_1 = 1.20\ \text{L} - 3.00\ \text{L} = -1.80\ \text{L}$$

ΔV is negative because the gas has been compressed.

$$w = -P_{ext}\Delta V = -(2.50\ \text{atm})(-1.80\ \text{L}) = +4.50\ \text{L·atm}$$

This should be converted to joules.

$$w = (4.50\ \text{L·atm})(101.32\ \text{J/L·atm}) = 456\ \text{J}$$

As w is defined to be the work done <u>to</u> the gas by the surroundings, the work done <u>by</u> the gas is $-w = -456$ J.

2. Because both bulbs are of equal volume, $V_2 = 2V_1$. As T is constant, Boyle's law applies and $P_2 = P_1V_1/V_2 = P_1/2$. Thus the final pressure is (2.40 atm)/2 = 1.20 atm. Since the external pressure is zero, no work is done by the gas on expanding. $w = -P_{ext}\Delta V = 0$.

3. The work done on the gas by the surroundings is

$$w = -P_{ext}\Delta V = -(2.00\ \text{atm})(5.90\ \text{L} - 1.40\ \text{L})$$

$$= -(2.00\ \text{atm})(4.50\ \text{L}) = -9.00\ \text{L·atm}$$

This should be converted to joules:

$$w = (-9.00\ \text{L·atm})(101.32\ \text{J/L·atm}) = -912\ \text{J}$$

The first law of thermodynamics is $\Delta E = q + w$. Since no heat has entered or left the system, $q = 0$. Thus,

$$\Delta E = w = -912\ \text{J}$$

The energy of the system has decreased by 912 J. The energy required to do the work of expansion must come from the internal energy of the gas, as there is no inflow of heat. The temperature is a measure of the average kinetic energy of the molecules, and if the energy decreases, the temperature decreases as well.

4. Since the gas expands against zero external pressure, it does no work. As no heat enters or leaves the system, q = 0. Thus $\Delta E = q + w = 0$. Since temperature is a measure of the average kinetic energy of the molecules, and the energy has not changed, the temperature of the gas must remain constant.

5. **(a)** $Cu(s) + O_2(g) + H_2(g) \rightleftharpoons Cu(OH)_2(s)$

(b) $2Na(s) + S(s) + (3/2)O_2(g) \rightleftharpoons Na_2SO_3(s)$

(c) $N_2(g) + (5/2)O_2(g) \rightleftharpoons N_2O_5(g)$

(d) $2C(s, gr) + 2H_2(g) + O_2(g) \rightleftharpoons CH_3COOH(liq)$

(e) $K(s) + Mn(s) + 2O_2(g) \rightleftharpoons KMnO_4(s)$

6. The heat of formation is zero only for elements in their standard states. Of those listed, the ones for which $\Delta H^o_f = 0$ are (a) Cd(s), (d) Li(s), and (g) $N_2(g)$. The standard state of chlorine is $Cl_2(g)$, not Cl(g). The standard state of Hg is liquid, not solid. The standard state of I_2 is solid, not gas. Water is a compound, not an element.

7. (a) $\Delta H^{\circ} = \Delta H_f^{\circ}(CaCO_3, s) = -1206.9$ kJ/mol. No calculation is necessary since the equation given is the formation of $CaCO_3$ from its elements in their standard states.

(b) $\Delta H^{\circ} = \Delta H_f^{\circ}(CaCO_3) - \Delta H_f^{\circ}(CaO) - \Delta H_f^{\circ}(CO_2)$

$= -1206.9 - (-635.5) - (-393.51) = -177.9$ kJ

8. (a) $\Delta H^{\circ} = \Delta H_f^{\circ}(C_2H_6) - \Delta H_f^{\circ}(H_2) - 2\Delta H_f^{\circ}(CH_4)$

$= -84.67 - 0 - 2(-74.81) = +64.95$ kJ

(b) $\Delta H^{\circ} = 2\Delta H_f^{\circ}(C_2H_6) - \Delta H_f^{\circ}(H_2) - \Delta H_f^{\circ}(C_4H_{10})$

$= 2(-84.67) - 0 - (-126.1) = -43.2$ kJ

9. (a) $\Delta H^{\circ} = 2\Delta H_f^{\circ}(H_2S) - 2\Delta H_f^{\circ}(H_2O, liq) - 2\Delta H_f^{\circ}(Ag_2S)$

$= 2(-20.6) - 2(-285.84) - 2(-31.8) = 594.1$ kJ

(b) $\Delta H^{\circ} = 3\Delta H_f^{\circ}(CO_2) - 3\Delta H_f^{\circ}(CO) - \Delta H_f^{\circ}(Al_2O_3)$

$= 3(-393.51) - 3(-110.52) - (-1676) = 827$ kJ

10. $C_5H_{12}(g) + 8O_2(g) \rightarrow 5CO_2(g) + 6H_2O(liq)$

$\Delta H^{\circ}_{comb} = 5\Delta H_f^{\circ}(CO_2) + 6\Delta H_f^{\circ}(H_2O, liq) - \Delta H_f^{\circ}(C_5H_{12})$

$-3536 = 5(-393.51) + 6(-285.84) - \Delta H_f^{\circ}(C_5H_{12})$

$\Delta H_f^{\circ}(C_5H_{12}) = -1967.6 - 1715.0 + 3536 = -147$ kJ/mol

11. $CH_3COOCH_2CH_3(liq) + 5O_2(g) \rightarrow 4CO_2(g) + 4H_2O(liq)$

$\Delta H^{\circ}_{comb} = 4\Delta H_f^{\circ}(CO_2) + 4\Delta H_f^{\circ}(H_2O, liq) - \Delta H_f^{\circ}(CH_3COOC_2H_5)$

$-2231 = 4(-393.51) + 4(-285.84) - \Delta H_f^{\circ}(CH_3COOC_2H_5)$

$\Delta H_f^{\circ}(CH_3COOC_2H_5) = -1574.0 - 1143.4 + 2231 = -486$ kJ/mol

12. $\Delta H_f^{\circ}(F, g)$ is the standard enthalpy change for the reaction $(1/2)F_2(g) \rightarrow F(g)$. This is just $(1/2)D(F_2)$ or (1/2)(158 kJ) = 79 kJ/mol of F(g). Similarly, $\Delta H_f^{\circ}(Cl, g)$ is

the standard enthalpy change for $(1/2)Cl_2(g) \rightarrow Cl(g)$. This is just $(1/2)D(Cl_2)$ or $(1/2)(243\ kJ) = 122$ kJ/mol of Cl(g).

13. $\Delta H_f^\circ(N,g)$ is the standard enthalpy change for the reaction $(1/2)N_2(g) \rightarrow N(g)$. There is a triple bond in N_2 and not a single bond, and Table 17.3 lists only single bond energies. The triple bond energy, $D(N_2)$, is listed in Table 17.4. $\Delta H_f^\circ(N,g) = (1/2)D(N_2) = 945/2 = 472$ kJ/mol.

14. The equation whose ΔH° is desired is

$$CH_3OH(g) \rightarrow C(g) + 4H(g) + O(g)$$

Equations whose ΔH° values we know and that can be combined to yield the desired equation are

$$H_2(g) \rightarrow 2H(g) \qquad D(H_2) = 436.\ kJ$$

$$O_2(g) \rightarrow 2O(g) \qquad D(O_2) = 495.0\ kJ$$

$$C(s) \rightarrow C(g) \qquad \Delta H^\circ_{subl}(C) = 716.7\ kJ$$

$$C(s) + H_2(g) + (1/2)O_2(g) \rightarrow CH_3OH \qquad \Delta H_f^\circ(CH_3OH) = -200.7\ kJ$$

$$\Delta H^\circ = 2(436) + (1/2)(495) + 716.7 - (-200.7) = 2037\ kJ$$

In CH_3OH there are 3 C–H bonds, 1 C–O bond, and 1 O–H bond.

Thus $\quad 2037\ kJ = 3(413) + 463 + \varepsilon(C\text{-}O) = 1702 + \varepsilon(C\text{-}O)$

and $\quad \varepsilon(C\text{-}O) = 335\ kJ$

15. (a) The equation whose ΔH° value is desired is

$$H_2C{=}CH_2(g) \rightarrow 2C(g) + 4H(g)$$

Equations whose ΔH° values we know that can be combined to give the desired equation are

$$H_2(g) \rightarrow 2H(g) \qquad D(H_2) = 436 \text{ kJ}$$

$$C(s) \rightarrow C(g) \qquad \Delta H^\circ_{subl}(C) = 716.7 \text{ kJ}$$

$$2C(s) + 2H_2(g) \rightarrow C_2H_4(g) \qquad \Delta H^\circ_f(C_2H_4) = 52.28 \text{ kJ}$$

$$\Delta H^\circ = 2D(H_2) + 2\Delta H^\circ_{subl}(C) - \Delta H^\circ_f(C_2H_4)$$

$$= 2(436) + 2(716.7) - 52.28 = 2253 \text{ kJ}$$

There are 4 C–H bonds and 1 C=C bond in ethylene. Thus,

$$2253 = 4(413) + \varepsilon(C{=}C) \quad \text{and} \quad \varepsilon(C{=}C) = 601 \text{ kJ}$$

(b) The C–C single bond energy is 348 kJ. Thus the double bond energy is less than twice the single bond energy. That is because the double bond in ethylene consists of one σ and one π bond, and a π bond is significantly weaker than a σ bond.

16. (a) On the right side of this equation there are 3 H–Cl bonds, 3 C–Cl bonds, and 1 C–H bond.

Total bond energy = 3(432) + 3(328) + 413 = 2693 kJ

On the left side there are 4 C–H bonds and 3 Cl–Cl bonds.

Total bond energy = 4(413) + 3(243) = 2381 kJ

When the reaction occurs, the bonds on the left-hand side are broken, expending 2381 kJ, and the bonds on the right-hand side are formed, releasing 2693 kJ. Thus,

$$\Delta H = 2381 - 2693 = -312 \text{ kJ}$$

(b) $\Delta H^\circ = 3\Delta H^\circ_f(HCl) + \Delta H^\circ_f(CHCl_3) - \Delta H^\circ_f(CH_4)$

$$= 3(-92.307) + (-103.1) - (-74.81) = -305.2 \text{ kJ}$$

$$\% \text{ error} = \left(\frac{-312 + 305.2}{305.2}\right) \times 100 = -2.2\%$$

17. The specific heat in $cal \cdot g^{-1}K^{-1}$ multiplied by the atomic weight in $g \cdot mol^{-1}$ yields the molar heat capacity in $cal \cdot mol^{-1}K^{-1}$. To convert to $J \cdot mol^{-1}K^{-1}$, multiply by 4.1840 J/cal.

element	spec. ht. ($cal \cdot g^{-1}K^{-1}$)	at. wt. (g/mol)	C_p ($cal \cdot mol^{-1}K^{-1}$)	C_p ($J \cdot mol^{-1}K^{-1}$)
Au	0.0308	196.97	6.07	25.4
C(gr)	0.170	12.011	2.04	8.54
Nd	0.0453	144.24	6.53	27.3
Pd	0.0583	106.42	6.20	26.0

The three elements other than graphite obey the Law of Dulong and Petit. In general, the lighter (low atomic weight) elements have molar heat capacities less than predicted by the law of Dulong and Petit. The deviation is largest for graphite. For Be, C_p is 16.4 $J \cdot mol^{-1}K^{-1}$ and for B, C_p is 11.1 $J \cdot mol^{-1}K^{-1}$.

18. Molar heat capacities are given in Table 17.5. The difference in temperature between 18° and 40° is 22°.

(a) For C_2H_6, the heat needed to raise the temperature 22° is (1 mol)(52.9 $J \cdot mol^{-1}K^{-1}$)(22 K) = 1.16×10^3 J = 1.16 kJ

(b) For N_2, the heat needed to raise the temperature 22° is (1 mol)(29.3 $J \cdot mol^{-1}K^{-1}$)(22 K) = 645 J = 0.645 kJ.

There are many more possibilities for vibration and rotation in C_2H_6 than in N_2, and therefore it takes more heat to raise the temperature an equal amount for C_2H_6 than for N_2.

19. The molecular weight of CO_2 is 44.01 g/mol. Thus there are (10.0 g)/(44.01 g/mol) = 0.227_2 mol CO_2. The value of $C_p = 37.2\ J\cdot mol^{-1}K^{-1}$ for CO_2, and

$C_p = C_v + R$ so that $C_v = 37.2 - 8.314 = 28.9\ J\cdot mol^{-1}K^{-1}$

Thus to raise the temperature of this sample 15° requires (0.2272 mol)(37.2 $J\cdot mol^{-1}K^{-1}$)(15 K) = 127 J at constant pressure, and (0.2272 mol)(28.9 $J\cdot mol^{-1}K^{-1}$)(15 K) = 98.5 J at constant volume. Less heat is required at constant volume than at constant pressure, because no work is done if the volume is constant, whereas some of the heat is needed for the expansion against the confining atmosphere at constant pressure.

20. Since Ar is a monatomic gas,

$$C_v = (3/2)R \quad \text{and} \quad C_p = (5/2)R$$

$$\Delta E = (3/2)nR\Delta T \quad \text{and} \quad \Delta H = (5/2)nR\Delta T$$

For this problem, $\Delta T = 60^{\circ}$ and $n = 0.500$ mol.

Thus $\Delta H = q_p = (0.500\ mol)(5/2)(8.3144\ J\cdot mol^{-1}K^{-1})(60\ K)$

$= 624\ J$ = heat required at constant pressure

$\Delta E = (3/2)(0.500)(8.3144)(60) = 375\ J$

21. The molecular weight of sucrose is 342.30 g/mol.

Thus, $$\text{No. mol sucrose} = \frac{1.583\ g}{342.30\ g/mol} = 4.625\text{x}10^{-3}\ mol$$

$$C_v(\text{calorimeter}) = \frac{-(n\ mol)(\Delta E\ kJ/mol)}{(\Delta T\ K)}$$

$$C_v = -(4.625\text{x}10^{-3})(-5647)/(4.29\ K) = 6.087\ kJ/K$$

The molecular weight of glucose, $C_6H_{12}O_6$, is 180.16 g/mol.

Thus, No. mol glucose $= \dfrac{1.420 \text{ g}}{180.16 \text{ g/mol}} = 7.882\text{x}10^{-3}$ mol

C_v(calorimeter) = 6.087 kJ/K = $-(7.882\text{x}10^{-3})(\Delta E)/(3.64 \text{ K})$

$\Delta E = (6.087)(3.64)/(7.882\text{x}10^{-3}) = -2811 = -2.81\text{x}10^3$ kJ/mol

22. No. mol sucrose $= \dfrac{2.783 \text{ g}}{342.30 \text{ g/mol}} = 8.130\text{x}10^{-3}$ mol

C_v(calorimeter) $= -(8.130\text{x}10^{-3})(-5647)/(4.63^\circ) = 9.916$ kJ/K

Let ΔE = heat absorbed on combustion of 1 gram of beef

$$C_v\Delta T = (9.916 \text{ kJ/K})(4.77 \text{ K}) = (4.178 \text{ g})(-\Delta E)$$

$$\Delta E(\text{beef}) = -11.32 \text{ kJ/g}$$

To convert to kcal (or Cal), divide by 4.1840:

$$\frac{(11.32 \text{ kJ/g})}{(4.1840 \text{ kJ/kcal})} = 2.706 \text{ kcal/g}$$

The calorie content of a quarter-pound hamburger is

$$(1/4)(453.6 \text{ g})(2.706 \text{ kcal/g}) = 307 \text{ kcal} = 307 \text{ Cal}$$

Solutions to Multiple Choice Questions, Chapter 17

1. (d) The left-hand side of a formation reaction can have only elements in their standard states. Option (a) is wrong because CO is not an element. Option (b) is wrong because the standard states of hydrogen and oxygen are H_2 and O_2 and not H(g) or O(g), and the standard state of carbon is graphite, not C(g). Option (c) is wrong because H_2O is not an element. Option (e) is wrong because the standard state of oxygen is not monatomic O.

2. <u>(e)</u> $\Delta H_f^\circ = 0$ only for an element in its standard state. The standard state of Br_2 is the liquid, not gas. The standard state of nitrogen is $N_2(g)$, and of carbon is solid graphite. Carbon monoxide is not an element.

3. <u>(b)</u> Krypton is a monatomic gas. The Law of Dulong and Petit applies to solid elements only.

4. <u>(b)</u>

$$\text{mass CaO needed} = \frac{(1000\ \text{kJ})(40.08\ \text{g/mol})}{(653.5\ \text{kJ/mol})} = 63.07\ \text{g}$$

5. <u>(e)</u>

$$\Delta H^\circ = \Delta H_f^\circ(CO_2, g) + 2\Delta H_f^\circ(H_2O, g) - \Delta H_f^\circ(CH_4)$$
$$= -393.51 + 2(-241.83) - (-74.81)$$

Note that -285.84 is ΔH_f° for <u>liquid</u> H_2O, not gaseous.

6. <u>(e)</u> Only elements in their standard states can be on the left-hand side of the formation reaction. Options (a) and (d) have compounds on the left-hand side. In both options (b) and (c) hydrogen is not in its standard state.

7. <u>(d)</u> $C_4H_{10}(g) + (13/2)O_2(g) \longrightarrow 4CO_2(g) + 5H_2O(liq)$

There are 13 O atoms on each side of the equation.

8. <u>(a)</u> Remember that the standard heat of combustion of an organic compound produces <u>liquid</u> water. Thus, to obtain the equation written, we must combine the following two equations:

(1) $C_2H_4(g) + 3O_2(g) \longrightarrow 2CO_2(g) + 2H_2O(liq) \qquad \Delta H_1^\circ = -1411$

(2) $2H_2O(liq) \longrightarrow 2H_2O(g) \qquad \Delta H_2^\circ = 2(44.0)$

$$\Delta H^\circ = -1411 + 88 = -1323\ \text{kJ}$$

9. **(b)** Neon is a monatomic gas, so that $C_v = (3/2)R$ and $C_p = (5/2)R = 20.8\ J\cdot mol^{-1}K^{-1}$. Since $q_p = nC_p\Delta T$,

$$\Delta T = (100.0\ J)/(20.8\ J\cdot K^{-1}) = 4.8^o$$

10. **(d)** To obtain the desired equation from the two that are given, we must multiply the second equation by 3 {to have $3O_2(g)$ on the left} and subtract twice the first equation (so that we have $2Fe_2O_3$ on the right, and 4Fe on the left).

11. **(e)** $w = -P_{ext}\Delta V = -(1.50\ atm)(-6.00\ L) = 9.00\ L\cdot atm$

$$w = (9.00\ L\cdot atm)(101.32\ J/L\cdot atm) = 912\ J$$

$$\Delta E = q + w = 100\ J + 912\ J = 1012\ J$$

12. **(a)** $\Delta H^o = \Delta H_f^o(N_2H_4, liq) + \Delta H_f^o(H_2O, liq) - \Delta H_f^o(N_2O)$

$$-316.97 = \Delta H_f^o(N_2H_4, liq) + (-285.84) - (82.05)$$

$$\Delta H_f^o(N_2H_4, liq) = -316.97 + 285.84 + 82.05$$

13. **(b)** Argon is monatomic, so $C_p = 20.8\ J\cdot mol^{-1}K^{-1}$

$$q_p = nC_p\Delta T = (0.250\ mol)(20.8\ J\cdot mol^{-1}K^{-1})(16\ K) = 83.2\ J$$

14. **(c)** $B(s) + (3/4)O_2(g) \longrightarrow (1/2)B_2O_3(s)$

By the definition of heat of combustion, only 1 mol of B(s) is burned, and this yields 1/2 mol of B_2O_3.

15. **(c)** The first law is $\Delta E = q + w$. For an adiabatic process $q = 0$, therefore $\Delta E = w$.

16. **(e)** The molecular weight of C_2H_4 = 28.054 g/mol. The 0.105 g sample contains $3.74_3 x10^{-3}$ mol C_2H_4.

$\Delta E = -C_v\Delta T/n = -(2.47\ kJ/K)(2.14^o)/(3.743x10^{-3}\ mol) = -1410$

17. <u>**(a)**</u> The standard state of bromine is the liquid. In Appendix G we find $\Delta H^0_f(Br_2,g) = 30.91$ kJ/mol. The molecular weight of $Br_2 = 159.808$ g/mol, so 10.00 g is 0.062675 mol. To vaporize 10.00 g of Br_2(liq) therefore requires

$$(0.062675 \text{ mol})(30.91 \text{ kJ/mol}) = 1.934 \text{ kJ}$$

18. <u>**(b)**</u> $w = -P_{ext}\Delta V = -(2.00 \text{ atm})(3.40 \text{ L}) = -6.80 \text{ L·atm}$

In joules, $w = (-6.80 \text{ L·atm})(101.32 \text{ J/L·atm}) = -689$ J

$$\Delta E = q + w = 400 - 689 = -289 \text{ J}$$

19. <u>**(b)**</u> The equation for the combustion of Al is

$$Al(s) + (3/4)O_2(g) \rightarrow (1/2)Al_2O_3(s) \quad \Delta H^0 = -834.9 \text{ kJ/mol}$$

To convert 250 kcal to kJ, multiply by 4.1840 kJ/kcal:

$$(250 \text{ kcal})(4.1840 \text{ kJ/kcal}) = 1046 \text{ kJ}$$

Combusting 1 mol Al yields 834.9 kJ, hence we must combust (1046 kJ)/(834.9 kJ/mol) = 1.253 mol Al to release 1046 kJ. The reaction of 1.253 mol Al is not one of the options, but that reaction will produce (1/2)(1.253 mol) = 0.626 mol Al_2O_3, which is option (b), the correct answer.

20. <u>**(d)**</u> We must calculate ΔH^0 for the reaction

$$CCl_4(g) \rightarrow C(g) + 4Cl(g)$$

The standard state of CCl_4 is the liquid, so $\Delta H^0_f(CCl_4,g)$ is the same as $\Delta H^0_{vap}(CCl_4)$. The series of reactions we need is: (1) $C(s) + 2Cl_2(g) \rightarrow CCl_4(\ell)$ (2) $CCl_4(\ell) \rightarrow CCl_4(g)$ (3) $C(s) \rightarrow C(g)$ and (4) $Cl_2(g) \rightarrow 2Cl(g)$ Thus we need the four ΔH values listed in option (d).

21. (a) On the right-hand side of the equation there are 6 C-H bonds and 1 C-C single bond. Thus the bond energy of the right side is $6\varepsilon_{C-H} + \varepsilon_{C-C}$. On the left-hand side of the equation there are 4 C-H bonds, 1 C=C double bond, and 1 H-H bond. Thus the bond energy of the left-hand side is $4\varepsilon_{C-H} + \varepsilon_{C=C} + \varepsilon_{H-H}$. When the reaction occurs, the bonds on the left side must be broken, expending the bond energy, and the bonds on the right side are formed, releasing that bond energy. Thus,

$$\Delta H^\circ = 4\varepsilon_{C-H} + \varepsilon_{C=C} + \varepsilon_{H-H} - (6\varepsilon_{C-H} + \varepsilon_{C-C})$$
$$= \varepsilon_{C=C} + \varepsilon_{H-H} - 2\varepsilon_{C-H} - \varepsilon_{C-C}$$

22. (c) The equation whose ΔH° is desired is obtained by adding the first equation given to twice the second. Thus $\Delta H^\circ = -26.8 + 2(16.5) = +6.2$ kJ

Solutions to Problems, Chapter 17

17.1. The enthalpy change for the reaction

$$(1/2)I_2(s) \rightarrow I(g)$$

is $\Delta H^\circ_f(I,g)$, since the standard state of I_2 is the solid. The I-I single bond energy in Table 17.3 is ΔH° for

$$I_2(g) \rightarrow 2I(g)$$

Hence, the additional information we need is the heat of sublimation of I_2, ΔH° for $I_2(s) \rightarrow I_2(g)$.

$$\Delta H^\circ_f(I,g) = (1/2)\{\Delta H^\circ_{subl}(I_2) + D(I_2)\}$$

17.2. (a) $$2CH_4(g) \rightleftharpoons C_2H_6(g) + H_2(g)$$

On the right-hand side there are 6 C-H bonds, 1 C-C bond, and 1 H-H bond. If we imagine these as being formed by the reaction

$$2C(g) + 8H(g) \rightarrow C_2H_6(g) + H_2(g)$$

then $\Delta H^\circ = -6(413) - 348 - 436 = -3262$ kJ

The signs are negative because energy is released when bonds are formed. On the left-hand side there are 8 C-H bonds. Thus for $2CH_4(g) \rightarrow 2C(g) + 8H(g)$

$$\Delta H^\circ = 8(413) = +3304 \text{ kJ}$$

For the reaction $\Delta H^\circ = 3304 - 3262 = 42$ kJ

In Exercise 8(a), ΔH° for this reaction was calculated to be 64.95 kJ. The error made using bond energies is

$$\% \text{ error} = \left(\frac{42 - 65}{65}\right) x100 = -35\%$$

(b) $$C_4H_{10}(g) + H_2(g) \rightleftharpoons 2C_2H_6(g)$$

On the right-hand side there are 2 C-C bonds and 12 C-H bonds. For the reaction

$$4C(g) + 12H(g) \rightarrow 2C_2H_6(g)$$

$$\Delta H^\circ = -2(348) - 12(413) = -5652 \text{ kJ}$$

On the left-hand side there are 3 C-C bonds, 10 C-H bonds, and 1 H-H bond, as the structure of butane is

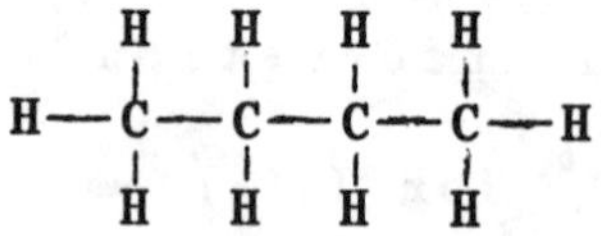

Thus for $C_4H_{10}(g) + H_2(g) \rightarrow 4C(g) + 12H(g)$

$$\Delta H^\circ = 3(348) + 10(413) + 436 = 5610 \text{ kJ}$$

Hence for the reaction $C_4H_{10}(g) + H_2(g) \rightleftharpoons 2C_2H_6(g)$

$$\Delta H^\circ = 5610 - 5652 = -42 \text{ kJ}$$

In Exercise 8(b) ΔH° for this reaction was calculated to be -43.2 kJ. The percent error using bond energies is

$$\% \text{ error} = \left(\frac{-41 + 43.2}{43.2}\right) x100 = 3\%$$

The error is lower for reaction (b) than for (a) because there are many more bonds involved, and the tabular values are the average of many bond energy calculations, rather than specific bond dissociations in particular molecules.

17.3. (a) The combustion reactions are

(1) $H_2C{=}O(g) + O_2(g) \longrightarrow H_2O(liq) + CO_2(g)$ $\quad \Delta H_1^\circ = -563$ kJ

(2) $HCOOH(liq) + \frac{1}{2}O_2(g) \longrightarrow H_2O(liq) + CO_2(g)$ $\quad \Delta H_2^\circ = -270$ kJ

The desired equation is Eq.(1) - Eq.(2), so

$$\Delta H^\circ = -563 + 270 = -293 \text{ kJ}$$

(b) Using ΔH_f° values we obtain

$$\Delta H^\circ = \Delta H_f^\circ(HCOOH, \ell) - \Delta H_f^\circ(H_2C{=}O) = -409 - (-116) = -293 \text{ kJ}$$

17.4.

$$\Delta H^\circ = \Delta H_f^\circ(N_2H_4, \ell) + \Delta H_f^\circ(H_2O, \ell) - 2\Delta H_f^\circ(NH_3, g)$$

$$-143.0 = \Delta H_f^\circ(N_2H_4, \ell) - 285.84 - 2(-46.11)$$

$$\Delta H_f^\circ(N_2H_4, \ell) = -143.0 + 285.84 - 92.22 = +50.6 \text{ kJ}$$

17.5. (a) $\quad C_3H_8(g) + 5O_2(g) \longrightarrow 3CO_2(g) + 4H_2O(liq)$

(b) The molecular weight of C_3H_8 is 44.10 g/mol. Thus the molar heat of combustion of propane is

$$(-50.33 \text{ kJ/g})(44.10 \text{ g/mol}) = -2219.6 = -2220 \text{ kJ/mol}$$

$$\Delta H^\circ_{comb} = 3\Delta H^\circ_f(CO_2,g) + 4\Delta H^\circ_f(H_2O,\ell) - 2\Delta H^\circ_f(C_3H_8,g)$$

$$-2220 = 3(-393.51) + 4(-285.84) - \Delta H^\circ_f(C_3H_8,g)$$

$$\Delta H^\circ_f(C_3H_8,g) = 2220 + 3(-393.51) + 4(-285.84) = -104 \text{ kJ}$$

The value listed in Appendix G is −103.8 kJ. Therefore, to the units place, which is all we are entitled to from the combustion data, this is the correct value.

17.6. To obtain the desired equation we must add Eq.(3) as it stands, as that is the only equation with X_2O_3, and it is on the right side. To eliminate the O_2, which does not appear in the desired equation, we must subtract 3xEq.(2). That will put $3CO_2$ on the left and 3CO on the right. As we only want CO_2 on the left and CO on the right, we must subtract 2xEq.(1). That will also eliminate the X(s), which does not appear in the desired equation. Thus the desired equation is

$$\text{Eq.}(3) - 3\text{Eq.}(2) - 2\text{Eq.}(1)$$

and $$\Delta H^\circ = \Delta H^\circ_3 - 3\Delta H^\circ_2 - 2\Delta H^\circ_1$$

17.7. The value of C_p, in $J \cdot mol^{-1}K^{-1}$, is 20.8 for He and 33.9 for Cl_2 (from Table 17.5).

$$q_p = nC_p\Delta T \quad \text{so that} \quad \Delta T = q_p/nC_p = (1000 \text{ J})/C_p$$

for each, since n = 1 mol.

$$\text{For He,} \quad \Delta T = 1000/20.8 = 48.1^\circ$$

$$\text{For } Cl_2, \quad \Delta T = 1000/33.9 = 29.5^\circ$$

For He, $T_2 = 293.15 + 48.1 = 341.2$ K

$$E_{trans} = \frac{3}{2}RT = \frac{3}{2}(8.3144\ J \cdot mol^{-1}K^{-1})(341.2\ K) = 4256\ J$$

For Cl_2, $T_2 = 293.15 + 29.5 = 322.6$ K

$$E_{trans} = \frac{3}{2}RT = \frac{3}{2}(8.3144\ J \cdot mol^{-1}K^{-1})(322.6\ K) = 4024\ J$$

All of the heat absorbed has gone into translational energy for He, as it is monatomic, whereas only part of the 1000 J absorbed went into translational energy for Cl_2, and some went into rotational and vibrational energy.

17.8. The formation of $Ca(OH)_2$ from its elements is

$$Ca(s) + O_2(g) + H_2(g) \rightleftharpoons Ca(OH)_2(s)$$

The sum of the three equations given is the desired equation, so $\Delta H_f^\circ = -285.84 - 65.2 - 635.5 = -986.5$ kJ

17.9. (a) The molecular weight of H_2O is 18.015 g/mol.

$$V_{gas} = \frac{18.015\ g/mol}{5.96x10^{-4}\ g/cm^3} = 3.02_3x10^4\ cm^3 = 30.2\ L$$

$$V_{liq} = \frac{18.015\ g/mol}{0.9584\ g/cm^3} = 18.80\ cm^3 = 0.01880\ L$$

$$\Delta V = V_{gas} - V_{liq} = 30.23 - 0.01880 = 30.21\ L = 30.2\ L$$

(b) $w = -P_{ext}\Delta V = -(1.00\ atm)(30.21\ L) = -30.21\ L \cdot atm$

$$w = (-30.21\ L \cdot atm)(101.32\ J/L \cdot atm) = -3.06x10^3\ J = -3.06\ kJ$$

(c) $$\Delta H_{vap} = \Delta E_{vap} + P\Delta V$$

$$40.66\ kJ = \Delta E_{vap} + 3.06\ kJ \quad \text{and} \quad \Delta E_{vap} = 37.6\ kJ$$

17.10. (a) $NCNH_2(s) + \frac{3}{2}O_2(g) \rightarrow CO_2(g) + N_2(g) + H_2O(\ell)$

(b) $$\Delta H^\circ_{comb} = \Delta H_f^\circ(CO_2, g) + \Delta H_f^\circ(H_2O, \ell) - \Delta H_f^\circ(NCNH_2, s)$$

$$-741 = -393.51 - 285.84 - \Delta H_f^\circ(NCNH_2, s)$$

$$\Delta H^\circ_f(NCNH_2,s) = 741 - 393.51 - 285.84 = +61.6 \text{ kJ}$$

17.11. (a) $5B(s) + \frac{9}{2}H_2(g) \rightarrow B_5H_9(g)$

(b) $B_5H_9(g) + 6O_2(g) \rightarrow \frac{5}{2}B_2O_3(s) + \frac{9}{2}H_2O(liq)$

$$\Delta H^\circ_{comb} = \frac{5}{2}\Delta H^\circ_f(B_2O_3,s) + \frac{9}{2}\Delta H^\circ_f(H_2O,\ell) - \Delta H^\circ_f(B_5H_9,g)$$

$$-4507.6 = \frac{5}{2}\Delta H^\circ_f(B_2O_3,s) + \frac{9}{2}(-285.84) - 62.76$$

$$\frac{5}{2}\Delta H^\circ_f(B_2O_3,s) = -4507.6 + \frac{9}{2}(285.84) + 62.76 = -3158.6 \text{ kJ}$$

$$\Delta H^\circ_f(B_2O_3,s) = (2/5)(-3158.6) = -1263.4 \text{ kJ}$$

17.12. (a) $2Al(s) + Fe_2O_3(s) \rightarrow Al_2O_3(s) + 2Fe(s)$

$$\Delta H^\circ = \Delta H^\circ_f(Al_2O_3,s) - \Delta H^\circ_f(Fe_2O_3,s)$$

$$= -1676 - (-824.2) = -851.8 = -852 \text{ kJ}$$

(b) The atomic weight of Cr is 51.996 g/mol. Thus,

No. mol Cr = (100 g)/(51.996 g/mol) = 1.923 mol Cr

Heat needed = (14.6 kJ/mol)(1.923 mol) = 28.08 kJ

Let x = No. mol Al needed to release 28.08 kJ of heat

$$\frac{2 \text{ mol Al}}{851.8 \text{ kJ}} = \frac{x}{28.08 \text{ kJ}}$$

$$x = 0.06593 = 0.0659 \text{ mol Al}$$

The atomic weight of Al is 26.98154 g/mol, so the mass of Al that must be used in the thermite reaction is

$$(0.06593 \text{ mol})(26.98154 \text{ g/mol}) = 1.78 \text{ g}$$

17.13. (a) $C_3H_6(g) + \frac{9}{2}O_2(g) \rightarrow 3CO_2(g) + 3H_2O(\ell)$

$$\Delta H^\circ_{comb} = 3\Delta H^\circ_f(CO_2,g) + 3\Delta H^\circ_f(H_2O,\ell) - \Delta H^\circ_f(C_3H_6,g)$$

$$-2091 = 3(-393.51) + 3(-285.84) - \Delta H^\circ_f(C_3H_6,g)$$

$$\Delta H^\circ_f(C_3H_6,g) = 2091 - 3(393.51) - 3(285.84) = +53 \text{ kJ}$$

(b) To calculate the C-C bond energy in C_3H_6 we need ΔH for

$$C_3H_6(g) \rightarrow 3C(g) + 6H(g)$$

The reactions that we can use whose ΔH° values we know, are

$$C(s) \rightarrow C(g) \qquad \Delta H_{subl} = 716.7 \text{ kJ}$$

$$H_2(g) \rightarrow 2H(g) \qquad D(H_2) = 435.9 \text{ kJ}$$

$$3C(s) + 3H_2(g) \rightarrow C_3H_6(g) \qquad \Delta H_f^\circ(C_3H_6, g) = 53 \text{ kJ}$$

Thus, $\Delta H^\circ = 3(716.7) + 3(435.9) - 53 = 3405$ kJ

This is the amount of energy required to break 3 C-C bonds and 6 C-H bonds in cyclopropane.

$$3\varepsilon_{C-C} + 6(413) = 3405 \quad \text{and} \quad \varepsilon_{C-C} = 309 \text{ kJ}$$

The value listed for a C-C bond in Table 17.3 is 348 kJ. Thus the C-C bond in cyclopropane is considerably weaker than a normal C-C bond, as the difference between 309 and 348 is significant. The reason is that the bond angle in cyclopropane is only 60°, whereas in typical organic compounds the bond angle is the tetrahedral angle, 109°28′. The ring strain weakens the bond as there is less overlap of bonding orbitals when the bond angle is only 60°.

17.14. (a) $q_p = (2000 \text{ g})(1.0 \frac{\text{cal}}{\text{g}\cdot\text{K}})(80^\circ) = 1.6\text{x}10^5$ cal

In joules this is $(1.6\text{x}10^5 \text{ cal})(4.1840 \text{ J/cal}) = 6.69\text{x}10^5$ J

As the kettle is open to the atmosphere this is $q_p = \Delta H$.

$$\Delta V = (1.03959 - 1.00087) \text{ mL/g} = 3.872\text{x}10^{-2} \text{ mL/g}$$

Hence for 2000 g, $\Delta V = (2000 \text{ g})(3.872\text{x}10^{-2} \text{ mL/g}) = 77.44$ mL

In liters, $\Delta V = 0.07744$ L. Thus $P\Delta V = 0.07744$ L·atm, as P is 1 atm. In joules this is (0.07744 L·atm)(101.32 J/L·atm) or 7.85 J.

$$\Delta H - \Delta E = P\Delta V = 7.85 \text{ J}$$

Since $\Delta H = 6.69\times10^5$ J, $\Delta E = (6.69\times10^5 - 7.85)$ J. As 7.85 is insignificant compared to 6.69×10^5, ΔH and ΔE for this process are the same, to the number of significant figures warranted by the data.

17.15. The molecular weight of urea, $CO(NH_2)_2$, is 60.056 g/mol. The heat released on burning 2.840 g of urea is

$$\left(\frac{2.840 \text{ g}}{60.056 \text{ g/mol}}\right)(632.90 \ \frac{\text{kJ}}{\text{mol}}) = 29.929 \text{ kJ}$$

This heat raised the temperature of the calorimeter and its contents by 3.16°. Thus

$$C_v(\text{calorimeter}) = \frac{29.929 \text{ kJ}}{3.16^\circ} = 9.471 \text{ kJ/K}$$

The molecular weight of alanine is 89.094 g/mol. Thus the heat released on burning 1.818 g of alanine is

$$-\left(\frac{1.818 \text{ g}}{89.094 \text{ g/mol}}\right)\Delta E_{comb} = C_v\Delta T = (9.471)(3.49^\circ) = 33.055 \text{ kJ}$$

and $$\Delta H_{comb} = \Delta E_{comb} = -1620 \text{ kJ/mol}$$

The balanced equation for the combustion of alanine is

$$C_3H_7NO_2(s) + \tfrac{15}{4}O_2(g) \longrightarrow 3CO_2(g) + \tfrac{7}{2}H_2O(\ell) + \tfrac{1}{2}N_2(g)$$

$$\Delta H^\circ_{comb} = 3\Delta H^\circ_f(CO_2,g) + (7/2)\Delta H^\circ_f(H_2O,\ell) - \Delta H^\circ_f(C_3H_7NO_2,s)$$

$$-1620 = 3(-393.51) + (7/2)(-285.84) - \Delta H^\circ_f(C_3H_7NO_2,s)$$

$$\Delta H^\circ_f(C_3H_7NO_2,s) = 1620 - 3(393.51) - (7/2)(285.84) = -561 \text{ kJ}$$

17.16. To calculate the bond energy we need to know ΔH° for $(CH_3)_2C{=}O(g) \rightarrow 3C(g) + 6H(g) + O(g)$

The equations we can use whose ΔH° values we know, are

(1)	$C(s) \rightarrow C(g)$	$\Delta H_1 = 716.7$ kJ
(2)	$H_2(g) \rightarrow 2H(g)$	$\Delta H_2 = 435.9$ kJ
(3)	$O_2(g) \rightarrow 2O(g)$	$\Delta H_3 = 498.3$ kJ
(4)	$3C(s) + 3H_2(g) + \frac{1}{2}O_2(g) \rightarrow (CH_3)_2CO(\ell)$	$\Delta H_4 = -248$ kJ
(5)	$(CH_3)_2CO(\ell) \rightarrow (CH_3)_2CO(g)$	$\Delta H_5 = 63$ kJ

The desired equation is

$$3\text{Eq.}(1) + 3\text{Eq.}(2) + \frac{1}{2}\text{Eq.}(3) - \text{Eq.}(4) - \text{Eq.}(5)$$

Hence $\Delta H^\circ = 3(716.7) + 3(435.9) + \frac{1}{2}(498.3) + 248 - 63$

$= 3892$ kJ

As the structure of acetone is 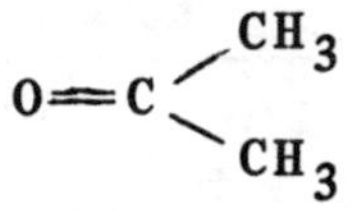 there are

6 C–H bonds, 2 C–C bonds and 1 C=O bond in acetone. Thus,

$$6(413) + 2(348) + \varepsilon_{C=O} = 3892 \text{ kJ}, \quad \text{and} \quad \varepsilon_{C=O} = 718 \text{ kJ}$$

17.17. To determine the bond energy we need ΔH° for

$$H_2O_2(g) \rightarrow 2H(g) + 2O(g)$$

We know

(1)	$H_2(g) \rightarrow 2H(g)$	$\Delta H_1 = 435.9$ kJ
(2)	$O_2(g) \rightarrow 2O(g)$	$\Delta H_2 = 498.3$ kJ
(3)	$H_2(g) + O_2(g) \rightarrow H_2O_2(g)$	$\Delta H_3 = -136.3$ kJ

The desired equation is Eq.(1) + Eq.(2) − Eq.(3). Thus,

$$\Delta H^\circ = 435.9 + 498.3 + 136.3 = 1070.5 \text{ kJ}$$

$$2\varepsilon_{O-H} + \varepsilon_{O-O} = 2(463) + \varepsilon_{O-O} = 1070.5 \quad \text{and} \quad \varepsilon_{O-O} = 144 \text{ kJ}$$

Relative to other single bonds, the O–O bond in H_2O_2 is weak. The H–H bond energy is 436 kJ, the Cl–Cl bond energy is 328 kJ, and so on. Examine Table 17.3 and you will see that the O–O single bond is the weakest single bond listed.

17.18. **(a)** Formula weight of Ag_2Se = 294.70 g/mol

$$C_v = C_p = \frac{\left(0.0693\ \frac{cal}{g\cdot K}\right)\left(4.1840\ \frac{J}{cal}\right)\left(294.70\ \frac{g}{mol}\right)}{3\ mol\ atoms/mol} = 28.5\ J/K$$

(b) Formula weight of AgCl = 143.32 g/mol

$$C_v = C_p = \frac{\left(0.0906\ \frac{cal}{g\cdot K}\right)\left(4.1840\ \frac{J}{cal}\right)\left(143.32\ \frac{g}{mol}\right)}{2\ mol\ atoms/mol} = 27.2\ J/K$$

(c) Formula weight of $PbWO_4$ = 455.04 g/mol

$$C_v = C_p = \frac{\left(0.0769\ \frac{cal}{g\cdot K}\right)\left(4.1840\ \frac{J}{cal}\right)\left(455.04\ \frac{g}{mol}\right)}{6\ mol\ atoms/mol} = 24.4\ J/K$$

(d) Formula weight of $PbBr_2$ = 367.01 g/mol

$$C_v = C_p = \frac{\left(0.0530\ \frac{cal}{g\cdot K}\right)\left(4.1840\ \frac{J}{cal}\right)\left(367.01\ \frac{g}{mol}\right)}{3\ mol\ atoms/mol} = 27.1\ J/K$$

A summary of the heat capacities in $J\cdot K^{-1}$ per mole of atoms for the 5 elements of Table 17.5 and these 4 compounds is

Compounds	Ag_2Se 28.5	AgCl 27.2	$PbWO_4$ 24.4	$PbBr_2$ 27.1	
Elements	Ag 25.5	Al 24.3	Cu 24.6	Fe 24.8	Pb 26.4

The C_p values for the compounds are slightly larger than those of the elements, and vary somewhat more widely, but the Law of Dulong and Petit seems reasonably good.

Solutions to Exercises, Chapter 18

1. When the stopcock is opened, the gases mix. Each gas occupies both bulbs. This process occurs spontaneously. The final, or mixed, state is one of greater molecular disorder than the initial state in which the two types of molecules are separated. In the final state, each molecule has greater freedom of motion than it had in the initial state. If the gases are ideal, $\Delta E = 0$, because the temperature is constant. The energy of an ideal gas is a function only of temperature.

2. $w = -P_{ext}\Delta V = 0$ because $P_{ext} = 0$, as the gas is expanding into a vacuum. $\Delta E = 0$ because for an ideal gas E is a function only of temperature, and the temperature is constant, so the energy must be constant. The first law of thermodynamics states $\Delta E = q + w$. As both w and ΔE are 0, q is also 0.

The final state has more molecular disorder than the initial state. The molecules have greater freedom of motion in a volume of 5.0 L than in the initial 3.0 L volume.

3. Since the temperature is constant, $P_1V_1 = P_2V_2$ and therefore $V_2 = P_1V_1/P_2 = (2.50\text{ atm})(3.00\text{ L})/(1.50\text{ atm}) = 5.00\text{ L}$. The work done to the gas, w, is

$$w = -P_{ext}\Delta V = -(1.50\text{ atm})(5.00\text{ L} - 3.00\text{ L}) = -3.00\text{ L·atm}$$

$$w = -(3.00\text{ L·atm})(101.32\text{ J/L·atm}) = -304\text{ J}$$

As the temperature is constant, $\Delta E = 0$, because the energy of an ideal gas is a function only of temperature. Since $\Delta E = q + w = 0$, $q = -w = +304$ J.

The initial and final states of the gas are the same and therefore the change in molecular disorder is the same for the two processes described in Exercises 2 and 3.

4. The fall of the object is irreversible. A reversible process must occur in a series of steps in each of which the system is in equilibrium with its surroundings. When an object falls, it is not at equilibrium with its surroundings during the fall.

5.
$$w_{rev} = -nRT \ln(V_2/V_1)$$

We can determine n by using the ideal gas law, and either the final or the initial state conditions.

$$n = \frac{PV}{RT} = \frac{(2.50\text{ atm})(3.00\text{ L})}{(0.08206\ \frac{\text{L}\cdot\text{atm}}{\text{mol}\cdot\text{K}})(303.15\text{ K})} = 0.30149 = 0.301\text{ mol}$$

$$w_{rev} = -(0.3015\text{ mol})(8.3144\ \frac{\text{J}}{\text{mol}\cdot\text{K}})(303.15\text{ K})\left(\ln\frac{5.00}{3.00}\right)$$
$$= -388\text{ J}$$

The maximum work done __by__ the gas is $-w_{rev} = +388$ J.

6. $$n = \frac{PV}{RT} = \frac{(4.00\text{ atm})(0.250\text{ L})}{(0.08206\ \frac{\text{L}\cdot\text{atm}}{\text{mol}\cdot\text{K}})(298.15\text{ K})} = 4.087\times10^{-2}\text{ mol}$$

$$w_{rev} = -nRT \ln(V_2/V_1) = -nRT \ln(P_1/P_2)$$

Since T is constant, $P_1V_1 = P_2V_2$ (Boyle's Law) and

$$V_2/V_1 = P_1/P_2 = 4.00/1.00 = 4.00$$

$w_{rev} = -(4.087 \times 10^{-2}\ mol)(8.3144\ \frac{J}{mol \cdot K})(298.15\ K)\ ln(4.00)$

$= -140\ J$

$\Delta E = 0$ because for an ideal gas the energy is a function only of temperature. If the temperature is constant, the energy is constant. Since $\Delta E = 0 = q + w$, $q = -w = +140\ J$.

7. Since the temperature is constant, and E is a function only of temperature for an ideal gas, $\Delta E = 0$ and $q_{rev} = -w_{rev} = +388\ J$.

$$\Delta S = q_{rev}/T = (388\ J)/(303.15\ K) = 1.28\ J \cdot K^{-1}$$

8. $\Delta S = q_{rev}/T = (140.5\ J)/(298.15\ K) = 0.471\ J \cdot K^{-1}$

9. To calculate ΔS, the temperature must be in kelvins. Then, $\Delta S_{fus} = \Delta H_{fus}/T_{mp}$ and $\Delta S_{vap} = \Delta H_{vap}/T_{bp}$. Convert ΔH values from kJ to J before dividing by T as entropy values are given in $J \cdot mol^{-1}K^{-1}$. Results are tabulated below.

Compound	T_{mp} (K)	ΔS_{fus} ($J \cdot mol^{-1}K^{-1}$)	T_{bp} (K)	ΔS_{vap} ($J \cdot mol^{-1}K^{-1}$)
$AsBr_3$	306.0	$\frac{11,800}{306.0} = 38.6$	494.2	$\frac{41,400}{494.2} = 83.8$
$CHCl_3$	209.6	$\frac{9200}{209.6} = 43.9$	334.8	$\frac{29,400}{334.8} = 87.8$
CH_3Cl	175.42	$\frac{6450}{175.42} = 36.8$	249.0	$\frac{21,600}{249.0} = 86.8$
CH_3SH	150.	$\frac{5910}{150} = 39.4$	279.4	$\frac{24,500}{279.4} = 87.7$

For each of these compounds, ΔS_{vap} is at least twice as large as ΔS_{fus}. The increase in molecular disorder for the process liquid $\rightleftharpoons$ gas is greater than the increase in molecular disorder for the process solid $\rightleftharpoons$ liquid. The freedom of motion of molecules in the gaseous state is considerably larger than in either of the condensed states. Note also that each of these liquids obeys Trouton's Rule.

10. Convert temperatures to the Kelvin scale, and each ΔH_{vap} to J/mol before dividing by T_{bp} to obtain ΔS_{vap}. Results are tabulated below.

Compound	T_{bp} (K)	$\Delta S_{vap} = \Delta H_{vap}/T_{bp}$ ($J \cdot mol^{-1}K^{-1}$)
BCl_3	285.6	$\frac{23,900}{285.6} = 83.7$
CH_3OH	338.11	$\frac{37,500}{338.11} = 110.9$
CH_3Br	276.71	$\frac{24,000}{276.71} = 86.7$
N_2H_4	386.6	$\frac{40,600}{386.6} = 105$
PCl_3	349	$\frac{30,500}{349} = 87.4$

Neither CH_3OH nor N_2H_4 obey Trouton's Rule. They have larger ΔS_{vap} values at the normal bp than is predicted by Trouton's Rule. There is a greater increase in molecular disorder when these liquids vaporize than when most liquids vaporize. The reason is that these liquids are hydrogen-bonded, and are more ordered than most. As the amount of molecular disorder in the gaseous state is roughly the same for all gases the increase in molecular disorder on vaporization of hydrogen-bonded liquids is larger than the increase for nonhydrogen-bonded liquids.

11. No, the argument is not a valid criticism of the theory of evolution. The second law of thermodynamics states that <u>in an isolated system</u> a spontaneous process is accompanied by an increase in entropy. Evolving creatures were certainly not in isolated systems, but continually exchanged energy with their surroundings.

12. (a) The entropy decreases when 2 moles of $NH_3(g)$ are formed from 4 moles of gas (1 of N_2 and 3 of H_2) so that ΔS^0 is negative.

(b) The entropy increases when a gas or gases are formed from condensed states. In this example 4 moles of gas are formed from 1 mol of solid, so ΔS^0 is large and positive.

(c) There are 2 moles of gas on the right-hand side and 4.5 moles of gas on the left-hand side of this equation. The decrease in the number of moles of gas results in a decrease in molecular order or randomness and ΔS^0 is negative. Note that you consider only the change in the number of moles of gases in predicting the sign of ΔS.

13. (a) He (g, 0.200 atm) has greater absolute entropy than He (g, 100 atm). At 0.200 atm, 1 mol of He(g) occupies a much larger volume than at 100 atm. The atoms have much greater freedom of motion, and therefore greater absolute entropy, at the lower pressure.

(b) The atomic number of Pt is 78, and of Fe is 26. The mass and the number of electrons, protons, and neutrons, is greater for Pt, so that Pt has a greater absolute entropy than Fe.

(c) As there are more atoms and a more complex structure for $(NH_4)_2CO_3$ than for NH_4F, the $(NH_4)_2CO_3$ has the greater absolute entropy.

(d) Entropy increases as temperature increases. Thus Cu at 373 K has greater absolute entropy than Cu at 273 K.

14.

$$\Delta H^\circ = 2\Delta H_f^\circ(H_2O,\ell) + \Delta H_f^\circ(CO_2,g) - \Delta H_f^\circ(CH_4,g)$$

$$= 2(-285.84) - 393.51 -(-74.81) = -890.38 \text{ kJ}$$

$$\Delta S^\circ = 2S^\circ(H_2O,\ell) + S^\circ(CO_2) - 2S^\circ(O_2) - S^\circ(CH_4)$$

$$= 2(69.9) + 213.6 - 2(205.0) - 186.2 = -242.8 \text{ J/K}$$

Note that the entropy decreases when this reaction occurs because only 1 mol of gas is formed and 3 moles of gas are used up.

The change in Gibbs Free Energy is calculated from the formula $\Delta G^\circ = \Delta H^\circ - T\Delta S^\circ$. To use this equation, both terms on the right must be in the same units. Convert ΔS° to kJ/K by multiplying by 10^{-3}, so that $T\Delta S^\circ$ has the same units as ΔH°, namely kJ.

$$\Delta G^\circ = -890.38 \text{ kJ} - (298.15 \text{ K})(-0.2428 \text{ kJ/K})$$

$$= -890.38 + 72.39 = -817.99 \text{ kJ}$$

The negative sign of ΔG° tells us that this is a spontaneous process at 1 atm. Methane, CH_4, is the principal component of natural gas, and the combustion of natural gas is widely used to heat our homes and to cook our food.

15. (a) $\Delta S^\circ = S^\circ(Fe_2O_3) - 2S^\circ(Fe) - \frac{3}{2}S^\circ(O_2)$

$= 87.40 - 2(27.2) - \frac{3}{2}(205.14) = -274.7 \text{ J/K}$

(b) $\Delta S^\circ = 2S^\circ(H_2O, \ell) - 2S^\circ(H_2) - S^\circ(O_2)$

$= 2(69.94) - 2(130.59) - 205.14 = -326.44 \text{ J/K}$

16. (a) $\Delta G^\circ = 2\Delta G_f^\circ(NO_2, g) - \Delta G_f^\circ(N_2O_5, s)$

$= 2(51.30) - 134 = -31 \text{ kJ}$

(b) $\Delta G^\circ = 2\Delta G_f^\circ(NO_2, g) = 2(51.30) = 102.6 \text{ kJ}$

(c) $\Delta G^\circ = 2\Delta G_f^\circ(NO_2, g) - 2\Delta G_f^\circ(NO, g)$

$= 2(51.30) - 2(86.57) = -70.54 \text{ kJ}$

17. (a) $\Delta G^\circ = \Delta G_f^\circ(C_6H_6, \ell) - 3\Delta G_f^\circ(C_2H_2, g)$

$= 124.5 - 3(209.2) = -503.1 \text{ kJ}$

Yes, this reaction goes spontaneously to the right when all species are at 1 atm and 25°C, as $\Delta G^\circ < 0$.

(b) $\Delta G^\circ = \Delta G_f^\circ(C_6H_6, \ell) - 3\Delta G_f^\circ(C_2H_6, g)$

$= 124.5 - 3(-32.89) = +223.2 \text{ kJ}$

No, this reaction will not proceed spontaneously to the right at 1 atm and 25°C, as $\Delta G^\circ > 0$.

18. (a) $\Delta H^\circ = \Delta H_f^\circ(C_6H_6, \ell) - 3\Delta H_f^\circ(C_2H_2, g)$

$= 49.028 - 3(226.75) = -631.22$ kJ

$\Delta S^\circ = S^\circ(C_6H_6, \ell) - 3S^\circ(C_2H_2, g)$

$= 172.8 - 3(200.8) = -429.6\ J\cdot K^{-1} = -0.4296\ kJ\cdot K^{-1}$

$T\Delta S^\circ = (298.15\ K)(-0.4296\ kJ\cdot K^{-1}) = -128.1$ kJ

$\Delta G^\circ = \Delta H^\circ - T\Delta S^\circ = -631.22 + 128.1 = -503.1$ kJ

Clearly, -631.22 predominates over +128.1 in determining the sign of ΔG°, so the enthalpy factor predominates over the entropy factor for this reaction at 25°C. We can also answer this question without doing any numerical calculations. The tendency to maximize entropy favors 3 moles of $C_2H_2(g)$ rather than 1 mole of liquid C_6H_6. Yet we found in Exercise 17(a) that ΔG° is negative. That means the reaction proceeds to the right, forming C_6H_6. The enthalpy factor must therefore predominate, since the reaction does not proceed in the direction that maximizes entropy.

(b) In Exercise 17(b) we found that ΔG° for this reaction is positive, indicating that the position of equilibrium is on the left at 25°C. It is the right-hand side, however, that maximizes entropy, as there are 6 moles of gas on the right and only 3 on the left. Since the reaction does not proceed in the direction that maximizes entropy, the enthalpy factor predominates in determining the sign of ΔG°.

At 25°C the enthalpy factor predominates over the entropy factor for most (but NOT all) reactions. As T increases, the entropy factor becomes more important.

19. **(a)** The formation reaction is

$$Cd(s) + O_2(g) + H_2(g) \rightleftharpoons Cd(OH)_2(s)$$

$$\Delta H_f^\circ\{Cd(OH)_2\} = -557.56\ kJ\cdot mol^{-1}$$

$$\Delta S_f^\circ = S^\circ\{Cd(OH)_2\} - S^\circ(O_2) - S^\circ(H_2) - S^\circ(Cd)$$

$$= 95.4 - 205.14 - 130.59 - 51.76 = -292.1\ J\cdot mol^{-1}K^{-1}$$

$$\Delta G_f^\circ = -557.56\ kJ/mol - (298.15\ K)(-0.2921\ kJ\cdot mol^{-1}K^{-1})$$

$$= -557.56 + 87.09 = -470.47\ kJ/mol$$

(b) The formation reaction is

$$N_2(g) + 2H_2(g) + C(s) + \frac{1}{2}O_2(g) \rightleftharpoons (NH_2)_2CO(s)$$

$$\Delta H_f^\circ\{(NH_2)_2CO\} = -333.2\ kJ\cdot mol^{-1}$$

$$\Delta S_f^\circ = S^\circ\{(NH_2)_2CO\} - S^\circ(N_2) - 2S^\circ(H_2) - S^\circ(C,s) - \frac{1}{2}S^\circ(O_2)$$

$$= 104.6 - 191.5 - 2(130.59) - 5.740 - \frac{1}{2}(205.14)$$

$$= -456.4\ J\cdot mol^{-1}K^{-1}$$

$$\Delta G_f^\circ = -333.2\ kJ/mol - (298.15\ K)(-0.4564\ kJ\cdot mol^{-1}K^{-1})$$

$$= -333.2 + 136.1 = -197.1\ kJ/mol$$

Rounding errors account for the very small differences in the last significant figure between these calculated values and the entries in Appendix G.

20. The formation reaction is

$$\frac{1}{2}N_2(g) + 2H_2(g) + \frac{1}{2}Cl_2(g) \rightleftharpoons NH_4Cl(s)$$

This reaction has a large negative entropy change, because

the reactants consist of 3 moles of gas, and the product is 1 mole of solid. Hence the entropy factor, $-T\Delta S^\circ_f$, is a large positive term. As $\Delta G^\circ_f = \Delta H^\circ_f - T\Delta S^\circ_f$, this positive term is added to ΔH°_f, which is negative. The result is that ΔG°_f is considerably more positive than ΔH°_f.

21. (a)

$$K_p = P_{O_2}^{1/2} P_{NO_2}^{2}$$

$$\Delta G^\circ = -31{,}000 \text{ J/mol} = -RT(\ln K_p) = -(8.3144)(298.15)\ln K_p$$

$$\ln K_p = \frac{31{,}000 \text{ J/mol}}{(8.3144 \frac{\text{J}}{\text{mol}\cdot\text{K}})(298.15 \text{ K})} = 12.5$$

$$K_p = e^{12.5} = 2.7\text{x}10^5 = 3\text{x}10^5$$

Note that ΔG° is negative and $K_{eq} > 1$. Both of these statements tell us that the position of equilibrium is on the right at 25°C and 1 atm.

(b)

$$K_p = P_{NO_2}^2 / P_{N_2} P_{O_2}^2$$

$$\Delta G^\circ = +102.6\text{x}10^3 \text{ J/mol} = -RT(\ln K_p)$$

$$\ln K_p = -\frac{102{,}600 \text{ J/mol}}{(8.3144 \frac{\text{J}}{\text{mol}\cdot\text{K}})(298.15 \text{ K})} = -41.39$$

$$K_p = e^{-41.39} = 1.1\text{x}10^{-18}$$

Note that ΔG° is positive and quite large, and $K_p \ll 1$. Both these results indicate that the position of equilibrium is far to the left at 25°C. That is a fact you should be familiar with because air is largely O_2 and N_2, and they do not combine to form $NO_2(g)$. The NO_2 that pollutes our air comes mainly from automobile exhausts. The combustion reaction in an automobile engine is at a high temperature, and the endothermic reaction between N_2 and O_2 is driven to the right at high temperatures.

(c) $$K_p = P^2_{NO_2}/P_{O_2}P^2_{NO}$$

$$\Delta G^\circ = -70.54\text{x}10^3 \text{ J/mol} = -RT(\ln K_p)$$

$$\ln K_p = \frac{70{,}540 \text{ J/mol}}{(8.3144 \frac{J}{mol \cdot K})(298.15 \text{ K})} = 28.46$$

$$K_p = e^{28.46} = 2.3\text{x}10^{12}$$

Both the negative sign of ΔG° and the large value of K_p indicate the position of equilibrium is on the right.

22. (a) $$\Delta G^\circ = \Delta G^\circ_f(PCl_3) - \Delta G^\circ_f(PCl_5)$$

$$= -268 - (-305) = +37 \text{ kJ}$$

(b) To determine in which direction a reaction will proceed we must compare the reaction quotient, Q, with the equilibrium constant, K_p.

$$Q = P_{Cl_2}P_{PCl_3}/P_{PCl_5} = (0.50)(2.0\text{x}10^{-3})/(0.25) = 4.0\text{x}10^{-3}$$

The value of K_p is calculated from ΔG°, which was determined in part (a).

$$\Delta G^\circ = +37{,}000 \text{ J/mol} = -RT(\ln K_p)$$

$$\ln K_p = \frac{-37{,}000 \text{ J/mol}}{(8.3144 \frac{J}{mol \cdot K})(298.15 \text{ K})} = -14.9$$

$$K_p = e^{-14.9} = 3\text{x}10^{-7}$$

Since $Q > K_p$, the reaction proceeds to the left, and more PCl_5 than is present initially will be formed.

23. (a) $\Delta G^\circ = \Delta G_f^\circ(NH_3,g) + \Delta G_f^\circ(HCl,g) - \Delta G_f^\circ(NH_4Cl,s)$

$$= -16.5 - 95.299 - (-201.5) = +89.7 \text{ kJ}$$

$$\Delta G^\circ = +89{,}700 \text{ J/mol} = -RT(\ln K_p)$$

$$\ln K_p = \frac{-89{,}700 \text{ J/mol}}{(8.3144 \frac{\text{J}}{\text{mol}\cdot\text{K}})(298.15 \text{ K})} = -36.2$$

$$K_p = e^{-36.2} = 2\text{x}10^{-16}$$

Since $K_p \ll 1$, the position of equilibrium is on the left. The entropy factor favors the production of the gases, NH_3 and HCl. Since the equilibrium favors the production of solid NH_4Cl, the enthalpy factor must predominate. The solid is at a lower energy than the two gases, and the decomposition of NH_4Cl is endothermic. At 25°C and 1 atm, the tendency to minimize the energy predominates over the tendency to maximize the entropy for this reaction.

(b) $$N_2(g) + CO(g) + 2H_2(g) \rightleftharpoons (NH_2)_2CO(s)$$

$$\Delta G^\circ = \Delta G_f^\circ\{(NH_2)_2CO, s\} - \Delta G_f^\circ(CO,g)$$

$$= -197.15 - (-137.15) = -60.00 \text{ kJ}$$

$$\Delta G^\circ = -60{,}000 \text{ J/mol} = -RT(\ln K_p)$$

$$\ln K_p = \frac{+60{,}000 \text{ J/mol}}{(8.3144 \frac{\text{J}}{\text{mol}\cdot\text{K}})(298.15 \text{ K})} = 24.20$$

$$K_p = e^{24.20} = 3.2\text{x}10^{10}$$

As $\Delta G^\circ < 0$ and $K_{eq} > 1$, this reaction proceeds spontaneously to the right. The tendency to maximize the entropy, however, favors the left side, which has 4 moles of gas, in contrast to the right side which has just 1 mole of solid.

$$\Delta H^\circ = \Delta H_f^\circ\{(NH_2)_2CO, s\} - \Delta H_f^\circ(CO, g)$$

$$= -333.2 - (-110.52) = -222.7 \text{ kJ}$$

This reaction is exothermic ($\Delta H^\circ < 0$), which means that the product, urea, is lower in energy than the reactants. Since the reaction proceeds to the right at 25°C, the enthalpy factor predominates over the entropy factor in determining the sign of ΔG°.

24. (a) anode: $Cu(s) \rightarrow Cu^{2+} + 2e^-$

cathode: $Ag^+ + e^- \rightarrow Ag(s)$

net cell: $Cu(s) + 2Ag^+ \rightarrow Cu^{2+} + 2Ag(s)$

$$\Delta G^\circ = \Delta G_f^\circ(Cu^{2+}, aq) - 2\Delta G_f^\circ(Ag^+, aq)$$

$$= 64.98 - 2(77.11) = -89.24 \text{ kJ}$$

(b) $\Delta G^\circ = -n\mathcal{F}\Delta\mathcal{E}^\circ_{cell}$ and $n = 2$ for this reaction.

$$\Delta\mathcal{E}^\circ_{cell} = \frac{+89{,}240 \text{ J}}{(2)(96{,}485 \text{ C})} = 0.4625 \text{ V}$$

The equilibrium constant can be calculated in either of two ways.

$$\Delta G^\circ = -89{,}240 \text{ J/mol} = -RT(\ln K_p)$$

$$\ln K_{eq} = \frac{+89{,}240 \text{ J/mol}}{(8.3144 \frac{\text{J}}{\text{mol}\cdot\text{K}})(298.15 \text{ K})} = 36.00$$

$$K_{eq} = e^{36.00} = 4.3\text{x}10^{15}$$

Also, $\log K_{eq} = \dfrac{2\Delta\mathcal{E}^\circ_{cell}}{0.05916} = 15.63$ and $K_{eq} = 4.3\text{x}10^{15}$

The sign of ΔG° is negative ($\Delta G^\circ < 0$), the sign of $\Delta\mathcal{E}^\circ_{cell}$ is positive ($\Delta\mathcal{E}^\circ_{cell} > 0$), and $K_{eq} >> 1$. All three criteria indicate that the reaction is spontaneous in the direction written.

25. **(a)** anode: $Ni(s) \rightarrow Ni^{2+} + 2e^-$

cathode: $AgBr(s) + e^- \rightarrow Ag(s) + Br^-$

net cell: $Ni(s) + 2AgBr \rightarrow Ni^{2+} + 2Ag(s) + 2Br^-$

$$\Delta\mathcal{E}^\circ_{cell} = 0.0713 - (-0.25) = +0.32\ V$$

(b) $\Delta G^\circ = -n\mathcal{F}\Delta\mathcal{E}^\circ_{cell} = -2(96{,}485\ C)(0.3213\ V) = -6.2\text{x}10^4\ J$

$$\Delta G^\circ = -62{,}000\ J/mol = -RT(\ln K_p)$$

$$\ln K_{eq} = \frac{+62{,}000\ J/mol}{(8.3144\ \frac{J}{mol\cdot K})(298.15\ K)} = 25.0$$

$$K_{eq} = e^{25.0} = 7\text{x}10^{10}$$

or $$\log K_{eq} = \frac{n\Delta\mathcal{E}^\circ_{cell}}{0.05916} = \frac{(2)(0.3213)}{0.05916} = 10.86$$

$$K_{eq} = 7\text{x}10^{10}$$

26. anode: $Cd(s) \rightarrow Cd^{2+} + 2e^-$

cathode: $Co^{2+} + 2e^- \rightarrow Co(s)$

net cell: $Cd(s) + Co^{2+} \rightarrow Cd^{2+} + Co(s)$

(a) $Q = [Cd^{2+}]/[Co^{2+}] = (0.050\ M)/(2.00\ M) = 2.5\text{x}10^{-2}$

$$\Delta\mathcal{E}^\circ_{cell} = \mathcal{E}^\circ_{right} - \mathcal{E}^\circ_{left} = -0.28 - (-0.403) = +0.12\ V$$

$$\Delta\mathcal{E}_{cell} = \Delta\mathcal{E}^\circ_{cell} - (0.05916/2)\log Q$$

$$= 0.123 - (0.02958)\log(2.5\text{x}10^{-2})$$

$$= 0.123 + 0.0474 = +0.17\ V$$

$\Delta G = -n\mathcal{F}\Delta\mathcal{E}_{cell} = -2(96{,}485\ C)(0.17\ V) = -3.3\text{x}10^4\ J = -33\ kJ$

(b) Yes, $\Delta G < 0$ and $\Delta\mathcal{E}_{cell} > 0$. Both these criteria tell us that the reaction proceeds spontaneously. We could also calculate K_{eq} and compare Q with K_{eq}, but that is not necessary to answer the question.

27. (a) For $NH_4Cl(s) \rightleftharpoons NH_3(g) + HCl(g)$

$\Delta G^o_{298} = +89.7$ kJ and $K_p = 2x10^{-16}$ [from Exercise 23(a)]

$$\Delta H^o = \Delta H^o_f(NH_3,g) + \Delta H^o_f(HCl,g) - \Delta H^o_f(NH_4Cl,s)$$

$$= -46.11 - 92.307 - (-314.4) = +175.98 = 176.0 \text{ kJ}$$

The decomposition reaction is endothermic.

$$\Delta S^o = S^o(NH_3) + S^o(HCl) - S^o(NH_4Cl)$$

$$= 192.3 + 186.80 - 94.6 = 284.5 \text{ J·mol}^{-1}\text{K}^{-1}$$

The entropy increases as gases are formed from a solid.

If ΔH^o and ΔS^o are constant,

$$\Delta G^o_{348} = 176.0 \text{ kJ} - (348.15 \text{ K})(0.2845 \text{ kJ/K}) = 176.0 - 99.05$$

$$= 77.0 \text{ kJ}$$

Note that ΔG^o_{348} is significantly less than ΔG^o_{298}. The equilibrium constant is larger at 348 K than at 298 K.

(b) From Exercise 23(b) we obtain $\Delta G^o_{298} = -60.00$ kJ, $\Delta H^o_{298} = -222.7$ kJ, and $K_{eq} = 3.2x10^{10}$ at 25°C.

$$\Delta S^o_{298} = S^o\{(NH_2)_2CO\} - S^o(N_2) - S^o(CO) - 2S^o(H_2)$$

$$= 104.6 - 191.5 - 197.56 - 2(130.59) = -545.6 \text{ J·K}^{-1}$$

Assuming ΔH^o and ΔS^o are constant,

$$\Delta G^o_{348} = -222.7 - (348.15 \text{ K})(-0.5456 \text{ kJ/K}) = -222.7 + 190.0$$

$$= -32.7 \text{ kJ}$$

Note that ΔG^o_{348} is more positive than ΔG^o_{298}. The entropy factor becomes more important as the temperature increases.

28. There is a large increase in entropy when solid $(NH_4)_2SO_4$ decomposes to yield 4 moles of gas. As $\Delta S^\circ > 0$, $T\Delta S$ becomes larger and more positive as T increases. This contributes a larger negative factor $(-T\Delta S^\circ)$ to ΔG°. Thus, ΔG°_{600} is more negative than ΔG°_{298}. Ammonium sulfate does not decompose at 25°C, but it does decompose when heated.

29. (a)

$$\Delta G^\circ_{343} = -R(343.15)\ln K_{343}$$

$$\Delta G^\circ_{343} = -(8.3144\text{x}10^{-3}\ \text{kJ/K})(343.15\ \text{K})\ln(0.408) = 2.56\ \text{kJ}$$

$$\Delta G^\circ_{298} = -R(298.15)\ln K_{298}$$

$$\Delta G^\circ_{298} = -(8.3144\text{x}10^{-3}\ \text{kJ/K})(298.15\ \text{K})\ln(33.2) = -8.68\ \text{kJ}$$

Note that ΔG° changes sign between 25°C and 70°C. The dimerization reaction is spontaneous at 25°C and 1 atm, but the decomposition of N_2O_4 is spontaneous at 70°C.

(b)

$$\ln\left(\frac{K_{363}}{K_{343}}\right) = -\frac{\Delta H^\circ}{R}\left(\frac{1}{363.15} - \frac{1}{343.15}\right)$$

$$= \frac{58,000}{8.3144}\left(\frac{-20}{(363.15)(343.15)}\right) = -1.12$$

$$K_{363}/K_{343} = e^{-1.12} = 0.3264$$

$$K_{363} = (0.3264)(K_{343}) = (0.3264)(0.408) = 0.133$$

As the temperature increases, the equilibrium constant for the dimerization of NO_2 decreases.

Solutions to Multiple Choice Questions, Chapter 18

1. **(e)** $\Delta S^\circ = S^\circ(C_2H_6) - 3S^\circ(H_2) - 2S^\circ(C,gr)$

$$= 229.5 - 3(130.59) - 2(5.740) = -173.7 \text{ J/K}$$

2. **(c)** $\Delta G^\circ = \Delta H^\circ - T\Delta S^\circ = -197.7 - (298.15)(-0.1880)$

$$= -197.7 + 56.05 = -141.6 \text{ kJ}$$

3. **(e)** For an ideal gas, E is a function only of temperature. Therefore at constant temperature $\Delta E = 0$. The entropy increases ($\Delta S > 0$) because the final volume is larger than the initial volume and the molecules have more freedom of motion in the final state.

4. **(b)** $\Delta G^\circ = \Delta G_f^\circ(H_2) + \Delta G_f^\circ(I_2) - 2\Delta G_f^\circ(HI)$

$$= 0 + 0 - 2(1.7) = -3.4 \text{ kJ} = -3400 \text{ J}$$

$$\Delta G^\circ = -3400 \text{ J} = -RT(\ln K_p) = -(8.3144)(298.15)(\ln K_p)$$

$$\ln K_p = (3400)/(8.3144)(298.15) = 1.37$$

$$K_p = e^{1.37} = 3.9$$

5. **(d)** Liquid water and water vapor are in equilibrium at 100°C and 1 atm pressure. Therefore, $\Delta G = 0 = \Delta H - T\Delta S$. Hence, $\Delta H = T\Delta S$ for this phase equilibrium.

6. **(b)** This is the formation reaction for propane as there are only elements in their standard states on the left-hand side. $\Delta G^\circ = \Delta G_f^\circ(C_3H_8) = -23{,}500 \text{ J} = -RT(\ln K_{eq})$

$$\ln K_{eq} = (23{,}500)/(8.3144)(298.15) = 9.48$$

$$K_{eq} = e^{9.48} = 1.3\times10^4$$

7. <u>(e)</u> Since the equilibrium constant is less than 1, ΔG^{o} must be positive. This means that options (a) and (b) are both wrong. To determine the sign of ΔG we must know the relative magnitudes of the reaction quotient, Q, and K_{eq}.

$$Q = P_C P_B / P_A = (1.0)(0.50)/(2.0) = 0.25$$

Since $Q > K_{eq}$, the reaction proceeds to the left, and therefore ΔG must be positive, that is, $\Delta G > 0$. You can also use the formula $\Delta G = RT\ \ln(Q/K)$ to calculate ΔG, but that is not necessary to answer the question.

8. <u>(c)</u> The side of an equation with more moles of gas is the side with higher entropy. For ΔS^{o} to be negative, there must be more moles of gas on the left side than on the right. This is only true for option (c).

9. <u>(d)</u> Since $\Delta G = \Delta G^{o} + RT(\ln Q)$, if $Q = 1$, $\ln Q = 0$, and $\Delta G = \Delta G^{o}$.

10. <u>(c)</u> $Q = P_{ICl}^2 / P_{Cl_2} = (0.800)^2/(2.1\text{x}10^{-3}) = 304.8$

$$\Delta G = \Delta G^{o} + RT(\ln Q) = -10.9 + (8.3144\text{x}10^{-3})(298.15)\ln(304.8)$$

$$= -10.9 + (2.4790)(5.7195) = -10.9 + 14.2 = 3.3$$

11. <u>(a)</u> $\Delta G^{o} = \Delta H^{o} - T\Delta S^{o} = 33.2 - (298.15)(-0.0609)$

$$= 33.2 + 18.16 = 51.4 \text{ kJ}$$

$$\Delta G^{o} = +51{,}360 = -RT(\ln K_{eq}) = -(8.3144)(298.15)(\ln K_{eq})$$

$$\ln K_{eq} = -20.7 \quad \text{and} \quad K_{eq} = e^{-20.7} = 1\text{x}10^{-9}$$

12. <u>(a)</u> For a reaction to be spontaneous, $\Delta G < 0$. Since $\Delta G = \Delta H - T\Delta S$, if $\Delta H > 0$ then ΔS must be greater than zero

to make ΔG less than zero.

13. __(b)__ Trouton's rule states that ΔS_{vap} at the normal boiling point is ~88 $J \cdot mol^{-1}K^{-1}$.

$$88\ J \cdot mol^{-1}K^{-1} = \frac{\Delta H_{vap}}{T_{bp}} = \frac{16,200}{T_{bp}} \quad \text{so that } T_{bp} = 184\ K = -89^{\circ}C$$

14. __(d)__ The standard state of bromine is liquid Br_2.

Thus $$\Delta G^{\circ} = \tfrac{1}{2}\Delta G_f^{\circ}(Br_2,g) + 0 - \Delta G_f^{\circ}(HBr)$$
$$= (0.5)(3.142) - (-53.43) = 55.00\ kJ$$

15. __(b)__ $$\Delta H^{\circ} = 2\Delta H_f^{\circ}(NH_3) = 2(-46.11) = -92.22\ kJ$$
$$\Delta S^{\circ} = 2S^{\circ}(NH_3) - 3S^{\circ}(H_2) - S^{\circ}(N_2)$$
$$= 2(192.3) - 3(130.59) - 191.5 = -198.7\ J/K$$
$$\Delta G^{\circ} = \Delta H^{\circ} - T\Delta S^{\circ} = -92.22 - (373.15)(-0.1987) = -18.07\ kJ$$

16. __(a)__ $\Delta G = -n\mathcal{F}\Delta\mathcal{E}_{cell}$ so that if $\Delta\mathcal{E}_{cell} > 0$, $\Delta G < 0$. Option (b) is wrong because it is not possible to know the sign of ΔG from $\Delta\mathcal{E}^{\circ}_{cell}$ alone, you must also know the value of Q. Options (d) and (e) are wrong because K_{eq} is determined from $\Delta\mathcal{E}^{\circ}_{cell}$ and not from $\Delta\mathcal{E}_{cell}$. Option (c) is wrong because if $\Delta\mathcal{E}^{\circ}_{cell}$ is negative, the position of equilibrium is on the left, and $K_{eq} < 1$.

17. __(d)__

$$\Delta\mathcal{E}^{\circ}_{cell} = \mathcal{E}^{\circ}_{right} - \mathcal{E}^{\circ}_{left} = -0.403 - (-0.763) = +0.360\ V$$
$$\Delta G^{\circ} = -n\mathcal{F}\Delta\mathcal{E}^{\circ}_{cell} = -2(96,485\ C)(0.360\ V) = -69,470\ J$$
$$= -69.47\ kJ$$

18. __(b)__ $$\Delta H_{vap} = \Delta H_f^{\circ}(CCl_4,g) - \Delta H_f^{\circ}(CCl_4,\ell)$$
$$= -102.9 - (-135.4) = 32.5\ kJ$$

$\Delta S_{vap} = S^\circ(CCl_4,g) - S^\circ(CCl_4,\ell) = 309.7 - 216.4 = 93.3$ J/K

These are the values at 25°C, and are not the values at the normal bp, although the differences are not large. Using these values we obtain

$$T_{bp} = \frac{\Delta H_{vap}}{\Delta S_{vap}} = \frac{32{,}500 \text{ J}}{93.3 \text{ J/K}} = 348 \text{ K} = 75^\circ\text{C}$$

The actual boiling point is 76.5°C.

19. <u>**(b)**</u> $\Delta G^\circ_{800} = -40{,}000 \text{ J} = -R(800 \text{ K})(\ln K_{eq})$

$$\ln K_{eq} = (40{,}000)/(8.3144)(800) = 6.01_4$$

$$K_{eq} = e^{6.014} = 409 = 4.1\text{x}10^2$$

20. <u>**(e)**</u> Spontaneity cannot be predicted from the standard state conditions, but only from the actual values of ΔG and $\Delta\mathcal{E}_{cell}$ with the concentrations used. A net cell reaction is spontaneous in the forward direction if ΔG < 0. In that case, $Q < K_{eq}$ and $\Delta\mathcal{E}_{cell} > 0$.

21. <u>**(b)**</u> Decompositions are endothermic, so ΔH > 0. There is more freedom of motion, that is, more molecular disorder, for the two separate molecules, PCl_3 and Cl_2, than when all the atoms are bound together as PCl_5. Therefore ΔS > 0 for this reaction.

<u>Solutions to Problems, Chapter 18</u>

18.1. (a)

$$\Delta G^\circ = 2\Delta G^\circ_f(H_2O,\ell) + \Delta G^\circ_f(H_2S,g) - \Delta G^\circ_f(SO_2,g)$$

$$= 2(-237.18) - 33.6 - (-300.19) = -207.8 \text{ kJ}$$

$$\Delta G^\circ = -207{,}800 \text{ J} = -RT(\ln K_p)$$

$$\ln K_p = 207{,}800/(8.3144)(298.15) = 83.81$$

$$K_p = e^{83.81} = 2.5\text{x}10^{36}$$

(b) $\Delta G^\circ = \Delta G_f^\circ(CO_2) - \Delta G_f^\circ(CaO) - \Delta G_f^\circ(CO)$

$$= -394.36 - (-604.2) - (-137.15) = 347.0 \text{ kJ}$$

$$\Delta G^\circ = 347{,}000 \text{ J} = -RT(\ln K_{eq})$$

$$\ln K_{eq} = -(347.0\text{x}10^3)/(8.3144)(298.15) = -140.0$$

$$K_{eq} = 1.6\text{x}10^{-61}$$

18.2. (a) $\Delta H^\circ = \Delta H_f^\circ(NH_3) - \Delta H_f^\circ(NH_4{}^+,aq)$

$$= -80.83 - (-132.8) = 51.97 = 52.0 \text{ kJ}$$

$$\Delta S^\circ = S^\circ(NH_3) - S^\circ(NH_4{}^+,aq) = 110 - 112.8 = -2.8 \text{ J}\cdot\text{K}^{-1}$$

$$\Delta G^\circ = \Delta H^\circ - T\Delta S^\circ = 52.0 - (298.15)(-0.0028) = 52.8 \text{ kJ}$$

$$\Delta G^\circ = 52{,}800 \text{ J} = -RT(\ln K_{eq})$$

$$\ln K_{eq} = -(52.8\text{x}10^3)/(8.3144)(298.15) = -21.3$$

$$K_{eq} = e^{-21.3} = 5.6\text{x}10^{-10}$$

Note that this K_{eq} is the acidity constant of ammonium ion.

(b) For this reaction ΔS° is negative, albeit of very small magnitude. This means there is more order on the right side than on the left side. The ordering is due to the hydration of these species. Water molecules orient themselves around the ions and the NH_3 molecules, due to ion-dipole and dipole-dipole attractive forces. There is more hydrogen bonding and more ordering of H_2O molecules around H^+ ions and NH_3 molecules than around $NH_4{}^+$ ions.

18.3. **(a)** The formation reaction is

$$2C(gr) + 3H_2(g) \rightleftharpoons C_2H_6(g)$$

$$\Delta S^\circ = S^\circ(C_2H_6) - 3S^\circ(H_2) - 2S^\circ(C,gr)$$

$$= 229.5 - 3(130.59) - 2(5.740) = -173.8\ J \cdot K^{-1}$$

(b) $$C_2H_4(g) + H_2(g) \rightleftharpoons C_2H_6(g)$$

$$\Delta S^\circ = S^\circ(C_2H_6) - S^\circ(H_2) - S^\circ(C_2H_4)$$

$$= 229.5 - 130.59 - 219.5 = -120.6\ J \cdot K^{-1}$$

(c) The decrease in entropy is greater for the formation reaction than for the reaction in (b) because the decrease in the number of moles of gas is larger for the formation reaction. Three moles of gas plus a mole of solid combine to form 1 mole of ethane gas in the formation reaction, whereas 2 moles of gas combine to form 1 mole of ethane gas in the reaction in (b). Thus the formation reaction has a more negative ΔS°.

18.4. $$KCl(s) \xrightarrow{H_2O} K^+(aq) + Cl^-(aq)$$

If the reaction is spontaneous, $\Delta G < 0$. Since $\Delta H > 0$, this must mean that $\Delta S > 0$, that is, there is an increase in entropy so that the entropy factor favors the products. Water molecules orient themselves about the ions due to ion-dipole forces of attraction. The hydrated ions are a more ordered arrangement of all these species than the separated KCl(s) and H_2O. In determining the sign of ΔG, the entropy factor predominates over the enthalpy factor.

18.5. $$AgBr(s) \rightleftharpoons Ag^+(aq) + Br^-(aq)$$

$$\Delta G^\circ = \Delta G_f^\circ(Ag^+) - \Delta G_f^\circ(Br^-) - \Delta G_f^\circ(AgBr)$$

$$= 77.11 - 102.8 - (-95.94) = 70.25 \text{ kJ}$$

$$\Delta G^\circ = 70{,}250 \text{ J} = -RT(\ln K_{eq})$$

$$\ln K_{eq} = -(70.2\text{x}10^3)/(8.3144)(298.15) = -28.3$$

$$K_{eq} = e^{-28.3} = 5\text{x}10^{-13} = K_{sp}(AgBr)$$

18.6. Even in the gas phase HF is hydrogen bonded. At its normal boiling point (and up to ~ 80°C) the gas phase consists of a mixture of hexameric molecules, $(HF)_6$, and HF monomers. Gaseous HF is much more ordered than typical gases that consist of discrete monomeric molecules. Therefore the entropy change on vaporization is less than predicted by Trouton's Rule.

18.7. $$\Delta H^\circ = \Delta H_f^\circ(SO_2) + \Delta H_f^\circ(H_2O,\ell) - \Delta H_f^\circ(H_2S,g)$$

$$= -269.83 - 285.84 - (-20.6) = -562.1 \text{ kJ}$$

$$\Delta S^\circ = S^\circ(SO_2) + S^\circ(H_2O,\ell) - \tfrac{3}{2}S^\circ(O_2) - S^\circ(H_2S,g)$$

$$= 248.1 + 69.94 - \tfrac{3}{2}(205.14) - 205.7$$

$$= -195.4 \text{ J·K}^{-1} = -0.1954 \text{ kJ·K}^{-1}$$

There are two equivalent ways of calculating ΔG°.

$$\Delta G^\circ = \Delta H^\circ - T\Delta S^\circ = -562.1 - (298.15)(-0.1954) = -503.8 \text{ kJ}$$

or, $$\Delta G^\circ = \Delta G_f^\circ(SO_2) + \Delta G_f^\circ(H_2O,\ell) - \Delta G_f^\circ(H_2S)$$

$$= -300.19 - 237.18 - (-33.6) = -503.8 \text{ kJ}$$

$$\Delta G^\circ = -503.8\text{x}10^3 \text{ J} = -RT(\ln K_{eq})$$

$$\ln K_{eq} = (503.8\text{x}10^3)/(8.3144)(298.15) = 203.2$$

$$K_{eq} = 1.8\text{x}10^{88} = 2\text{x}10^{88}$$

(b) This is an exothermic reaction, as $\Delta H^{\circ} < 0$. Thus the products are at a lower energy than the reactants, and the tendency to minimize the energy favors the products, $H_2O(\ell)$ and SO_2.

(c) For this reaction, the change in entropy is negative, $\Delta S^{\circ} < 0$. Two and one half moles of gas combine to form 1 mole of liquid and 1 mole of gas. Thus there is a decrease in entropy, and the tendency to maximize the entropy favors the reactants, H_2S and O_2.

(d) The enthalpy factor predominates in determining the position of equilibrium. The equilibrium constant for this reaction is very large, $2\text{x}10^{88} \gg 1$. The position of equilibrium is far to the right, the side favored by the large negative enthalpy change.

18.8. Let P_0 = initial pressure of N_2O_4

x = decrease in pressure of N_2O_4

Then, $P_{N_2O_4} = P_0 - x$ and $P_{NO_2} = 2x$ at equilibrium

If 27.2% is dissociated, 72.8% is not dissociated, and

$$P_{N_2O_4} = 0.728P_0 = P_0 - x \quad \text{so that} \quad x = 0.272P_0$$

$$P_{NO_2} = 2x = 0.544P_0$$

$$P_{total} = P_{N_2O_4} + P_{NO_2} = 0.728P_0 + 0.544P_0 = 1.000 \text{ atm}$$

$$1.272P_0 = 1.000 \text{ atm} \quad \text{and} \quad P_0 = 0.786 \text{ atm}$$

Thus, $P_{NO_2} = (0.786)(0.544) = 0.428$ atm

$$P_{N_2O_4} = (0.728)(0.786) = 0.572 \text{ atm}$$

$$K_p = P^2_{NO_2}/P_{N_2O_4} = (0.428)^2/0.572 = 0.320 \text{ atm}$$

$$\Delta G^\circ = -RT(\ln K_p) = -(8.3144)(308.15)\ln(0.320) = +2.9\text{x}10^3 \text{ J}$$

18.9. (a) $PCl_3(g) + Cl_2(g) \rightleftharpoons PCl_5(g)$

$$\Delta H^\circ = \Delta H^\circ_f(PCl_5) - \Delta H^\circ_f(PCl_3) = -375 - (-287) = -88 \text{ kJ}$$

$$\Delta S^\circ = S^\circ(PCl_5) - S^\circ(Cl_2) - S^\circ(PCl_3)$$

$$= 364.5 - 222.96 - 311.7 = -170.2 \text{ J}\cdot\text{K}^{-1}$$

$$\Delta G^\circ = \Delta G^\circ_f(PCl_5) - \Delta G^\circ_f(PCl_3) = -305 - (-268) = -37 \text{ kJ}$$

or, $\Delta G^\circ = \Delta H^\circ - T\Delta S^\circ = -88 - (298.15)(-0.1702) = -37 \text{ kJ}$

$$\ln K_{298} = -\Delta G^\circ/RT = 37\text{x}10^3/(8.3144)(298.15) = 15.0$$

$$K_{eq} = 3\text{x}10^6$$

(b) This is an exothermic reaction, so the product, PCl_5, is at lower energy than the reactants. The enthalpy factor favors the product. The entropy is larger for the reactants than for the product, as 2 moles of gas combine to yield 1 mole of gas. The entropy factor favors the reactants. Since $\Delta G^\circ < 0$ and $K_{eq} > 1$, the reaction proceeds spontaneously to form PCl_5 and the enthalpy factor is the principal driving force at 25°C.

(c)
$$\ln \frac{K_{400}}{K_{298}} = \frac{+88\text{x}10^3}{8.3144}\left(\frac{1}{400} - \frac{1}{298}\right)$$

$$= (1.058\text{x}10^4)\left(\frac{-102}{(400)(298)}\right) = -9.05$$

$$\frac{K_{400}}{K_{298}} = e^{-9.05} = 1.17\text{x}10^{-4}$$

$$K_{400} = K_{298}(1.17\text{x}10^{-4}) = (3\text{x}10^6)(1.18\text{x}10^{-4}) = 4\text{x}10^2$$

The equilibrium constant has decreased from $3x10^6$ to $4x10^2$ as the temperature increased from 298 K to 400 K. According to Le Chatelier's Principle, if the temperature is increased the reaction shifts in the direction that uses up heat, that is, to the left in this case, as the backward reaction is endothermic. There is more PCl_3 and Cl_2 and less PCl_5 at 400 K than at 298 K, and K_{eq} is less at the higher temperature.

18.10. anode: $Ag(s) \rightarrow Ag^+ + e^-$

cathode: $e^- + AgCl(s) \rightarrow Ag(s) + Cl^-$

net cell: $AgCl(s) \rightarrow Ag^+ + Cl^-$

$$\Delta\mathcal{E}^\circ_{cell} = \mathcal{E}^\circ_{right} - \mathcal{E}^\circ_{left} = 0.2223 - 0.799 = -0.577 \text{ V}$$

$$\Delta G^\circ = -n\mathcal{F}\Delta\mathcal{E}^\circ_{cell} = -(1)(96{,}485 \text{ C})(-0.577 \text{ V})$$

$$= +5.57x10^4 \text{ J}$$

$$\ln K = \frac{-5.57x10^4}{(8.3144)(298.15)} = -22.47$$

$$K = e^{-22.47} = 1.7x10^{-10} = [Ag^+][Cl^-]$$

Note that the net cell reaction is simply the dissolution of AgCl, and therefore K is the solubility product of AgCl, $K_{sp}(AgCl)$.

18.11. (a) This can be balanced using oxidation numbers.

NO: N has oxidation number +2
N_2: N has oxidation number 0
CO: C has oxidation number +2
CO_2: C has oxidation number +4

Note that NO is being reduced and CO oxidized. The partly balanced half-reactions are

$$2NO + 4e^- \rightarrow N_2$$

$$CO \rightarrow CO_2 + 2e^-$$

and in order for the overall equation to be balanced in electrons, the second half-reaction has to be multiplied by two. This also leads to balancing in terms of oxygen:

$$2NO + 2CO \rightarrow N_2 + 2CO_2$$

(b)

$$K_p = \frac{P_{N_2}P^2_{CO_2}}{P^2_{NO}P^2_{CO}}$$

Although equilibrium problems can be worked with concentrations expressed either in molarity or in partial pressure, when K is to be related to thermodynamic parameters such as ΔG°, partial pressure must be used for gases and molarity for substances in solution. The only acceptable version of K_{eq} for this problem is, therefore, K_p.

(c)

$$\Delta H^\circ = 2\Delta H^\circ_f(CO_2) - 2\Delta H^\circ_f(NO) - 2\Delta H^\circ_f(CO)$$

$$= 2(-393.51) - 90.25 - (-110.52) \text{ kJ}$$

$$= -746.48 \text{ kJ}$$

Note that for both ΔH° and ΔG° there is no contribution from N_2, since it is an element in its standard state.

$$\Delta G^\circ = 2\Delta G^\circ_f(CO_2) - 2\Delta G^\circ_f(NO) - 2\Delta G^\circ_f(CO)$$

$$= 2(-394.36) - 86.57 - (-137.15) \text{ kJ}$$

$$= -687.56 \text{ kJ}$$

Already it is plain that under standard conditions equilibrium favors the products, since $\Delta G^\circ < 0$. Thus we should also expect that $K_{eq} > 1$.

$$\Delta G^\circ = -RT\ln K_{eq}$$

$$K_{eq} = e^{-\Delta G^\circ/RT}$$

$$= e^{+(687{,}560\ J)/(8.3144\ J/K)(298\ K)} = e^{277.36}$$

Most calculators cannot evaluate this expression. Convert to base 10 logarithms to calculate $e^{277.36}$.

$$\log(e^{277.36}) = 277.36(\log e) = (277.36)(0.43429) = 120.46$$

$$\log K_{298} = 120.46$$

$$K_{298} = \text{antilog}(0.46)\text{x}10^{120} = 3\text{x}10^{120}$$

(d) We evaluate Q for the conditions stated. This requires substituting the given values of the partial pressures into the expression for K_p.

$$Q = \frac{(0.781)(3.1\text{x}10^{-4})^2}{(5.0\text{x}10^{-7})^2(5.0\text{x}10^{-5})^2} = 1.2\text{x}10^{14}$$

Since $Q \ll K$, the reaction will proceed to the right.

(e) Since $\Delta H^\circ < 0$ (the reaction is exothermic), the equilibrium will shift to the left with higher temperatures, in accord with Le Chatelier's principle. Thus K_p will be smaller at higher temperatures than at 25°C.

18.12. The problem asks for S°_{298} for N_2H_4. We start by calculating ΔS°_f at 298 K.

$$\Delta G^\circ_f = \Delta H^\circ_f - T\Delta S^\circ_f$$

$$\Delta S^\circ_{f,298} = \frac{\Delta H^\circ_f - \Delta G^\circ_f}{298.15\ K} = \frac{(95.4 - 159.3)}{298.15\ K}\ kJ/mol$$

$$= -0.2143\ kJ\cdot mol^{-1}K^{-1}$$

$$= -214.3\ J\cdot mol^{-1}K^{-1}$$

The formation reaction is

$$2H_2 + N_2 \rightleftharpoons N_2H_4$$

$$\Delta S^\circ_f(N_2H_4) = S^\circ_{N_2H_4} - 2S^\circ_{H_2} - S^\circ_{N_2}$$

We have just calculated ΔS°_f, and $S^\circ_{H_2}$ and $S^\circ_{N_2}$ are readily available from tables; thus

$$S^\circ_{N_2H_4} = \Delta S^\circ_f(N_2H_4) + 2S^\circ_{H_2} + S^\circ_{N_2}$$

$$= \{-214.3 + 2(130.59) + 191.5\}\ J\cdot mol^{-1}K^{-1}$$

$$= 238.4\ J\cdot mol^{-1}K^{-1}$$

18.13. (a) We calculate ΔH° from tabulated values of ΔH°_f, and ΔS° from tabulated values of S°.

$$\Delta H^\circ = \Delta H^\circ_f(\text{urea}) + \Delta H^\circ_f(H_2O,\ell) - \Delta H^\circ_f(CO_2) - 2\Delta H^\circ_f(NH_3)$$

$$= -333.2 - 285.84 - 2(-46.11) - (-393.51)\ kJ$$

$$= -133.3\ kJ$$

$$\Delta S^\circ = S^\circ(\text{urea}) + S^\circ(H_2O,\ell) - 2S^\circ(NH_3) - S^\circ(CO_2)$$

$$= 104.6 + 69.94 - 2(192.3) - 213.64\ J/K$$

$$= -423.7\ J\cdot mol^{-1}K^{-1}$$

(b)

$$\Delta G^\circ = \Delta H^\circ - T\Delta S^\circ$$

$$\Delta G^\circ = -133.3\ kJ - (298\ K)(-0.4237\ kJ/K) = -7.0\ kJ$$

Since $\Delta G^\circ < 0$, the reaction is spontaneous under standard conditions (where each gas has a partial pressure of 1 atm) at 25°C.

18.14. (a) $SO_2Cl_2(g) \rightleftharpoons SO_2(g) + Cl_2(g)$

We first calculate the total and partial pressures before reaction has occurred. Then use a "before-after" table. The molecular weight of SO_2Cl_2 is 134.97 g/mol. In 4.386 g there are (4.386 g)/(134.97 g/mol) = 0.03250 mol. Then, before reaction takes place, the total pressure is

$$P_T = (0.03250 \text{ mol})(0.08206 \text{ L·atm/mol·K})(375 \text{ K})/(1.000 \text{ L})$$

$$= 1.000 \text{ atm}$$

If we let x be the pressure in atmospheres by which $P_{SO_2Cl_2}$ has diminished, then the reaction stoichiometry gives $P_{SO_2} = P_{Cl_2} = x$. This leads to the following table:

	$P_{SO_2Cl_2}$	P_{SO_2}	P_{Cl_2}	P_T (atm)
<u>before</u>	1.000	0	0	1.000
<u>after</u>	1.000−x	x	x	1.000+x

P_T(after) is calculated by adding the partial pressures of all the gases present. Since we are told that P_T(after) is 1.76 atm, then 1.000+x = 1.76 and

$$x = 0.76 \text{ atm} = P_{SO_2} = P_{Cl_2}$$

Thus $P_{SO_2Cl_2} = 1.00 - 0.76 = 0.24$ atm at equilibrium.

(b) $$K_p = \frac{P_{SO_2}P_{Cl_2}}{P_{SO_2Cl_2}} = \frac{(0.76)^2}{0.24} = 2.4$$

(c) $$\Delta G^\circ = -RT(\ln K) = -(8.314 \text{ J/K})(375 \text{ K})(\ln 2.4)$$

$$= -2730 \text{ J} = -2.7 \text{ kJ}$$

(d) First, note that the reaction is spontaneous at 375 K. Second, recall that the reaction is endothermic, which favors the reverse reaction. Thus, it must be the entropy change that causes the reaction to be spontaneous. Note that this implies that ΔS must be positive, since positive entropy changes facilitate spontaneity. Note further that the reaction involves forming two moles of gas from one, which is, in fact, associated with a positive ΔS.

18.15. (a) First of all, note that the reaction involves condensing 5.5 moles of gas into 4 moles of solid and liquid, so that ΔS° is expected to be large and negative. We calculate ΔS° from tabulated values of absolute entropies.

$$\begin{aligned}\Delta S^\circ &= S^\circ_{gly} + 3S^\circ(H_2O, \ell) - S^\circ(NH_3) - 2S^\circ(CH_4) - (5/2)S^\circ(O_2)\\ &= 103.5 + 3(69.94) - 192.3 - 2(186.15) - (5/2)(205.14)\\ &= -764.1 \text{ J/K}\end{aligned}$$

As implied by the introductory sentence, the reason ΔS° is negative is that so much translational freedom is lost in the condensation from the gaseous reactants to the solid and liquid products.

(b) In order to make a statement about spontaneity under standard conditions, we need to know ΔG°, which can be determined directly from a table. Alternatively, ΔH° can be obtained from the tabulated values of ΔH°_f, and ΔG°

calculated from ΔS° and ΔH°. Because part (d), below, involves the temperature variation of K_{eq}, and ΔH° is needed to determine this, it makes sense to employ the latter approach. Note that since O_2 is an element in its standard state, its ΔH_f° is zero. It does not, therefore, appear in the following equation:

$$\Delta H^\circ = \Delta H_f^\circ(\text{glycine}) + 3\Delta H^\circ(H_2O, \ell) - \Delta H_f^\circ(NH_3) - 2\Delta H_f^\circ(CH_4)$$

$$= -537.2 + 3(-285.84) - (-46.11) - 2(-74.81) \text{ kJ}$$

$$= -1199.0 \text{ kJ}$$

At 298 K: $\Delta G^\circ = \Delta H^\circ - T\Delta S^\circ$

$$= -1199.0 \text{ kJ} - (298.15 \text{ K})(-0.7641 \text{ kJ/K})$$

$$= -971.3 \text{ kJ}$$

Since $\Delta G_{298}^\circ < 0$, the reaction is spontaneous at 298 K.

(c) $$K_{298} = e^{-\Delta G_{298}^\circ/RT}$$

$$= e^{-(-971.3 \text{ kJ})/(0.0083144 \text{ kJ/K})(298 \text{ K})}$$

$$= e^{+392.0}$$

Calculators cannot evaluate a number as large as e^{392} directly. You must convert to base 10 logarithms.

$$K_{298} = e^{392.0} = 10^{(392.0/2.3026)} = 10^{170.25}$$

$$= 10^{0.25}10^{170} = 2x10^{170}$$

See the solution to Problem 18.11. for an explanation of how to change from powers of e to powers of 10. Note that

$$(\log e)^{-1} = (0.43429)^{-1} = 2.3026$$

To calculate K_{eq} at 37°C, first convert the temperature to the Kelvin scale. We obtain T = (273 + 37) = 310 K. It is easiest at this point to use ΔG^{o}_{310} to calculate K_{310}.

$$\Delta G^{o}_{310} = \Delta H^{o} + (310\ K)\Delta S^{o}$$

$$= -1199.0\ kJ - (310\ K)(-0.7641\ kJ/K)$$

$$= -962.1\ kJ$$

$$K_{310} = e^{-\Delta G^{o}_{310}/RT}$$

$$= e^{-(-962.1\ kJ)/(0.0083144\ kJ/K)(310\ K)}$$

$$= e^{373.3}$$

Once again we must convert to base 10 logarithms as most calculators cannot directly evaluate a number as large as $e^{373.3}$.

$$K_{310} = e^{373.3} = 10^{(373.3/2.3026)}$$

$$= 10^{162.11} = 10^{0.11}10^{162} = 1x10^{162}$$

The equilibrium constant, K, gets smaller with increasing temperature because the reaction is exothermic ($\Delta H < 0$).

Solutions to Exercises, Chapter 19

1. (a) Adding water decreases all concentrations and thereby decreases the rate of reaction. It has no effect on the specific rate constant k.

(b) Adding NH_3 decreases the $[H^+]$ since NH_3 and H^+ ions react to form $NH_4{}^+$. Since $[H^+]$ decreases, the rate of reaction decreases. Adding NH_3 has no effect on the specific rate constant k.

(c) Heating the solution from 20° to 35°C increases both the rate of reaction and the specific rate constant k.

2. (a) Overall 4th order, 1st order in ClO_3^- and I^-, 2nd order in H^+.

(b) Overall 3/2 order, 1st order in $CHCl_3$, 1/2 order in Cl_2.

(c) Overall 2nd order, 2nd order in NOBr.

(d) Overall 5/2 order, 1st order in CO, 3/2 order in Cl_2.

(e) Overall 2nd order, 1st order in I^-, 1st order in $S_2O_8{}^{2-}$.

3. (a) $\text{Rate} = \frac{-d[CO]}{dt} = \frac{+d[COCl_2]}{dt}$

As the reaction proceeds, CO is consumed, $COCl_2$ is produced, and the ratio ([CO] used)/($[COCl_2]$ formed) = 1:1.

(b) $\text{Rate} = \frac{-d[Cl_2]}{dt} = \frac{+d[COCl_2]}{dt}$

The units of this reaction rate are $mol\cdot L^{-1}time^{-1}$, e.g. $mol\cdot L^{-1}s^{-1}$ or $mol\cdot L^{-1}min^{-1}$.

4. (a) The average rate of reaction between t = 0 and t = 1000 s is

$$\frac{-\Delta P_{azo}}{\Delta t} = \frac{-(5.72\times10^{-2} - 8.20\times10^{-2})\ \text{mmHg}}{(1000 - 0)\ \text{s}}$$

$$= 2.48\times10^{-5}\ \text{mmHg/s}$$

The rate can also be expressed in $mol\cdot L^{-1}s^{-1}$ by using the ideal gas law: $\frac{\Delta n}{V} = \frac{\Delta P}{RT}$, where T = 600 K and

$$R = 62.363\ L\cdot mmHg\cdot mol^{-1}K^{-1}$$

$$\text{Rate} = \frac{\Delta P/RT}{\Delta t} = (2.48\times10^{-5})/(62.363)(600)$$

$$= 6.63\times10^{-10}\ mol\cdot L^{-1}s^{-1}$$

(Note, however, that for gaseous reactions, it is more convenient to express the reaction rate in units of pressure per unit time.)

(b) Between t = 3000 s and t = 4000 s, the average reaction rate is

$$\frac{-\Delta P_{azo}}{\Delta t} = \frac{-(1.94\times10^{-2} - 2.78\times10^{-2})\ \text{mmHg}}{(4000 - 3000)\ \text{s}}$$

$$= 8.4\times10^{-6}\ mmHg\cdot s^{-1}$$

The rate for the later time interval is significantly less than the rate for the first 1000 seconds. As the reaction proceeds, the moles of azomethane (and thus the pressure of azomethane) decreases, for a constant reaction volume. Since the pressure of azomethane decreases, the reaction rate decreases.

5. $$3H_2(g) + N_2(g) \rightarrow 2NH_3(g)$$

(a) $$\text{Rate} = -\frac{1}{3}\frac{d[H_2]}{dt} = -\frac{d[N_2]}{dt}$$

since 3 moles of H_2 are consumed for every 1 mole of N_2.

(b) $$\text{Rate} = -\frac{d[N_2]}{dt} = +\frac{1}{2}\frac{d[NH_3]}{dt}$$

since 1/2 mole of NH_3 is produced for every 1 mole of N_2 consumed.

6. (a) The units of the reaction rate are $mol{\cdot}L^{-1}s^{-1}$ (or $mol{\cdot}L^{-1}min^{-1}$, etc.). The units of the reaction rate do <u>not</u> depend on the order of the reaction.

(b) $$\text{Rate} = -\,d[NO]/dt = k[NO]^2[H_2]$$

This is a 3rd order reaction overall.

$$(\text{Units of } k)(mol{\cdot}L^{-1})^3 = mol{\cdot}L^{-1}s^{-1}$$

$$\text{Units of } k = L^2mol^{-2}s^{-1}$$

7. $$\text{Rate} = -dP_{azo}/dt \text{ in units of } atm{\cdot}min^{-1} = k_1P_{azo}$$

$$atm{\cdot}min^{-1} = (\text{Units of } k_1)(atm)$$

$$\text{Units of } k_1 = min^{-1}$$

8. See the plot on the following page. Note that to determine the initial rate, it is not necessary to use all the data points. For the most accurate determination, the scales on the two axes should be as large as reasonable.

There is no need for the ordinate axis to start at zero. Choose a scale that is easy to read and large enough to read all the significant figures.

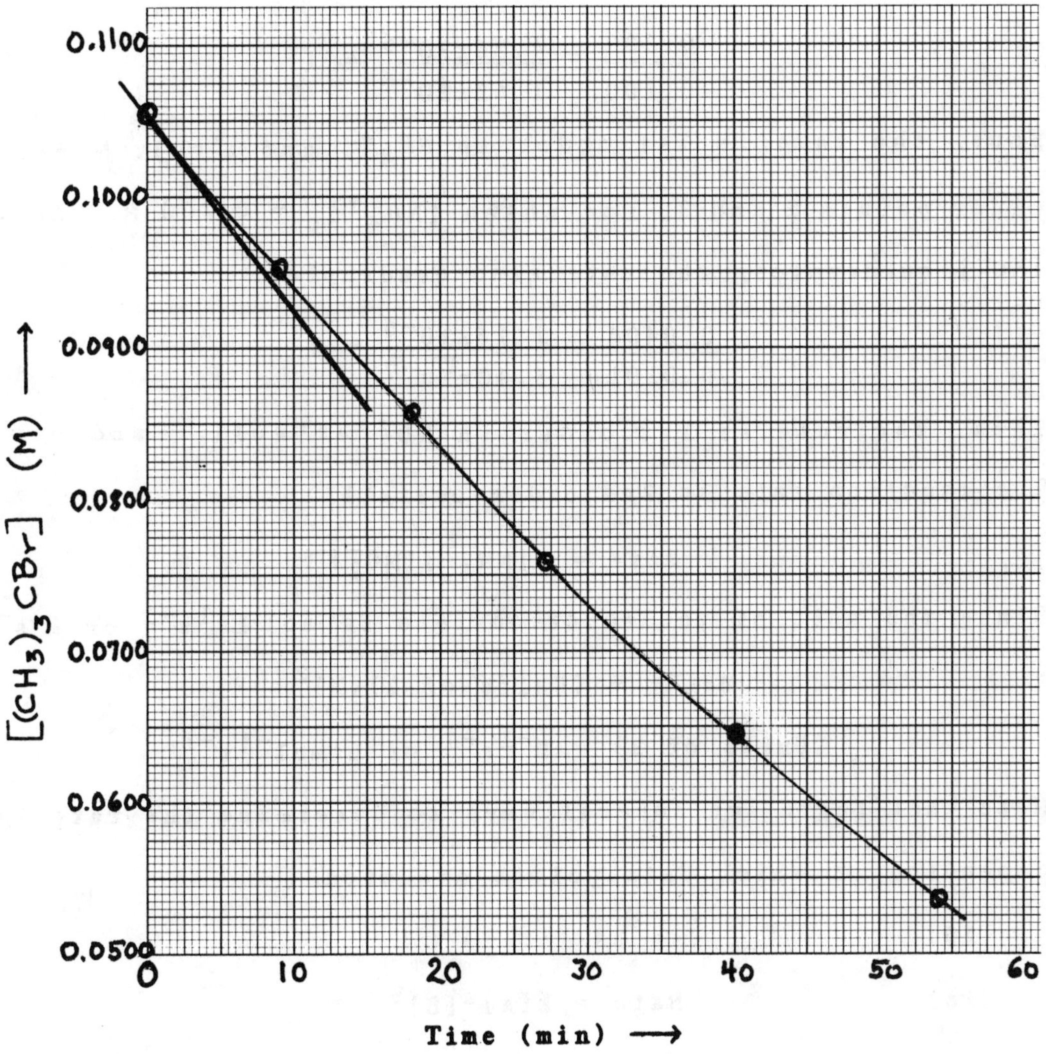

The slope of the tangent at t = 0 is

$$\text{initial slope} = \frac{0.0925 - 0.1056}{10.00 - 0.00} = -1.31\times10^{-3}$$

$$\text{initial rate} = 1.31\times10^{-3}\ \text{mol}\cdot\text{L}^{-1}\text{min}^{-1}$$

9. $$\text{Rate} = k[NH_4^+]^a[NO_2^-]^b$$

To determine a and b, we use the data given. First consider points 1 and 4, for which $[NO_2^-]_o = 0.0606$ M. The initial rate triples as $[NH_4^+]$ triples:

$$\frac{0.300}{0.100} = \frac{4.86\text{x}10^{-6}}{1.62\text{x}10^{-6}} = 3$$

Thus, the rate is 1st order in NH_4^+, and a = 1. Now consider points 2 and 3, for which $[NH_4^+]_o = 0.200$ M. As the $[NO_2^-]$ quadruples, the rate also quadruples:

$$\frac{0.0404}{0.0101} = \frac{2.16\text{x}10^{-6}}{5.40\text{x}10^{-7}} = 4$$

Thus, the rate is 1st order in NO_2^- as well, and b = 1. The reaction rate is 2nd order overall.

$$\text{Rate} = k[NH_4^+][NO_2^-]$$

Since the unit of the reaction rate is $\text{mol}\cdot L^{-1}s^{-1}$ or $M\cdot s^{-1}$

$$M\cdot s^{-1} = (\text{Units of } k)(M)^2$$

$$(\text{Units of } k) = M^{-1}s^{-1} \text{ or } L\cdot\text{mol}^{-1}s^{-1}$$

Note that there are several ways to determine the rate law, depending on which data points are used.

10. $$2A + B \longrightarrow C$$

(a) $$\text{Rate} = k[A]^a[B]^b$$

From experiments 2 and 3, with $[A]_o$ kept constant, we see that doubling $[B]_o$ quadruples the rate:

$$\frac{\text{Rate 3}}{\text{Rate 2}} = \frac{14.4\text{x}10^4}{3.60\text{x}10^3} = \left(\frac{0.80}{0.40}\right)^b = 2^b = 4$$

Thus, b = 2, and the rate is 2nd order with respect to [B].

Next, considering experiments 1 and 2:

$$\frac{\text{Rate 2}}{\text{Rate 1}} = \frac{3.60\text{x}10^3}{3.00\text{x}10^2} = \left(\frac{0.4}{0.2}\right)^2\left(\frac{0.30}{0.10}\right)^a$$

$$12 = (2^2)(3^a) \quad \text{so that } 3 = 3^a$$

Thus, a = 1, and the rate is 1st order with respect to [A].

(b)

$$\text{Rate} = k[A][B]^2$$

$$\text{mol}\cdot L^{-1}s^{-1} = k(\text{mol}\cdot L^{-1})(\text{mol}\cdot L^{-1})^2$$

Therefore k has units of $L^2\cdot mol^{-2}s^{-1}$. The value of k can be determined using any of the 3 experiments. From experiment 1:

$$k = \text{Rate}/[A]_o[B]_o^2$$

$$= (3.00\text{x}10^2)/(0.10)(0.20)^2 \; L^2mol^{-2}s^{-1}$$

$$= 7.5\text{x}10^4 \; L^2mol^{-2}s^{-1}$$

11.

Time (min)	0.00	9.00	18.0	27.0	40.0
$[(CH_3)_3CBr]$ (M)	0.1056	0.0951	0.0856	0.0767	0.0645
$\ln[(CH_3)_3CBr]$	-2.248	-2.353	-2.458	-2.568	-2.741

Time (min)	54.0	72.0	105.0	135.0
$[(CH_3)_3CBr]$ (M)	0.0536	0.0432	0.0270	0.0174
$\ln[(CH_3)_3CBr]$	-2.926	-3.142	-3.612	-4.051

A plot of $\ln[(CH_3)_3CBr]$ versus time must yield a straight line with slope = -k, since this is a first-order reaction.

$$\text{Rate} = k[(CH_3)_3CBr]$$

$$\text{mol}\cdot L^{-1}\text{min}^{-1} = k(\text{mol}\cdot L^{-1})$$

Therefore k is in units of min^{-1}. From the plot on the next page, a value of k = 0.0132 min^{-1} is obtained.

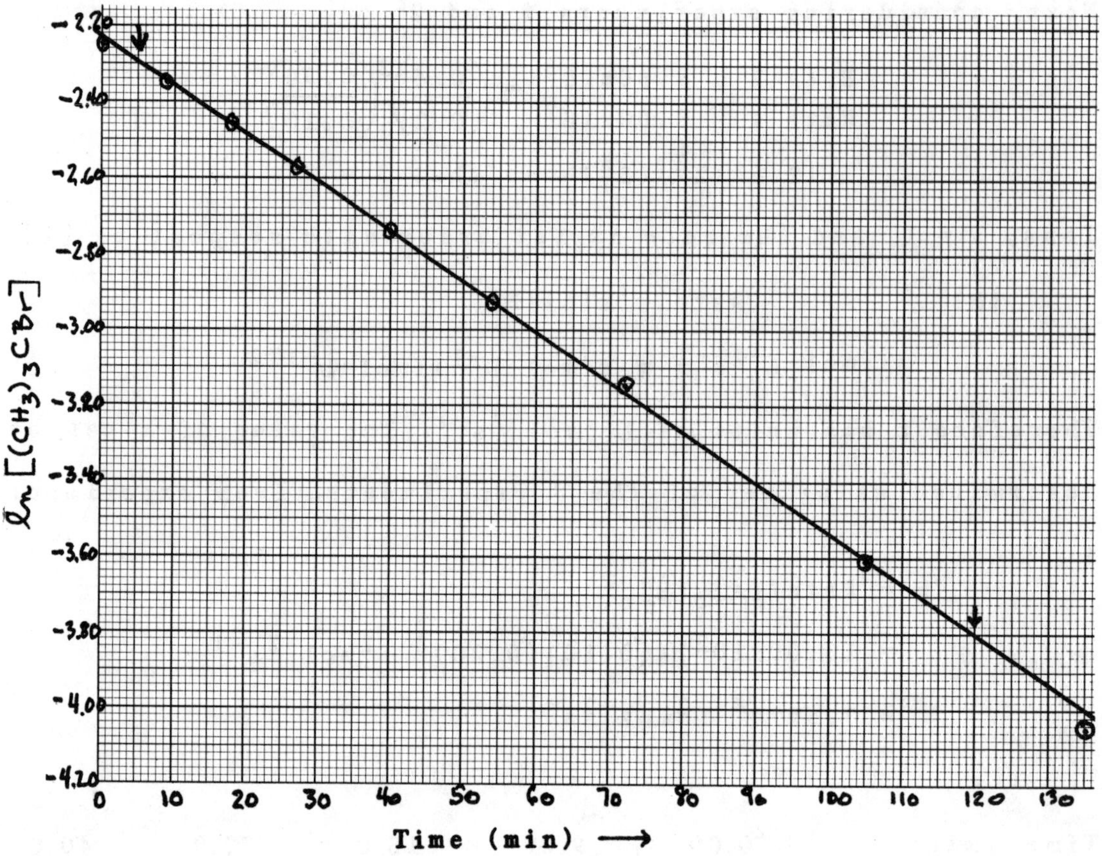

The slope is determined from the points marked with arrows on the plot.

$$\text{Slope} = \frac{-3.805 - (-2.290)}{120.0 - 5.00} = \frac{-1.515}{115.0} = -1.32\text{x}10^{-2}$$

$$\text{Therefore } k = +1.32\text{x}10^{-2}\ \text{min}^{-1}$$

12. One half the initial concentration is 0.0528 M, and occurs at t = 55 min. One quarter the initial concentration is 0.0264 M, and occurs at t = 106 min, which makes one half-life equal to 53 min. Note that using this plot yields a value of $\tau_{1/2}$ with a large experimental uncertainty,

namely 54±1 min. From the value of k obtained in Exercise 11, $k = 0.0132\ min^{-1}$, a better value of $\tau_{1/2}$ is obtained.

$$\tau_{1/2} = (\ln 2)/k = 0.6931/0.0132 = 52.5\ min$$

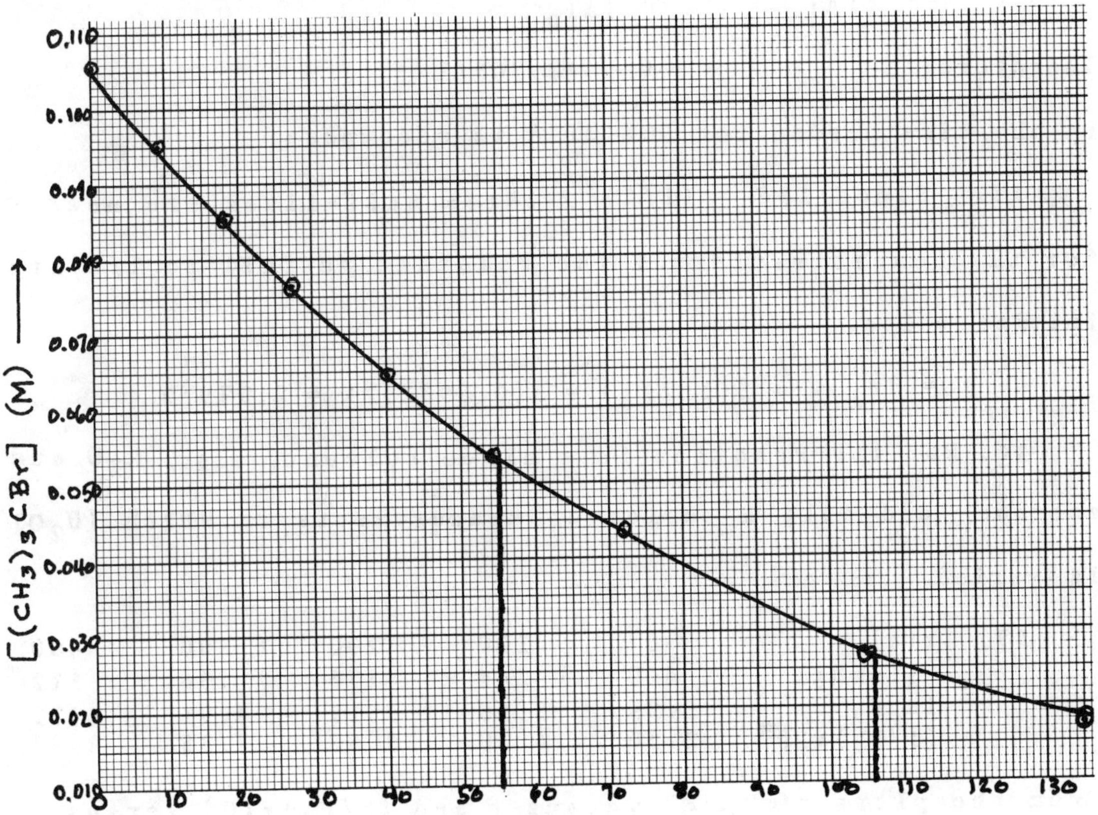

13. Since radioactive decay is a first-order process,

$$\ln \frac{1775}{14,200} = -kt = -\frac{\ln 2}{\tau_{1/2}}\ t = -\ \frac{0.6931}{8.07}\ t$$

$$\ln (0.125) = -2.079 = -0.08589t$$

Therefore $t = 24.2$ days

It is far easier, however, to think a bit about the ratio 1775/14,200 and to realize that it is $1:8 = (1:2)^3$. Thus, three half-lives have elapsed, and 3(8.07) = 24.2 days.

14. If 90% of the reactant has decomposed, then 10% has not decomposed, and $[A] = 0.10[A]_o$.

$$\ln\frac{[A]}{[A]_o} = \ln\frac{0.10[A]_o}{[A]_o} = \ln(0.10) = -kt$$

Therefore $$t = +2.303/k$$

is the time needed for 90% of A to decompose.

15. Since $1/8 = (1/2)^3$, three half-lives are needed for the concentration of the reactant to fall to 1/8 its initial value:

$$t = 3\tau_{1/2} = 3(\ln 2/k) = 3(0.6931)/k = 2.079/k$$

16. Run the reaction in a mixed solvent, e.g., H_2O and acetone, and make a series of measurements in which $[H_2O]$ is varied.

17.

t(s)	0	100	200	300	400
P_A(mmHg)	400	244	176	136	112
$\ln P_A$	5.99	5.50	5.17	4.91	4.72
$(1/P_A)\times10^3$	2.50	4.10	5.68	7.35	8.93

From the plots of $\ln P_A$ versus t and $(1/P_A)\times10^3$ versus t, which appear on the following page, it is seen that the latter gives a straight line. The reaction is thus second order in A.

$$\text{Rate} = kP_A^2$$

The value of the specific rate constant, k, is given by the slope of the plot of $1/P_A$ versus t. Using the 2 points indicated by the arrows:

$$\text{Slope} = \frac{(8.13 - 3.30)\times10^{-3}\ (\text{mmHg})^{-1}}{(350 - 50)\ \text{s}} = 1.61\times10^{-5}\ (\text{mmHg})^{-1}\text{s}^{-1}$$

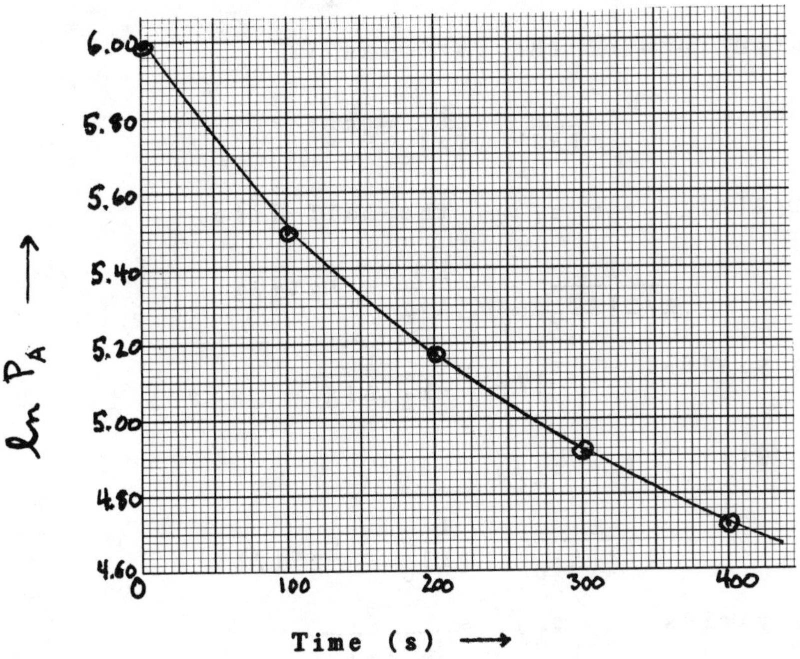
6.00
5.80
5.60
5.40
5.20
5.00
4.80
4.60
0
100
200
300
400
ln P_A →
Time (s) →

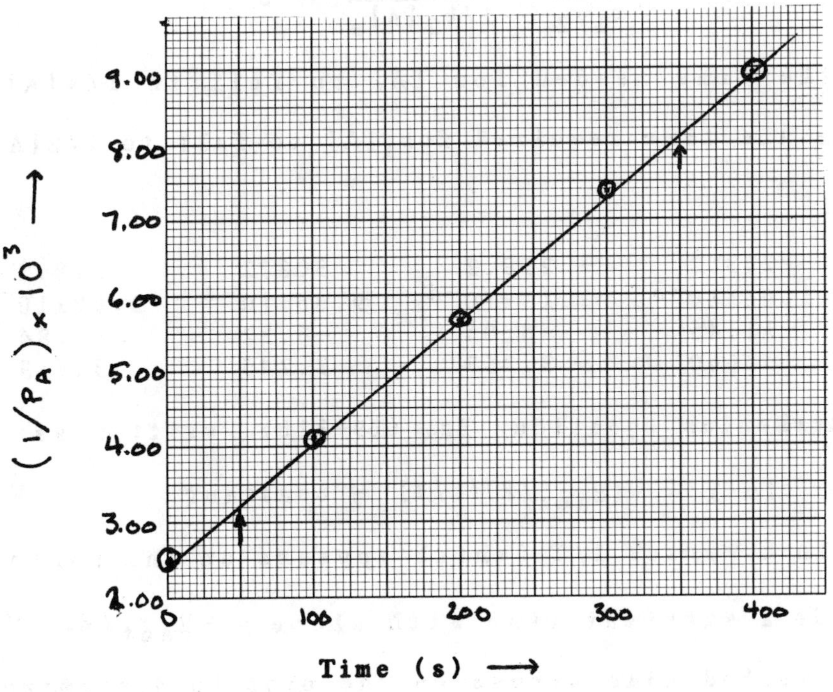
9.00
8.00
7.00
6.00
5.00
4.00
3.00
2.00
0
100
200
300
400
$(1/P_A) \times 10^3$ →
Time (s) →

18. $$\text{Rate} = -d[A]/dt = k_2[A]^2$$

The integrated form of the rate law is

$$\frac{1}{[A]} - \frac{1}{[A]_o} = k_2 t$$

For $[A] = 1/2[A]_o$, $t = \tau_{1/2}$, the half-life,

$$\frac{1}{1/2[A]_o} - \frac{1}{[A]_o} = k_2\tau_{1/2}$$

Rearranging yields: $$\tau_{1/2} = \frac{1}{k_2[A]_o}$$

For $[A] = 1/4[A]_o$, $t = \tau_{1/4}$

$$\frac{1}{1/4[A]_o} - \frac{1}{[A]_o} = k_2\tau_{1/4}$$

Rearranging yields: $$\tau_{1/4} = \frac{3}{k_2[A]_o}$$

Thus, $$\frac{\tau_{1/4}}{\tau_{1/2}} = \frac{3/k_2[A]_o}{1/k_2[A]_o} = 3$$

That is, the time needed for [A] to fall to $1/4[A]_o$ is three times the time required for [A] to fall to $1/2[A]_o$.

19.

T(K)	273.2	298.2	308.2	318.2
$k(s^{-1})$	1.06×10^{-3}	3.19×10^{-4}	9.86×10^{-4}	2.92×10^{-3}
ln k	-11.45	-8.05	-6.92	-5.84
$(1/T)\times10^3$	3.660	3.353	3.245	3.143

From the Arrhenius equation, Eq. (19-31b), written as:

$$\ln k = -(E_{act}/R)(1/T) + \text{constant}$$

a plot of ln k versus 1/T (which appears on the following page) yields a straight line with slope = $-E_{act}/R$. Using the points marked with arrows on the plot to determine the slope, we obtain E_{act} = 88.3 kJ/mol.

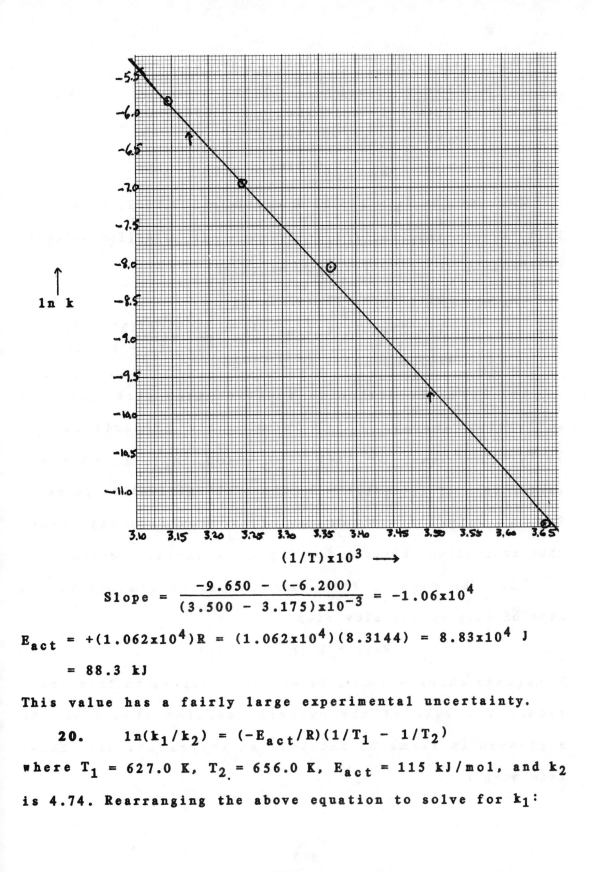

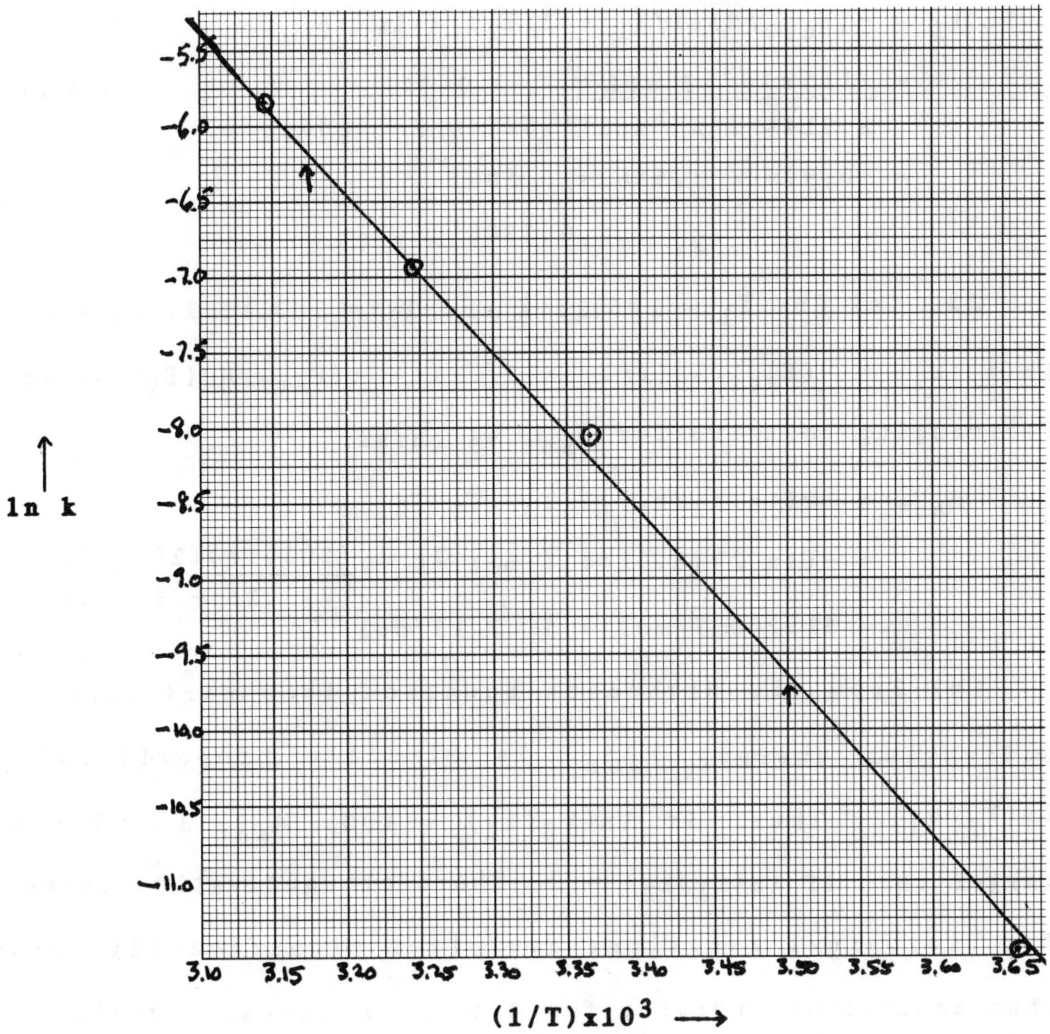

$$\text{Slope} = \frac{-9.650 - (-6.200)}{(3.500 - 3.175)\text{x}10^{-3}} = -1.06\text{x}10^4$$

$E_{act} = +(1.062\text{x}10^4)R = (1.062\text{x}10^4)(8.3144) = 8.83\text{x}10^4$ J

$= 88.3$ kJ

This value has a fairly large experimental uncertainty.

20. $\ln(k_1/k_2) = (-E_{act}/R)(1/T_1 - 1/T_2)$

where $T_1 = 627.0$ K, $T_2 = 656.0$ K, $E_{act} = 115$ kJ/mol, and k_2 is 4.74. Rearranging the above equation to solve for k_1:

$$\ln k_1 = -(E_{act}/R)(1/T_1 - 1/T_2) + \ln k_2$$

$$= \frac{-115\times10^3\ \text{J}\cdot\text{mol}^{-1}}{8.3144\ \text{J}\cdot\text{K}^{-1}\text{mol}^{-1}}\left(\frac{1}{627.0\ \text{K}} - \frac{1}{656.0\ \text{K}}\right) + \ln(4.74)$$

$$= -0.975 + 1.556 = 0.5808$$

$$k_1 = e^{0.5808} = 1.79$$

21. (a) For $T_1 = 293.15$ K and $T_2 = 303.15$ K, $k_2 = 2k_1$.

$\ln(k_2/k_1) = -(E_{act}/R)(1/T_2 - 1/T_1) = -(E_{act}/R)(T_1-T_2)/T_1T_2$

Rearranging to solve for E_{act} we obtain

$$E_{act} = -R\{\ln(k_2/k_1)\}T_1T_2/(T_1-T_2)$$

$$= -(\ln 2)(8.3144\ \text{J}\cdot\text{mol}^{-1}\text{K}^{-1})\frac{(303.15)(293.15)}{293.15 - 303.15}$$

$$= 51{,}200\ \text{J/mol} = 51.2\ \text{kJ/mol}$$

(b) From the Arrhenius equation {see part (a)}, the activation energy, E_{act}, is directly proportional to $\ln(k_2/k_1)$. Thus, if $\ln(k_2/k_1) = 100$, E_{act} is 50 times larger than if $\ln(k_2/k_1) = 2$. Therefore activation energies for biological reactions are often significantly larger than activation energies for typical chemical reactions.

22. The rate of this reaction is determined by the rate of step 2, the slow step:

$$\text{Rate} = k_2[\text{Cl}\cdot][\text{CHCl}_3]$$

Monatomic chlorine, Cl·, is an intermediate in this reaction. The rate of the overall reaction should not be expressed in terms of short-lived intermediates. Thus, from step 1:

$$\frac{[Cl\cdot]^2}{[Cl_2]} = K_{eq} \text{ or } [Cl\cdot] = K_{eq}^{1/2}[Cl_2]^{1/2}$$

Substituting this expression for [Cl·] into the rate equation, we obtain

$$\text{Rate} = k_2 K_{eq}^{1/2}[Cl_2]^{1/2}[CHCl_3] = k[Cl_2]^{1/2}[CHCl_3]$$

Since k_2 and K_{eq} are both constants, $k_2 K_{eq}^{1/2}$ is a new constant, k, the observed specific rate constant for the reaction.

23. For mechanism I, the rate determining step is the slow step.

$$\text{Rate} = k_2[I^-][HOCl]$$

From the first equilibrium, $K_{eq} = [HOCl][OH^-]/[OCl^-]$, (since the $[H_2O]$ term is incorporated into K_{eq}). Rearranging we obtain

$$[HOCl] = K_{eq}\ [OCl^-]/[OH^-]$$

Substituting this into the rate equation yields

$$\text{Rate} = k_2 K_{eq}[OCl^-][I^-]/[OH^-] = k[OCl^-][I^-]/[OH^-]$$

which is the observed rate expression. Mechanism I, therefore, is a possible mechanism.

For mechanism II, $\text{Rate} = k_2'[I^-][HOCl]$, and

$$K_{eq} = \frac{[HOCl][OH^-]}{[OCl^-]} \text{ or } [HOCl] = K_{eq}[OCl^-]/[OH^-]$$

By substitution: $\text{Rate} = k_2' K_{eq}[I^-][OCl^-]/[OH^-]$

$$= k[I^-][OCl^-]/[OH^-]$$

which is the observed rate expression. Hence mechanism II is also possible. Note that unless there is additional experimental evidence to prove or disprove either mechanism, <u>both</u> mechanisms are possible.

24. (a) The overall stoichiometry can be obtained by adding the two steps:

$$(CH_3)_2C{=\!=}CH_2 + H_2O \longrightarrow (CH_3)_3COH$$

(b) The intermediate species is the carbonium ion, $(CH_3)_2\overset{\oplus}{C}CH_3$.

(c) This reaction is acid-catalyzed, with H^+ as the catalyst. Note that H^+ is consumed in step 1 (the slow, or rate-determining step), but is regenerated in the subsequent fast step and therefore does not appear in the overall stoichiometry.

(d) Rate = $k[(CH_3)_2C{=\!=}CH_2][H^+]$

(e) Since $[H^+]$ is essentially constant, the observed rate law will be: Rate = $k_1[(CH_3)_2C{=\!=}CH_2]$. For a given aqueous acidic solution, only the first-order dependence on $(CH_3)_2C{=\!=}CH_2$ will be observed. The first-order rate constant, k_1, however, will depend on $[H^+]$:

$$k_1 = k[H^+]$$

To determine k, the reaction should be run in a series of aqueous acidic solutions of known pH and the dependence of k_1 on $[H^+]$ observed.

25.

step 1	$H_2 + O_2 \rightarrow HO_2\cdot + H\cdot$	chain initiation
step 2	$H\cdot + O_2 \rightarrow HO\cdot + O\cdot$	chain propagation
step 3	$HO_2\cdot + H_2 \rightarrow HO\cdot + H_2O$	chain propagation
step 4	$H_2 + HO\cdot \rightarrow H\cdot + H_2O$	chain propagation
step 5	$O\cdot + H_2 \rightarrow HO\cdot + H\cdot$	chain propagation
step 6	$H\cdot + HO\cdot \rightarrow H_2O$	chain termination

Both steps 2 and 5 increase the number of radicals in the system and can lead to the reaction becoming explosive.

Solutions to Multiple Choice Questions, Chapter 19

1. (a) If concentrations are given in moles per liter and time in minutes, then the rate of reaction of any order is in units of $mol\cdot L^{-1}min^{-1}$.

2. (b) $$mol\cdot L^{-1}min^{-1} = rate = k_3(mol\cdot L^{-1})^3$$ for a 3rd order reaction. Hence, k_3 will have units of $L^2mol^{-2}min^{-1}$ so that both sides of the equation have the same units.

3. (e) The order of a reaction can be zero, fractional, or integral. The order indicates nothing about the molecularity unless it is an elementary process. Order is temperature independent.

4. (b) This is just stoichiometry. Every time an A molecule is used up, two B molecules are used up. Thus, B disappears twice as fast as A.

$$-d[B]/dt = -2(d[A]/dt) = 2(2.6x10^{-2}\ M\cdot s^{-1})$$
$$= 5.2x10^{-2}\ M\cdot s^{-1}$$

5. (e)

No. mol C formed = No. mol A used = 1/2 No. mol B used

Since the partial pressure of a gas is directly proportional to the number of moles at constant T and V, when

$$P_C = 0.20 \text{ atm}, \quad P_A = (0.6 - 0.2) = 0.4 \text{ atm}$$

$$P_B = 0.8 - 2(0.2) = 0.4 \text{ atm}$$

Since this is an elementary process,

$$\text{rate} = kP_AP_B^2$$

Initially: $\text{rate} = k(0.6)(0.8)^2$

When $P_C = 0.2$ atm: $\text{rate} = k(0.4)(0.4)^2$

$$\text{Ratio of rates} = 0.4(0.4)^2/(0.6)(0.8)^2 = (2/3)(1/4) = 1/6$$

6. (c) The rate is directly proportional to $[Cl_2]$, since doubling the $[Cl_2]$ doubles the rate. Hence, doubling [NO] must increase the rate of a factor of 4. This means the order of the reaction with respect to NO is 2.

7. (c) Comparing runs 1 and 2, we see that keeping $[I^-]_o$ constant while doubling $[S_2O_8^{-2}]_o$ doubles the reaction rate, since it takes only half as long (22 s compared to 44 s) for the blue color to appear. This means that the order of the reaction with respect to $S_2O_8^{2-}$ is 2. (Note that this same conclusion can be drawn using some other combination of runs.)

8. (d) A comparison of runs 4 and 1 shows that doubling $[I^-]_o$ while keeping $[S_2O_8^{2-}]_o$ constant, halves the time (44 s compared to 88 s) and thus doubles the rate. The

reaction is therefore first order with respect to $[I^-]$. Comparing runs 1 and 3 shows that doubling $[I^-]_o$ while simultaneously halving $[S_2O_8^{2-}]_o$ leaves the rate unchanged ($t \cong 44$ s in both runs). Hence, rate = $k[I^-][S_2O_8^{2-}]$. The overall order of the reaction is 2.

9. **(a)** Compare run 4 with this run, in which $[S_2O_8^{2-}]_o$ is also 0.0400M, but $[I^-]_o$ is three times higher. Thus, the rate should be 3 times higher and the time required for the blue color to appear 1/3 of the time for run 4.

$$(1/3)(88.0) = 29.3 \text{ s}$$

10. **(d)**

$$\frac{d[C]}{dt} = -3\frac{d[A]}{dt} = \frac{-3}{2}\frac{d[B]}{dt}$$

From the stoichiometry of the reaction we see that C is formed 3 times as fast as A is used up and 3/2 times as fast as B is used up.

11. **(d)** Option (a) is wrong because there is no relationship between the magnitude of the activation energy and the sign of ΔH. Option (e) is wrong because for some reactions with complex mechanisms there can be several slow steps.

12. **(b)** $T_1 = 45 + 273.15 = 318.15$ K, and $k_1 = 6.2\text{x}10^{-4}$

$T_2 = 55 + 273.15 = 328.15$ K, and $k_2 = 2.1\text{x}10^{-3}$

$$\ln \frac{6.2\text{x}10^{-4}}{2.1\text{x}10^{-3}} = \frac{-E_{act}}{R}\left(\frac{1}{318.15} - \frac{1}{328.15}\right)$$

$$-1.22 = \frac{-E_{act}}{R}\left(\frac{10}{(318.15)(328.15)}\right)$$

$$E_{act}/R = \frac{(1.22)(318.15)(328.15)}{10} = 1.27\text{x}10^4$$

$$E_{act} = (8.3144\ \text{J}\cdot\text{mol}^{-1}\text{K}^{-1})(1.27\text{x}10^4\ \text{K}) = 1.06\text{x}10^5\ \text{J/mol}$$

$$= 1.1\text{x}10^2\ \text{kJ/mol}$$

13. <u>(e)</u> The rate law must be determined by experiment. It cannot, in general, be determined from the overall reaction stoichiometry.

14. <u>(e)</u> All the other choices change only $[NO_2]$. The value of k does not depend on $[NO_2]$, but on temperature, solvent, and the concentration of any catalyst.

15. <u>(b)</u> From Eq. (19-33), $E_{a_f} - E_{a_b} = \Delta H$

If $E_{a_f} = E_{a_b}$, then ΔH must be zero.

16. <u>(e)</u> The other four options involve <u>strong</u> acids while acetic acid is a weak acid. In 0.10 F HOAc, $[H^+] = 1.3\text{x}10^{-3}$ M. (To find the $[H^+]$,use the procedure given in Example 9.6 in Chapter 9.) Thus, in the solution of (e),

$$\text{rate} = k[H^+][TA] = k(1.3\text{x}10^{-3})(0.15) = (1.95\text{x}10^{-4})k$$

The next lowest rate is in (d), where $[H^+][TA] = 6.0\text{x}10^{-3}$.

17. <u>(a)</u> Sodium acetate, NaOAc, is a basic salt. Adding OAc^- decreases the $[H^+]$ and therefore decreases the rate. It does not affect k, which is a constant at constant T.

18. <u>(d)</u> The value of k increases with increasing T and thus the rate increases.

Solutions to Problems, Chapter 19

19.1. Since the rate constant is in s^{-1}, the time must be in s. There are 3600 s in 1.00 h. As the decomposition of SO_2Cl_2 is a first-order reaction:

$$\ln\frac{[SO_2Cl_2]_t}{[SO_2Cl_2]_o} = -kt = -(2.20\times10^{-5}\ s^{-1})(3600\ s) = -0.0792$$

$$\frac{[SO_2Cl_2]_t}{[SO_2Cl_2]_o} = e^{-0.0792} = 0.924$$

As the $[SO_2Cl_2]$ remaining after heating at 595 K for one hour is 92.4% of the original concentration, then 7.6% has decomposed.

19.2. (a) The units of a reaction rate are $mol{\cdot}L^{-1}s^{-1}$, regardless of the order of the reaction.

(b) $$rate = k[A][B]^{1/2}$$

$$mol{\cdot}L^{-1}s^{-1} = (\text{units of k})(mol{\cdot}L^{-1})(mol^{1/2}L^{-1/2})$$

Therefore, $$(\text{units of k}) = (mol{\cdot}L^{-1}s^{-1})(mol^{-3/2}L^{3/2})$$

$$= L^{1/2}mol^{-1/2}s^{-1}$$

19.3. For a first-order reaction (or a pseudo-first order reaction such as the hydrolysis of sucrose):

$$\ln\frac{[C_{12}H_{22}O_{11}]_t}{[C_{12}H_{22}O_{11}]_o} = -kt$$

Note that it is the <u>ratio</u> of the concentration at time t to the initial concentration that matters, not the initial concentration (or amount). Thus, it will take the same amount of time to hydrolyze 80.0% of a kilogram of sucrose as it does to hydrolyze 80.0% of a pound of sucrose. If

80.0% has hydrolyzed, then 20.0% remains as sucrose.

$$\ln(0.200) = -(3.47\times10^{-3}\ \text{min}^{-1})t$$

$$-1.61 = -(3.47\times10^{-3}\ \text{min}^{-1})t$$

$$t = (1.61/3.47\times10^{-3})\ \text{min} = 464\ \text{min}$$

19.4. (a) The stoichiometric equation for the overall reaction is obtained by adding steps 1 and 2:

step 1	$O_3 \rightleftharpoons O_2 + O$
step 2	$O + O_3 \rightarrow 2O_2$
Overall	$2O_3 \rightarrow 3O_2$

(b) The rate is determined by the slow step, step 2:

$$\text{rate} = k_2[O][O_3]$$

Since the overall rate should not be expressed in terms of any intermediates (the monatomic O), we use step 1 to obtain an expression for [O]:

$$K_{eq} = [O_2][O]/[O_3]$$

or

$$[O] = K_{eq}[O_3]/[O_2]$$

Substitution into the rate law gives

$$\text{rate} = k_2K_{eq}[O_3]^2/[O_2] = k[O_3]^2/[O_2]$$

(c) $k_2K_{eq} = k$, the observed specific rate constant.

19.5. $3HNO_2(aq) \rightleftharpoons H^+(aq) + NO_3^-(aq) + 2NO(g) + H_2O(\ell)$

$$K_{eq} = \frac{[H^+][NO_3^-][NO]^2}{[HNO_2]^3}$$

As usual, the $[H_2O]$ has been included in the value of K_{eq}. From Eq. (19-44), $K_{eq} = k_f/k_r$. At equilibrium, rate of forward reaction = rate of reverse reaction

$$k_f[HNO_2]/[NO]^2 = k_r\{X\}$$

where {X} stands for the concentration expression for the reverse reaction.

Thus, $$k_f/k_r = \frac{\{X\}[NO]^2}{[HNO_2]} = K_{eq} = \frac{[H^+][NO_3^-][NO]^2}{[HNO_2]^3}$$

and $$\{X\} = [H^+][NO_3^-]/[HNO_2]^2$$

Thus, for the reverse reaction,

$$\text{rate} = k_r[H^+][NO_3^-]/[HNO_2]^2$$

19.6. $$2N_2O_5(soln) \rightarrow 2NO_2(soln) + 1/2\ O_2(g)$$

To determine the order of the reaction we must plot both $\ln[N_2O_5]$ and $1/[N_2O_5]$ versus t and show that one is linear and the other is not linear.

t (s)	$[N_2O_5]$ (M)	$\ln[N_2O_5]$	$1/[N_2O_5]$
0	2.33	0.846	0.429
184	2.08	0.732	0.481
319	1.91	0.647	0.524
526	1.67	0.513	0.599
867	1.36	0.307	0.735
1189	1.11	0.104	0.901
1877	0.72	-0.329	1.39
2315	0.55	-0.598	1.82
2724	0.43	-0.844	2.33

The plots are shown on the following two pages. It is clear that the plot of $1/[N_2O_5]$ versus time is not linear, and therefore the reaction is not second order with respect to N_2O_5. The plot of $\ln[N_2O_5]$ versus time <u>is</u> linear, so the reaction is first order in $[N_2O_5]$, and

$$k_1 = -(\text{slope of plot of } \ln[N_2O_5] \text{ versus t})$$

Plot of $\ln[N_2O_5]$ vs. t in s

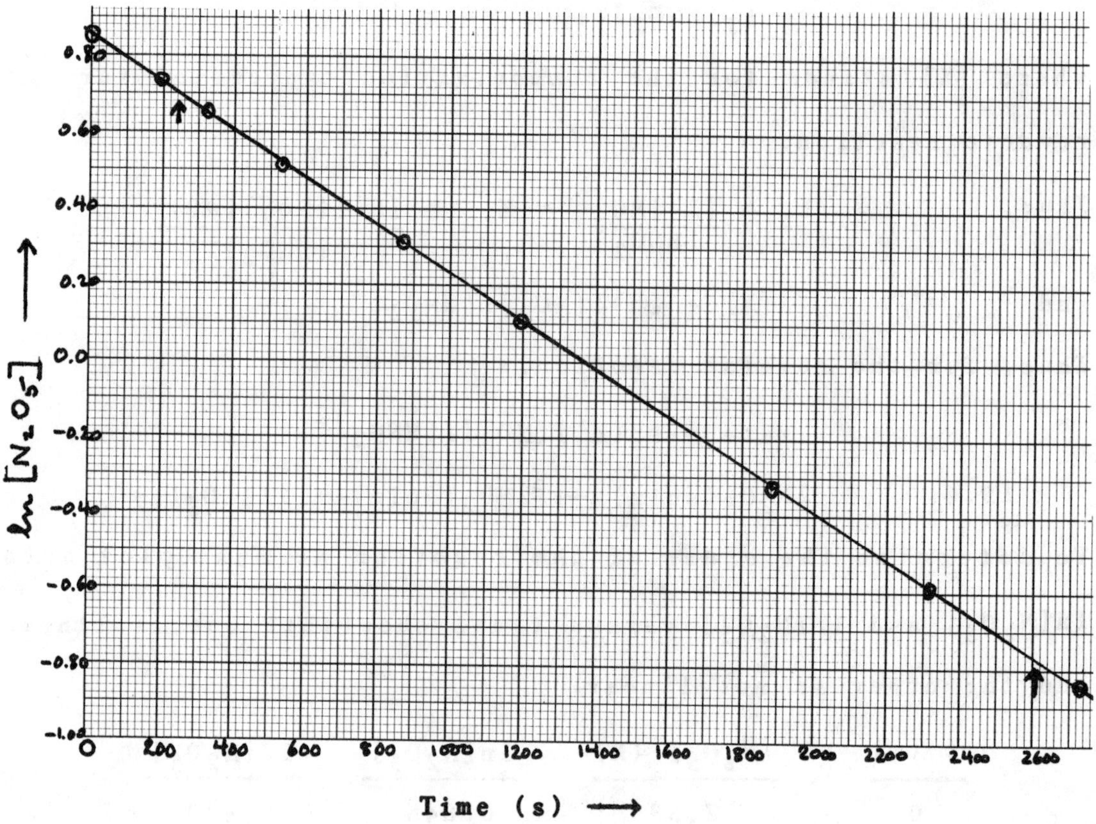

Using the points parked with arrows to determine the slope, we obtain

$$\text{slope} = \frac{-0.762 - (0.705)}{2600 - 240} = \frac{-1.467}{2360} = -6.22\text{x}10^{-4}$$

Therefore $\qquad k_1 = +6.22\text{x}10^{-4}\ s^{-1}$

If it is preferred to have k_1 in units of $\min^{-1}$, the conversion is shown below:

$$(6.22\text{x}10^{-4}\ s^{-1})(60\ s\cdot\min^{-1}) = 3.73\text{x}10^{-2}\ \min^{-1}$$

Plot of $1/[N_2O_5]$ vs. t in s

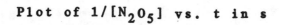

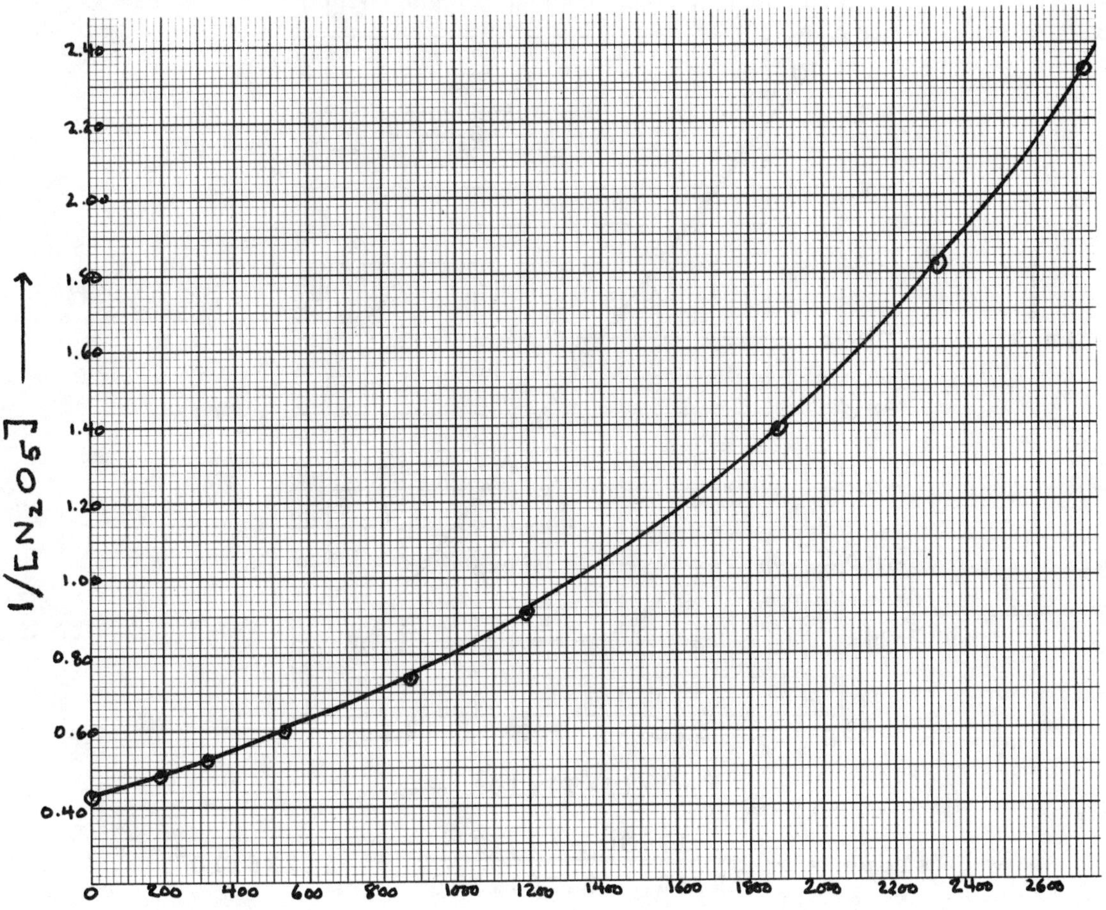

Time (s) ⟶

19.7. (a) The Arrhenius equation, Eq. (19-31b), can be written as $\ln k = -E_{act}/RT + \text{constant}$. Therefore a plot of $\ln k$ versus $1/T$ yields a straight line with slope $-E_{act}/R$.

T (K)	k (s^{-1})	ln k	$(1/T)\times10^3$
273.15	7.87×10^{-7}	-14.06	3.66
298.15	3.46×10^{-5}	-10.27	3.35
308.15	1.35×10^{-4}	- 8.91	3.25
318.15	4.98×10^{-4}	- 7.60	3.14
328.15	1.50×10^{-3}	- 6.50	3.05

Plot of ln k vs. 1/T for $N_2O_5(g) \rightarrow 2NO_2(g) + 1/2\ O_2(g)$

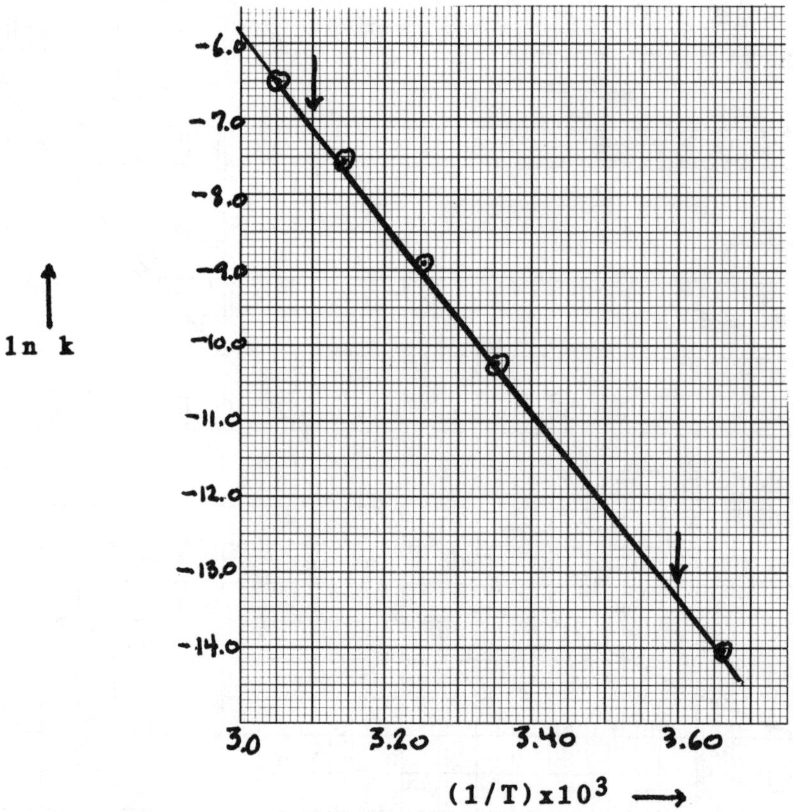

$$\text{slope} = -\frac{13.30 - 7.12}{(3.60 - 3.10)\times10^{-3}} = -1.236\times10^{4}$$

$$E_{act} = -(\text{Slope})(R) = -(1.236\times10^{4}\ K)(8.3144\ J\cdot mol^{-1}K^{-1})$$

$$= 1.028\times10^{5}\ J/mol = 103\ kJ/mol$$

(b) The slope of the best straight line through all the data points yields a more accurate value for E_{act}. There is always scatter (experimental uncertainty) in a set of data. Assuming the scatter is random, the + and - fluctuations tend to cancel out. A calculation using only two points, which could both be slightly in error, may yield a poor value of E_{act}.

19.8. (a) For a first-order reaction, the rate constant is related to the half-life by the equation

$$k = \ln 2/\tau_{1/2} = 0.6931/\tau_{1/2}$$

Thus the specific rate constant at any temperature is inversely proportional to the half-life at that temperature. The Arrhenius equation is

$$\ln(k_2/k_1) = -(E_{act}/R)(1/T_2 - 1/T_1)$$

With $T_1 = 37°C = 310.15$ K, $T_2 = 50°C = 323.15$ K, and E_{act} equal to $420\text{x}10^3$ J/mol, we obtain

$$\ln(k_2/k_1) = -\left(\frac{420\text{x}10^3 \text{ J}\cdot\text{mol}^{-1}}{8.3144 \text{ J}\cdot\text{mol}^{-1}\text{K}^{-1}}\right)\left(\frac{1}{323.15} - \frac{1}{310.15}\right)$$

$$= \frac{(5.051\text{x}10^4)(13.0)}{(323.15)(310.15)} = 6.552$$

$$k_2/k_1 = e^{6.552} = 700.8$$

Thus,

$$\frac{\tau_{1/2} \text{ at } T_1}{\tau_{1/2} \text{ at } T_2} = k_2/k_1 = 700.8$$

$$\tau_{1/2} \text{ at } T_1 = (700.8)(\tau_{1/2} \text{ at } T_2) = (700.8)(2 \text{ min})$$

$$= 1402 \text{ min} = 23.4 \text{ h}$$

(b) Both protein denaturation and DNA uncoiling are processes with large activation energies. Thus, both processes are highly sensitive to temperature changes. Their rates go up very rapidly as temperature increases, even by a few degrees. In order to survive, keeping all proteins and DNA intact for reasonable lengths of time, living organisms must somehow regulate their temperatures fairly closely and must particularly avoid becoming too hot.

19.9. To find the half-life of the nuclide, $\tau_{1/2}$, we use the relation $\tau_{1/2} = \ln 2/\lambda = 0.6931/\lambda$, where λ is the first-order decay constant. From the first-order decay law

$$\ln N = -\lambda t + \ln No$$

where N is the activity, we see that a plot of ln N versus time yields a straight line with slope = $-\lambda$.

Time (days)	0.00	5.00	10.00	15.00	20.00	25.00
Activity (cpm)	5640	5300	4981	4681	4398	4133
ln N	8.638	8.575	8.513	8.451	8.389	8.327

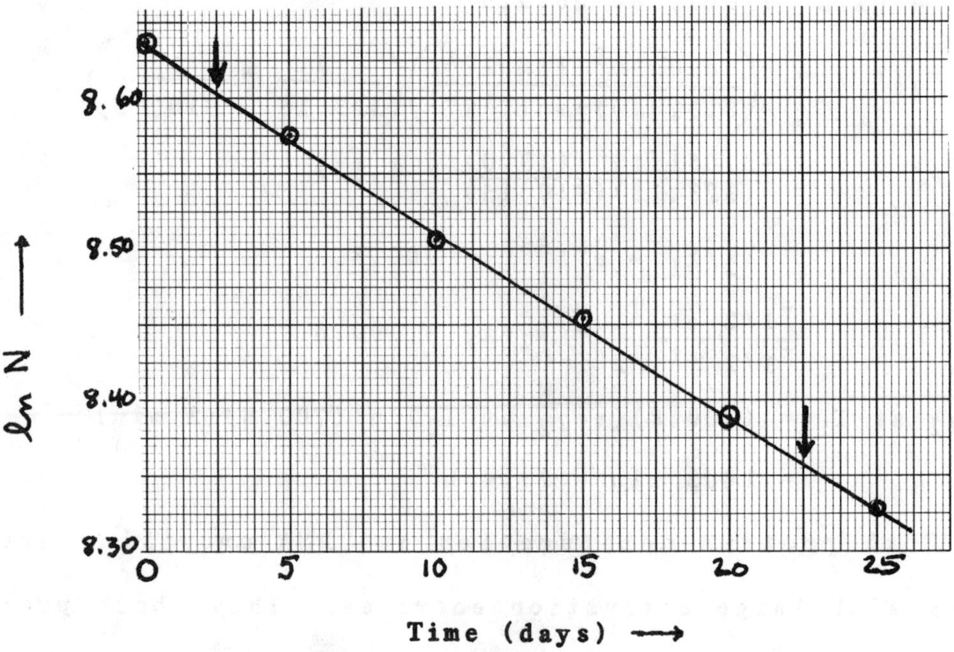

Using the points marked with arrows to determine the slope, we obtain

$$\text{slope} = \frac{8.359 - 8.607}{22.5 - 2.5} = -0.0124$$

$$\text{Decay constant, } \lambda, = +0.0124 \text{ days}^{-1}$$

$$\tau_{1/2} = (\ln 2)/\lambda = (0.69315)/(0.0124) = 55.9 \text{ days}$$

19.10. $Cl_2(g) + CO(g) \rightarrow Cl_2CO(g)$

$$\text{Observed rate} = -d[CO]/dt = k[Cl_2]^{3/2}[CO]$$

The slow step in the mechanism is the rate-determining step, so the rate of the reaction is the rate of step 3:

$$\text{rate} = k_3[ClCO][Cl_2]$$

We must find an expression for [ClCO] from the two preceding fast equilibria.

$$K_1 = [Cl]^2[M]/[Cl_2][M] = [Cl]^2/[Cl_2]$$

so that $$[Cl] = \{K_1[Cl_2]\}^{1/2}$$

$$K_2 = [ClCO][M]/[Cl][CO][M] = [ClCO]/[Cl][CO]$$

so that $$[ClCO] = K_2[Cl][CO]$$

Substituting the expression for [Cl] into the expression for [ClCO] yields

$$[ClCO] = K_2(K_1)^{1/2}[Cl_2]^{1/2}[CO]$$

Substitution of this expression for [ClCO] into the rate expression yields

$$\text{rate} = k_3[ClCO][Cl_2] = k_3K_2(K_1)^{1/2}[Cl_2]^{3/2}[CO]$$

which is the observed rate expression.

The composite or observed specific rate constant is

$$k = k_3K_2(K_1)^{1/2}$$

19.11. (a) $N_2O_5(g) \rightarrow 2NO_2(g) + 1/2\ O_2(g)$

The observed reaction rate is the rate of the slow or rate-determining step, step 2:

$$\text{rate} = k_2[NO_2][NO_3]$$

We can determine $[NO_2][NO_3]$ from the preceding fast equilibrium:

$$K_{eq} = [NO_2][NO_3]/[N_2O_5]$$

so that

$$[NO_2][NO_3] = K_{eq}[N_2O_5]$$

and

$$\text{rate} = k_2K_{eq}[N_2O_5] = k[N_2O_5]$$

where $k = k_2K_{eq}$. Thus, this mechanism gives a rate law that is first order in N_2O_5, consistent with the experimental data.

Note that since the rate-determining step precedes step 3, the rate constant k_3 does not appear as a factor in the observed rate constant k.

(b) Since this is a first order reaction

$$\ln\frac{[N_2O_5]_t}{[N_2O_5]_o} = -kt$$

For $[N_2O_5]_t = (1/10)[N_2O_5]_o$, $\ln(0.10) = -2.303 = -kt$

$$t = \frac{2.303}{5.0\text{x}10^{-4}\ s^{-1}} = 4.6\text{x}10^{2}\ s$$

To convert to hours, use

$$(4605\ s)/(3600\ s\cdot h^{-1}) = 1.28\ h = 1.3\ h$$

19.12. $2NO_2(g) + F_2(g) \rightarrow 2NO_2F(g)$

$$\text{rate} = \frac{-d[NO_2]}{dt} = k[NO_2][F_2]$$

A possible mechanism is

step 1: $F_2 + NO_2 \rightarrow FNO_2 + F\cdot$ (slow)

step 2: $F\cdot + NO_2 \rightarrow FNO_2$ (fast)

$$\text{rate} = \text{rate of step 1} = k_1[F_2][NO_2]$$

The 2 steps must add up to yield the overall stoichiometry.

19.13. If the stoichiometry

$$Tl^+(aq) + 2Ce^{4+}(aq) \longrightarrow 2Ce^{3+}(aq) + Tl^{3+}(aq)$$

represents an elementary process, it means that a 3-body collision (one Tl^+ and two Ce^{4+}) is required. This occurs much less frequently than 2-body collisions, which are the only ones needed in all three steps of the mechanism involving the Mn^{2+} catalyst. Consequently, the catalyzed reaction, even though it occurs in three steps, is faster than the uncatalyzed reaction.

19.14. (a) $$\text{rate} = k[H_2]^a[NO]^b$$

From runs 1 and 2, in which $[H_2]_0$ is kept constant, but $[NO]_0$ is halved, we see that

$$\frac{\text{rate}_1}{\text{rate}_2} = \frac{2.6\text{x}10^{-7}}{6.5\text{x}10^{-8}} = \frac{4}{1} = \left(\frac{0.010}{0.0050}\right)^b = 2^b$$

Therefore b = 2 and the reaction is 2nd order in NO. We can use any other pair of runs to determine the dependence on $[H_2]$ once we know the reaction is 2nd order in NO. If we choose to compare runs 1 and 3 we obtain

$$\frac{\text{rate}_3}{\text{rate}_1} = \frac{7.8\text{x}10^{-7}}{2.6\text{x}10^{-7}} = \frac{3}{1} = \left(\frac{0.020}{0.060}\right)^a\left(\frac{0.030}{0.010}\right)^2$$

Therefore $3 = (1/3)^a(3^2)$ and $a = 1$

The reaction is 1st order in H_2, 2nd order in NO, and the rate law is

$$\text{rate} = k[H_2][NO_2]^2$$

The specific rate constant can be calculated from any of

the three runs. From run 1:

$$2.6\text{x}10^{-7}\ \text{mol}\cdot\text{L}^{-1}\text{s}^{-1} = k(0.060\ \text{mol}\cdot\text{L}^{-1})(0.010\ \text{mol}\cdot\text{L}^{-1})^2$$

$$= k(6.0\text{x}10^{-6}\ \text{mol}^3\text{L}^{-3})$$

$$k = 4.3\text{x}10^{-2}\ \text{L}^2\text{mol}^{-2}\text{s}^{-1}$$

(b) $$2NO(g) + 2H_2(g) \rightarrow N_2(g) + 2H_2O(g)$$

The sum of all the steps in a mechanism must be the overall stoichiometry of the reaction. We try to avoid any three-body collisions, that is, any termolecular step. A possible mechanism for this gas-phase reaction is

step 1: $2NO \rightleftharpoons N_2O_2$ (fast equilibrium)

step 2: $N_2O_2 + H_2 \rightarrow N_2O + H_2O$ (slow)

step 3: $N_2O + H_2 \rightarrow N_2 + H_2O$ (fast)

$$\text{rate} = \text{rate of step 2} = k_2[N_2O_2][H_2]$$

From step 1, $K_{eq} = [N_2O_2]/[NO]^2$, or $[N_2O_2] = K_{eq}[NO]^2$

Thus, $\text{rate} = k_2K_{eq}[NO]^2[H_2] = k[NO]^2[H_2]$

consistent with the observed rate law.

19.15. (a) $2X + Y \rightarrow Z$ and $\text{rate} = k[X]^a[Y]^b$

From runs 1 and 2 we see that if $[X]_o$ is kept constant and $[Y]_o$ is doubled, the rate also doubles, so the reaction must be first order in [Y].

From runs 2 and 3 we see that if $[Y]_o$ is kept constant and $[X]_o$ is doubled, the rate does not change at all. The rate does not depend on the [X].

We can check this by comparing runs 1 and 4. The $[Y]_o$

is multiplied by a factor of 6, and the rate is also multiplied by a factor of 6. The change in $[X]_0$ has no effect on the rate. Thus

$$\text{rate} = k[Y]$$

$$7.0\text{x}10^{-4}\ \text{mol}\cdot\text{L}^{-1}\text{s}^{-1} = k(0.10\ \text{mol}\cdot\text{L}^{-1}) \quad \text{(from run 1)}$$

$$k = (7.0\text{x}10^{-4})/(0.10)\text{s}^{-1} = 7.0\text{x}10^{-3}\ \text{s}^{-1}$$

(b) In each mechanism, the rate is given by the rate of the slow step.

Mechanism I rate = $k_I[X][Y]$

which is <u>not</u> consistent with the observed rate law.

Mechanism II rate = $k_{II}[Y][M]$

which is <u>not</u> consistent with the observed rate law.

Mechanism III rate = $k_{III}[Y]$

which is consistent with the observed rate law. This does not prove that mechanism III is correct, only that it is a possible mechanism.

19.16. (a) ΔH for E + S ⇌ ES complex = +4200 kcal (since ES is at a higher potential energy than E + S).

(b) ΔH for E + P ⇌ EP complex = −1200 kcal

(c) ΔH for S + H_2O ⇌ P is just the ΔH for the overall reaction.

ΔH for E + S ⟶ E + P = −3600 kcal

(d) E_{a_b} = the difference in energy between the transition state and the EP complex

$$E_{a_b} = +1200 + 3600 + 4200 + 6100 = 15{,}100\ \text{kcal}$$

Solutions to Exercises, Chapter 20

1. (a) The coordination number (C.N.) of Ni in $Ni(en)_2Cl_2$ is 6. Ethylenediamine (en) is a bidentate ligand. Each en attaches at two N atoms, so the two en ligands occupy 4 coordination sites, and the two Cl^- ligands occupy one each, for a total of 6.

(b) This is an ionic compound with cation $Co(NH_3)_6{}^{2+}$ and a $SO_4{}^{2-}$ anion. The C.N. of Co in $Co(NH_3)_6{}^{2+}$ is 6. The SO_4^{2-} is not coordinated. It is the anion to make a neutral molecule.

(c) The C.N. of Fe in $Fe(CO)_5$ is 5. Carbon monoxide, CO, is a monodentate ligand.

(d) The C.N. of Cu in $Cu(acac)_2$ is 4. Acetylacetonate (acac) is a bidentate ligand.

(e) The C.N. of Cr in $Cr(C_2O_4)_3{}^{3-}$ is 6. Oxalate ion, $C_2O_4^{2-}$, is bidentate. This compound is ionic, with K^+ as the cation and the trioxalatochromate ion as the anion.

2. (a) The oxidation state of Cr is +3 in $Cr(H_2O)_4Br_2^+$. The H_2O ligands are uncharged, and each Br^- ligand has a charge of -1. The sum of the oxidation state of Cr and the charges on the two Br^- ligands must be +1, the charge on the complex ion.

(b) The oxidation state of Ag is +3 in AgF_4^-.

(c) The oxidation state of Ru is +2 in $[Ru(bipy)_3]^{2+}$.

The bidentate ligand bipy is uncharged (neutral).

(d) The oxidation state of Ni is +2 in $Ni(CN)_5^{3-}$. Each CN^- has a charge of −1.

(e) The oxidation state of Au is +1 in $AuCl_2^-$.

(f) In $[Co(NH_3)_2(CN)_4]^-$ the NH_3 ligands are neutral and each cyano ligand has a charge of −1, so the oxidation state of Co must be +3 to make the charge on the ion −1.

(g) The oxidation state of Rh is +3 in $[Rh(NH_3)_5Cl]^{+2}$.

3. There is a lone pair of electrons on the N atom in NH_3, whereas CH_4 has 4 bonded pairs and no lone pair.

4. (a) The Ba^{2+} ion is not a Lewis acid; it has the electronic configuration of Xe with completely filled electron shells.

(b) The Pd^{2+} ion is a Lewis acid. The atomic number of Pd is 46, so there are $44e^-$ in Pd^{2+}, which has electronic configuration $(Kr)^{36}(4d)^8$. There are vacant 'd' atomic orbitals, i.e., 4d orbitals that can accept electrons.

(c) Thallic ion, Tl^{3+}, is a Lewis acid. The atomic number of Tl is 81, so there are $78e^-$ in Tl^{3+}. Its electronic configuration is $(Xe)^{54}(4f)^{14}(5d)^{10}$. The 6s and 6p atomic orbitals are vacant, and the 5d, 6s, and 6p orbitals are fairly close in energy at Z = 81.

(d) The Al^{3+} ion is not a Lewis acid. The electronic configuration of Al^{3+} is isoelectronic with neon.

(e) The Zr^{2+} ion is a Lewis acid. The atomic number of Zr is 40, so that Zr^{2+} has $38e^-$, and electronic configuration $(Kr)^{36}(4d)^2$. There are vacant 4d orbitals that can accept electrons.

5. The following hydrated metal ions are acidic in aqueous solution: $Rh^{3+}(aq)$, $Hg^{2+}(aq)$, $Fe^{3+}(aq)$ and $Co^{2+}(aq)$. These are all highly charged cations that are Lewis acids and form strong metal-oxygen bonds. The Rb^+ ion is a large, singly-charged ion with rare gas electronic configuration. Cations with charge +1 are not acidic. Strontium ion, Sr^{2+}, is a large cation with rare gas configuration. It is not a Lewis acid.

6. Both Ba^{2+} and Be^{2+} are alkaline earth ions with rare gas electronic configurations, but Be^{2+} is very small, whereas Ba^{2+} is much larger. Because of the small size of Be^{2+}, the Be-O bond is short and the electrostatic attraction between Be^{2+} and the O end of H_2O is much larger than that between Ba^{2+} and H_2O. The stronger Be-O bond makes it easier for the H_2O to donate a proton.

7. Both Cr^{3+} and Cu^{2+} are Lewis acids. The +3 charge on Cr^{3+} makes the coulombic attraction to the O end of H_2O significantly larger than for Cu^{2+}. The bond between Cr^{3+} and O is stronger than that between Cu^{2+} and O and it is easier for $Cr(OH_2)_6^{3+}$ to donate a proton than for $Cu(OH_2)_4^{2+}$.

8. The Sr^{2+} ion has rare gas configuration, whereas Sn^{2+} does not. Thus Sn^{2+} is a Lewis acid and is much more efficient at polarizing the electron cloud around O in H_2O (pulling it towards itself) than is Sr^{2+}. The bond between Sn^{2+} and O is significantly stronger than the ion-dipole attraction between Sr^{2+} and H_2O.

9. (a) $Zn(OH)_4^{2-} + 4H^+(aq) \rightleftharpoons Zn^{2+}(aq) + 4H_2O$

(b) $Cr^{3+}(aq) + 3NH_3 + 3H_2O \rightarrow Cr(OH)_3\downarrow + 3NH_4^+$

The Cr^{3+} ion forms inert complexes and $Cr(NH_3)_6^{3+}$ is not formed on mixing these reagents.

(c) No reaction occurs. The $Co(NH_3)_6^{3+}$ ion is inert.

(d) $Zn^{2+}(aq) + 4NH_3 \rightleftharpoons Zn(NH_3)_4^{2+}$

(e) $Ni(NH_3)_6{}^{2+} + 6H^+(aq) \rightleftharpoons Ni^{2+}(aq) + 6NH_4{}^+$

(f) $AgCl(s) + 2NH_3 \rightleftharpoons Ag(NH_3)_2^+ + Cl^-$

(g) No reaction occurs. The Ba^{2+} ion forms few complexes, and does not form an OH^- complex.

(h) $Al(OH)_3 + OH^- \rightleftharpoons Al(OH)_4^-$ The Al^{3+} ion is small and highly charged, and the Al—O bond is strong.

10. Of this list, only (c) $Rh(NH_3)_6{}^{3+}$, (e) $Co(NO_2)_6{}^{3-}$, and (g) $Cr(NH_3)_6{}^{3+}$ are inert.

Octahedral complexes of tripositive ions with either three or six d electrons form inert complexes. (This corresponds to having the lower t_{2g} level either half-full or completely filled.) The Rh^{3+} ion has 42 electrons, with electronic configuration $(Kr)^{36}(4d)^6$. The Co^{3+} ion has $24e^-$ and electronic configuration $(Ar)^{18}(3d)^6$. The Cr^{3+} ion has $21e^-$, with electronic configuration $(Ar)^{18}(3d)^3$.

11. Since only two of the three Cl^- ions in the compound precipitate as AgCl when Ag^+ ions are added, one Cl^- must be tightly bound in the coordination complex. Since no $NH_4{}^+$ ions are formed on adding H^+, all five NH_3 molecules are coordinated to the Co^{2+}. Thus, the cation is $Co(NH_3)_5Cl^{2+}$, and the compound is $[Co(NH_3)_5Cl]Cl_2$. The molar conductance of 245 ohm^{-1} (see Table 20.4) indicates a 2:1 compound, confirming the formula.

12. Adding $H^+(aq)$ does not produce NH_4^+ ions, but only HCl gas, and all five NH_3 remain tightly bound to the Co^{3+}, so there must be five NH_3 ligands. The new compound has 2 Co^{3+} ions and 5 moles of H_2O, of which 3 are just waters of hydration since they are lost on drying at room temperature. Thus, 2 moles of H_2O are bound per 2 moles of Co^{3+}, or one H_2O per Co^{3+}. The original compound is therefore $[Co(NH_3)_5H_2O]Cl_3$, and the cation is $[Co(NH_3)_5H_2O]^{3+}$. The new compound is $[Co(NH_3)_5(H_2O)]_2(SO_4)_3 \cdot 3H_2O$. Note that the cation:anion ratio in each compound is determined by the necessity of having an uncharged molecule.

13. $\Delta T_f = +0.206^\circ = K_f \nu m = (1.86)(0.0400)\nu$

$$\nu = 0.206/(1.86)(0.0400) = 2.77$$

There are 3 ions, $2K^+$ and one $[Fe(CN)_5NO]^{2-}$. The value of ν is somewhat less than 3 because interionic forces cause solutions of $K_2[Fe(CN)_5NO]$ to deviate from ideality. The attractions between cation and anion result in some ion-pair formation and the solute particles do not behave as independently as molecular (neutral) solutes do.

14. In order of increasing molar conductivity:

(c)	$Co(py)_3(CN)_3$	a neutral molecular complex
(b)	$K^+ + Co(EDTA)^-$	2 ions/formula unit
(d)	$[Cr(NH_3)_5Cl]^{2+} + 2Cl^-$	3 ions/formula unit
(a)	$3Na^+ + Co(NO_2)_6^{3-}$	4 ions/formula unit
(e)	$Pt(NH_3)_6^{4+} + 4Br^-$	5 ions/formula unit

15.

(a) Dinitrotetramminecobalt(III) nitrite

(b) Tetrachloroethylenediamineplatinum(IV)

(c) Sodium dithiosulfatoargentate(I)

(d) Potassium hexanitrocobaltate(III)

(e) Sodium ethylenediaminetetraacetatozincate(II)

(f) Dibromobis(ethylenediamine)ruthenium(III) bromide

16. **(a)** $Cs[IFCl_3]$

(b) $[Ni(en)_3](NO_3)_2$

(c) $K_3[Co(C_2O_4)_2Br_2]$

(d) $Na_4[Fe(CN)_6]$

(e) $[Cr(NH_3)_5Cl]SO_4$

17. (a) $[Rh(en)_2Cl_2]^+$

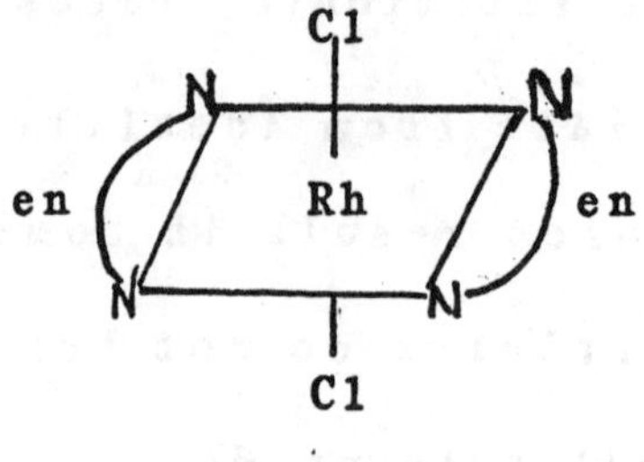

trans

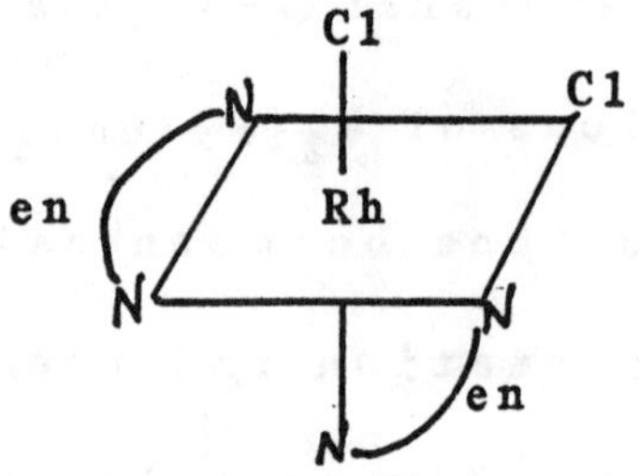

cis

(b) $[Co(NH_3)_4(NO_2)_2]^+$

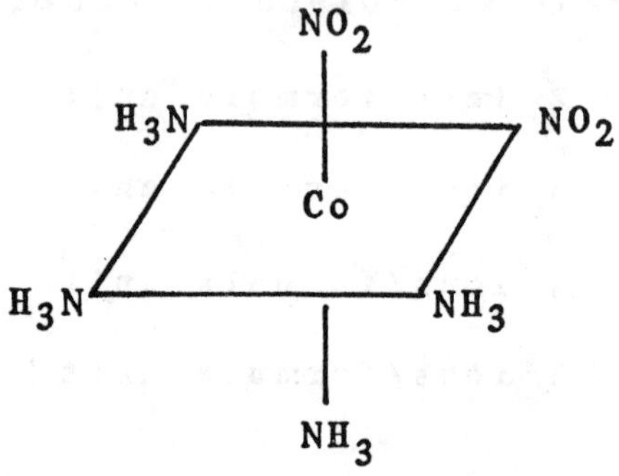

cis

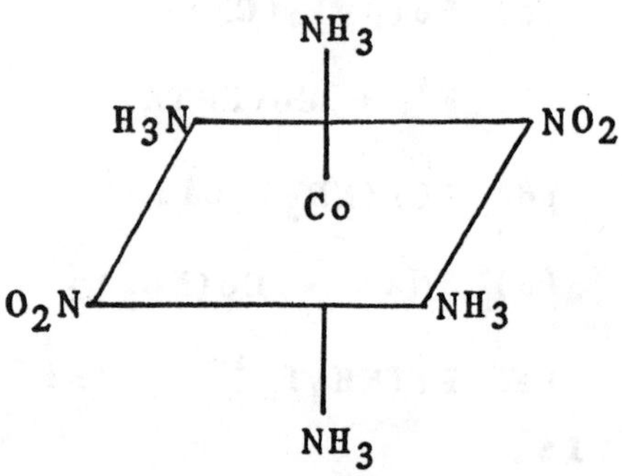

trans

(c) $Pd(gly)_2$ Note that this complex is square planar (C.N. of Pd^{2+} = 4)

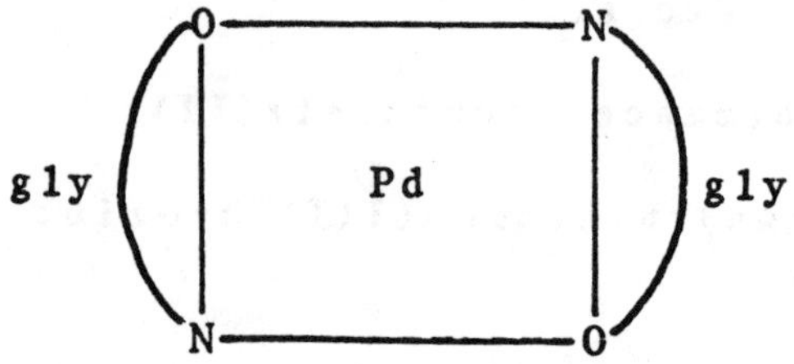

trans

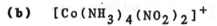

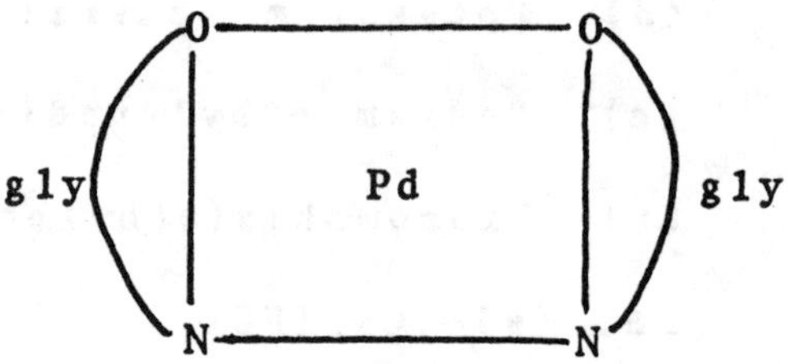

cis

18. Six-coordinate complexes with 3 identical bidentate ligands, or with two identical bidentate ligands and two identical monodentate ligands, have enantiomers. Thus only (b) and (e) have optical isomers.

(b) $[Cr(NH_3)_2(C_2O_4)_2]^-$

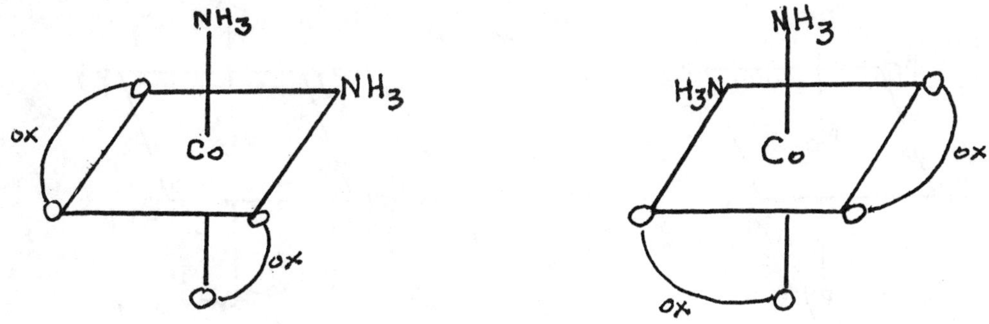

(e) $Cr(C_2O_4)^{3-}$

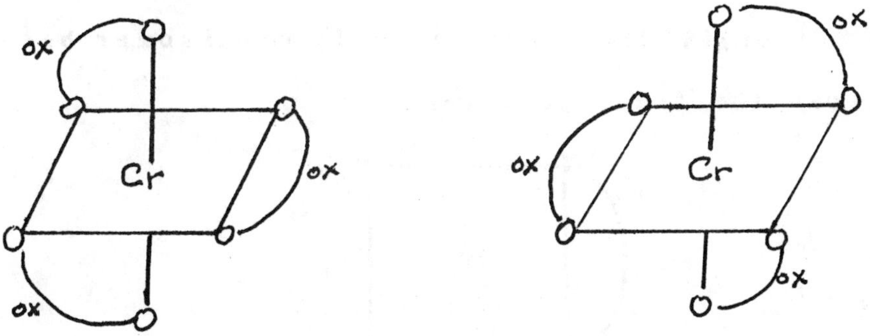

19. (a) The dicarbonatodiamminecobaltate(III) ion, $[Co(NH_3)_2(CO_3)_2]^{-1}$, has a cis and a trans form. The cis isomer exists as a pair of enantiomers.

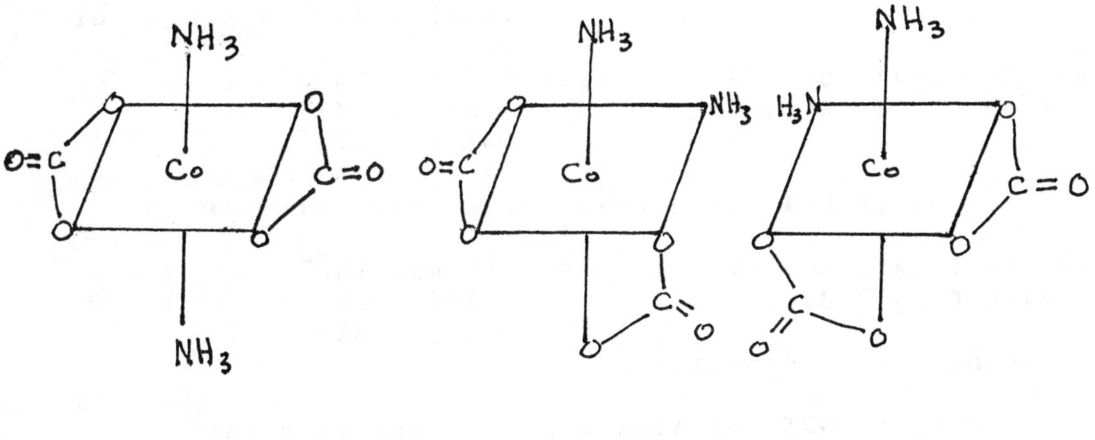

trans

the cis enantiomers

(b) $[Pt(py)_3Br_3]^+$

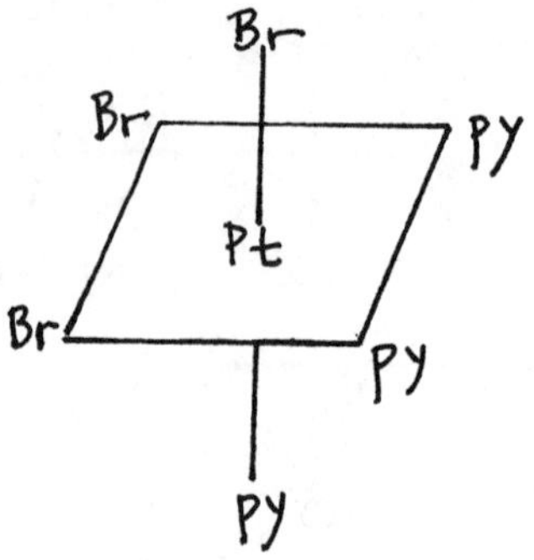

cis

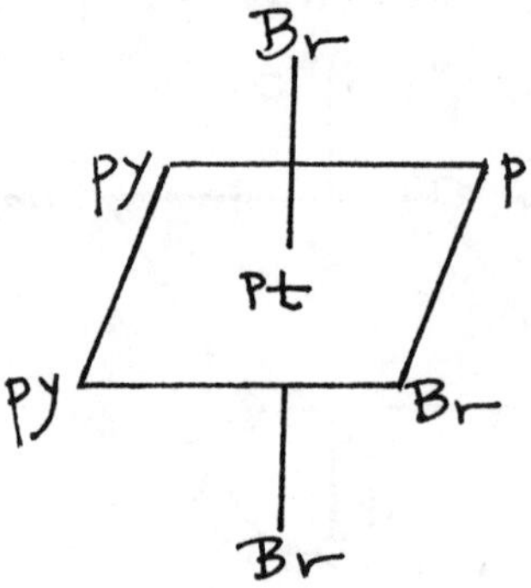

trans

(c) $Pt(en)(SCN)_2$ There is only one isomer because en cannot span the trans position.

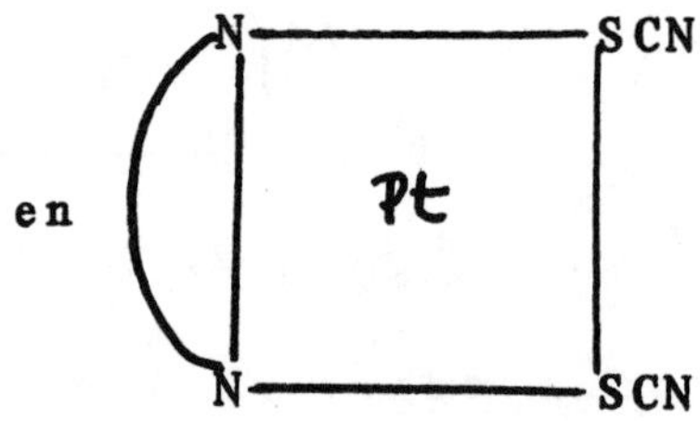

20.

(a) Fe is at. no. 26, so Fe^{2+} has $24e^-$
each CN^- donates $2e^-$: $6x2 = 12e^-$
Total = $36e^-$ = E.A.N. of Kr

(b) Au is at. no. 79, so Au^+ has $78e^-$
each Cl^- donates $2e^-$: $2x2 = 4e^-$
Total = $82e^-$

82 is NOT the atomic no. of any rare gas

(c) Al is at. no. 13, so Al^{3+} has $10e^-$
each $C_2O_4^{2-}$ donates $4e^-$: $3x4 = 12e^-$
Total = $22e^-$
($C_2O_4^{2-}$ is bidentate)

22 is NOT the atomic no. of any rare gas

(d) Cd is at. no. 48, so Cd^{2+} has $46e^-$
each I^- donates $2e^-$: $4x2 = 8e^-$
Total = $54e^-$ = E.A.N. of Xe

(e) Cr is at. no. 24, so Cr^{2+} has $22e^-$
each ligand donates $2e^-$: $6x2 = 12e^-$
Total = $34e^-$

34 is NOT the atomic no. of any rare gas

(f) Co is at. no. 27, so Co^{3+} has $24e^-$
each NO_2^- donates $2e^-$: $6x2 = 12e^-$
Total = $36e^-$ = E.A.N. of Kr

(g) Fe is at. no. 26, so Fe^0 has $26e^-$
each CO donates $2e^-$: $5x2 = 10e^-$
Total = $36e^-$ = E.A.N. of Kr

There are clearly many exceptions to Sidgwick's E.A.N. rule. It certainly is not an infallible predictor of coordination number.

21. The value of the magnetic moment, μ, given for each complex tells you how many unpaired electrons there are in the complex, since $\mu_{spin-only} = \sqrt{n(n+2)}$, where n is the nnumber of unpaired electrons. The number of unpaired electrons in the complex should then be compared with the number of unpaired electrons in the free metal ion. If there are fewer unpaired electrons in the complex than in the free ion, the complex is low spin. If the numbers are identical, the complex is high spin.

(a) This is a high-spin complex as $\mu \doteq 5.94$ BM indicates 5 unpaired e^-, the maximum value possible. There is one e^- in each of the five d orbitals.

(b) This is a low-spin complex as μ = 1.9 BM indicates 1 unpaired e^-. (For a spin-only magnetic moment, μ = 1.73

BM for 1 unpaired electron, but there is a very small contribution to the magnetic moment from the orbital angular momentum of the electron.) A free Co^{2+} ion has 7 e^- in the <u>3d</u> orbitals, and therefore has 3 unpaired electrons with configuration $\underline{\uparrow\downarrow}$ $\underline{\uparrow\downarrow}$ $\underline{\downarrow}$ $\underline{\downarrow}$ $\underline{\downarrow}$ Since there are fewer unpaired electrons in the complex than in the free ion, this is a low-spin complex.

(c) This is a high-spin complex as μ = 4.9 BM indicates 4 unpaired e^-. The free Mn^{3+} ion has $22e^-$, configuration $(Ar)^{18}(3d)^4$, and therefore 4 unpaired electrons.

(d) This is a high-spin complex as μ = 4.9 BM indicates 4 unpaired e^-. The free Cr^{2+} ion has $22e^-$, configuration $(Ar)^{18}(3d)^4$, and therefore 4 unpaired electrons.

(e) This is a low-spin complex. A zero magnetic moment means that there are no unpaired electrons in the complex. The free Fe^{2+} ion has $24e^-$, configuration $(Ar)^{18}(3d)^6$, and 4 unpaired e-: $\underline{\uparrow\downarrow}$ $\underline{\downarrow}$ $\underline{\downarrow}$ $\underline{\downarrow}$ $\underline{\downarrow}$

(f) This is a high-spin complex. The value μ = 4.6 BM is due to 3 unpaired electrons plus a contribution to the total magnetic moment from the orbital angular momentum of the electrons. A free Co^{2+} ion has $25e^-$, configuration $(Ar)^{18}(3d)^7$, and therefore 3 unpaired e^-: $\underline{\uparrow\downarrow}$ $\underline{\uparrow\downarrow}$ $\underline{\uparrow}$ $\underline{\uparrow}$ $\underline{\uparrow}$ Note that if μ is less than 4.9 BM, there cannot be 4 unpaired electrons.

22. (a) The electron configuration of Zn^{2+} is $Ar^{18}3d^{10}$. All the d orbitals are filled, so n = 0 and μ = 0 always, and there are no low-spin or high-spin complexes.

(b) The electron configuration of Rh^{3+} is $Kr^{36}4d^6$. It is possible to have low-spin complexes. For octahedral complexes, low-spin and high-spin complexes are possible if the number of d electrons is 4, 5, 6, or 7.

(c) The electron configuration of Zr^{2+} is $Kr^{36}4d^2$. Only one kind of complex is possible with 2 unpaired electrons.

(d) The electron configuration of Ag^+ is $Kr^{36}4d^{10}$. The 4d orbitals are filled and there are no unpaired electrons. All complexes have zero magnetic moment.

(e) The electron configuration of Mn^{3+} is $Ar^{18}3d^4$. Both low-spin and high-spin octahedral complexes are possible. High-spin complexes have 4 unpaired e^-, low-spin complexes have 2 unpaired e^-.

23. The electron configuration of Ni^{2+} is $Ar^{18}3d^8$. There are 8 electrons in the 3d orbitals. Since the orbitals are more than half-full, in addition to the spin-only magnetic moment, there is also a contribution to μ from the orbital angular momentum of the electrons. In any octahedral Ni^{2+} complex, there are 2 unpaired electrons:

↑↓ ↑↓ ↑↓ ↑ ↑ and $\mu_{spin-only} = \sqrt{2(4)} = \sqrt{8} = 2.83$ BM

The orbital contribution is therefore (3.2 − 2.8) = 0.4 BM.

24. The electron configuration of Fe^{3+} is $Ar^{18}3d^5$. In octahedral complexes, the five originally degenerate (equal energy) d orbitals are split into two sets of orbitals. The magnitude of this crystal field splitting, Δ_o, depends on the ligands for a given metal ion. When Δ_o is small, as for $Fe(H_2O)_6{}^{3+}$, the number of unpaired electrons is the same as for the free ion (high-spin complex). When Δ_o is large, as for $Fe(CN)_6^{3-}$, a low-spin complex results.

High-spin	Low-spin
e_g ↑ ↑	e_g — —
Δ_o small	Δ_o large
t_{2g} ↑ ↑ ↑	t_{2g} ↑↓ ↑↓ ↑
$n = 5$, $\mu_{spin-only} = 5.92$ BM	$n = 1$, $\mu_{spin-only} = 1.73$ BM
High-spin	Low-spin

25. **(a)** The electron configuration of Cr^{2+} is $Ar^{18}3d^4$. As the ligand field due to H_2O is weak, a high-spin complex results. The electron configuration is now $(t_{2g})^3(e_g)$, and there are 4 unpaired electrons.

$$\mu_{spin-only} = \sqrt{4(6)} = \sqrt{24} = 4.90 \text{ BM}$$

$$\text{CFSE} = 3(0.4\Delta_o) - (0.6\Delta_o) = 0.6\Delta_o$$

Since there are only four d electrons, the orbital contribution to the total magnetic moment is insignificant.

(b) The electron configuration of Co^{2+} is $Ar^{18}3d^7$ and we are given that $Co(en)_3{}^{2+}$ is a high-spin complex (i.e., en exerts a weak ligand field). The electron configuration is now $(t_{2g})^5(e_g)^2$, and there are 3 unpaired electrons.

$$\mu_{spin\text{-}only} = \sqrt{3(5)} = 3.87 \text{ BM}$$

$$CFSE = 5(0.4\Delta_o) - 2(0.6\Delta_o) = 0.8\Delta_o$$

In addition to $\mu_{spin\text{-}only}$, there is also an orbital contribution to the total μ because there are more than five d electrons.

(c) The electron configuration of Rh^{3+} is $Kr^{36}4d^6$, and $Rh(C_2O_4)_3{}^{3-}$ is a low-spin complex ($C_2O_4^{2-}$ exerts a strong ligand field). All 6 electrons are in the t_{2g} level, and there are no unpaired electrons, μ is zero.

$$CFSE = 6(0.4\Delta_o) = 2.4\Delta_o$$

When n = 0 the orbital contribution to μ is also zero.

(d) The electron configuration of Mn^{2+} is $Ar^{18}3d^5$ and $Mn(CN)_6{}^{4-}$ is a low-spin complex since CN^- is at the strong field end of the spectrochemical series. All 5 electrons are in the t_{2g} orbitals, and there is 1 unpaired e^-.

$$\mu_{spin\text{-}only} = \sqrt{1(3)} = 1.73 \text{ BM}$$

$$CFSE = 5(0.4\Delta_o) = 2.0\Delta_o$$

Since there are 5 <u>d</u> electrons, there will be a (very) small orbital contribution to μ.

(e) The electron configuration of Mn^{2+} is $Ar^{18}3d^5$, as in part (d), but $Mn(NH_3)_6{}^{2+}$ is a high-spin complex. The electron configuration is now $(t_{2g})^3(e_g)^2$, and there are 5 unpaired e^-.

$$\mu_{spin-only} = \sqrt{5(7)} = 5.92 \text{ BM}$$

$$CFSE = 3(0.4\Delta_o) - 2(0.6\Delta_o) = 0$$

As in (d), there is a very small orbital contribution to μ.

26. (a) Ethylenediamine (en) exerts a stronger ligand field than F^-. Thus, $Mn(en)_3^{3+}$ has a larger Δ_o than MnF_6^{3-}.

(b) Rhodium is in the second transition series, directly below Co. The crystal field splitting, Δ_o, is ~30% larger for Rh^{3+} than for Co^{3+} (given the same ligand).

(c) The F^- ion exerts a larger crystal field splitting than does the I^- ion. The much larger I^- ligand cannot approach the Pt^{2+} cation as closely as the F^- ion, and the bond between the metal ion and the ligand is thus stronger for the smaller F^-. Note that these are square-planar complexes, so that the crystal field splitting should not be denoted as Δ_o, which refers to the CFS for octahedral complexes, but as Δ_{sp}.

(d) The crystal field splitting for $Cr(H_2O)_6^{3+}$ is larger than for $Cr(H_2O)_6^{2+}$ because a +3 charge pulls the ligands towards the metal ion more closely than a +2 charge, and there is a stronger interaction between ligands and metal electrons.

(e) The value of Δ_o is larger for $Fe(CN)_6^{3-}$ than for $Fe(SCN)_6^{3-}$. In the spectrochemical series, CN^- produces a much stronger ligand field than SCN^-.

27. $Ni(H_2O)_6^{2+} + 6NH_3 \rightleftharpoons Ni(NH_3)_6^{2+} + 6H_2O$

green blue-violet

The ligand field produced by NH_3 is stronger than that of H_2O. Therefore Δ_o is larger for $Ni(NH_3)_6^{2+}$ than for $Ni(H_2O)_6^{2+}$. The light absorbed by the hexammine complex is of higher frequency (shorter wavelength) than that absorbed by the aquo complex. The $Ni(NH_3)_6^{2+}$ absorbs yellow light, and reflects blue-violet, which we see. The $Ni(H_2O)_6^{2+}$ absorbs red light and we see the reflected green light.

28. $Cu(H_2O)_4^{2+} + 4Cl^- \rightleftharpoons CuCl_4^{2-} + 4H_2O$

blue green

The H_2O exerts a stronger ligand field than the Cl^-, producing a larger CFS, so that higher frequency (shorter wavelength) light is absorbed. The $Cu(H_2O)_4^{2+}$ ion absorbs orange light and reflects blue. The $CuCl_4^{2-}$ ion absorbs red light and reflects green.

29. In joules per molecule, $\Delta_o = h\nu = hc/\lambda$, where h is 6.626×10^{-34} $J\cdot s^{-1}$ and $c = 3.00\times10^{10}$ $cm\cdot s^{-1}$ We can use c in $cm\cdot s^{-1}$ since the cm will cancel with the cm^{-1} from $1/\lambda$.

$$(\Delta_o \frac{J}{molecule})(6.022\times10^{23} \frac{molecules}{mol})(10^{-3} \frac{kJ}{J}) = \Delta_o \text{ (kJ/mol)}$$

Complex	$\tilde{\nu}$ (cm^{-1})	$\Delta_o = hc/\lambda$ (J/molecule)	Δ_o (kJ/mol)
$Co(NH_3)_6^{3+}$	2.3×10^4	4.57×10^{-19}	2.8×10^2
$Rh(NH_3)_6^{3+}$	3.4×10^4	6.76×10^{-19}	4.1×10^2
$Ir(NH_3)_6^{3+}$	4.1×10^4	8.15×10^{-19}	4.9×10^2

30. The NO_2^- causes a stronger ligand field than H_2O. Substituting H_2O for NO_2^- decreases Δ_o, so that the second

complex absorbs light of a lower frequency than the first. The Δ_o is decreased even more as one NH_3 and one H_2O are replaced by two Cl^-.

Complex	Color seen	Color absorbed
$[Co(NH_3)_5NO_2]^{2+}$	yellow	blue-violet
$[Co(NH_3)_5H_2O]^{3+}$	red	green
$[Co(NH_3)_4Cl_2]^+$	violet	yellow-orange

Solutions to Multiple Choice Questions, Chapter 20

1. (e) Option (a) is wrong because most metal ions can exhibit several coordination numbers, although there is often one that predominates. Option (b) is wrong for multidentate ligands. The most common coordination numbers are 4 and 6; 8 is uncommon. All values from 2 to 12 have been observed.

2. (b) Zinc(II) hydroxide, $Zn(OH)_2(s)$, is an insoluble solid. Ammonia is a weak base, so that the $[OH^-]$ is not very large and reaction (c) does not occur to any significant extent. There is no such species as NH_4OH!

3. (c) The electron configuration of Zn^{2+} is $Ar^{18}3d^{10}$. All the d orbitals are filled. In all the other species, there are empty, or half-empty d orbitals. Since the crystal field produces a splitting into at least 2 levels (depending on the geometry), the metal ion can absorb visible light of some frequency as an electron in a lower

energy d orbital is promoted to a higher energy d orbital.

4. (a)

5. (a) The electron configuration of Fe^{2+} is $Ar^{18}3d^6$. Since CN^- exerts a strong ligand field, the ground state electron configuration of $Fe(CN)_6^{4-}$ is $(t_{2g})^6$, with all 6 electrons paired (n = 0) and $\mu = 0$.

6. (c) Magnesium hydroxide, $Mg(OH)_2$, precipitates when concentrated NH_3 is added to a solution containing Mg^{2+} ions, as ammonia is a weak base. All the other metal ions form coordination complexes with NH_3.

$$Ni^{2+}(aq) + 6NH_3 \rightleftharpoons Ni(NH_3)_6^{2+}$$

$$Cu^{2+}(aq) + 4NH_3 \rightleftharpoons Cu(NH_3)_4^{2+}$$

$$Co^{2+}(aq) + 6NH_3 \rightleftharpoons Co(NH_3)_6^{2+}$$

$$Zn^{2+}(aq) + 4NH_3 \rightleftharpoons Zn(NH_3)_4^{2+}$$

The reaction with $Mg^{2+}(aq)$ (which has rare gas electronic configuration and forms relatively few complexes) is

$$Mg^{2+}(aq) + 2NH_3 + 2H_2O \rightleftharpoons Mg(OH)_2(s) + 2NH_4^+$$

7. (e) A potentiometer measures voltage, a refractometer measures the refractive index, a Gouy balance measures the magnetic moment, and a UV spectrometer measures the frequency of radiation absorbed in the ultraviolet region.

8. (a) $$CFSE = 3(0.4\Delta_o) - 2(0.6\Delta_o) = 0$$

9. (a) The electron configuration of Sc^{3+} is Ar^{18}, so there are no unpaired electrons.

10. <u>**(e)**</u> A chelate is formed with multidentate ligands. Neither CN^- nor SCN^- is multidentate, but dimethylglyoxime, ethylenediamine, carbonate, and glycine are all bidentate.

11. <u>**(b)**</u> See the drawings for Exercise 19(a).

12. <u>**(c)**</u> $\Delta T_f = \nu K_f m$, and $\nu = \Delta T_f / K_f m$

Thus, $\nu = 0.142/(1.86)(0.020) = 3.82$

A value of ν somewhat smaller than 4 indicates that there are 4 ions per formula unit. There are 2 ions per formula unit for (a), 3 for (b), 4 for (c), one $[Cr(NH_3)_6]^{3+}$ and $3Cl^-$ ions, none for (d) and 2 for (e).

13. <u>**(d)**</u> The cyanide ion causes a stronger ligand field than any of the other ligands, and Ru is in the second transition series. Larger crystal field splittings are observed for cations of the second transition series than for those of the first series.

14. <u>**(d)**</u>

$$AgBr(s) \rightleftharpoons Ag^+ + Br^- \qquad K_{sp} = 7.7\times10^{-13}$$

$$Ag^+ + 2S_2O_3^{2-} \rightleftharpoons Ag(S_2O_3)_2^{3-} \qquad K_{stab} = 1.0\times10^{13}$$

$$AgBr(s) + 2S_2O_3^{2-} \rightleftharpoons Ag(S_2O_3)_2^{3-} + Br^-$$

The third reaction is the sum of the first two, so that the equilibrium constant for the third reaction is the <u>product</u> of the equilibrium constants for the first two.

$$K_{overall} = K_{sp} \cdot K_{stab} = 7.7$$

15. <u>**(b)**</u> The electron configuration of a d^7 low-spin complex is $(t_{2g})^6(e_g)^1$. CFSE = $6(0.4\Delta_o) - (0.6\Delta_o) = 1.8\Delta_o$

16. (b) The electron configuration of a d^7 high-spin complex is $(t_{2g})^5(e_g)^2$. $CFSE = 5(0.4\Delta_o) - 2(0.6\Delta_o) = 0.8\Delta_o$

17. (d) The electron configuration of Ni^{2+} is $Ar^{18}3d^8$.

	Ni^{2+} has $26e^-$
each CN^- donates $2e^-$:	$4x2 = 8e^-$
	Total $= 34e^- =$ EAN

18. (e) $$Zn^{2+} + 4NH_3 \rightleftharpoons Zn(NH_3)_4{}^{2+}$$

$$K_{stab} = \frac{[Zn(NH_3)_4{}^{2+}]}{[Zn^{2+}][NH_3]^4}$$

$$[Zn^{2+}]/[Zn(NH_3)_4{}^{2+}] = 1/(K_{stab})[NH_3]^4 = 1/(3x10^9)(10)^4$$

$$= 1/(3x10^{13}) = 3x10^{-14}$$

19. (c) For Co, Z = 27, so that a Co atom has $27e^-$. The Co–Co bond contributes $1e^-$ to each Co. Each CO ligand contributes $2e^-$, and there are n CO ligands per Co. Thus the number of electrons around each Co is

27 from the Co atom
1 from the Co–Co bond
2n from the n CO ligands

Total = EAN = (28 + 2n)

Metal carbonyls always obey Sidgwick's EAN rule, so that (28 + 2n) must be equal to the atomic number of one of the rare gases. The rare gas that terminates the 4th row of the periodic table is Kr, with Z = 36. Thus

$$28 + 2n = 36, \quad \text{and } n = 4$$

The formula for the dicobalt carbonyl is thus $Co_2(CO)_8$.

20. <u>(c)</u> Only the Cl^- that is not tightly bound to the Co(III) as a ligand will react with Ag^+ ions. Since there is one such Cl^- in $[Co(en)_2Cl_2]Cl$, the number of moles of AgCl precipitated will be

$$(100.0\ mL)(10^{-3}\ L/mL)(0.0240\ F) = 0.00240\ mol$$

Solutions to Problems, Chapter 20

20.1. The formula weight of $Pt(NH_3)_2Cl_2$ is

$$195.08 + 2(14.0067) + 6(1.00794) + 2(35.453) = 300.05$$

If the molecular weight of the compound is close to 600, the compound must be a dimer, with formula $Pt_2(NH_3)_4Cl_4$.

Since no AgCl precipitates when Ag^+ ions (from the $AgNO_3$ solution) are added to an aqueous solution of this compound, all the Cl^- in the complex must be tightly bound to Pt, and the complex must be inert. Similarly, since no NH_4^+ is formed upon addition of H_3O^+ ions (from the sulfuric acid) all the NH_3 must be ligands. The molar conductivity measurements indicate that this is a salt similar to $MgSO_4$, that is, with a cation of charge +2 and an anion of charge −2, and 2 ions/formula unit. All Pt(II) complexes are 4-coordinate. The compound must, of course, be electrically neutral. The cation must therefore be $[Pt(NH_3)_4]^{2+}$ and the anion $[PtCl_4]^{2-}$. The formula of the compound is

$$[Pt(NH_3)_4][PtCl_4]$$

20.2. Metal carbonyls obey Sidgwick's EAN rule. The number of electrons around each Mn atom is

25 from the Mn atom
1 from the Mn–Mn bond
2n from n CO ligands

Total = 26 + 2n = 36 = EAN of Kr

Therefore, n = 5 and the formula for the carbonyl compound is $Mn_2(CO)_{10}$.

20.3. (a)

$$K_{stab} = \frac{[Ag(NH_3)_2^+]}{[Ag^+][NH_3]^2} = 1.6\text{x}10^7$$

$$K_{sp} = [Ag^+][Cl^-] = 1.7\text{x}10^{-10}$$

When one drop of 0.010 F $AgNO_3$ is added to a large excess of 2.00 F NH_3, the reaction is

$$Ag^+ + 2NH_3 \rightleftharpoons Ag(NH_3)_2^+$$

Rearranging the K_{stab} expression we obtain

$$\frac{[Ag^+]}{[Ag(NH_3)_2{}^+]} = \frac{1}{K_{stab}[NH_3]^2} = \frac{1}{(1.6\text{x}10^7)(2.00)^2}$$

$$= 1.56\text{x}10^{-8} = 1.56\text{x}10^{-6}\ \%$$

Note that adding one drop of $AgNO_3$ does not change the $[NH_3]$ significantly. Virtually all the silver is in the complexed form.

(b)

$$AgCl(s) + 2NH_3(aq) \rightleftharpoons Ag(NH_3)_2^+ + Cl^-$$

The equilibrium constant for this reaction is

$$K_{eq} = \frac{[Ag(NH_3)_2^+][Cl^-]}{[NH_3]^2} = \frac{[Ag(NH_3)_2^+][Ag^+][Cl^-]}{[NH_3]^2[Ag^+]} = K_{stab}\cdot K_{sp}$$

$$= (1.6\text{x}10^7)(1.7\text{x}10^{-10}) = 2.7\text{x}10^{-3}$$

(c) Let x = No. mol AgCl that dissolve in 1.00 L 2F NH_3

Then $[Ag(NH_3)_2^+] = [Cl^-] = x$ and $[NH_3] = 2.00 - 2x$

since 2 NH_3 molecules are tied up in each $Ag(NH_3)_2^+$.

$$K_{eq} = \frac{[Ag(NH_3)_2^+][Cl^-]}{[NH_3]^2} = \frac{x^2}{(2-2x)^2} = \frac{x^2}{4(1-x)^2} = 2.7\text{x}10^{-3}$$

Taking the square root of both sides we obtain

$$\frac{x}{2(1-x)} = (2.7\text{x}10^{-3})^{1/2} = 0.052$$

$$x/(1-x) = 0.104$$

$$x = 0.104 - 0.104x \quad \text{so that} \quad 1.104x = 0.104$$

and $x = 0.094$ mol in 1.00 L 2F NH_3

Hence the molar solubility of AgCl in 2F NH_3 is $9.4\text{x}10^{-2}$ M

20.4. First, we find the empirical formula of the compound. Consider exactly 100.00 g of compound. The number of moles of each element is

Pt: 46.2/195.09 = 0.2368 Cl: 33.6/35.453 = 0.9478

N: 16.6/14.007 = 1.185 H: 3.6/1.0079 = 3.57

The molar ratios are exact integers to three significant figures, (except for H, for which the weight % is only known to 2 figures). The molar ratios are

Pt:Cl:N:H = 1:4:5:15

Thus the empirical formula is $PtCl_4N_5H_{15}$, or $PtCl_4{\cdot}5NH_3$. (Remember that an empirical formula provides no information about the structure and bonding of the compound.)

A molar conductivity of 420 ohm^{-1} for a 0.001 M solution of the compound means this is a 3:1 type of salt (see

Table 20.4), with 4 ions per formula unit formed when the salt is dissolved in water.

No. mmol compound used = (50 mL)(0.0320 F) = 1.6 mmol

No. mol compound used = $1.6x10^{-3}$ mol

No. mol AgCl precipitated = (0.6879 g)/(143.33 g/mol)

= $4.8x10^{-3}$ mol AgCl

Thus 3 moles of AgCl precipitate per mole of compound. Since there are 4 Cl^- in each molecule, one of the Cl^- must be a ligand, tightly bound to the Pt in an inert complex, and there must be 3 Cl^- anions needed to make an electrically neutral compound. The oxidation state of the Pt must therefore be +4. The formula for the compound is therefore $[Pt(NH_3)_5Cl]Cl_3$. The IUPAC name of the compound is

chloropentaammineplatinum(IV) chloride

With six ligands around the central Pt(IV) the geometry is octahedral.

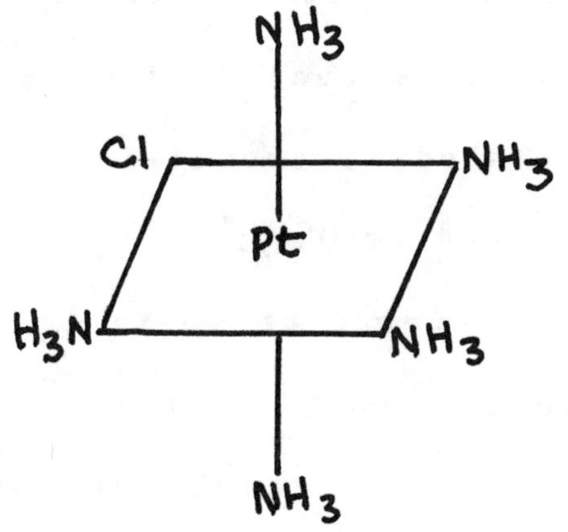

20.5. For the zincate ion, $r_c/r_L = 0.74/1.40 = 0.53$, which predicts either a square-planar (C.N. = 4) or octahedral (C.N. = 6) geometry, that is, either $Zn(OH)_4{}^{2-}$ or $Zn(OH)_6{}^{4-}$, but not $ZnO_2{}^{-}$. As Zn^{2+} has $28e^-$, with configuration $Ar^{18}3d^{10}$, $8e^-$ are required from the ligands to achieve an EAN = 36 (the atomic number of Kr). As 4 ligands provide $8e^-$, the complex is predicted to be $Zn(OH)_4{}^{2-}$. This is indeed the formula for the zincate ion, but the actual geometry is tetrahedral. Thus, both the radius ratio and Sidgwick's EAN rule are useful, but not infallible in determining the structure of coordination complexes.

For the chromite ion, $r_c/r_L = 0.55/1.40 = 0.39$, which predicts a tetrahedral (C.N. = 4) geometry, i.e., $Cr(OH)_4^-$. Sidgwick's EAN rule does not work at all, since Cr^{3+} has $21e^-$, an odd number, and both O^{2-} and OH^- are ligands donating $2e^-$ each. There is no way to achieve the atomic number of a rare gas. Actual Cr^{3+} complexes display both tetrahedral and octahedral geometries. The formula of the chromite ion is indeed $Cr(OH)_4^-$.

20.6. The atomic number of Mo is 42, so that Mo(II) has $40e^-$. Each ligand donates $2e^-$ to a complex, so that n ligands donate $(2n)e^-$. To reach the EAN of Xe, $14e^-$ are needed beyond the $40e^-$ of Mo(II). Thus

$$40 + 2n = 54 \quad \text{and} \quad n = 7$$

Therefore if Sidgwick's EAN rule is obeyed by Mo(II), this ion is a good candidate for forming complexes with C.N. = 7

20.7. (a) We can write the desired equation as the sum of

$$Ag^+(aq) + 2NH_3 \rightleftharpoons Ag(NH_3)_2^+ \qquad \Delta G^\circ = -41.4 \text{ kJ/mol}$$

$$AgCl(s) \rightleftharpoons Ag^+(aq) + Cl^-(aq) \qquad \Delta G^\circ = +55.6 \text{ kJ/mol}$$

Note that the second equation written here is the reverse of the one given in the text, so the sign of ΔG° for this reaction is the negative of that in the text. Thus for

$$AgCl(s) + 2NH_3 \rightleftharpoons Ag(NH_3)_2^+ + Cl^-(aq)$$

$$\Delta G^\circ = -41.4 + 55.6 = +14.2 \text{ kJ/mol}$$

(b) $\Delta G^\circ = -RT(\ln K_{eq})$ or $K_{eq} = e^{-\Delta G^\circ/RT}$

$$K_{eq} = \exp[(-14{,}200 \text{ J}\cdot\text{mol}^{-1})/(8.3144 \text{ J}\cdot\text{mol}^{-1}\text{K}^{-1})(298.15 \text{ K})]$$

$$= e^{-5.73} = 0.0032 = 3.2\text{x}10^{-3}$$

Since ΔG° is positive, and $K_{eq} < 1$, the reaction in part (a) will <u>not</u> be spontaneous from left to right if all the substances are in their standard states.

(c) $\Delta G = \Delta G^\circ + RT(\ln Q)$ Eq. (18-27)

$$= \Delta G^\circ + RT \ln\frac{[Ag(NH_3)_2^+][Cl^-]}{[NH_3]^2}$$

in which we have used concentrations as an approximation for activities.

$$Q = (0.10)(0.10)/(6.00)^2 = 2.78\text{x}10^{-4} \quad \text{and} \quad \ln Q = -8.19$$

$$\Delta G^\circ = +14{,}200 \text{ J/mol} + (8.3144 \text{ J}\cdot\text{mol}^{-1}\text{K}^{-1})(298.15 \text{ K})(-8.19)$$

$$= -6100 \text{ J/mol} = -6.1 \text{ kJ/mol}$$

Since ΔG is negative under these conditions, the reaction is spontaneous. Although K_{eq} is small, the large excess of NH_3 drives the reaction to the right, in accordance with Le Chatelier's Principle. Note also that $Q < K_{eq}$, which indicates that the reaction will proceed to the right.

20.8. (a) (i) $$Mg^{2+} + ATP^{4-} \rightleftharpoons Mg(ATP)^{2-}$$

$$K_1 = [Mg(ATP)^{2-}]/[Mg^{2+}][ATP^{4-}]$$

(ii) $$Cu^{2+} + 4py \rightleftharpoons Cu(py)_4{}^{2+}$$

$$\beta_4 = \frac{[Cu(py)_4{}^{2+}]}{[Cu^{2+}][py]^4}$$

(iii) The geometry of Co^{3+} complexes is invariably octahedral, so that 3 ethylenediamine molecules (bidentate ligand) are needed for a C.N. = 6. If we consider this as a stepwise process, the second step is

$$Co(en)^{3+} + en \rightleftharpoons Co(en)_2{}^{3+}$$

$$K_2 = [Co(en)_2{}^{3+}]/[Co(en)^{3+}][en]$$

(b)

$$Ag^+ + NH_3 = Ag(NH_3)^+ \quad \text{and} \quad K_1 = [Ag(NH_3)^+]/[Ag^+][NH_3]$$

$$Ag(NH_3)^+ + NH_3 \rightleftharpoons Ag(NH_3)_2{}^+$$

$$K_2 = [Ag(NH_3)_2{}^+]/[Ag(NH_3)^+][NH_3]$$

The overall reaction is the sum of these two, so the K_{eq} for the overall reaction is the product K_1K_2. In detail,

$$Ag^+ + 2NH_3 \rightleftharpoons Ag(NH_3)_2^+$$

$$\beta_2 = \frac{[Ag(NH_3)_2^+]}{[Ag^+][NH_3]^2}$$

$$K_1K_2 = \frac{[Ag(NH_3)^+]}{[Ag^+][NH_3]} \; \frac{[Ag(NH_3)_2{}^+]}{[Ag(NH_3)^+][NH_3]} = \beta_2$$

20.9. **(a)** Solid $Zn(OH)_2$ dissolves in excess OH^- because of the formation of the complex $Zn(OH)_4{}^{2-}$ ion

$$Zn(OH)_2(s) + 2OH^- \rightleftharpoons Zn(OH)_4{}^{2-}$$

(b) Solid $Zn(OH)_2$ dissolves in excess NH_3 because of the formation of the $Zn(NH_3)_4{}^{2+}$ complex ion

$$Zn(OH)_2(s) + 4NH_3 \rightleftharpoons Zn(NH_3)_4{}^{2+} + 2OH^-$$

(c) Solid $Zn(OH)_2$ dissolves in strong acid (HCl) because of the acid-base reaction

$$Zn(OH)_2(s) + 2H^+ \rightleftharpoons Zn^{2+}(aq) + 2H_2O$$

(d) Solid $Zn(OH)_2$ also dissolves in a weak acid (CH_3COOH), but the acid must be written in molecular form

$$Zn(OH)_2(s) + 2CH_3COOH \rightleftharpoons Zn^{2+} + 2CH_3COO^- + 2H_2O$$

20.10. **(a)** The geometry of Co(III) complexes is octahedral, so that the C.N. = 6. Remember that en is a bidentate ligand. Possible ions are therefore $Co(CN)_6{}^{3-}$, $Co(en)(CN)_4{}^-$, $Co(en)_2(CN)_2{}^+$ (<u>cis</u> and <u>trans</u>) and $Co(en)_3{}^{3+}$. The geometrical isomers of $Co(en)_2(CN)_2$ are shown below. Remember that en is too short to span the trans positions.

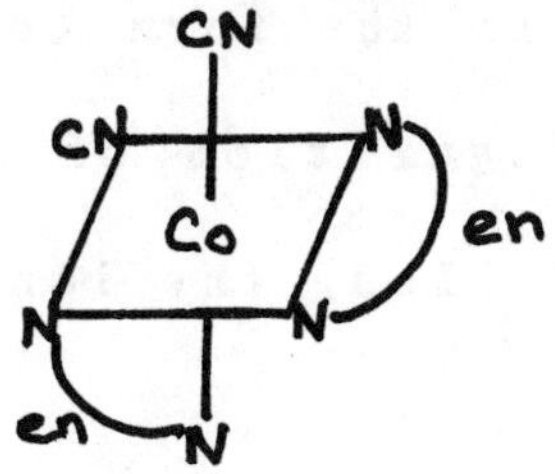

cis

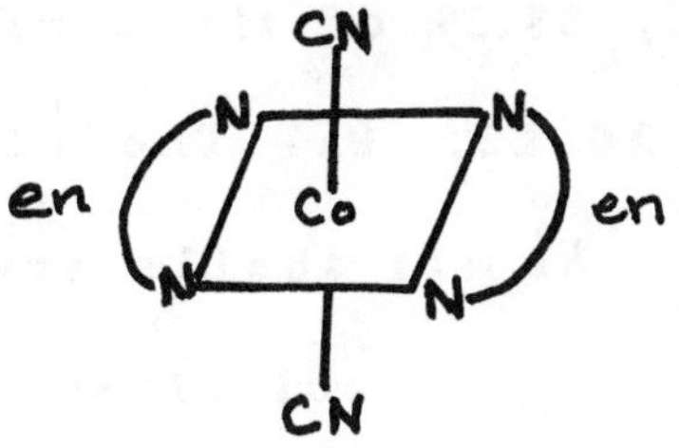

trans

Formula	Name
$(NH_4)_3[Co(CN)_6]$	Ammonium hexacyanocobaltate(III)
$NH_4[Co(en)(CN)_4]$	Ammonium tetracyanobis(ethylenediamine)-cobaltate(III)
$[Co(en)_2(CN)_2]CN$ and	*cis*-Dicyanobis(ethylenediamine)-cobalt(III) cyanide *trans*-Dicyanobis(ethylenediamine)-cobalt(III) cyanide
$[Co(en)_3](CN)_3$	tris(ethylenediamine)cobalt(III) cyanide

20.11.

$$\frac{[Co(gly)^+]}{[Co^{2+}][gly^-]} = K_1 = 10^{4.95} = 8.91x10^4$$

$$\frac{[Co(ala)^+]}{[Co^{2+}][ala^-]} = K_2 = 10^{4.83} = 6.76x10^4$$

$$\frac{K_1}{K_2} = \frac{[Co(gly)^+]/[Co^{2+}][gly^-]}{[Co(ala)^+]/[Co^{2+}][ala^-]} = \frac{[Co(gly)^+][ala^-]}{[Co(ala)^+][gly^-]}$$

$$= \frac{8.91x10^4}{6.76x10^4} = 1.32$$

If $\frac{[ala^-]}{[gly^-]} = 3/2$, then $\frac{[Co(gly)^+]}{[Co(ala)^+]}(3/2) = 1.32$

or, $$[Co(gly)^+] = 0.88[Co(ala)^+]$$

The fraction of Co as $Co(ala)^+$ is

$$\frac{[Co(ala)^+]}{[Co(ala)^+] + [Co(gly)^+]} = \frac{[Co(ala)^+]}{[Co(ala)^+] + 0.88[Co(ala)^+]}$$

$$= \frac{1}{1 + 0.88} = 0.532$$

Thus, 53.2% of the complexed Co^{2+} is in the form $Co(ala)^+$.

20.12. (a) The electronic configuration of La^{3+} is Xe^{54}. As all shells are completely filled, the ion should be (and is) colorless.

(b) The $Fe(SCN)_2^+$ ion has an intense, deep blood-red color. The electron configuration of Fe^{3+} is $Ar^{18}3d^5$, not a rare gas configuration. The crystal field splitting due to the SCN^- ligands allows the d electrons to be promoted from a lower energy d orbital to a higher energy d orbital when the substance absorbs light of some frequency and reflects light of other frequencies. We see the color of the reflected frequencies.

(c) The insoluble solid MnO_2 is black. The electron configuration of Mn(IV) is $Ar^{18}3d^3$, and the d electrons can be excited from a lower to a higher energy orbital.

(d) The Ti^{4+} ion is colorless. It has the same electronic configuration as Ar and no d electrons.

(e) The electron configuration of Ni^{2+} is $Ar^{18}3d^8$, not a rare gas configuration. Actually $Ni(ClO_4)_2$ exists as the hexahydrate $Ni(ClO_4)_2 \cdot 6H_2O$, in which the six waters are ligands in an octahedral complex. This compound is green.

(f) The zincate ion, $Zn(OH)_4^{2-}$, is colorless. The electron configuration of Zn^{2+} is $Ar^{18}3d^{10}$. All the d orbitals are filled, and the electrons cannot be promoted from one orbital to another.

(g) Both the cis and trans forms of $Cr(NH_3)_3Br_3$ are colored (they have different colors). The electron configuration of Cr^{3+} is $Ar^{18}3d^3$. The octahedral ligand field splits the five $\underline{d}$ orbitals into the t_{2g} and e_g levels, and visible light of specific frequencies is absorbed when electrons are promoted from a lower to a higher energy $\underline{d}$ orbital.

20.13. (a) The NO_2^- ion is at the strong field end of the spectrochemical series and therefore produces a large crystal field splitting. The $Fe(NO_2)_6^{4-}$ complex is therefore low-spin. The ground-state $\underline{d}$ electron configuration is $(t_{2g})^6$, with CFSE = $6(0.4\Delta_o)$ = $2.4\Delta_o$, the maximum possible. The transition state in a ligand-substitution reaction may involve a 7th ligand, if the new one is added before an old one leaves, or may involve only 5 ligands. In either case, the octahedral ligand field no longer exists and the transition state is very high in energy relative to the ground state of the octahedral complex. The activation energy for ligand substitution is therefore very large, and these reactions are so slow that the $Fe(NO_2)_6^{4-}$ is inert. Do not confuse inertness (a kinetic property) with stability (a thermodynamic property).

In contrast, FeF_6^{4-} is a high-spin complex since the F^- exerts a weak ligand field. The ground-state $\underline{d}$ electron configuration of FeF_6^{4-} is $(t_{2g})^4(e_g)^2$, and the CFSE is only $4(0.4\Delta_o) - 2(0.6\Delta_o) = 0.4\Delta_o$, considerably less than the CFSE of $Fe(NO_2)_6^{4-}$ since Δ_o is very much smaller. The activation energy required to reach the transition state is therefore significantly less than for the low-spin complex, and FeF_6^{4-} is labile.

(b) As a ligand, H_2O exerts a stronger crystal field than does Cl^-. In addition, there are only 4 Cl^- ligands in the tetrahedral complex, and 6 H_2O ligands in the octahedral complex. As a result, the crystal field splitting for the octahedral complex, Δ_o, is larger than the CFS for the tetrahedral complex, Δ_t. (In fact, it can be shown that for a given metal ion and the same ligands and the same metal-ligand distance in the octahedral and tetrahedral geometries, $\Delta_t = 4/9\ \Delta_o$, so that Δ_t is <u>always</u> smaller than Δ_o.) We expect, therefore, that the $Co(H_2O)_6^{2+}$ octahedral complex absorbs light of higher frequency than that absorbed by the $CoCl_4^{2-}$ tetrahedral complex. Since the $Co(H_2O)_6^{2+}$ complex is light red, it absorbs green light, which is of higher frequency and energy than the orange light absorbed by the blue tetrahedral complex $CoCl_4^{2-}$.

20.14. If a solution is green, then red light is being absorbed. In the visible region, red light is the lowest frequency, lowest energy radiation. If a solution is yellow, blue-violet or violet light is being absorbed. Violet light is of much higher frequency than red light. Thus the splitting produced by CN^- ligands is much larger than that produced by H_2O, as higher energy radiation is absorbed by the $[Fe(CN)_6]^{4-}$ complex than by $Fe(H_2O)_6{}^{2+}$.

20.15. **(a)** Potassium dioxalatobis(pyridine)rhodate(III)

(b)

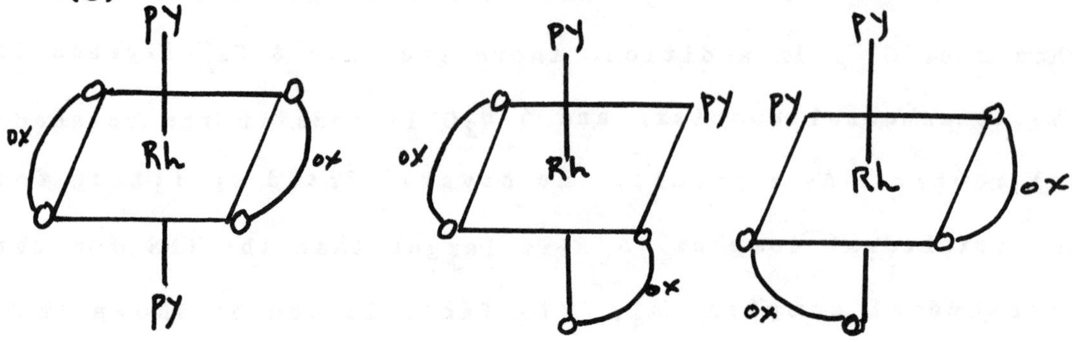

<u>trans</u> <u>cis enantiomers</u>

20.16. **(a)** To a solution initially 0.10 M in both Ni^{2+} and Mn^{2+}, excess ethylenediamine is added. Because of the large values of the formation constants, β_2 for $Mn(en)_2{}^{2+}$, and β_2' for $Ni(en)_2{}^{2+}$, when the final solution is 1.0 M in en, most of the Ni^{2+} and Mn^{2+} will be tied up in their respective complexes, and $[Ni^{2+}]$ and $[Mn^{2+}]$ will both be much less than their initial values of 0.10 M. Let us therefore calculate the $[Mn^{2+}]$ and $[Ni^{2+}]$ <u>before</u> the addition of NaOH.

$$Mn^{2+} + 2en \rightleftharpoons Mn(en)_2{}^{2+}$$

$$\beta_2 = 6.25\text{x}10^4 = [Mn(en)_2{}^{2+}]/[Mn^{2+}][en]^2$$

Let x = $[Mn^{2+}]$ in this solution BEFORE adding OH^-

Then, $[Mn(en)_2{}^{2+}] = 0.10 - x$, and [en] = 1.0 M

$$\beta_2' = (0.10-x)/(x)(1.0)^2 = 6.25\text{x}10^4$$

Assume $x \ll 0.10$, so that $(0.10 - x) \cong 0.10$

Then, $6.25 \times 10^4 = (0.10)/x$, and $x = 1.6 \times 10^{-6}$ M = $[Mn^{2+}]$

As 1.6×10^{-6} is indeed $\ll 0.10$, our assumption is valid.

For $Mn(OH)_2$, $K_{sp} = 1.6 \times 10^{-13} = [Mn^{2+}][OH^-]^2$

If $[OH^-] = 0.010$ M, then the <u>equilibrium</u> concentration of free $Mn^{2+}(aq)$ is

$$[Mn^{2+}] = K_{sp}/[OH^-]^2 = 1.6 \times 10^{-13}/(0.010)^2 = 1.6 \times 10^{-9} \text{ M}$$

In a solution in which $[Mn^{2+}]$ is initially larger than 1.6×10^{-9} M, $Mn(OH)_2(s)$ will precipitate if $[OH^-] = 0.010$ M. As we have just calculated that $[Mn^{2+}] = 1.6 \times 10^{-6}$ M before the addition of the OH^- ions, $Mn(OH)_2$ will precipitate from the solution that is 1.0 M in ethylenediamine.

We repeat the calculation for the $[Ni^{2+}]$.

$$Ni^{2+} + 2en \rightleftharpoons Ni(en)_2{}^{2+}$$

$$\beta_2' = 4.8 \times 10^{13} = [Ni(en)_2{}^{2+}]/[Ni^{2+}][en]^2$$

Let $y = [Ni^{2+}]$ in this solution BEFORE adding OH^-

Then, $[Ni(en)_2{}^{2+}] = 0.10 - y$, and $[en] = 1.0$ M

$$\beta_2' = (0.10-y)/(y)(1.0)^2 = 4.8 \times 10^{13}$$

Assume $y \ll 0.10$, so that $(0.10 - y) \cong 0.10$

Then, $4.8 \times 10^{13} = (0.10)/y$, and $y = 2.1 \times 10^{-15}$ M = $[Ni^{2+}]$

As 2.1×10^{-15} is indeed $\ll 0.10$, our assumption is valid.

For $Ni(OH)_2$, $K_{sp} = 2 \times 10^{-15} = [Ni^{2+}][OH^-]^2$

The equilibrium $[Ni^{2+}]$ if $[OH^-] = 0.010$ M is

$$[Ni^{2+}] = K_{sp}/[OH^-]^2 = 2 \times 10^{-15}/(0.01)^2 = 2 \times 10^{-11} \text{ M}$$

If $[Ni^{2+}]$ is greater than 2×10^{-11}, then $Ni(OH)_2(s)$ will precipitate. We have just calculated that in the 1.0 M en solution, $[Ni^{2+}] = 2.1\times10^{-15}$ M. As $2.1\times10^{-15} < 2\times10^{-11}$, no $Ni(OH)_2$ will precipitate.

(b) As calculated in part (a), after the precipitation of the $Mn(OH)_2$, $[Mn^{2+}] = 1.6\times10^{-9}$ M and [en] = 1.0 M.

$$\beta_2 = \frac{[Mn(en)_2{}^{2+}]}{[Mn^{2+}][en]^2} = 6.25\times10^4 = \frac{[Mn(en)_2{}^{2+}]}{(1.6\times10^{-9})(1.0)^2}$$

$$[Mn(en)_2{}^{2+}] = (6.25\times10^4)(1.6\times10^{-9})(1.0)^2 = 1.0\times10^{-4} M$$

The calculations show that Mn^{2+} and Ni^{2+} can be separated analytically by using en to tie up the Ni^{2+} in the $Ni(en)_2{}^{2+}$ complex, thus keeping the free, unbound $[Ni^{2+}]$ extremely low. The formation constant for $Mn(en)_2{}^{2+}$ is much smaller (though both β_2 and β_2' are large numbers), so that $[Mn^{2+}]$ will exceed that required to precipitate $Mn(OH)_2$ when OH^- is added.

We began with $[Mn^{2+}]$ = 0.10 M (before addition of either en or OH^-) and ended with $[Mn^{2+}] = 1.6\times10^{-9}$ M, and $[Mn(en)_2{}^{2+}] = 1\times10^{-4}$ M. Thus, to within about one part per thousand, all the Mn^{2+} is precipitated as $Mn(OH)_2$ and can be separated from the Ni^{2+}.

20.17. Consider an octahedral complex ML_6 and in your mind stretch it along the Z-axis (the vertical axis; see diagrams on the following page) and a tetragonal complex, ML_4L_2', results. (Note that the same effect can be achieved if the two L′ ligands are kept at the same distance from M, but are different from the four L ligands with the L′ ligands exerting a weaker ligand field than the L ligands.) Since the electrostatic repulsion between the outer electrons of M and the L′ ligands is decreased, the energies of the d orbitals with electron density having a Z-component will be lowered compared to the other d orbitals. (Refer to Fig. 13.8 for sketches of the atomic d orbitals.)

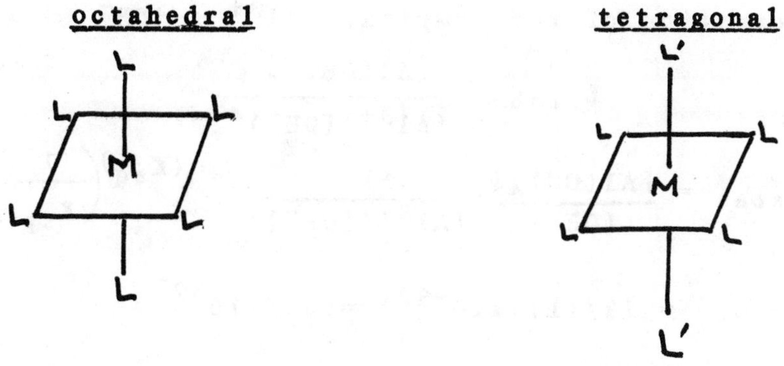

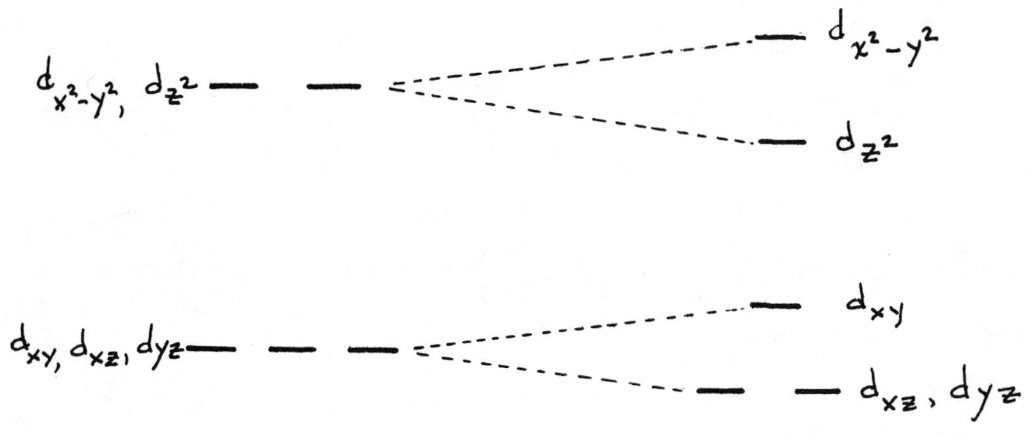

Thus, of the two degenerate (equal energy) e_g orbitals in an octahedral complex, the d_{z^2} will be lowered with respect to the $d_{x^2-y^2}$ orbital. Of the three t_{2g} orbitals, the d_{xz} and the d_{yz} orbitals will be lowered below the d_{xy}.

20.18. $$Al(OH)_3(s) + OH^- \rightleftharpoons Al(OH)_4^-$$

$$K_{eq} = \frac{[Al(OH)_4^-]}{[OH^-]} = 13 \quad \text{at } 30^\circ C$$

$$K_{sp}\{Al(OH)_3\} = 1.9\text{x}10^{-32} = [Al^{3+}][OH^-]^3$$

For the formation of the complex, $Al^{3+} + 4OH^- \rightleftharpoons Al(OH)_4^-$

$$K_{stab} = \frac{[Al(OH)_4^-]}{[Al^{3+}][OH^-]^4}$$

$$K_{stab} = \frac{[Al(OH)_4^-]}{[OH^-]} \cdot \frac{1}{[Al^{3+}][OH^-]^3} = (K_{eq})\left(\frac{1}{K_{sp}}\right)$$

$$= 13/(1.9\text{x}10^{-32}) = 6.8\text{x}10^{32}$$

Solutions to Multiple Choice Questions, Chapter 21

1. **(c)** In the body-centered cubic arrangement of K, the unit cell is a cube with one atom at each corner and one in the center. Since a cube has eight corners, the atom at the center has eight nearest neighbors. Furthermore, since each corner is shared by eight cubes, a corner atom also has eight neighbors, which are the center atoms of the eight adjacent cubes. Alternatively, any given K atom can be visualized as being at the body-center of a unit cell. In fact, all atoms are in identical environments.

2. **(d)** In MgO, both ions are doubly charged (Mg^{2+} and O^{2-}). All the other choices are crystals with singly charged ions. Thus, in Eq. (21-6), the product z_+z_- is 4 for MgO and 1 for all the other crystals. This product is the most important factor in determining lattice energies. It far outweighs variations due to differences in interionic distance and Madelung constant.

3. **(b)** One eighth of each corner and one half of each face center are in the unit cell. There are 8 corners, and 2 faces with lattice points at the centers. Thus,

$$8(1/8) + 2(1/2) = 2$$

There are therefore 2 lattice points per unit cell, and if there is a molecule at each lattice site, there are 2 molecules per unit cell.

4. **(c)**

No. X atoms per unit cell = (8 corners)(1/8 per corner) = 1

No. Y atoms per unit cell = 1

The simplest formula is therefore XY.

5. **(b)** The three crystals in which both ions are doubly charged are NiS, SrO, and BaS. (Refer to the answer to Exercise 2). Of these, the one with the smallest cation is NiS. Refer to Fig. 21.22 and note that Ni is in the the 4th period of the periodic table, while Sr and Ba are in the 5th and 6th periods, respectively, and are not transition metals. The O^{2-} ion is smaller than the S^{2-} ion.

For NiS, $r_c + r_a = 0.70 + 1.84 = 2.54$ Å

For SrO, $r_c + r_a = 1.13 + 1.40 = 2.53$ Å

Thus, the interionic distance is essentially the same for NiS and SrO, but is considerably larger for BaS, so that BaS has the smallest lattice energy of these 3.

The Ni^{2+} ion is the only cation of the three that does not have a rare gas electron configuration and the S^{2-} anion is large and polarizable. Polarization of the anion by the cation increases the lattice energy, and this effect is maximized for small cations without rare gas configuration and for large anions. Because Ni^{2+} has partly filled d-orbitals and S^{2-} has low-lying empty d-orbitals there is considerable covalent character to the NiS bond, so that the lattice energy of NiS is larger than that of SrO.

6. (e) All the ions in the two compounds are singly charged and have rare gas electron configuration. Because Na^+ and F^- are much smaller than Rb^+ and Cl^-, respectively, the internuclear distance in NaF is significantly smaller than that in RbCl. As a result, the lattice energy is larger for NaF, which is therefore more tightly bound and has a higher melting point.

7. (e) In an fcc arrangement, the atoms make contact along the face diagonals. If the unit cell axial length is denoted a, the length of a face diagonal is $\sqrt{2}a$ and is equal to four atomic radii. Thus

$$4r = \sqrt{2}a \quad \text{where r is the atomic radius}$$

Setting r = 2.0 Å, we obtain $a = 4\sqrt{2}$ Å = 5.657 Å. The volume of a unit cell is

$$a^3 = (5.657)^3 \times 10^{-24}\ \text{cm}^3 = 181 \times 10^{-24}\ \text{cm}^3 = 1.81 \times 10^{-22}\ \text{cm}^3$$

Recall that 1 Å = 10^{-8} cm, so that $(1\ \text{Å})^3 = 10^{-24}\ \text{cm}^3$.

8. (a) The only cation of these compounds that does not have a rare gas electron configuration is Cd^{2+}. The S^{2-} anion is large and polarizable. Thus the bond in CdS has the largest amount of covalent character of those listed.

9. (b) The only crystal system with three unequal unit-cell axial lengths but three 90° cell angles is the orthorhombic.

10. (c) Because Ni and Ti are in the 4th row of the periodic table, while Zr and Cd are in the 5th row, and Pt in the 6th, the two smallest cations are Ti^{2+} and Ni^{2+}. As one goes across a transition metal series from left to right, ions of the same charge decrease slightly in size, as the d electrons being added do not shield each other very well, and the increasing nuclear charge pulls the electron cloud in more tightly.

11. (e) The smallest of these anions is F^-, because F is in the second row of the periodic table, and F^- is singly charged. Remember that for isoelectronic anions, the more negative the charge, the larger the anion. The largest of these anions is I^-, because I is in the fifth period of the table. This leaves only sequences (b) and (e) to compare. As Br^- is larger than O^{2-} (fourth vs. second period), (e) must be the correct sequence.

12. (d) Anion-anion contact occurs when the anions are very large compared to the cations. Of the compounds listed, NaI has the largest anion:cation radius ratio.

13. (b) Small, highly-charged ions have the largest heats of hydration. Cations are generally smaller than anions, and Al^{3+} is the most highly charged and the smallest of the ions listed.

14. **(d)** Larger, more highly charged anions are more easily polarized than smaller anions. By far the largest anion of those listed is Te^{2-}.

15. **(e)** The only compound of those given with both ions doubly charged is NiO, which therefore has the largest lattice energy and the highest melting point (see the answer to Exercise 2). Like SO_2, SeO_2 is covalent.

16. **(d)** Electron affinities are difficult to measure, and are often calculated theoretically instead.

17. **(a)** The total amounts of positive and negative charge in the unit cell must be equal, so the M^{3+}:X^- molar ratio must be 1:3. An M^{3+} at each corner means 1 M^{3+} ion per unit cell. An X^- at each body center means 1 X^- ion per unit cell (wrong molar ratio) whereas an X^- at each face center means 6(1/2) = 3 X^- ions per unit cell, the correct molar ratio, consistent with the formula MX_3.

18. **(b)** See Fig. 21.14. For the orthorhombic, tetragonal, and cubic systems, all three angles are 90°. For the rhombohedral system, all angles are equal, but are not, in general, 90°. In the hexagonal system, 2 angles are 90° but the third is 120°.

19. **(a)** Metals tend to form cations, which are smaller in size than the neutral atoms.

Solutions to Problems, Chapter 21

21.1. (a)

Simple cubic lattice: The atoms are at the 8 corners and make contact along an edge. If the radius is r, and the unit cell axial length is a, $a = 2r$

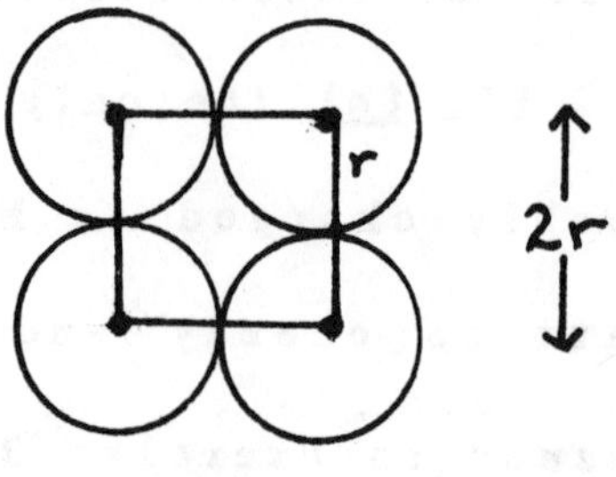

Face-centered cubic: The atoms make contact along a face diagonal. A face diagonal has length 4r (see Fig. 21.20). If a = unit cell length, the length of a face diagonal is $\sqrt{2}a$, so that $\sqrt{2}a = 4r$ or $a = 2\sqrt{2}r$

Body-centered cubic: Three atoms make contact along the body diagonal of the cube, which is 4r in length. Refer to Fig. 21.23(b) to see that the length of the body diagonal is $\sqrt{3}$ times the length of a side, so that $\sqrt{3}a = 4r$ and

$$a = 4r/\sqrt{3} = 2.31r$$

(b) For all the cubic lattices, the total volume (V_T) is the cube of the edge length, a^3, while the occupied volume (V_o) is equal to the number of atoms times the volume of a single atom, which is $(4/3)\pi r^3$.

Simple cubic: 1 atom/unit cell so that $V_o = (4/3)\pi r^3$

From part (a), $a = 2r$, so that $V_T = a^3 = 8r^3$

$$\text{Fraction occupied} = V_o/V_T = \frac{(4/3)\pi r^3}{8r^3} = \pi/6 = 0.5236$$

$$\text{Percentage filled} = (\pi/6)(100) = 52.36\ \%$$

Face-centered cubic: 4 atoms/unit cell, $V_o = (16/3)\pi r^3$

From part (a), $V_T = a^3 = (2\sqrt{2})^3 r^3 = 16\sqrt{2}r^3$

$$\text{Fraction occupied} = \frac{(16/3)\pi r^3}{16\sqrt{2}r^3} = \frac{\pi}{3\sqrt{2}} = 0.7405$$

Percentage filled = 74.05 %

Body-centered cubic: 2 atoms/unit cell, $V_o = (8/3)\pi r^3$

From part (a), $V_T = a^3 = (4/\sqrt{3})^3 r^3 = (64r^3)/3\sqrt{3}$

$$\text{Fraction occupied} = \frac{(8/3)\pi r^3}{\{64/(3\sqrt{3})\}r^3} = (\pi/8)(\sqrt{3}) = 0.6802$$

Percentage filled = 68.02 %

Thus space is filled most efficiently in the face-centered cubic system, with close to three-quarters of the total volume occupied.

21.2. (a) This is a metallic crystal, so we assume atom-atom contact. In Problem 21.1. (a) we showed that in a body-centered cubic unit cell, the relation between a (axial length) and r (atomic radius) is $a = 4r/\sqrt{3}$, so

$$r = (\sqrt{3}/4)a = (\sqrt{3}/4)(2.8664\ \text{Å}) = 1.24\ \text{Å}$$

An atom does not have a rigid boundary. The electron charge cloud is diffuse and the atomic radius depends on the number of nearest neighbors, the cell geometry, temperature, pressure, etc. An atomic radius is not valid to five significant figures.

(b) One unit cell contains 2 Fe atoms (bcc lattice) and has a volume = $a^3 = (2.8664)^3 \times 10^{-24}$ cm^3 = 23.551×10^{-24} cm^3 The volume occupied by Avogadro's number of Fe atoms is therefore

$$\frac{(6.02205\times10^{23})(2.35511\times10^{-23}\ \text{cm}^3)}{2} = 7.091\ \text{cm}^3/\text{mol}$$

One mole of Fe weighs 55.847 g, so that the density is

$$\rho = \frac{55.847\ \text{g/mol}}{7.091\ \text{cm}^3/\text{mol}} = 7.88\ \text{g/cm}^3$$

21.3. One unit cell contains 4 Fe atoms (fcc lattice) and the relation between a (unit cell length) and r (atomic radius) is $a = 2\sqrt{2}r$, as shown in Problem 21.1.(a). Hence, for γ-Fe, $a = 2\sqrt{2}(1.26\ \text{Å}) = 3.564\ \text{Å}$

volume of unit cell = $(3.564)^3 \times 10^{-24}$ cm^3 = 45.27×10^{-24} cm^3

The volume containing Avogadro's number of atoms is

$$\frac{(6.022\times10^{23})(4.527\times10^{-23}\ \text{cm}^3)}{4} = 6.815\ \text{cm}^3/\text{mol}$$

One mole of Fe weighs 55.847 g, so that the density is

$$\rho = \frac{55.847\ \text{g/mol}}{6.815\ \text{cm}^3/\text{mol}} = 8.20\ \text{g/cm}^3$$

This is denser than α-Fe because, as we showed in Problem 21.1. (b), a face-centered cubic arrangement packs spheres more efficiently than a body-centered cubic arrangement.

21.4. For the two crystals, the stoichiometry is the same and the charge types are the same and all ions have rare gas electron configuration. Thus the lattice energies could differ either because the crystals are not isomorphous, that is, because of different values of the Madelung constant, A, in Eq. (21-6) or because of different interionic distances (r_0 in the same equation). Madelung constants for crystals with different structures differ only slightly, and a significant difference in the interionic distance will always be a more important factor than a difference in the value of A. Note that $CaCl_2$, which has the larger of the two anions, has the lower lattice energy.

For CaF_2, $r_0 = r_c + r_a = 0.99 + 1.36 = 2.35$ Å

For $CaCl_2$, $r_0 = r_c + r_a = 0.99 + 1.81 = 2.80$ Å

The ratio of the interionic distances should be inversely proportional to the ratio of the lattice energies if this is the predominant reason for the difference.

$$\frac{r_0(CaCl_2)}{r_0(CaF_2)} = \frac{2.80}{2.35} = 1.19$$

$$\frac{\Delta H_{latt}(CaF_2)}{\Delta H_{latt}(CaCl_2)} = \frac{2630\ \text{kJ/mol}}{2250\ \text{kJ/mol}} = 1.17$$

The agreement between these ratios is convincing evidence that the principal reason for the difference between the two lattice energies is the difference in the radii of the two anions.

21.5. The interionic distances in the two compounds are very similar, as the two cations are very close in size. Note that Cu^+ is larger than Cu^{2+} because of the smaller positive charge. (The ionic radius of Cu^+ has been given as 0.96 Å) The large difference in lattice energy is due to the fact that Cu^+ does not have a rare gas electron configuration, and is therefore an effective polarizer of anions. The I^- anion is large and polarizable. There is a significant amount of covalent character to the bond in CuI, which increases the lattice energy relative to that of NaI.

21.6. Both BaO and CdS have doubly charged ions, while the ions in RbCl are singly charged. The charge factor, z_+z_-, is therefore 4 for BaO and CdS, and only 1 for RbCl. This accounts for the fact that the lattice energy of RbCl is roughly 4 times less than that of BaO.

Using Fig. 21.22 we can calculate the interionic distances, $r_0 = r_c + r_a$, in these three compounds.

For BaO, $r_0 = 1.35 + 1.70 = 2.75$ Å

For CdS, $r_0 = 0.97 + 1.84 = 2.81$ Å

For RbCl, $r_0 = 1.49 + 1.81 = 3.29$ Å

Since RbCl has the largest value of r_0 by a significant amount, its lattice energy is less than 1/4 that of BaO.

The values of $r_c + r_a$ for BaO and CdS are quite similar but the lattice energy of CdS is significantly larger than that of BaO. This is because Cd^{2+} does not have rare gas electron configuration, whereas Ba^{2+} does. Furthermore, S^{2-} is larger than O^{2-} and more polarizable. The Cd^{2+} ion polarizes the S^{2-} ion, and there is considerable covalent character to the bond in CdS, increasing the lattice energy relative to that of BaO.

We would expect the lattice energies of BaO and RbCl to be well described by a 'pure ionic' model, but such a model underestimates the CdS lattice energy significantly.

21.7. There is anion-anion contact in LiBr, since Br^- ions are much larger than Li^+ ions (refer to Fig. 21.21). The anion-anion contact is along the face diagonal of the unit cell, which has length $\sqrt{2}a$, if a is the length of the side of the unit cell. The length of a face diagonal is also $4r_{Br^-}$ {see Prob. 21.1. (a)} so that

$$4r_{Br^-} = \sqrt{2}a = (\sqrt{2})(5.501\ \text{Å}) = 7.780\ \text{Å}$$

and $$r_{Br^-} = 1.945\ \text{Å} = 1.94\ \text{Å}$$

in excellent agreement with Fig. 21.22.

If the Li^+ and Br^- ions are in contact along the edge of the unit cell, then

$$2r_{Br^-} + 2r_{Li^+} = 5.501\ \text{Å}$$

and $$r_{Li^+} = (5.501/2) - r_{Br^-} = 2.751 - 1.945 = 0.81\ \text{Å}$$

This value is considerably larger than that in Fig. 21.22, which tells us that Li^+ ions are too small to be in contact with the Br^- ions. The actual value of r_{Li^+} is 0.60 Å. The face of a unit cell of LiBr is best represented as in Fig. 21.21. (a).

21.8. In the orthorhombic system all interfacial angles are 90°, so the volume of the unit cell is just the product of the edge lengths. A mole of unit cells thus occupies a volume

$$V = (6.022\text{x}10^{23})(14.75\ \text{Å})(17.60\ \text{Å})(13.91\ \text{Å})(10^{-24}\ \text{cm}^3/\text{Å}^3)$$
$$= 2175\ \text{cm}^3$$

The mass of this volume is obtained by multiplying the volume by the density

$$(2175\ \text{cm}^3)(1.17\ \text{g/cm}^3) = 2544\ \text{g}$$

The molecular weight of $C_{11}H_{29}N_5B_2Cu$ is 316.6 g/mol. Therefore, in one mole of unit cells

$$\text{No. mol complex} = (2544\ \text{g})/(316.6\ \text{g/mol}) = 8.04\ \text{mol}$$

This number must, of course, be an exact integer. As the experimental error in the density is in the 3rd significant (and is ~ 1 %), the 8.04 is also uncertain in the 3rd figure, and there are exactly 8 moles of complex per mole of unit cells. Thus a unit cell contains 8 molecules.

21.9. In a face-centered cubic cell, atoms make contact along a face diagonal, and {see Problem 21.1. (a)} $4r = \sqrt{2}a$ where r is the atomic radius, and a the unit cell length. Thus,

$$4r_{Ca} = \sqrt{2}(5.57\text{Å})$$
$$r = (\sqrt{2}/4)(5.57\text{Å}) = 1.97\text{Å}$$

The volume of one unit cell is

$$a^3 = (5.57\text{x}10^{-8}\ \text{cm})^3 = (5.57)^3\text{x}10^{-24}\ \text{cm}^3 = 1.728\text{x}10^{-22}\ \text{cm}^3$$

An fcc unit cell contains 4 atoms. Thus the volume containing exactly 1 mol of atoms is

$$\frac{(6.022\times10^{23})(1.728\times10^{-22}\ \text{cm}^3)}{4} = 26.0\ \text{cm}^3$$

The mass of 1 mol of Ca is 40.08 g. The density is therefore

$$\rho = \frac{40.08\ \text{g}}{26.0\ \text{cm}^3} = 1.54\ \text{g/cm}^3$$

21.10. There are two reasons why the lattice energy of CuI is larger than the lattice energy of AgI. Since Cu is in the 4th period and Ag in the 5th period of the periodic table, $r_{Cu^+} < r_{Ag^+}$, so that the interionic distance is smaller for CuI, which leads to a larger lattice energy. In addition, both Cu^+ and Ag^+ are transition metal ions, and tend to polarize a large anion like I^-. However, smaller cations are more efficient polarizers than larger ones, so we expect that the strengthening of the bond due to polarization of the anion charge cloud is somewhat greater for CuI than for AgI. Both of these factors contribute to making the lattice energy of CuI larger than that of AgI.

21.11. The lattice energy is ΔH for the reaction

$$KF(s) \longrightarrow K^+(g) + F^-(g)$$

If we write a list of equations which sum to this equation, then their ΔH's will sum to U, the lattice energy. The appropriate reactions, and their thermodynamic parameters, are given below:

Reaction	Parameter	Value (kJ)
$KF(s) \rightarrow K(s) + (1/2)F_2(g)$	$-\Delta H^\circ_f(KF)$	562.6
$K(s) \rightarrow K(g)$	$\Delta H^\circ_{sub}(K)$	89.9
$K(g) \rightarrow K^+(g) + e^-$	IE(K)	418.6
$(1/2)F_2(g) \rightarrow F(g)$	$(1/2)D(F_2)$	79.0
$F(g) + e^- \rightarrow F^-(g)$	-EA(F)	333.
$KF(s) \text{ -- } K(g) + F^-(g)$	U(KF)	817

Thus the lattice energy of KF is 817 kJ/mol.

21.12. The radii of Na^+ and F^- are smaller than those of Ag^+ and Cl^-, respectively, but Ag^+ (which does not have the electron configuration of a rare gas) is a better polarizer than Na^+, and Cl^- is easier to polarize than F^-, so that the bonds in AgCl have more covalent character than those in NaF. The larger interionic distance for AgCl would make the lattice energy of AgCl lower than that of NaF, but the covalent contribution to the bonding in AgCl is just sufficient to negate that effect.

21.13. The volume of one unit cell is

$$(3.9231\times10^{-8}\ cm)^3 = (3.9231)^3\times10^{-24}\ cm^3 = 60.379\times10^{-24}\ cm^3$$

In a face-centered cubic cell there are 4 atoms/unit cell. The volume of 1 mol of this metal is therefore

$$\frac{(6.022045\times10^{23})(6.0379\times10^{-23}\ cm^3)}{4} = 9.0901\ cm^3$$

To obtain the mass of 1 mol multiply this volume by the density:

$$(21.45\ g/cm^3)(9.0901\ cm^3) = 195.0\ g$$

The element is platinum (at. wt. 195.08 ± .03)

21.14. Bragg's law states $n\lambda = 2d\ \sin\theta$

As this is the minimum value of θ, n = 1 in Bragg's law. (For small angles, sin θ increases as θ increases.) Thus,

$$\lambda = 0.7093\ \text{Å} = 2d\ \sin(9.045°) = (2d)(0.1572)$$

$$d = (0.7093\ \text{Å})/(2)(0.1572) = 2.256\ \text{Å}$$

21.15. Since Cu^+ does not have rare gas electron configuration it is an effective polarizer of anions, leading to stronger bonds (larger lattice energies) than the pure ionic model (Born-Mayer equation) predicts. The larger the anion the greater the polarization, so that the deviations from the lattice energies calculated using a pure ionic model become greater as we go from CuCl to CuBr to CuI.

21.16. Because the charge factor z_+z_- is 4 for MgO and 1 for LiF, the lattice energy is roughly 4 times larger for MgO. As the interionic distance in MgO is a little larger than that in LiF, the ratio of the lattice energies is somewhat smaller than 4. The higher melting point and hardness, and the lower solubility of MgO, are due to its larger lattice energy. The different densities result from differences in the respective internuclear distances and formula weights.

21.17. (a) There is anion-cation contact in NaCl. From Fig. 21.13(c) it is clear that the edge length of the unit cell is twice the Na-Cl distance. Therefore, the unit cell axial length is $2(2.820\ \text{Å}) = 5.640\times10^{-8}$ cm, and the volume of a unit cell is

$$V_{cell} = (5.640\times10^{-8}\ \text{cm})^3 = 1.794\times10^{-22}\ \text{cm}^3$$

(b) The mass of 1 mol of NaCl is 58.443 g. The volume of 1 mol is therefore

$$\frac{\text{mass}}{\text{density}} = \frac{58.443\ \text{g}}{2.163\ \text{g/cm}^3} = 27.019\ \text{cm}^3$$

The number of unit cells per mole of NaCl is therefore

$$\frac{(27.019\ \text{cm}^3/\text{mol})}{1.794\times10^{-22}\ \text{cm}^3/\text{cell}} = 1.506\times10^{23}$$

(c) The unit cell contains $4Na^+$ ions and $4Cl^-$ ions. This can be seen by counting the cations in Fig. 21.13(c), and noting that, from the formula, there is one anion per cation. We also know that a face-centered cubic cell has 4 molecules (in NaCl, ion-pairs) per unit cell.

$$(4\ \frac{\text{ion-pairs}}{\text{cell}})(1.506\times10^{23}\ \frac{\text{unit cells}}{\text{mol}}) = 6.024\times10^{23}\ \frac{\text{ion-pairs}}{\text{mol}}$$

Thus, $N_A = 6.024\times10^{23}$, with uncertainty in the 4th significant figure, as both the density and the interionic distance have experimental uncertainty in the 4th figure.

Solutions to Exercises, Chapter 22

1. The equation defining the binding energy of $^{60}_{28}Ni$ is

$$32n + 28p + 28e^- \rightarrow {}^{60}_{28}Ni(atom) + BE$$

$$\text{mass of } 28p + 28e^- = \text{mass of } 28({}^1_1H)$$

$$\text{mass of } 28({}^1_1H) = 28(1.00782505) = 28.21910$$

$$+ \text{ mass of } 32n = 32(1.00866501) = \underline{32.27728}$$

$$\text{total mass of left-hand side} = 60.49638$$

$$\text{mass loss} = 60.49638 - 59.9332 = 0.05632 \text{ amu}$$

which is equivalent to

$$(0.05632 \text{ amu})(931.50 \frac{\text{MeV}}{\text{amu}}) = 524.6 \text{ MeV}$$

The binding energy per nucleon is thus

$$BE/A = 524.6/60 = 8.74 \text{ MeV/nucleon}$$

2. (a) $^{14}_{7}N + {}^4_2He \rightarrow {}^{17}_{8}O + {}^1_1H$

14 + 4 = 17 + 1 so that A of missing product = 1

7 + 2 = 8 + 1 so that Z of missing product = 1

(b) $^{10}_{5}B + {}^1_0n \rightarrow {}^3_1H + 2({}^4_2He)$

10 + 1 = 3 + 8 so that A of missing reactant = 1

5 + 0 = 1 + 4 so that Z of missing reactant = 0

(c) $^{235}_{92}U + {}^1_0n \rightarrow {}^{90}_{38}Sr + {}^{143}_{54}Xe + 3({}^1_0n)$

235 + 1 = 90 + 143 + 3 thus total A of missing product = 3

92 + 0 = 38 + 54 + 0 therefore the product has no charge

(d) $^{238}_{92}U + {}^4_2He \rightarrow {}^{239}_{94}Pu + 3({}^1_0n)$

238 + 4 = 239 + 3 so that A of missing product = 239

92 + 2 = 94 + 0 so that Z of missing product = 94

(e) $^{232}_{90}Th + ^{12}_{6}C \rightarrow ^{240}_{94}Cm + 4(^{1}_{0}n)$

232 + 12 = 240 + 4 so that A of missing reactant = 12

90 + 6 = 96 so that Z of missing reactant = 6

3. $^{6}_{3}Li + ^{6}_{3}Li \rightarrow ^{12}_{6}C + BE$

mass loss = 2(6.015126) - 12.00000 = 0.030252 amu

so the binding energy released is

$$(0.030252 \text{ amu})(931.50 \frac{\text{MeV}}{\text{amu}}) = 28.18 \text{ MeV}$$

The conversion to kilojoules per mole is

$$BE = (28.1797\text{x}10^{6} \frac{\text{eV}}{\text{atom}})(1.6022\text{x}10^{-19} \frac{\text{J}}{\text{eV}})(6.022\text{x}10^{23} \frac{\text{atoms}}{\text{mol}})$$

$$= 2.719\text{x}10^{12} \text{ J/mol} = 2.719\text{x}10^{9} \text{ kJ/mol}$$

Note that the binding energy is extremely large.

Alternatively, we could use the conversion factor given in Eq. (22-7):

$$(28.1797 \text{ MeV})(9.6485\text{x}10^{7} \frac{\text{kJ/mol}}{\text{MeV}}) = 2.719\text{x}10^{9} \text{ kJ/mol}$$

4. The nuclear reaction $2(^{4}_{2}He) + ^{1}_{0}n \rightarrow ^{9}_{4}Be$ would release energy because the total binding energy is higher for $^{9}_{4}Be$ than for two $^{4}_{2}He$ plus a neutron.

Total BE on left-hand side: (2)(4)(7.075) = 56.60 MeV

Total BE on right-hand side: (9)(6.46) = 58.14 MeV

Thus, BE released = 58.1 - 56.60 = 1.5 MeV

Note that while the BE per nucleon is less for $^{9}_{4}Be$ than for $^{4}_{2}He$ (see Fig. 22.1), there is an extra neutron bound in $^{9}_{4}Be$, which makes the total BE greater.

5. (a) Nuclei with even Z, even N:

$^{4}_{2}He$, $^{12}_{6}C$, $^{16}_{8}O$, $^{20}_{10}Ne$, $^{24}_{12}Mg$, $^{28}_{14}Si$, $^{32}_{16}S$, $^{40}_{18}Ar$, $^{40}_{20}Ca$

There are 9 nuclei in this category.

(b) Nuclei with odd Z, even N:

$^{1}_{1}H$, $^{7}_{3}Li$, $^{11}_{5}B$, $^{19}_{9}F$, $^{23}_{11}Na$, $^{27}_{13}Al$, $^{31}_{15}P$, $^{35}_{17}Cl$, $^{37}_{17}Cl$, $^{39}_{10}K$

There are 10 nuclei in this category.

(c) Only one nucleus with even Z, odd N: $^{9}_{4}Be$

(d) Only one nucleus with odd Z, odd N: $^{14}_{7}N$

These are the most stable and abundant of all the light nuclides. These results are evidence for the preference of even numbers for Z and/or N, which leads to the conclusion that 'like nucleons pair off in some way.' Note also that for all nuclides containing more than 1 nucleon, the n/p ratio is never less than 1.0 and is usually as close to 1.0 as is possible, consistent with having an even number of either neutrons or protons. Thus, for all the odd Z elements, except for nitrogen, rather than have n/p = 1.0 exactly, n is one more than p so that n is even.

6. (a) For $^{206}_{86}Rn$ $\qquad$ n/p = 120/86 = 1.395

This ratio is too low for stability at Z = 86. The most likely modes of decay are electron capture and α emission. In fact, both occur.

$$^{206}_{86}Rn \xrightarrow{EC} {}^{206}_{85}At$$

$$^{206}_{86}Rn \rightarrow {}^{202}_{84}Po^{2-} + {}^{4}_{2}He^{2+}$$

For $^{206}_{85}At$, n/p = 121/85 = 1.424, which is still too low for stability at Z = 85. The first product, $^{206}_{85}At$, therefore also decays via α emission and electron capture.

For $^{202}_{84}Po$, n/p = 118/84 = 1.405, which is also too low for stability at Z = 84. The nuclide $^{202}_{84}Po$ primarily decays by electron capture, but also emits α-particles.

(b) For $^{120}_{49}In$ n/p = 71/49 = 1.449

This ratio is too high for stability at Z = 49, therefore $^{120}_{49}In$ emits a β^- particle.

$$^{120}_{49}In \rightarrow {}^{0}_{-1}\beta^- + {}^{120}_{50}Sn + \nu$$

For $^{120}_{50}Sn$, n/p = 70/50 = 1.40. The nuclide $^{120}_{50}Sn$ is a stable isotope. Recall that Z = 50 is one of the nuclear magic numbers. The element Sn has 10 stable isotopes.

(c) For $^{20}_{12}Mg$ n/p = 8/12 = 0.67

This ratio is too low for stability. The most likely decay mode is positron emission.

$$^{20}_{12}Mg \rightarrow {}^{20}_{11}Na^- + {}^{0}_{+1}\beta^+ + \nu$$

For $^{20}_{11}Na$, n/p = 9/11 = 0.82, which is still too low for stability. Thus $^{20}_{11}Na$ decays further, also emitting a positron.

(d) For $^{84}_{39}Y$ n/p = 1.154

This ratio is too low for stability at Z = 39. At this value of Z, both β^+ emission and EC are likely. In fact, both processes do occur.

$$^{84}_{39}Y \rightarrow ^{84}_{38}Sr + ^{0}_{+1}\beta^{+} + \nu$$

$$^{84}_{39}Y \xrightarrow{EC} ^{84}_{38}Sr$$

For $^{84}_{38}Sr$, n/p = 46/38 = 1.21. This is a stable isotope, having a natural abundance of 0.56% of strontium.

7. An energy of 0.4387 MeV is equivalent to

$$(0.4387\times10^{6}\ eV)(1.6022\times10^{-19}\ J/eV) = 7.029\times10^{-14}\ J$$

$$\nu = E/h = \frac{7.029\times10^{-14}\ J}{6.6262\times10^{-34}\ J\cdot s} = 1.061\times10^{20}\ s^{-1}$$

$$\lambda = c/\nu = hc/E = \frac{(6.6262\times10^{-34}\ J\cdot s)(2.997925\times10^{8}\ m\cdot s^{-1})}{7.029\times10^{-14}\ J}$$

$$= \frac{(6.6262)(2.997925)\times10^{-12}\ m}{7.029} = 2.826\times10^{-12}\ m$$

$$= 2.826\times10^{-3}\ nm = 0.02826\ \text{Å}$$

This is a typical value for the wavelength of a gamma ray, and is shorter than the wavelengths of x-rays.

8. Both ^{17}F and ^{18}F are neutron-poor nuclei. Since Z is so small, positron emission is most likely. In fact, both ^{17}F and ^{18}F do emit positrons.

Both ^{20}F and ^{21}F are neutron-rich nuclei. The only possible decay mode for these nuclei is β^- emission.

9. $$^{214}_{85}At \rightarrow ^{210}_{83}Bi^{2-} + ^{4}_{2}He^{2+}$$

$$\text{Mass of } ^{214}_{85}At = 213.9963$$

Mass of right-hand side = 209.9841 + 4.0026 = 213.9867 amu

Mass loss = 213.9963 - 213.9867 = 0.0096 amu, which is

$$(0.0096\ amu)(931.50\ \frac{MeV}{amu}) = 8.94\ MeV$$

According to the law of conservation of momentum, the lighter α-particle carries away (210/214)(8.94) = 8.78MeV.

10. Since 1 Ci = 3.700×10^{10} dps, we will first convert $\tau_{1/2}$ and λ into seconds and $(\text{seconds})^{-1}$, respectively.

$$\tau_{1/2} = (3.82 \text{ days})(24 \frac{\text{h}}{\text{day}})(60 \frac{\text{min}}{\text{h}})(60 \frac{\text{s}}{\text{min}}) = 3.30\times10^{5} \text{ s}$$

$$\lambda = (0.6931)/\tau_{1/2} = 0.6931/(3.30\times10^{5} \text{ s}) = 2.10\times10^{-6} \text{ s}^{-1}$$

$$\lambda N = (2.10\times10^{-6} \text{ N}) = 3.700\times10^{10} \text{ dps} = \text{activity of 1 Ci}$$

Solving for N we obtain

$$N = (3.700/2.10)\times10^{16} \text{ atoms} = 1.762\times10^{16} \text{ atoms}$$

$$\frac{1.762\times10^{16} \text{ atoms}}{6.022\times10^{23} \text{ atoms}\cdot\text{mol}^{-1}} = 2.92_6\times10^{-8} \text{ mol of } ^{222}\text{Rn}$$

The atomic weight of ^{222}Rn = 222 to 3 significant figures.

$$(2.92_6\times10^{-8} \text{ mol})(222 \text{ g/mol}) = 6.49_5\times10^{-6} \text{ g}$$
$$= 6.50 \ \mu\text{g of } ^{222}\text{Rn}$$

11. Since 0.100 mg = 1.00×10^{-4} g

$$\text{No. mol } ^{239}\text{Pu} = \frac{1.00\times10^{-4} \text{ g}}{239\text{g/mol}} = 4.184\times10^{-7} \text{ mol}$$

$$\text{No. atoms } ^{239}\text{Pu} = (6.022\times10^{23} \frac{\text{atoms}}{\text{mol}})(4.184\times10^{-7} \text{ mol})$$
$$= 2.52\times10^{17} \text{ atoms of } ^{239}\text{Pu}$$

$$\lambda N = \text{activity} = \lambda(2.52\times10^{17}) = 1.36\times10^{7} \text{ dpm}$$

$$\lambda = \frac{1.36\times10^{7}}{2.52\times10^{17}} = 5.40\times10^{-11} \text{ min}^{-1}$$

$$\tau_{1/2} = (0.6931)/(5.40\times10^{-11}) \text{ min} = 1.28_4\times10^{10} \text{ min}$$

Converting to years we obtain:

$$\tau_{1/2} = (1.28_4\times10^{10} \text{ min})\left(\frac{1 \text{ h}}{60 \text{ min}}\right)\left(\frac{1 \text{ day}}{24 \text{ h}}\right)\left(\frac{1 \text{ yr}}{365 \text{ day}}\right) = 2.44\times10^{4} \text{ yr}$$

12. $(5.8\times10^4 \text{ cpm})\left(\frac{1 \text{ min}}{60 \text{ s}}\right)\left(\frac{1\ \mu\text{Ci}}{3.700\times10^4 \text{ cps}}\right) = 2.6\times10^{-2}\ \mu\text{Ci}$

$= 0.026\ \mu\text{Ci}$

13. $\ln(N/N_o) = \ln\left(\frac{3.00}{5.00}\right) = -\lambda t = -\left(\frac{0.6931}{\tau_{1/2}}\right)t = \frac{-0.6931}{5.26}t$

$$\ln(0.600) = -0.5108 = -\frac{0.6931}{5.26}t$$

$$t = \frac{(0.5108)(5.26 \text{ yr})}{(0.6931)} = 3.88 \text{ yr}$$

14. Let $f = N/N_o$ = fraction left after decay

Then, $$\ln f = -\left(\frac{0.6931}{\tau_{1/2}}\right)t$$

(a) After 3 days, $\ln f = -\frac{(0.6931)(3 \text{ days})}{8.06 \text{ days}} = -0.258$

$$f = e^{-0.258} = 0.773$$

Therefore 77.3% of the ^{131}I remains after 3 days.

(b) After 30 days, $\ln f = -\frac{(0.6931)(30 \text{ days})}{8.06 \text{ days}} = -2.58$

$$f = e^{-2.58} = 0.0758$$

Therefore 7.58% of the original ^{131}I remains after 30 days.

15. As ^{14}C has a relatively long half-life (5730 yr), its total activity during this isotope dilution procedure is essentially unchanged.

Total activity before mixing = (10.0 mg)(0.785 μCi/mg)

= 7.85 μCi

Total activity after mixing = (W + 10.0)(0.102) μCi

As these are equal, (W + 10.0)(0.102) = 7.85

W + 10.00 = 7.85/0.102 = 76.96, so that W = 66.96 = 67.0 mg

Note that you do not need to know exactly how much pure penicillin was isolated, but only that some pure penicillin was isolated.

16. For ^{14}C, $\tau_{1/2}$ = 5730 yr $\ln (N/N_o) = -\left(\frac{0.6931}{\tau_{1/2}}\right)t$

N_o = 15.3 dpm per gram of ^{14}C in living organisms

N = 11.9 dpm per gram of ^{14}C from the wooden bowl

$$\ln(11.9/15.3) = \ln(0.7778) = -0.2513 = -0.6931t/(5730\text{ yr})$$

$$t = \frac{(0.2513)(5730\text{ yr})}{0.6931} = 2078\text{ yr} = 2.08\text{x}10^3\text{ yr}$$

17. Use H_2O labeled with ^{18}O. If the P-O bond cleaves at 'a', all the ^{18}O will be in the ADP, and none will be in H_3PO_4. If the P-O bond cleaves at 'b', all the ^{18}O will be in the H_3PO_4, and none in the ADP.

Solutions to Multiple Choice Questions, Chapter 22

1. (d) $\frac{N}{N_o} = \frac{\text{mass after 3 h}}{\text{mass shipped}} = \frac{10.0\text{ mg}}{x}$

$$\ln (N/N_o) = -\left(\frac{0.6931}{\tau_{1/2}}\right)t = -\frac{(0.6931)(3.00\text{ h})}{(6.00\text{ h})} = -0.3466$$

Thus, $N/N_o = e^{-0.3466} = 0.707$

Hence (10.00 mg)/(x mg) = 0.707 and x = 14.1 mg shipped

2. (b) Isobars are nuclides with the same mass number, A, but different atomic number, Z.

3. (e) An α-particle has 2n + 2p. A triton has 2n but only a single p.

4. **(a)** $^{25}_{13}Al \rightarrow \,^{25}_{12}Mg^- + \,^{0}_{+1}\beta^+ + \nu$

After emitting a positron, the resulting atom has one less proton, one more neutron, but the same number of electrons as the atom that decayed. Of course $^{25}_{12}Mg^-$ will quickly lose the extra electron and become a neutral Mg atom.

5. **(c)** For $^{13}_{7}N$, n/p = 6/7 = 0.67, too low for stability. At low Z, the most likely decay mode is β^+ emission.

6. **(b)** For $^{25}_{11}Na$, n/p = 1.27, too high at Z = 11. Neutron-rich nuclides decay via β^- emission.

7. **(a)** The plot of BE/A versus A (Fig. 22.1) has a maximum close to A ~ 60. The nuclide $^{56}_{26}Fe$ has close to the maximum BE/A value.

8. **(e)** The injected activity is N_o, and the activity after 36.0 h is N = 0.01 μCi. The relation between them is

$$\ln (N/N_o) = -(0.6931)(t)/\tau_{1/2} = -(0.6931)(36.0 \text{ h})/(6.0 \text{ h})$$
$$= -4.159$$

Thus, $$N/N_o = e^{-4.159} = 1.562\times10^{-2}$$

Since $(0.01\ \mu Ci)/N_o = 1.562\times10^{-2}$, $N_o = 0.64\ \mu Ci$

9. **(d)**

10. **(e)** The neutrino has no rest mass.

11. **(c)** 1 amu = (1/12)(mass of one ^{12}C atom)

By definition, Avogadro's number is the number of ^{12}C atoms in exactly 12 g of ^{12}C. Thus the mass of one ^{12}C atom is $(12\text{ g})/N_A = (12\times10^{-3}\text{ kg})/N_A$. 1 amu = $(1/12)(12\times10^{-3}\text{ kg})/N_A$

12. (b) $^{235}_{92}U + ^{1}_{0}n \longrightarrow ^{146}_{57}La + ^{87}_{35}Br + 3(^{1}_{0}n)$

For the missing product, Z must be 92 − 57 = 35

For the missing product, A must be 235 + 1 − (146 + 3) = 87

13. (a) $^{246}_{96}Cm + ^{12}_{6}C \longrightarrow ^{254}_{102}No + 4(^{1}_{0}n)$

The target atom must have Z = 102 − 6 = 96 and

$$A = (254 + 4) - 12 = 246$$

14. (d) The only atom of those listed with an odd Z is $_{45}Rh$. Nuclei with odd Z have fewer stable isotopes than those with even Z. Values of 20, 28, and 50 are magic numbers, so Ca, Ni, and Sn have many stable isotopes. Krypton, with Z = 36, has 6 stable isotopes.

15. (b) $^{118}_{51}Sb \longrightarrow {}^{0}_{+1}\beta^{+} + ^{118}_{50}Sn^{-} + \nu$

16. (d) $$\frac{N}{N_0} = \frac{3.00\times10^8}{2.40\times10^9} = \frac{1}{8} = \left(\frac{1}{2}\right)^3$$

which means that 3 half lives must pass for the activity to fall to 3.00×10^8 cpm.

$$t = 3\tau_{1/2} = 3(12.26) = 36.78 \text{ days}$$

Of course, this problem can also be done by direct substitution into the equation $\ln(N/N_0) = -(0.6931)(t)/\tau_{1/2}$, but it is a good idea to look first at the relation between N and N_0 and see if an integral number of half-lives are involved, so you can do the arithmetic in your head.

17. (c) $$\frac{N}{N_0} = \frac{3.83}{15.3} = 0.2503$$

Since 0.2503 is very close to 1/4, essentially two half

lives must have passed, and as two half lives are 11,460 years, the only possible answer is (c). If you are concerned about the third significant figure, then you must do all the calculations to 4 significant figures, and round to 3 figures at the end, as shown below, but for a multiple choice question that is unnecessary and should be avoided.

$$\ln(0.2503) = -1.385 = -(0.69315)(t)/(5730\ \text{yr})$$

$$t = (1.385)(5730)/0.69315 = 11{,}449\ \text{yr} = 11{,}400\ \text{yr}$$

to 3 significant figures.

18. <u>(b)</u> $^{226}_{88}Ra \rightarrow {}^{4}_{2}He^{2+} + {}^{222}_{86}Rn^{2-}$

19. <u>(c)</u> If the fraction remaining is $1/8 = (1/2)^3$, that means 3 half lives have elapsed. Thus, 96 min = $3\tau_{1/2}$, and

$$\tau_{1/2} = 32\ \text{min}$$

20. <u>(c)</u>

$$^{228}_{88}Ra \rightarrow {}^{0}_{-1}\beta^- + {}^{228}_{89}Ac$$

$$^{228}_{89}Ac \rightarrow {}^{0}_{-1}\beta^- + {}^{228}_{90}Th$$

$$^{228}_{90}Th \rightarrow {}^{4}_{2}He^{2+} + {}^{224}_{88}Ra^{2-}$$

Emitting a β^- particle increases Z by 1 ($n \rightarrow p^+ + \beta^-$). So emitting 2 β^- particles increases Z by 2. Since emitting an α-particle decreases Z by 2, the emission sequence β^-, β^-, α leaves Z unchanged. We start with one isotope of Ra and end with another.

Solutions to Problems, Chapter 22

22.1.(a) At. wt. = 0.5182(106.90509) + 0.4818(108.9047)

$$= 55.39_8 + 52.47_0 = 107.86_8 = 107.87$$

(b) The emission of a β^- particle is always accompanied by the emission of a neutrino. These two particles have a combined kinetic energy equal to 1.05 MeV, the energy equivalent of the mass loss that results when the nuclear reaction occurs. The greater the kinetic energy of the neutrino, the less the kinetic energy of the β^- particle, but the sum is always 1.05 MeV.

(c) $$^{111}_{47}Ag \rightarrow {}^{0}_{-1}\beta^- + {}^{111}_{48}Cd^+ + \nu$$

Mass of right-hand side = 110.9042 amu

Mass of left-hand side = mass of ^{111}Ag

$$\text{Mass loss} = \left(\frac{1 \text{ amu}}{931.5 \text{ MeV}}\right)(1.05 \text{ Mev}) = 0.00113 \text{ amu}$$

Therefore, mass of ^{111}Ag = 110.9042 + 0.00113 = 110.9053

22.2. Odd-odd nuclei are uncommon, and those that are stable, except for the lightest ones, usually constitute a small percentage of the naturally occurring isotopes. Of the three isotopes, only $^{40}_{19}K$ is an odd-odd nucleus.

isotope	No. protons	No. neutrons	natural abundance
^{39}K	19	20	93.1 %
^{40}K	19	21	0.00118 %
^{41}K	19	22	6.88 %

22.3. $$^{238}_{92}U \rightarrow {}^{4}_{2}He^{2+} + {}^{234}_{90}Th^{2-}$$

$$^{234}_{90}Th \rightarrow {}^{0}_{-1}\beta^- + {}^{234}_{91}Pa^+ + \nu$$

$$^{234}_{91}Pa \rightarrow {}^{0}_{-1}\beta^- + {}^{234}_{92}U^+ + \nu$$

$$^{234}_{92}U \rightarrow {}^{4}_{2}He^{2+} + {}^{230}_{90}Th^{2-}$$

22.4. For $^{16}_{8}O$: $8n + 8p^+ + 8e^- \rightarrow {}^{16}_{8}O + BE$

Mass of left-hand side = mass of 8n + mass of $8(^{1}_{1}H)$

$$= 8(1.00866501) + 8(1.00782505)$$

$$= 16.1319205$$

$$\text{Mass loss} = 16.1319205 - 15.9949149 = 0.137006 \text{ amu}$$

$$BE = (931.50 \frac{\text{MeV}}{\text{amu}})(0.137006 \text{ amu}) = 127.62 \text{ MeV}$$

$$BE/A = 127.62/16 = 7.976 \text{ MeV/nucleon}$$

For $^{17}_{8}O$: $9n + 8p + 8e \rightarrow {}^{17}_{8}O + BE$

Mass of left-hand side = mass of 9n + mass of $8(^{1}_{1}H)$

$$= 9(1.00866501) + 8(1.00782505)$$

$$= 17.1405855$$

$$\text{Mass loss} = 17.1405855 - 16.999133 = 0.1414525 \text{ amu}$$

$$BE = (931.50 \frac{\text{MeV}}{\text{amu}})(0.1414525 \text{ amu}) = 131.76 \text{ MeV}$$

$$BE/A = 131.76/17 = 7.751 \text{ MeV/nucleon}$$

The binding energy per nucleon is larger for $^{16}_{8}O$ (7.98 MeV) than for $^{17}_{8}O$ (7.75 MeV). This suggests that the ninth neutron in $^{17}_{8}O$ is going into a higher energy level than that of the first eight, since it does not provide as much binding energy as each of the first eight. Note also the greater stability of even-even nuclei with n/p = 1, relative to an even-odd nucleus at the same Z value.

22.5. Remember, tritium is a gas! Using the ideal gas law, the number of moles of $^{3}_{1}H$ at 25°C and 0.0100 atm pressure in a 1.00 mL sample is

$$n = \frac{PV}{RT} = \frac{(0.0100\ \text{atm})(1.00\text{x}10^{-3}\ \text{L})}{(0.082057\ \text{L·atm·mol}^{-1}\text{K}^{-1})(298.15\ \text{K})}$$

$$= 4.087\text{x}10^{-7}\ \text{mol tritium}$$

No. atoms $^{3}_{1}H = N = (4.087\text{x}10^{-7}\ \text{mol})(6.022\text{x}10^{23}\ \text{atoms/mol})$

$$= 2.461\text{x}10^{17}\ \text{atoms}$$

Since activity = λN, we need λ in s^{-1} for the activity to be in mCi. We obtain λ from the half life, $\lambda = 0.6931/\tau_{1/2}$

$$\tau_{1/2} = (12.26\ \text{yr})(365\ \frac{\text{days}}{\text{yr}})(24\ \frac{\text{h}}{\text{day}})(60\ \frac{\text{min}}{\text{h}})(60\ \frac{\text{s}}{\text{min}})$$

$$= 3.866\text{x}10^{8}\ \text{s}$$

$$\lambda = 0.6931/(3.866\text{x}10^{8}\ \text{s}) = 1.793\text{x}10^{-9}\ \text{s}^{-1}$$

$$\text{Activity} = \lambda N = (1.793\text{x}10^{-9}\ \text{s}^{-1})(2.461\text{x}10^{17}\ \text{atoms})$$

$$= 4.412\text{x}10^{8}\ \text{dps}$$

$$1\ \text{millicurie (mCi)} = 3.700\text{x}10^{7}\ \text{dps}$$

Hence the activity of the tritium in mCi is

$$\frac{4.412\text{x}10^{8}\ \text{dps}}{3.700\text{x}10^{7}\ \text{dps/mCi}} = 11.9\ \text{mCi}$$

22.6. $^{52}_{25}Mn + ^{1}_{1}H \rightarrow ^{53}_{26}Fe + BE$

Mass of left-hand side = 51.94556 + 1.00782505

= 52.95339

Mass of right-hand side = 52.94558

Mass loss = 52.95339 - 52.94558 = 0.00781 amu

$$BE = (0.00781\ \text{amu})(931.50\ \frac{\text{MeV}}{\text{amu}}) = 7.27\ \text{MeV}$$

22.7. Only nuclear reactions for which there is a mass loss can occur. If there is a mass gain, the energy required to cause the reaction to occur is so very large that it prohibits the reaction from occurring. For the reaction

$$^{38}_{18}Ar \rightarrow \, ^{34}_{16}S + \, ^{4}_{2}He$$

Mass of left-hand side = 37.96272

Mass of right-hand side = 33.96786 + 4.00260 = 37.97046

Since the right-hand side has more mass than the left-hand side, this reaction is not possible. An enormous (prohibitive) amount of energy would be required in order for it to occur.

22.8.
$$\ln\left(\frac{N}{N_o}\right) = \ln\left(\frac{1}{15.3}\right) = -\left(\frac{0.6931}{\tau_{1/2}}\right)t = -\frac{0.6931}{5730 \text{ yr}}\,t$$

$$t = \frac{(2.728)(5730 \text{ yr})}{0.6931} = 22,600 \text{ yr}$$

Thus, the oldest objects that can be reliably dated using ^{14}C are approximately 22,600 years old.

22.9. The Einstein relation, Eq. (22-3), is $\Delta E = (\Delta m)c^2$

By substitution,
$$\Delta m = \frac{\Delta E}{c^2} = \frac{393.51\text{x}10^3 \text{ J}}{(2.997925\text{x}10^8 \text{ m/s})^2}$$

$$= 4.378\text{x}10^{-12} \text{ kg} = 4.378\text{x}10^{-9} \text{ g}$$

For the relationship between joules and other SI units, see Appendix A (Derived SI Units).

A mass loss of $4.4\text{x}10^{-9}$ g (4.4 nanograms) is much too small to be detected, hence we observe the conservation of mass in this reaction.

22.10.
$$^{239}_{94}Pu \rightarrow \, ^{4}_{2}He^{2+} + \, ^{235}_{92}U^{2-} + 5.243 \text{ MeV}$$

Mass of left-hand side = 239.05216 amu

$$\text{Mass equivalent to 5.243 MeV} = \frac{5.243 \text{ MeV}}{931.5 \text{ MeV/amu}} = 0.005629 \text{ amu}$$

$$\text{Mass } ^{239}_{94}\text{Pu} = 239.05216 = 4.00260 + \text{Mass } ^{235}_{92}\text{U} + 0.005629$$

$$\text{Mass } ^{235}_{92}\text{U} = 239.05216 - 4.00260 - 0.005629 = 235.04393 \text{ amu}$$

22.11. The ratio $^{206}Pb/^{238}U = 0.297/1.000$ at the present time. Consider a sample currently containing 1.000 g ^{238}U and 0.297 g ^{206}Pb. At the time the mineral was formed, what is now 0.297 g of ^{206}Pb was still ^{238}U. The mass of this amount of ^{238}U was (238/206)(0.297) = 0.343 g.

Thus, originally the mineral sample contained

$$1.000 + 0.343 = 1.343 \text{ g of } ^{238}\text{U}$$

$$\ln\frac{N}{N_o} = \ln\frac{1.000}{1.343} = -0.2949 = \frac{-0.6931}{\tau_{1/2}}(t) = -\frac{0.6931}{4.5\times10^9 \text{ yr}}(t)$$

$$t = (0.2949)(4.5\times10^9 \text{ yr})/(0.6931) = 1.9\times10^9 \text{ yr}$$

The rock was formed 1.9 billion years ago.

22.12. (a) At first, essentially all the SO_4^{2-} added is precipitated as $BaSO_4$. Thus, all the radioactivity will be found in the $BaSO_4$ precipitate and almost none in the remaining solution. Since the aliquot withdrawn is filtered, the first aliquots will show no radioactivity.

After all the Ba^{2+} has been precipitated as the sulfate, however, further addition of the $^{35}SO_4^{2-}$ solution will render the solution radioactive since the $^{35}SO_4^{2-}$ now stays in solution. Thus, by plotting radioactivity of the solution (in cpm) versus volume of SO_4^{2-} added, we can extrapolate back to zero activity. This will correspond to the volume of SO_4^{2-} needed to precipitate all the Ba^{2+}.

(b)

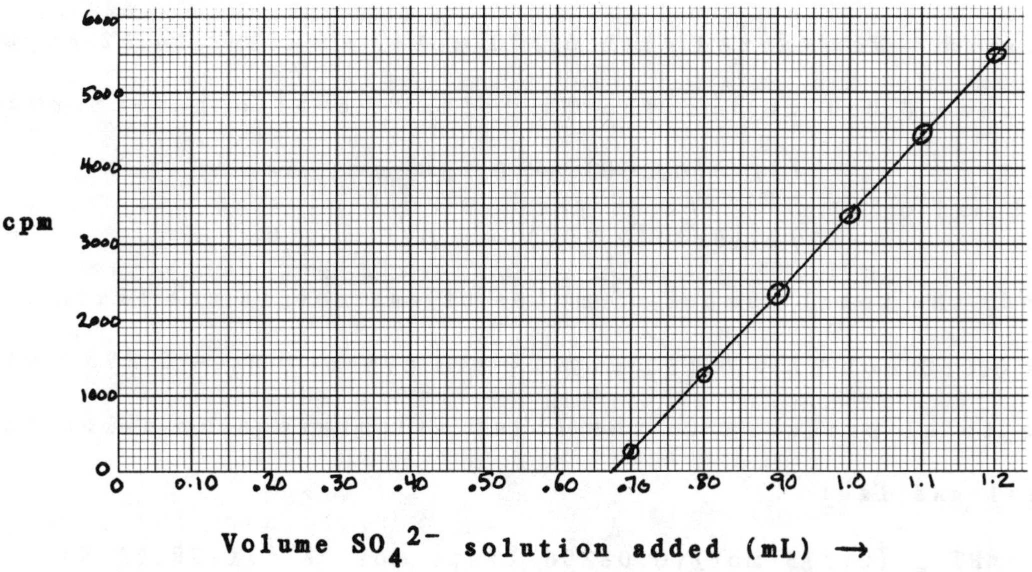

Extrapolating to zero activity we find that the plot intersects the x-axis at 0.68 mL of added SO_4^{2-}. This is the volume required to precipitate all the Ba^{2+} ions in the 20.00 mL sample. Thus,

$$(20.00\ \text{mL})(M_{Ba^{2+}}) = (0.68\ \text{mL})(0.0100\ M)$$

since Ba^{2+} and SO_4^{2-} react in a 1:1 molar ratio.

$$M_{Ba^{2+}} = \frac{(0.68)(0.0100)}{20.00} = 3.4 \times 10^{-4}\ M$$

22.13. $$^{131}_{53}I \rightarrow {}^{0}_{-1}\beta^- + {}^{131}_{54}Xe^+ + \nu$$

This is the __nuclear__ reaction occurring. The Xe^+ very quickly picks up an electron and becomes Xe gas.

(a) $$2H^{131}I(g) \rightarrow H_2(g) + 2Xe(g)$$

This is the __chemical__ reaction or decomposition resulting from the radioactive decay of ^{131}I to Xe.

(b) Note that 16.12 days is 2 half lives. After this much time, only 1/4 of the original HI is left since 3/4 decayed. We started with 0.200 mole, so after 16.12 days, we have 0.050 mol of the HI left. We also have formed

$$(3/4)(0.200) = 0.150 \text{ mol Xe}$$

and $$(1/2)(3/4)(0.200) = 0.075 \text{ mol } H_2$$

Thus, the total number of moles of gas now in the flask is

$n = 0.050 \text{ mol HI} + 0.150 \text{ mol Xe} + 0.075 \text{ mol } H_2 = 0.275 \text{ mol}$

The total pressure in the flask is obtained by using the ideal gas law:

$$P = \frac{nRT}{V} = \frac{(0.275 \text{ mol})(0.08206 \text{ L·atm·mol}^{-1}\text{K}^{-1})(298.15 \text{ K})}{4.00 \text{ L}}$$
$$= 1.68_2 \text{ atm}$$

22.14. $$^{21}_{11}Na \rightarrow {}^{0}_{+1}\beta^{+} + {}^{21}_{10}Ne^{-} + \nu$$

As there were 11 orbital electrons around the Na atom, immediately after decay there are 11 electrons around the Ne nucleus, so we have a positron, a Ne atom, plus an extra electron as the products in this nuclear reaction. Since the mass of an electron is identical with the mass of a positron,

Mass of right-hand side = 20.99385 + 2(0.000549) = 20.99495

Mass of left-hand side = mass of $^{21}_{11}Na$ atom = 20.99764 amu

Mass loss = 20.99764 − 20.99495 = 0.00269 amu

The energy equivalent of this mass loss is the energy released when the reaction occurs.

$$E = (931.50\ \frac{\text{MeV}}{\text{amu}})(0.00269\ \text{amu}) = 2.51\ \text{MeV}$$

The total kinetic energy of the emitted neutrino and positron is 2.51 MeV. A spectrum of energies, from 0 to 2.51 MeV will be observed for all the positrons. The maximum kinetic energy of an emitted positron is therefore 2.51 MeV, in which case the accompanying neutrino has zero kinetic energy.

22.15. (a)

$$\ln \frac{N}{N_0} = \ln\left(\frac{\text{activity at 60 min}}{\text{activity at zero } t}\right) = \frac{-0.6931}{\tau_{1/2}}(60\ \text{min})$$

$$\ln\left(\frac{31,900}{39,400}\right) = \ln(0.8096) = -0.2112 = \frac{-0.6931}{\tau_{1/2}}(60\ \text{min})$$

$$\tau_{1/2} = \frac{(0.6931)(60\ \text{min})}{0.2112} = 196.9_6 = 197\ \text{min}$$

(b) Plot ln(activity) versus time. We will obtain a straight line with slope $-\lambda$, from which the half life is obtained, as

$$\tau_{1/2} = (\ln 2)/\lambda = 0.69315/\lambda$$

Time	0.00	30.00	60.00	90.00	120.00	150.00
Activity	39,400	35,500	31,900	28,800	25,900	23,300
ln(activity)	10.582	10.477	10.370	10.268	10.162	10.056

The plot appears on the following page. The slope has been determined using the two points marked with arrows.

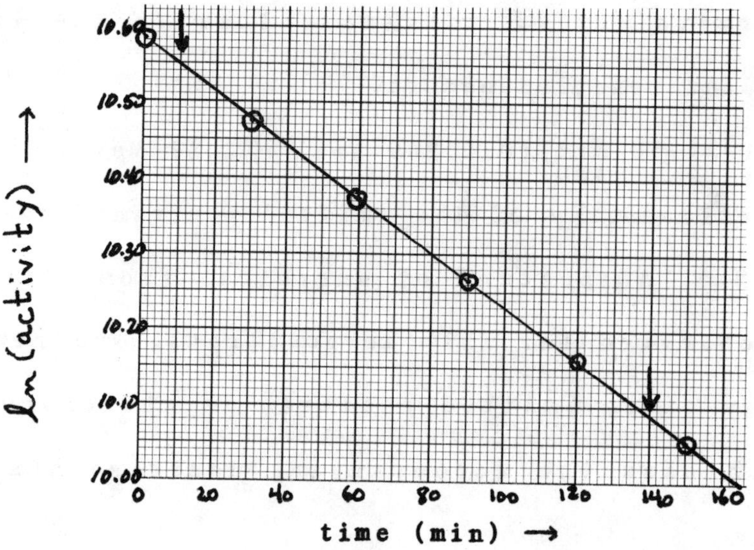

$$\text{slope} = \frac{10.546 - 10.093}{10.00 - 140.00} = -\frac{0.453}{130.00} = -3.485\text{x}10^{-3}$$

$$\lambda = 3.48_5\text{x}10^{-3}\ \text{min}^{-1}$$

$$\tau_{1/2} = (0.69315)/(3.485\text{x}10^{-3}) = 199\ \text{min}$$

(c) The value using all six points is more reliable. Each experimental point has a random uncertainty, some +, some −. Using as many points as available, these uncertainties average out.

22.16. $$4(^1_1H) \longrightarrow {}^4_2He^{2-} + 2({}^{\ 0}_{+1}\beta^+)$$

Mass of left-hand side = 4(1.00782505) = 4.0313002 amu

The right-hand side consists of a helium atom, two electrons, and two positrons. Since the mass of an electron and a positron are identical,

Mass of right-hand side = 4.00260 + 4(0.0005485803)

= 4.004794 amu

$$\text{Mass loss} = 4.0313002 - 4.004794 = 0.026506 \text{ amu}$$

$$\text{Energy equivalent} = \left(931.50 \frac{\text{MeV}}{\text{amu}}\right)(0.026506 \text{ amu}) = 24.690 \text{ MeV}$$

This is the energy released when 4 single ^1H atoms are fused. We can convert this to kJ per 4 moles of ^1H atoms by using Eq. (22-7), $1 \text{ MeV} = 9.6485 \times 10^7 \text{ kJ/mol}$

$$(24.690 \text{ MeV})\left(9.6485 \times 10^7 \frac{\text{kJ}}{\text{MeV}}\right) = 238.22 \times 10^7 \text{ kJ per 4 mol H}$$

The fusion of 1 mol of ^1H therefore produces

$$\frac{238.22 \times 10^7 \text{ kJ}}{4} = 5.9555 \times 10^8 \text{ kJ}$$

In one second, the sun produces 3×10^{22} kJ, so that

$$\frac{3 \times 10^{22} \text{ kJ/s}}{5.9555 \times 10^8 \text{ kJ/mol}} = 5 \times 10^{13} \text{ mol of } {}^1H \text{ consumed per second}$$

The mass of hydrogen that is fused in the sun each second is certainly impressive!

Solutions to Multiple Choice Questions, Chapter 23

1. (b) The linkage shown is an amide linkage. Glycogen, (b), is a starch and contains only C, H, and O. Of the other substances, (a), nylon, is a synthetic polyamide, (c), protein, is a naturally occurring polyamide (polypeptide), (d), valylglycine, is a dipeptide and (e), N-ethylacetamide, is a simple amide.

2. (c) This is the only choice for which both carbons flanking the double bond have two different substituents. For the others, both substituents are the same on at least one of the carbons, thus precluding cis-trans isomerism.

3. (e) This is a matter of definition.

4. (a) Compound (a) is methyl ethyl ether. Ethers tend to be less soluble than the other classes of compounds exemplified. Compound (b) is an alcohol, (c) a ketone, (d) an aldehyde, and (e) a carboxylic acid. These molecules are sufficiently polar to be water soluble.

5. (e) The longest chain has five carbons, so the compound must be a pentane. We number substituents so as to give the first one encountered the lowest possible number. In this case that means starting from the right. The second and third carbons in the chain then have methyl group substituents, leading to the name 2,3-dimethylpentane. The compound has been redrawn below, with the numbering in-

cluded, so that the name is immediately apparent.

$$\overset{5}{C}H_3 - \overset{4}{C}H_2 - \overset{3}{C}H - \overset{2}{C}H - \overset{1}{C}H_3$$
$$\underset{CH_3}{|} \quad \underset{CH_3}{|}$$

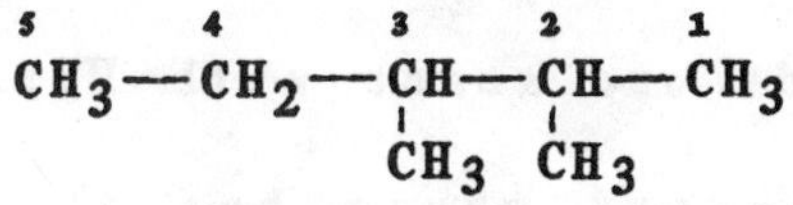

6. **(e)** This is a definition. Hetero- is a combining form meaning 'other than usual.' In this context it means 'other than carbon.' A cyclic compound contains a ring of atoms.

7. **(a)** None of the compounds has a tetrahedral carbon with four different substituents (a usually sufficient but not necessary condition for optical isomerism), and none is non-superimposable on its mirror-image (the necessary condition).

8. **(e)** (Sorry; you just have to know this!)

9. **(d)** The longest chain containing the double bond has four carbons; therefore the compound is a butene. The carbon chain is numbered so that the double-bonded carbons receive the lowest possible numbers, so this is a 1-butene; then the methyl group is on the second carbon. The correct name is therefore 2-methyl-1-butene.

10. **(a)** Note that what is given in parentheses has two $-(CH_2CCl_2)-$ units, so that $-(CH_2CCl_2)-$ is really the basic repeating unit. The polymer has two connected carbons, one attached to two H's, one attached to two Cl's, and (a) is the only choice which also exhibits this property.

11. <u>(c)</u> Compound II is the only alkene; alkenes have reactive double bonds and react with HBr.

12. <u>(d)</u> The longest chain has five carbons; if you start numbering from either ethyl group the methyl substituent is on carbon number 3.

13. <u>(a)</u> Compounds III and IV are both $C_5H_{10}O$.

14. <u>(c)</u> Only trimethylamine, the compound in (c), has a nitrogen with three carbons attached to it. All three H atoms of NH_3 have been replaced by $-CH_3$.

15. <u>(b)</u> Only compound (b) has a tetrahedral carbon bearing four different substituents.

16. <u>(c)</u> The carboxyl group carbon, $—\overset{\overset{\displaystyle O}{\|}}{C}—OH$, gets no contribution to its oxidation number from the methyl group to which it is attached. Of the other atoms in this group, the two oxygens have oxidation number −2 each, and the H has +1, so this C must have +3.

17. <u>(e)</u> Only compounds I, III, and IV exhibit the pattern of three alternating single and double bonds in a ring, which is the simplest way of depicting aromaticity.

18. <u>(d)</u> This is a definition.

19. <u>(b)</u> The structure of 2-butene is $CH_3-CH=CH-CH_3$. The addition of HBr to the double bond yields $CH_3-CH_2-CHBr-CH_2$. The carbon chain is numbered from the end closer to the Br, in order to give the lower numbering scheme (2-bromobutane,

not 3-bromobutane).

20. **(b)** If you forget that amylose is a starch, you might remember that nylon is a polyamide and that penicillin is a small molecule (not poly-anything!). Compounds (c) and (e) are, from their names, not saccharides.

Solutions to Problems, Chapter 23

23.1.

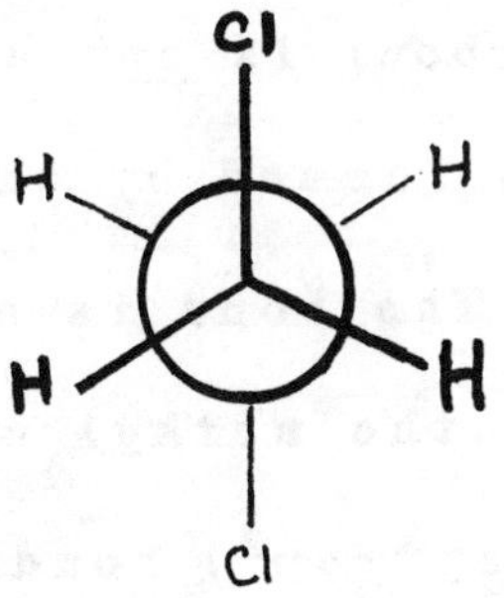

lowest energy
dihedral angle = 180°

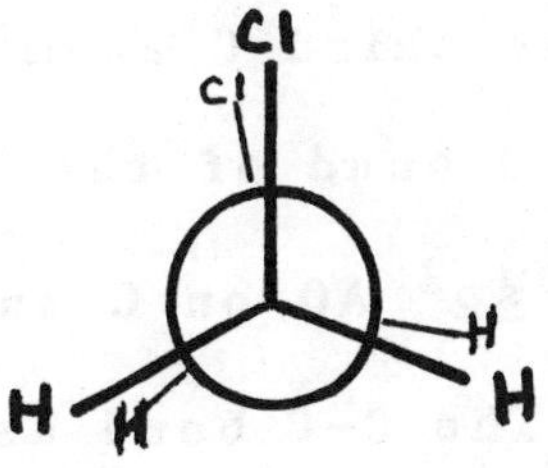

highest energy
dihedral angle = 0°

In the conformation of lowest potential energy, the Cl atoms are as far apart as possible. Conversely, in the conformation of highest potential energy, the Cl atoms are as close as possible.

23.2. **(a)** Two isomers, cis and trans, would be possible if the molecule were square planar (See text, Example 20.6) **(b)** Only one isomer is possible for tetrahedral dichloromethane. In fact, there is only one isomer.

23.3. (a)

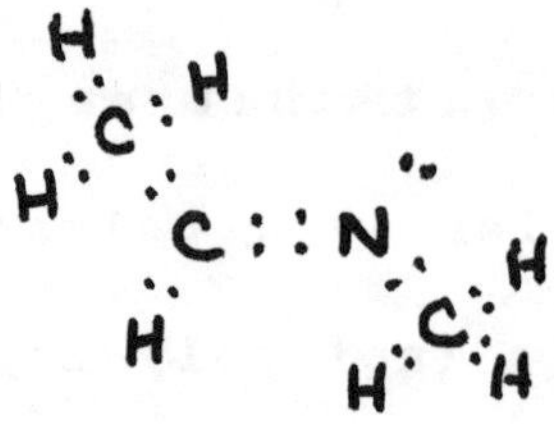

(b) There are 6 C-H bonds in the two $-CH_3$ groups. Each bond is formed by the overlap of an sp^3 hybrid AO on C and the 1s AO on H. The bond is called a $\sigma(sp^3-s)$ bond.

The third C atom (not a $-CH_3$ carbon) is sp^2 hybridized. The C-H bond of the third carbon is formed by the overlap of an sp^2 AO on C and the 1s on H. The bond is a $\sigma(sp^2-s)$ bond. The C-C bond uses an sp^3 AO of the methyl carbon and an sp^2 AO of the third C. It is a $\sigma(sp^3-sp^2)$ bond.

The N atom is also sp^2 hybridized. The C=N double bond consists of a σ bond formed by the overlap of an sp^2 AO on C and an sp^2 AO on N, and a π bond formed by overlapping p orbitals on both C and N. The N-C single bond uses an sp^2 AO of N and an sp^3 AO of the methyl C. The lone pair (unbonded) electrons of N are in an sp^2 hybrid AO.

(c) The methyl group on the C can be either cis or trans to the methyl group on the N, so there are two geometric isomers. The C-N-C angle is 120°, and the N has an sp^2 lone pair. Such compounds are called imines, or Schiff's bases.

23.4. Compounds (b), (c), and (f) exhibit cis-trans isomerism. The isomers of compound (f) are shown below:

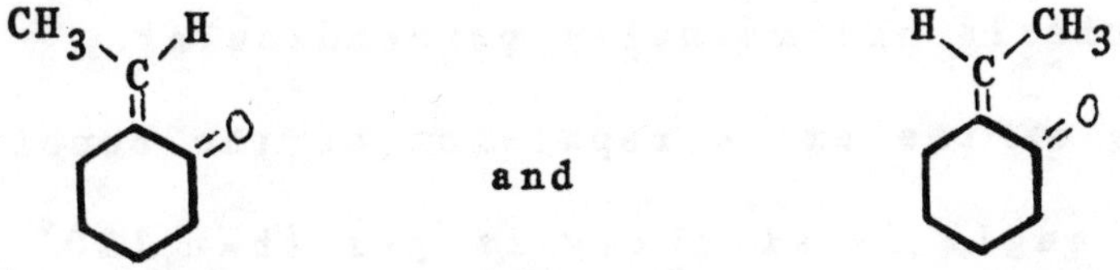

23.5. The C–C≡C–C group must be linear, since the triple-bonded carbons are sp-hybridized, and sp hybrids are 180° apart. Clearly, the remaining two carbons cannot reach far enough to close a six-membered ring, and cyclohexyne does not exist.

23.6. The end carbons in allene are sp^2 hybridized, and the center carbon is sp hybridized. The C–H σ-bonds involve a carbon sp^2 AO and the 1s AO on H. The C═C bonds consist of a σ bond formed by the overlap of an sp^2 AO on the end carbon and an sp AO on the center carbon, plus a π bond formed by overlapping p orbitals on the carbons. The C–C–C angle is 180° (linear) as the central carbon uses two different sp orbitals and two different p orbitals to bond with its neighbors. The H–C–C and H–C–H angles are ~ 120°, but the two CH_2 groups are mutually perpendicular as shown below.

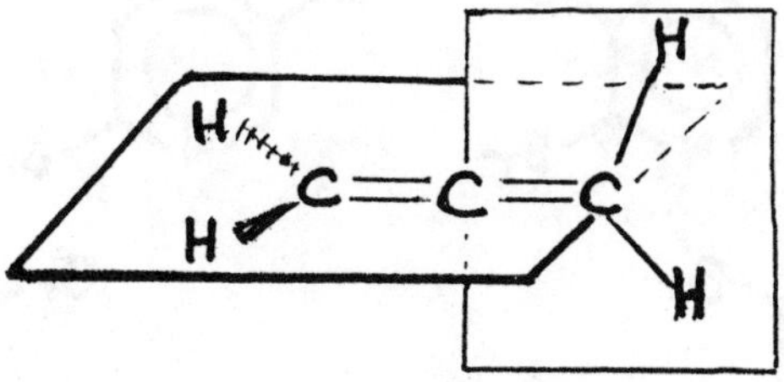

This geometry is required because different p orbitals on the central carbon are needed for the two π bonds, and these p orbitals are mutually perpendicular.

Because of the extra repulsion of the double bond, the H-C-C bond angle is slightly larger than 120° (122°), and the H-C-H bond angle is slightly smaller than 120° (116°).

23.7. (a) There are 3 isomers of dibromobenzene, shown here with their names:

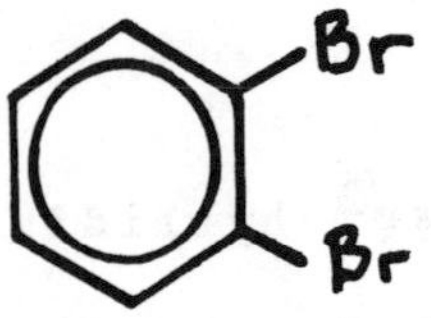

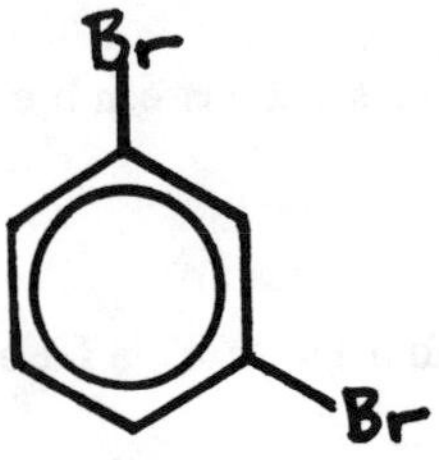

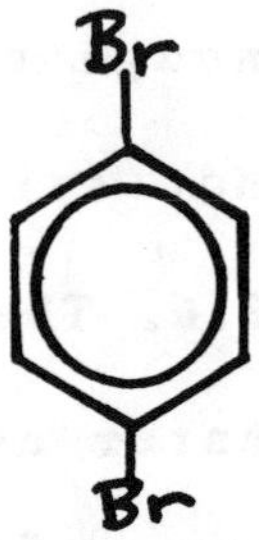

ortho or 1,2-dibromobenzene   meta or 1,3-dibromobenzene   para or 1,4-dibromobenzene

(b) If the Kekulé localized bond structure were correct there would be <u>two</u> ortho isomers, differing in whether the two Br substituents flanked a single or a double bond, for a total of 4 isomers. In fact, there are only 3 isomers of dibromobenzene.

23.8. There are 6 isomers of dibromopyridine.

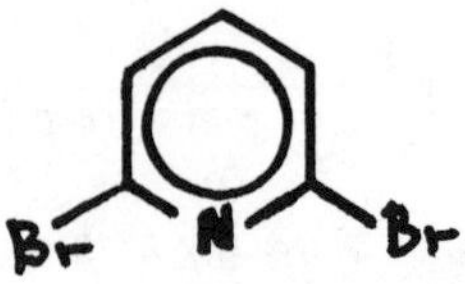

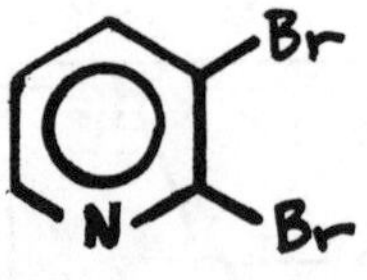

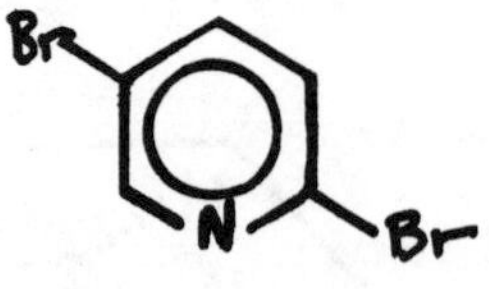

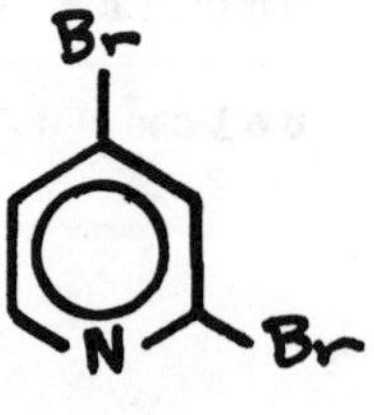

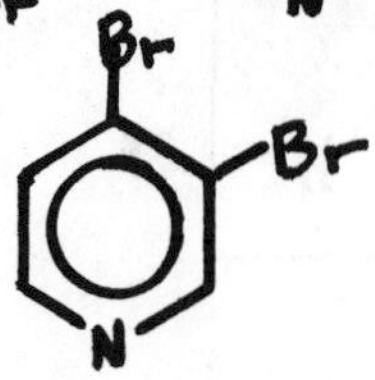

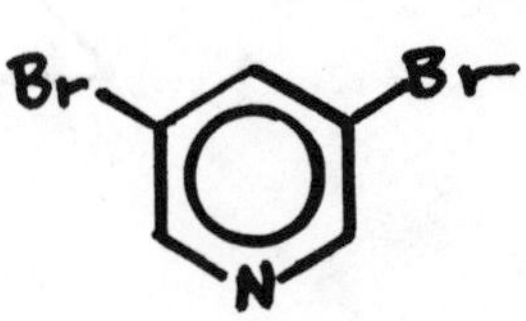

23.9. (a) The longest chain that includes the double bond has five carbon atoms. The name of the compound is 2-ethyl-3-methyl-1-pentene. The structure is redrawn below to make the numbering system clear.

$$\overset{1}{C}H_2 = \overset{2}{C} - \overset{3}{C}H - \overset{4}{C}H_2 - \overset{5}{C}H_3$$
$$\underset{CH_3}{\overset{|}{}} \underset{CH_2}{\overset{|}{}} \underset{CH_3}{\overset{|}{}}$$

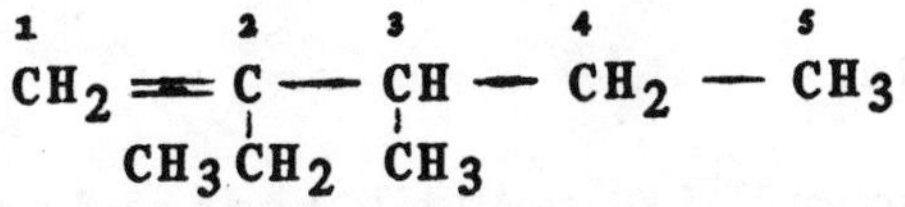

(b) This compound is 4-ethyl-2,5,5-trimethylheptane. The longest chain has seven carbon atoms. To count, start at the bottom ethyl group and continue to the upper right. Number the carbons from right to left.

(c) This compound is 3-methyl-1-butanol. It is numbered so that the -OH is on the carbon with the lowest number.

(d) This compound is ethyl isopropyl ether. Once you see this is an ether, you just prepend the names of the alkyl groups in alphabetical order.

(e) The correct name is N,N-dimethylaniline. Aniline is an aromatic amine with an $-NH_2$ group as a substituent on benzene. Another name, less likely to be used by organic chemists, but in use by other chemists, is phenyldimethyl-amine. Phenyl is the name for a benzene ring when it is considered as a substituent.

(f) This is an aldehyde, 2-methylbutanal. The numbering starts with the aldehydic carbon, which will always be 1, since the aldehyde group must occur at the end of a chain.

(g) This compound is pentanoic acid.

(h) The systematic name is 3-pentanone. More commonly, this compound is called diethyl ketone. Ketones are named like ethers: first the substituents, then the name of the class of compounds.

(i) This compound is called benzamide. It is the amide of benzoic acid, which consists of a benzene ring with a $-COOH$ group substituent.

23.10 There are five isomeric hexanes:

$CH_3-CH_2-CH_2-CH_2-CH_2-CH_3$ $CH_3-\underset{\underset{CH_3}{|}}{CH}-CH_2-CH_2-CH_3$

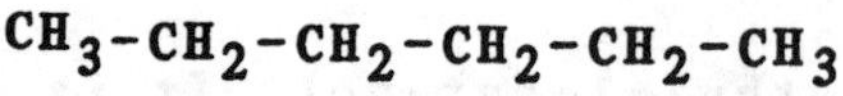

n-hexane or hexane   2-methylpentane

$CH_3-CH_2-\underset{\underset{CH_3}{|}}{CH}-CH_2-CH_3$ $CH_3-\underset{\underset{H_3C}{|}}{CH}-\underset{\underset{CH_3}{|}}{CH}-CH_3$

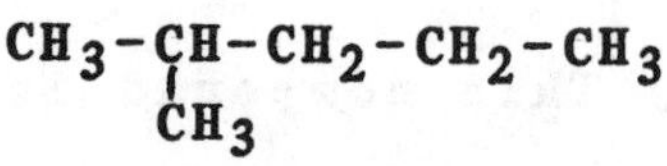

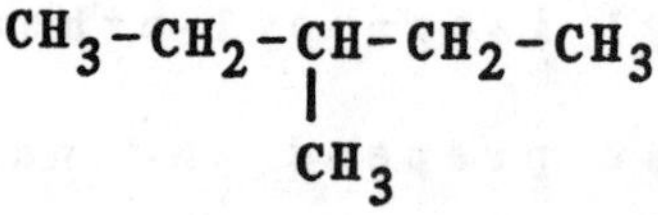

3-methylpentane   2,3-dimethylbutane

$CH_3-\overset{\overset{CH_3}{|}}{\underset{\underset{CH_3}{|}}{CH}}-CH-CH_3$

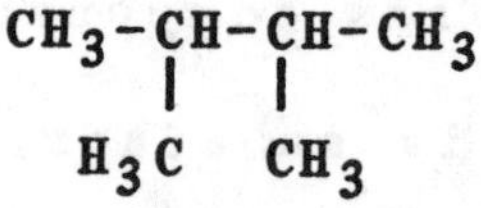

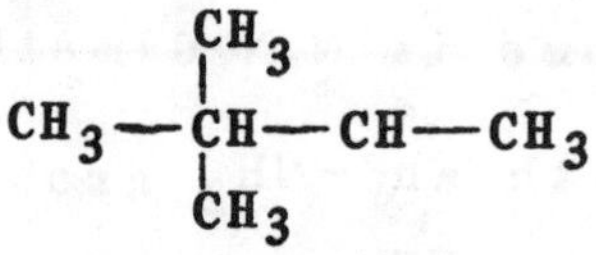

2,2-dimethylbutane

23.11. Neither compound (a) nor (c) can exist as enantiomers. Neither has a carbon with four different substituents, nor is there any other way that they are not superimposable on their mirror images. The enantiomers of compounds (b), (d), and (e) are shown on the following page.

(b)

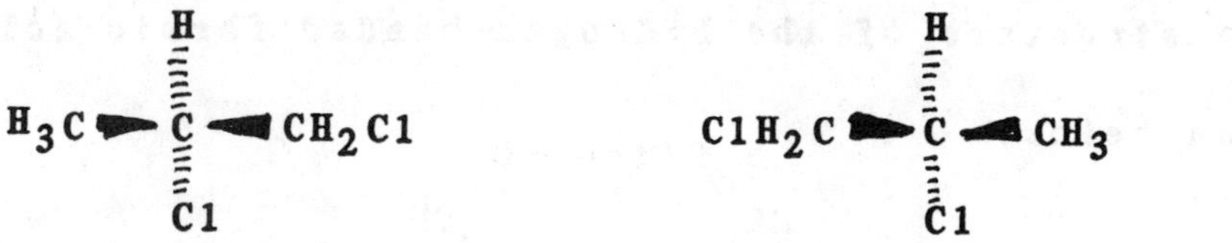

$$H_3C \blacktriangleright \overset{\overset{\text{H}}{\vdots}}{\underset{\underset{\text{Cl}}{\vdots}}{C}} \blacktriangleleft CH_2Cl \qquad ClH_2C \blacktriangleright \overset{\overset{\text{H}}{\vdots}}{\underset{\underset{\text{Cl}}{\vdots}}{C}} \blacktriangleleft CH_3$$

(d)

$$H_2N \blacktriangleright \overset{\overset{\text{H}}{\vdots}}{\underset{\underset{\text{CH}_2\text{OH}}{\vdots}}{C}} \blacktriangleleft COOH \qquad HOOC \blacktriangleright \overset{\overset{\text{H}}{\vdots}}{\underset{\underset{\text{CH}_2\text{OH}}{\vdots}}{C}} \blacktriangleleft NH_2$$

(e)

$$H_3C-CH_2 \blacktriangleright \overset{\overset{\text{Br}}{\vdots}}{\underset{\underset{\text{I}}{\vdots}}{C}} \blacktriangleleft CH_2Br \qquad BrH_2C \blacktriangleright \overset{\overset{\text{Br}}{\vdots}}{\underset{\underset{\text{I}}{\vdots}}{C}} \blacktriangleleft CH_2-CH_3$$

23.12. Step 1:

$$CH_3-CH_2-CH=CH-CH_3 + HI \rightarrow I^- + CH_3-CH_2-CH_2-\overset{+}{C}H-CH_3$$

$$\text{or}$$

$$CH_3-CH_2-\overset{+}{C}H-CH_2-CH_3$$

Step 2:

$$CH_3-CH_2-CH_2-\overset{+}{C}H-CH_3 + I^- \rightarrow CH_3-CH_2-CH_2-CHI-CH_3$$
$$\text{2-iodopentane}$$

or $\quad CH_2-CH_2-\overset{+}{C}H-CH_2CH_3 + I^- \rightarrow CH_3-CH_2-CHI-CH_2-CH_3$
$$\text{3-iodopentane}$$

A mixture of 2-iodopentane and 3-iodopentane is formed, depending on which carbon forms the carbocation. Actually, there are 3 products, because 2-iodopentane exists as a pair of enantiomers, and both of them will form.

23.13.

	order	compound	reason	bp (^{o}C)
(c)	lowest bp	propane	nonpolar	-42
(a)	next	dimethylether	slightly polar	-23
(e)	next	acetaldehyde	more polar	$+20.8$
(d)	next	ethanol	hydrogen-bonded	$+78.5$
(b)	highest bp	formic acid	dimerizes	$+100.7$

The structure of the hydrogen-bonded formic acid dimers is shown below:

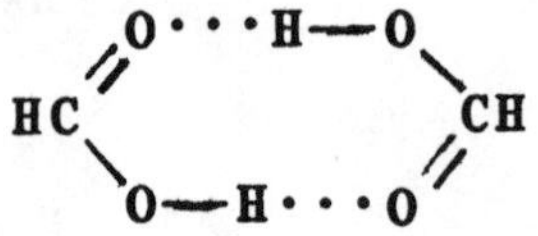

23.14. In all of these reactions, water is also formed.

(a)

$\bigcirc$—$\overset{\overset{\displaystyle O}{\|}}{C}$—O—$CH_2$–$CH_3$ ethyl benzoate

(b) This is primarily a simple proton-transfer (acid-base) reaction, with product dimethylammonium benzoate, because of the presence of water:

$$C_6H_5COOH + HN(CH_3)_2 \rightleftharpoons H_2N(CH_3)_2^+ + C_6H_5COO^-$$

If the reaction is run at high temperature to drive off water, the product is then N,N-dimethylbenzamide:

$\bigcirc$—$\overset{\overset{\displaystyle O}{\|}}{C}$—N$\overset{\displaystyle CH_3}{\underset{\displaystyle CH_3}{}}$ N,N-dimethylbenzamide

(c) This is primarily a simple proton-transfer (acid-base) reaction, with product ammonium acetate, because of the presence of water:

$$CH_3COOH + NH_3 \rightleftharpoons CH_3COO^- + NH_4^+$$

If the reaction is run at high temperature to drive off water, the product is then acetamide:

$$CH_3-\overset{\overset{\displaystyle O}{\|}}{C}-NH_2 \qquad\qquad \text{acetamide}$$

(d)

$$CH_3-\overset{\overset{\displaystyle O}{\|}}{C}-OCH_2-CH_2-CH_2-CH_3 \qquad \text{butyl acetate}$$

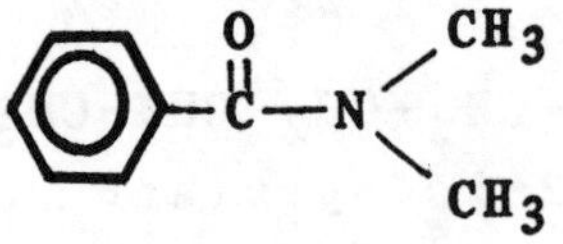

23.15. (a) This is an oxidation (remember that MnO_4^- is a powerful oxidizing agent). Carbon atoms numbered 2 and 3 are oxidized from the −1 to the 0 state.

(b) This is a reduction. The carbonyl carbon is reduced from the +2 to the −2 oxidation state.

(c) This is a reduction. The originally double-bonded carbons (numbers 2 and 3) are reduced from the −1 to the −2 state.

(d) This is an oxidation. The alcohol is oxidized to an aldehyde. Carbon number 1 is oxidized from the −1 to the +1 oxidation state.

(e) This is a reduction. The carboxyl carbon is reduced from the +3 to the −1 state, as the carboxylic acid is reduced to the alcohol.

23.16. In sequence (from left to right as shown), the amino acids are named and categorized as follows:
serine - polar, hydrophilic; valine - hydrophobic; histidine - hydrophilic (because of the electron density on the two N atoms); tyrosine - in neither category, despite the -OH group, because of the large organic part; glycine - in neither category; cysteine - in neither category. The -SH group does not hydrogen-bond.

23.17. (a) Polystyrene is an addition polymer. The mechanism is a free-radical chain reaction, and no water is released as the reaction proceeds.

(b) Dacron polyester is a condensation polymer, with water being lost during the esterifications.

(c) This is an addition polymer, the styrene, butadiene copolymer. No water is extruded as the reaction proceeds.

In condensation polymers, the polymer differs in formula from its subunits by the elements of water (or some other extruded small molecule). In an addition polymer, the poylmer formula is the sum of the constituent formulae.

23.18. The six isomers of C_4H_8 are

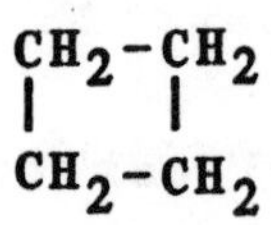

$$\begin{array}{c} CH_2-CH_2 \\ | \qquad | \\ CH_2-CH_2 \end{array}$$
cyclobutane

$$\begin{array}{c} CH_2 \\ \diagup \; \diagdown \\ CH_2 - CH-CH_3 \end{array}$$
methylcyclopropane

$$CH_2=CH-CH_2-CH_3$$
1-butene

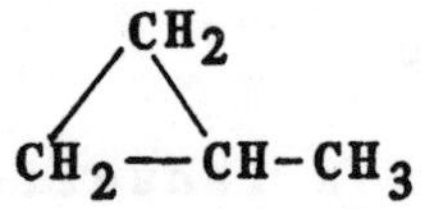

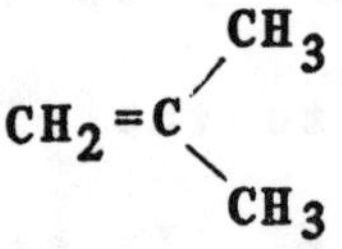

$$CH_2=C\begin{array}{c} CH_3 \\ \diagup \\ \diagdown \\ CH_3 \end{array}$$
2-methylpropene

$$\begin{array}{c} CH_3 \diagdown \qquad \diagup CH_3 \\ CH=CH \end{array}$$
cis-2-butene

$$\begin{array}{c} CH_3 \diagdown \\ CH=CH \\ \diagdown CH_3 \end{array}$$
trans-2-butene

23.19. The six **alkene** isomers with formula C_5H_{10} are

$$H_2C=CH-CH_2-CH_2-CH_3$$
1-pentene

$$\begin{array}{c} CH_3 \diagdown \qquad \diagup CH_3 \\ C=C \\ CH_3 \diagup \qquad \diagdown H \end{array}$$
2-methyl-2-butene

$$\begin{array}{c} CH_3 \diagdown \\ CH=CH \\ \diagdown CH_2-CH_3 \end{array}$$
trans-2-pentene

$$\begin{array}{c} CH_3 \diagdown \qquad \diagup CH_2-CH_3 \\ CH=CH \end{array}$$
cis-2-pentene

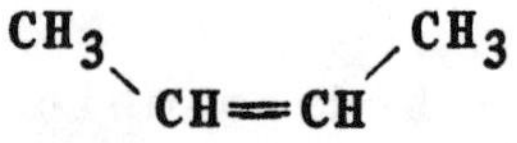

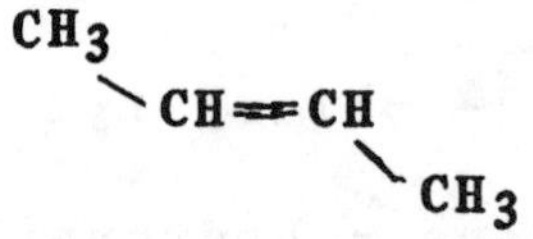

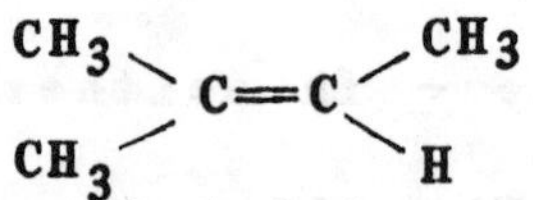

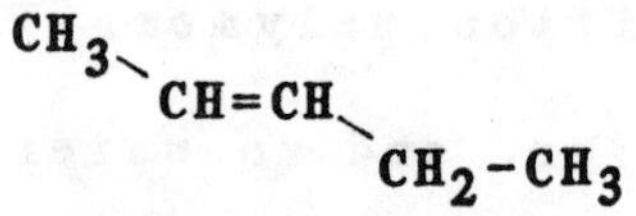

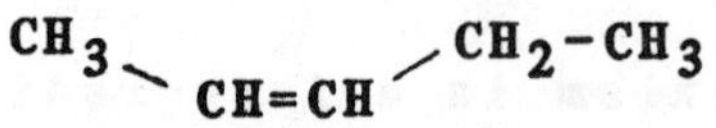

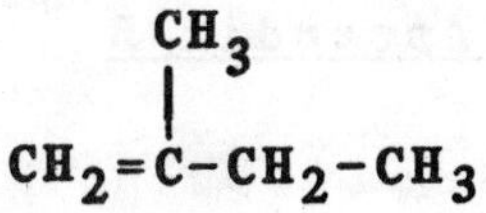

2-methyl-1-butene

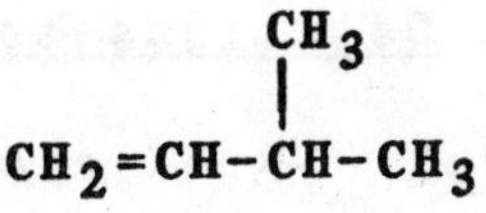

3-methyl-1-butene

23.20. The four cyclic isomers of formula C_5H_{10} are

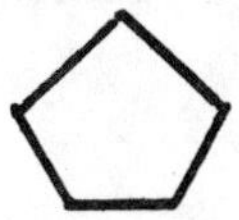

cyclopentane

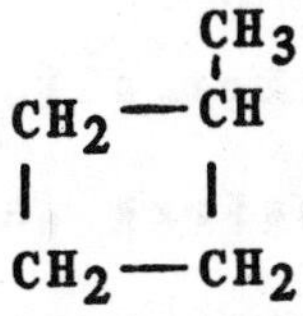

methylcyclobutane

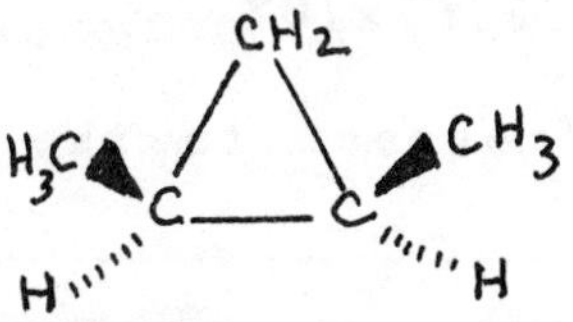

<u>cis</u>-dimethylcyclopropane

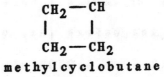

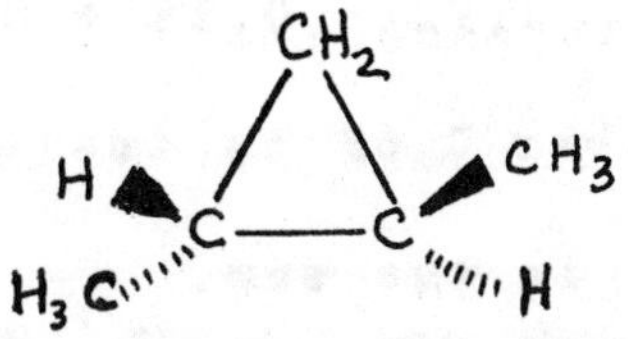

<u>trans</u>-dimethylcyclopropane

<u>Trans</u>-dimethylcyclopropane exists as a pair of enantiomers, so that strictly speaking there are five isomers.

Solutions to Exercises, Appendix B

B1. $(17.2 - 9.47)\text{x}10^4 = 7.7\text{x}10^4$

B2. $(4.51 + 0.0640 - 0.827)\text{x}10^{-3} = (4.51 - 0.763)\text{x}10^{-3}$

$$= 3.75\text{x}10^{-3}$$

Remember that all terms must be expressed with the same power of ten before they can be summed.

B3. $(2.50 + 0.0703)\text{x}10^{-6} = 2.57\text{x}10^{-6}$

B4. $(3.92 - 0.25 + 0.000163)\text{x}10^4 = 3.67\text{x}10^4$

The number 1.63 is insignificant with respect to the other numbers in the sum.

B5. $(1.643)(7.2)(6.03)\text{x}10^{-6} = 71.33\text{x}10^{-6} = 7.1\text{x}10^{-5}$

B6. $(2.10)(6.591)(4.20)(1.093)\text{x}10^{-4} = 63.54\text{x}10^{-4}$

$$= 6.35\text{x}10^{-3}$$

B7. $\dfrac{4.637}{7.20}\text{x}10^{-3} = 0.644\text{x}10^{-3} = 6.44\text{x}10^{-4}$

B8. $\dfrac{(3.8037)(4.19)}{(2.068)(9.108)}\text{x}10^{-2} = 0.846\text{x}10^{-2} = 8.46\text{x}10^{-3}$

B9. $\dfrac{(3.70)^2\text{x}10^{-6}\text{x}(850.3\text{x}10^6)^{1/3}}{(6.421\text{x}10^{-4})(95.6\text{x}10^2)^{1/2}} = \dfrac{(3.70)^2(850.3)^{1/3}}{(6.421)(9.778)}\text{x}10^{-1}$

$$= \frac{(13.69)(9.4738)}{(6.421)(9.778)}\text{x}10^{-1} = 0.2066 = 0.207$$

B10. $\dfrac{-0.491 + 0.08536}{6.3704\text{x}10^{-4}} = \dfrac{-0.406\text{x}10^4}{6.3704} = -637$

B11. $\dfrac{(56.3 - 8.72)^{1/2}\text{x}10^1}{(0.09686 + 2.058)\text{x}10^{-2}} = \dfrac{68.98}{2.155\text{x}10^{-2}} = 320.1 = 320$

B12. (a) $\log(6.022\text{x}10^{23}) = 23.7797$

(b) $\log(4.87\text{x}10^{-11}) = -11 + 0.6875 = -10.312$

(c) $\log(0.00519) = \log(5.19\text{x}10^{-3}) = -2.285$

(d) $\log(8\text{x}10^{124}) = 124 + \log 8 = 124.9$

Note that the characteristic of the logarithm gives the power of ten. Therefore, the number of significant figures in the logarithm is only the number in the mantissa. Thus, in (d), as there is only one significant figure in $8\text{x}10^{124}$, the mantissa of the logarithm should only be given to one figure.

B13. (a) $x = 10^{15.314} = 2.06\text{x}10^{15}$

(b) $x = 10^{-12.410} = 3.89\text{x}10^{-13}$

Note that -12.410 can be expressed as -13 + 0.590. The mantissa of this logarithm is 0.590, and $x = 10^{-13} \cdot 10^{0.590}$

(c) $x = 10^{-0.3307} = 0.4670$

(d) $x = 10^{99.84} = 10^{99} \cdot 10^{0.84} = 6.9\text{x}10^{99}$

(e) $x = 10^{-115.7} = 10^{-116} \cdot 10^{0.3} = 2\text{x}10^{-116}$

B14. (a)
$$4y^2 - 7y - 3 = 0$$

$$y = \frac{7 \pm (49 + 48)^{1/2}}{8} = \frac{7 \pm 9.849}{8}$$

$$y = 16.849/8 = 2.106 \quad \text{or} \quad y = -2.849/8 - -0.3561$$

As the coefficients in the quadratic equation were not given as experimental numbers, we have assumed they were exact integers and expressed the answers to 4 significant figures arbitrarily. The number of significant figures has meaning only when you are dealing with experimental values.

(b) $$2x^2 + 5x + 1 = 0$$

$$x = \frac{-5 \pm (25 - 8)^{1/2}}{4} = \frac{-5 \pm 4.123}{4}$$

$$x = (-9.123)/4 = -2.281 \quad \text{or} \quad x = (-0.877)/4 = -\ 0.219$$

B15. First rearrange the equation to put it into the form suitable for using the quadratic formula:

$$z^2 + (5.0\times10^{-2})z - 4.0\times10^{-3} = 0$$

$$z = \frac{-5.0\times10^{-2} \pm (25\times10^{-4} + 16\times10^{-3})^{1/2}}{2}$$

Since we are to find only the positive root,

$$z = \frac{-5.0\times10^{-2} + (18.5\times10^{-3})^{1/2}}{2} = \frac{-5.0\times10^{-2} + 1.36\times10^{-1}}{2}$$

$$= \frac{0.0860}{2} = 0.043 = 4.3\times10^{-2}$$

B16. $$x^2 + kx - ka = 0$$

$$x^2 + (6.3\times10^{-4})x - 6.3\times10^{-6} = 0$$

$$x = \frac{-6.3\times10^{-4} + (39.69\times10^{-8} + 25.2\times10^{-6})^{1/2}}{2}$$

$$x = \frac{-6.3\times10^{-4} + (0.397 + 25.2)^{1/2}\times10^{-3}}{2}$$

$$x = \frac{-6.3\times10^{-4} + 5.06\times10^{-3}}{2} = \frac{(5.06 - 0.63)\times10^{-3}}{2} = \frac{4.43\times10^{-3}}{2}$$

$$x = 2.2\times10^{-3}$$